Conditional Markov Processes and Their Application to the Theory of Optimal Control

MODERN ANALYTIC AND COMPUTATIONAL
METHODS IN SCIENCE AND MATHEMATICS
A Group of Monographs and Advanced Textbooks

Editor: RICHARD BELLMAN, University of Southern California

Already Published:

1. R. E. Bellman, R. E. Kalaba, and Marcia C. Prestrud
INVARIANT IMBEDDING AND RADIATIVE TRANSFER IN SLABS OF FINITE THICKNESS, 1963

2. R. E. Bellman, Harriet H. Kagiwada, R. E. Kalaba, and Marcia C. Prestrud
INVARIANT IMBEDDING AND TIME-DEPENDENT TRANSPORT PROCESSES, 1964

3. R. E. Bellman and R. E. Kalaba, QUASILINEARIZATION AND NONLINEAR BOUNDARY-VALUE PROBLEMS, 1965

4. R. E. Bellman, R. E. Kalaba, and Jo Ann Lockett, NUMERICAL INVERSION OF THE LAPLACE TRANSFORM: Applications to Biology, Economics, Engineering, and Physics, 1966

5. S. G. Mikhlin and K. L. Smolitskiy, APPROXIMATE METHODS FOR SOLUTION OF DIFFERENTIAL AND INTEGRAL EQUATIONS, 1967

6. R. N. Adams and E. D. Denman, WAVE PROPAGATION AND TURBULENT MEDIA, 1966

7. R. L. Stratonovich, CONDITIONAL MARKOV PROCESSES AND THEIR APPLICATION TO THE THEORY OF OPTIMAL CONTROL, 1968

8. A. G. Ivakhnenko and V. G. Lapa, CYBERNETICS AND FORECASTING TECHNIQUES, 1967

9. G. A. Chebotarev, ANALYTICAL AND NUMERICAL METHODS OF CELESTIAL MECHANICS, 1967

10. S. F. Feshchenko, N. I. Shkil', and L. D. Nikolenko, ASYMPTOTIC METHODS IN THE THEORY OF LINEAR DIFFERENTIAL EQUATIONS, 1967

In Preparation:

A. G. Butkovskii, OPTIMAL CONTROL THEORY FOR DISTRIBUTED PARAMETERS

R. E. Larson, STATE INCREMENT DYNAMIC PROGRAMMING

MODERN ANALYTIC AND COMPUTATIONAL METHODS IN SCIENCE AND MATHEMATICS

MÉTHODES MODERNES D'ANALYSE ET DE COMPUTATION EN SCIENCE ET MATHÉMATIQUE

NEUE ANALYTISCHE UND NUMERISCHE METHODEN IN DER WISSENSCHAFT UND DER MATHEMATIK

НОВЫЕ АНАЛИТИЧЕСКИЕ И ВЫЧИСЛИТЕЛЬНЫЕ МЕТОДЫ В НАУКЕ И МАТЕМАТИКЕ

Editor

RICHARD BELLMAN, UNIVERSITY OF SOUTHERN CALIFORNIA

Conditional Markov Processes and Their Application to the Theory of Optimal Control

by

R. L. STRATONOVICH
Moscow State University

Translated from the Russian by
R. N. and N. B. McDONOUGH
for *Scripta Technica, Inc.*

With a Preface by
RICHARD BELLMAN

AMERICAN ELSEVIER PUBLISHING COMPANY, INC.
NEW YORK 1968

ORIGINALLY PUBLISHED AS
Uslovnyye markovskiye protsessy i ikh primeneniye k teorii optimal'nogo upravleniya
Moscow University Press, Moscow, 1966

The English language edition of this book contains numerous changes as well as additions which have been made by the author after the Russian edition was published. The present work may be considered as a REVISED, SECOND EDITION.

AMERICAN ELSEVIER PUBLISHING COMPANY, INC.
52 Vanderbilt Avenue
New York, N. Y. 10017

ELSEVIER PUBLISHING CO. LTD.
Barking, Essex, England

ELSEVIER PUBLISHING COMPANY
335 Jan Van Galenstraat
P.O. Box 211, Amsterdam, The Netherlands

Library of Congress Catalog Card Number 67-28450

MANUFACTURED IN THE UNITED STATES OF AMERICA

Editor's Preface

Over the last twenty-five years two of the most important mathematical and scientific developments have been the creations of the theories of stochastic processes, and of control and decision-making. As usual in the history of mathematics, these theories have been firmly rooted in specific fields of science. Equally the case, the mathematical techniques, once developed in connection with specific problems, have then been extensively applied to many other problems, some surprisingly far from the original focus of attention. Such is the strange power of mathematics.

The contemporary theory of stochastic control processes represents a remarkable fusion of these two mainstreams of analysis. Although a significant and useful theory of stochastic control processes can be rigorously constructed on a fairly elementary level, it is quite essential for a variety of reasons to formulate a theory of continuous type. As we know, there is a considerable degree of subtlety and sophistication to the continuous versions of both variational analysis and probability theory. It is to be expected therefore that it will be no easy matter to lay the proper foundations for a continuous variational theory, particularly one constructed along the lines of dynamic programming, which is to say, one emphasizing multi-stage aspects and information. Stratonovich has carried out this presentation very carefully and very adroitly, with full awareness both of the needs of rigor and the needs of those mathematicians and scientists who wish to utilize these powerful and versatile methods.

Also important about this work is that it provides new vantage points from which to view the theory of partial differential equations, another of the principal domains of modern mathematics. Furthermore, the emphasis upon observables and sufficient statistics paves the way for the more general theory of adaptive processes, and also provides a tool for the study of the feasible operation and control of large systems.

From what we have said above, we feel very safe in declaring that Stratonovich's book represents a major step forward in the current endeavor to create unified mathematical theories with wide-ranging applications in both mathematics itself and in science. It is therefore of particular pleasure to welcome this work into a series specifically devoted to this objective. The English translation which follows is an expanded and amended version of the original Russian edition prepared under the supervision of the author himself. I wish to thank R. L. Stratonovich for his kind and continuing assistance in this effort.

RICHARD BELLMAN

Preface

The purpose of this book is to discuss a mathematical apparatus which can be used for the construction of optimal cybernetic systems processing statistical input information, in particular, systems of optimal filtering, optimal detection, and optimal control in the presence of noise.

It is unnecessary to discuss the practical value of a stochastic theory of optimal system synthesis. Its area of application is difficult to survey. This theory includes optimal filtering theory, Wald's sequential analysis, and the stochastic form of Bellman's dynamic programming, and is one of the most important divisions of theoretical cybernetics.

From the mathematical point of view the synthesis of optimal systems, or alternatively the theory of optimal transformations of observed statistical information, relates to mathematical statistics. In the present volume we will concentrate our attention on Bayesian problems, in which *a priori* probability distributions are assumed to be known. The theory can also be generalized to non-Bayesian problems, since their solution can be obtained by solving selected Bayesian problems in a particular way. However, we will not consider such cases. In addition to this, we will limit ourselves to a cursory examination of questions of game theory. It will be shown that almost all results relevant to nongame cases can be generalized to a game situation.

Our primary interest is in effective methods of problem solution, which actually facilitate the construction of optimal systems. In regard to the efficiency of the synthesis methods, to a certain extent the same pattern is followed as in regard to methods of analysis of stochastic systems. Two basic kinds of methods can be distinguished:

1. methods of linear algebra, especially suitable for the examination of linear transformations of Gaussian processes, and of other processes within the framework of the first two moments;
2. methods of differential equations and recursive transformations, especially suitable for the study of Markov processes.

In contrast to the first methods, nonlinear transformations are also included among the second ones. The recursive form of the transformations is in good agreement with the spirit of cybernetics, where transformations are usually carried out in stages.

The linear methods are simpler, and as a rule were developed earlier. Thus, the application of correlation theory to problems of analysis of statistical systems preceded the application of Markov methods for this purpose.

Something similar is also observed in stochastic problems of optimal system synthesis. The application of the inverse probability formula (Bayes' formula) does not provide a practical solution to the problem in complicated cases. An acceptable solution requires the use of more effective methods. In the first stage a theory of linear optimal filtering was developed, in which only linear transformations were compared and only linear methods used. The most important steps here were: the establishment of regression (filtering) equations; Kolmogorov's solution for stationary random sequences; Wiener's solution for stationary random processes in continuous time; and the construction of nonstationary solutions.

Along with this, the methods of sufficient statistics were developed in the theory of parameter estimation, permitting a satisfactory solution to be obtained in complex cases (for example, parameters dependent on sampling or varying parameters) if the processes are Gaussian.

When non-Gaussian processes are studied in complex statistical problems, if the examiner does not limit his choice to linear transformations, the linear methods described above are not suitable.

Of course some sort of limitations along another line are needed in order to construct effective methods. In the light of what was said above it should be clear to the reader that we have in mind the condition that the processes in question be Markov.

Without this condition we would have to use the apparatus of moments or correlation functions. Effective methods have not yet been created on this basis.

One favorable circumstance is that a non-Markov process, as is known, can be approximated to within any required precision by a multidimensional Markov process, perhaps a rather complicated one. Thus while remaining within the framework of Markov processes, we will have a complication of solution corresponding to the complication of the problem.

From the above the fact seems entirely natural that, at the present time, there is a great interest in Markov processes. The appearance of a series of monographs devoted to them is evidence of this. However, monographs which deal with the statistics of Markov processes (i.e., which deal with those cases when some function of a Markov process is observed) unfortunately do not exist. The present book will try to fill this gap to whatever extent is feasible.

If some function $y_t = f(x_t)$ of a Markov process x_t is observed, then as a result of this observation the *a posteriori* probabilities, say, $\mathbf{P}(dx_t \mid y_\tau, \tau \leqslant t)$, differ from the *a priori* ones. The study of these *a posteriori* probabilities and their evolution in time is the subject of the theory of conditional Markov processes.

The first results of this theory and of the optimal nonlinear filtering based on it were presented by the author at the All-Union Conference on Statistical Radiophysics in Gorki (1958) and in a seminar in the Department of Probability Theory of Moscow University (Stratonovich [1]). The results of this period were published by the author [2].

The differential equation

$$\frac{\partial w_t(x)}{\partial t} = (Bw_t)(x) - w(x) \int (Bw_t)(x')\, dx'$$

for the *a posteriori* probability distribution density (relative to Lebesgue measure)

$$w_t(x) = \mathbf{P}(dx_t \mid y_\tau, \tau \leqslant t)/dx_t$$

relates to those results. Here x_t is a point of a multidimensional state space; B is the basic *a posteriori* operator, depending on the observed process y_t and on *a priori* statistical data.

This equation is unusual in that it is nonlinear in w_t. Apparently for the first time in probability theory, we meet a nonlinear equation for probabilities.

Later, a specific unnormalized (i.e., nonprobabilistic) basic *a posteriori* measure $V_s^t(x_s, \Gamma)$ was introduced, which has Markov properties (satisfies the Chapman–Kolmogorov equation). Its density

$$v(x_s, s;\ x_t, t) = V_s^t(x_s, dx_t)/dx_t$$

satisfies the linear equation

$$\frac{\partial v}{\partial t} = Bv$$

with the same operator. Various *a posteriori* probabilities can be expressed in terms of this measure.

In the trivial special case of little practical interest when the observed process y_t is itself Markov, the equation given first is linear and the need to introduce the auxiliary measure V disappears. It is precisely to this case that the results given without proof in the note of C. S. Lyan [1] apply. In addition to the assumption about the existence of conditional distributions, this introduces topological limitations on the state space (its separability is assumed). In our opinion, the introduction of topology into the state space is not necessary for the theory.

One aspect of a Markov process is its infinitesimal operator. The *a priori* Markov process is characterized by the *a priori* operator. The basic *a posteriori* measure is described by the basic *a posteriori* operator (B in the above equation). Other *a posteriori* operators can be expressed in terms of it. The form of the basic *a posteriori* operator depends on the *a priori* operator and on the method of observation. Obtaining the form of the *a posteriori* operator for various specific cases is the central problem of the theory of conditional Markov processes. In this book this problem is solved for several important special cases corresponding to diffusion processes. For discrete time recursive transformations (recurrence relations) are used in place of differential equations.

A nonlinear filter in its main section realizes these equations or transformations. In place of the *a posteriori* probabilities it is also possible to consider parameters replacing them. If the *a posteriori* operator is found, the algorithm of the recursive transformations is determined without particular difficulties. The resulting complicated transformation is the result of simpler single-stage transformations. Thus the synthesis of a filter does not necessitate laborious calculations.

Problems connected with the derivation or simulation of the equations (recursive transformations) for the *a posteriori* probabilities or parameters replacing them are called primary, and the corresponding equations, the primary *a posteriori* equations.

The theory of conditional Markov processes also facilitates the solution of secondary problems, in which functions of the *a posteriori* probabilities or the parameters replacing them are considered. For these functions it is possible to obtain differential equations (secondary equations), the operator of which can be called the secondary *a posteriori* operator. Its derivation is also an important problem of the theory.

In the theory of optimal control a conditional risk is a function depending on the sufficient coordinates, i.e., in addition to other variables, and on the *a posteriori* probabilities or the parameters replacing them. Optimal control results from minimizing this risk. The determination of optimal solutions and optimal conditional risks is carried out simultaneously. Moreover, the determination of conditional risks helps in finding an optimal solution, and thus the great role played by conditional risks in the theory of optimal control becomes apparent.

Knowing the secondary *a posteriori* operator, we can easily derive the equation for the reduced conditional risks, which is the main equation of the theory. The standard route recommended by the theory of optimal control consist in the establishment of this equation and its solution.

In generalizing the theory to the case of continuous time it is convenient to use the concept of optimal conditional risks (defined using conditional minimizations and the mean of the penalty functions) as the more fundamental, rather than the concept of optimal solution. The introduction of a stepped index aids in the transition to continuous time. The case of continuous time and a stepped index (when time is changing continuously and the information arrives at discrete instants) occupies an intermediate position between the case of discrete time and the case of continuous time and continuous index (continuous accumulation of information). In the latter (doubly continuous) case, it is difficult to determine the optimal solution in a useful form, but it is not difficult to determine the "optimal" conditional risks. After this determination, a stepped approximation to the continuous index is made and an optimal solution constructed for it. The risks of these solutions can be made as close as desired to the "optimal" risks corresponding to the continuous index. In this sense these solutions are ε-optimal for the continuous index. The purely formal difficulties involved in generalizing the theory to the case of continuous time are circumvented in this manner, and an efficient theory is built.

The formulation of optimal control theory presented in this book came about through generalization of various concrete problems which arose in the author's work. The possibility of extending the methods used to new problems resulted in the abstract form of the theory. The language of measurable functions and measure theory is adequate for this degree of generalization. Thus we chose this language for the presentation here, although from the pedagogical point of view this method of presentation can be considered the least expedient. We assume that the reader will master the basic material, while becoming acquainted with concrete problems and examples in order to understand what is behind the abstract formulations. Active participation on the part of the reader is required. It is useful to keep in mind in reading the book that turning the pages towards the front is as useful as towards the back.

Since the theoretical significance of various points of the book is in inverse proportion to their availability, we will not attempt to put part of the material into smaller type, but will instead leave the method of reading the material up to the various categories of readers. The reader who is familiar with the language of measure theory and who has had the experience of working in adjacent areas can begin immediately with the abstract formulation. A less prepared reader should pay more attention to the examples, of which there are many in the book. Persons interested in applications may transfer the methods of solution from the given problems to their own, avoiding the theoretical material and the proofs. A wide circle of readers, specializing in applications, can, in addition, use the book for the elevation of their mathematical level. Finally, to persons who are working independently the book can be of great value as a handbook, containing various formulas and results not found in books.

The reader will quickly note that the given sources and list of literature in the book are not complete. In defense, the author would like to say that he did not carry out any detailed bibliographic analysis, and considers a historical handling of the questions premature.

In conclusion the author would like to express his gratitude to Yu. L. Klimontovich, M. S. Pinsker, V. I. Tikhonov, S. V. Fomin, E. M. Khazen and R. Z. Khas'minskiy, who read the manuscript and made many useful comments.

R. L. STRATONOVICH

Contents

Part 2

THE MAIN RESULTS OF THE THEORY OF CONDITIONAL MARKOV PROCESSES

Part 3

APPLICATION OF THE THEORY OF CONDITIONAL MARKOV PROCESSES TO THE THEORY OF OPTIMAL CONTROL

PART 1

Some Auxiliary Questions in the Theory of Markov Processes

CHAPTER 1

The Convergence of Non-Markov to Markov Processes

1.1 Presentation of the Problem

The mechanism of Markov processes is very effective, mainly because it is associated with the apparatus of differential equations which are satisfied by probabilities of Markov processes in the case of continuous time. In discrete time, definite recursion relations correspond to these equations. This circumstance helps in obtaining various results.

However, the application of the results of the theory to physical and technical problems is often accompanied with difficulties. In such applications, the time function usually possesses a series of "good" characteristics: smoothness and even analyticity, which, as is known, is incompatible with Markov characteristics of the process. Thus the application of the theory of exact Markov processes is essentially connected with some approximations.

There arises the practically important problem of principal interest of the convergence of Markov and non-Markov processes, the study of conditions of their interchangeability and errors connected with this. At the present time this situation has almost not been studied, except for several trivial special cases. Previous general studies of this question are described in Sect. 4 of the monograph by Stratonovich [8].

The verification of the convergence of non-Markov to Markov processes to a certain extent resembles the central limit theorem, having to do with the convergence of a non-Gaussian distribution law to the Gaussian. This analogy shows the wide scope of this problem. A concrete definition of "convergence" of Markov and non-Markov processes and a study of convergence conditions and rate of convergence could form the content of a separate chapter on the theory of probability.

Here we will examine only one specific result. Under certain assumptions we will prove the convergence of the distribution of a non-Markov process to the distribution of a diffusion Markov process. Generally speaking, this result is contained in the results of the above monograph, which were developed from a more general point of view, but here it will be studied and proved in more detail.

Let us assume that the non-Markov process $\{x(t)\}=\{x(t), t, \omega, \mu\}$ is determined by a differential equation

$$\frac{dx(t)}{dt} = G(x(t), t, \omega, \mu) \tag{1.1}$$

as is often done in applications. Here ω is a point of the basic probability space $(\Omega, \mathcal{M}, \mathbf{P})$. For simplicity, we will consider the process $\{x(t)\}$ to be one-dimensional, i.e., we will assume that its state space is the interval I. Without further loss of generality it is possible to assume $I=(-a, a)$. In addition to this interval we will also examine the circle $R=\{|x|\leqslant a\}$ in the complex plane. Let the time t be a point on the real axis, and μ a positive number. We formulate a series of assumptions in regard to the function on the right side.

1. A_1. With fixed t, μ, x $(\in R)$ it is an $\mathcal{M}$-measurable function of ω where the moments

$$\mathbf{M}G(x_1, t_1, \omega) \dots G(x_r, t_r, \omega) \tag{1.2}$$

of all possible orders $r = 1, 2, \dots$ are finite.

1. A_2. With fixed ω, t, μ it forms a regular analytic function of x in the circle R with probability 1. Analogously, its moments (1.2) are regular in $R\times \dots \times R$.

1. A_3. With fixed x, ω, μ it is a continuous function of t with probability 1.

1. A_4. With fixed x, μ it is a stationary random function (in the narrow sense).

If we are given the initial condition

$$x(s) = y \in I, \tag{1.3}$$

Eq. (1.1) will almost everywhere determine the process

$$x(t) = f(s, y; t, \omega, \mu) \equiv f_s^t(y) \tag{1.4}$$

in those time intervals $s<t<\Theta(s, y, \omega, \mu) \equiv \Theta(\omega)$, i.e., in those sets

$$\Omega'(s, y, t, \mu) = \{\omega : t < \Theta(s, y, \omega, \mu)\}$$

where this process does not go beyond the boundaries of I. Here $\Theta(s, y, \omega, \mu)$ is the first time of exit from the I of the trajectory which begins at y. This follows from known conditions of the theory of differential equations if $1.A_3$ is taken into account. Obviously, the function (1.4) will be $\mathcal{M}$-measurable with fixed remaining arguments. $\mathcal{M}$-measurability is retained if in the initial condition (1.3) the value $y=y(\omega)$ is considered an $\mathcal{M}$-measurable function of ω. Thus, we construct the random process $x(t, \omega, \mu)$.

The differential equation (1.1) can be changed into the integral equation

$$x(t) = y + \int_s^t G(x(\tau), \tau, \omega, \mu)\, d\tau.$$

This can be solved by the method of successive approximations using the formula

$$\begin{gathered} x^{(j+1)}(t) = y + \int_s^t G(x^{(j)}(\tau), \tau, \omega, \mu)\, d\tau, \\ j = 0, 1, \ldots; \quad x^{(0)}(t) = y. \end{gathered} \tag{1.5}$$

As could be expected from the theory of differential equations (see, for example, Smirnov [1], pp. 152-156), these approximations will certainly converge for points ω corresponding to functions G continuous in t (i.e., almost everywhere) on the segment $[s, \theta'(\omega)]$. Here

$$\begin{gathered} \theta'(\omega) = M_G^{-1} \min(a - y,\ a + y); \\ M_G = \sup\{|G|;\ x \in I,\ s \leqslant t \leqslant \theta(\omega)\}. \end{gathered} \tag{1.6}$$

On this interval no approximation (1.5) extends beyond $[-a, a]$.

For the differences $x^j = x^{(j)} - x^{(j-1)}$, according to (1.5), we have the recursion relation

$$\begin{aligned} x^{j+1}(t) = \int_s^t [G(y + x^1 + \ldots + x^{j-1} + x^j, \tau, \omega, \mu) - \\ - G(y + x^1 + \ldots + x^{j-1}, \tau, \omega, \mu)]\, d\tau. \end{aligned}$$

Using the analyticity of the function G with respect to x, we expand the functions under the integral in a Taylor series

$$x^{j+1}(t)=\sum_{l=1}^{\infty}\frac{1}{l!}\int_s^t\frac{\partial^l G}{\partial y^l}(y,\tau,\omega,\mu)\,[(x^1+\ldots+x^{j-1}+x^j)^l-$$
$$-(x^1+\ldots+x^{j-1})^l]\,d\tau,$$

which converges on $[s,\ \theta'(\omega)]$.

Using these relations, we can explicitly express all x^j in terms of the function G and its derivatives. Thus, the lower-order formulas have the form

$$x^1(t)=\int_s^t G(y,\tau,\omega,\mu)\,d\tau;$$
$$x^2(t)=\sum_{l=1}^{\infty}\frac{1}{l!}\int_s^t\frac{\partial^l G}{\partial y^l}(y,\tau,\omega,\mu)\left[\int_s^{\tau}G(y,\tau_1,\omega,\mu)\,d\tau_1\right]^l d\tau, \tag{1.7}$$
$$\ldots\ldots\ldots\ldots\ldots\ldots\ldots\ldots\ldots\ldots\ldots\ldots$$

The exact value of $x(t)$ is the almost certainly converging series

$$x(t)=f_s^t(y)=y+\sum_{j=1}^{\infty}x^j(t). \tag{1.8}$$

It is easy to see that the substitution of expressions of the type (1.7) into (1.8) leads to a sum of multilinear expressions of the function G and its derivatives of the type

$$x(t)=\sum_{q\rho_1\ldots\rho_q}\frac{\partial^{\rho_1+\ldots+\rho_q}}{\partial y_1^{\rho_1}\ldots\partial y_q^{\rho_q}}\int_s^t\ldots\int_s^t G(y_1,\tau_1,\omega,\mu)\ldots G(y_q,\tau_q,\omega,\mu)\times$$
$$\times\, Q_{q\rho_1\ldots\rho_q}(\tau_1,\ldots,\tau_q)\,d\tau_1\ldots d\tau_q \tag{1.9}$$

(after differentiation it is necessary to assume $y_1=\ldots=y_q=y$), where $Q_{q\rho_1\ldots\rho_q}$ $(\tau_1,\ldots,\tau_q)$ are certain bounded positive functions of $\tau_1,\ldots,\tau_q$, not dependent on y, ω, or μ. This will be taken into consideration in the future.

The "closeness" of the process $x(t)$ to a Markov process is ensured by a small parameter μ with a special choice of the dependence of G on μ. In the interest of examining the convergence of the process to a diffusion process, we will assume

$$G(x,t,\omega,\mu)=\mu^2 m(x)+\mu g(x,t,\omega), \tag{1.10}$$

where

$$\mu^2 m(x)=\mathbf{M}G(x,t,\omega,\mu),$$

i.e.,

$$\mathbf{M}\, g(x, t, \omega) = 0. \tag{1.11}$$

Functions m and g do not depend on μ.

Introducing a new time scale, we will assume $\tilde{t}=\mu^2 t$. If we designate

$$x\left(\frac{\tilde{t}}{\mu^2}\right) = \tilde{x}(\tilde{t}); \quad g(x, t, \omega) = \tilde{g}(x, \tilde{t}, \omega),$$

we will get

$$\frac{d\tilde{x}}{d\tilde{t}} = m(\tilde{x}) + \frac{1}{\mu}\tilde{g}(\tilde{x}, \tilde{t}, \omega), \ \tilde{x}(\tilde{t}) = \tilde{f}_{\tilde{s}}^{\tilde{t}}(y). \tag{1.12}$$

The substitution of (1.10) into (1.9) will increase the number of terms. Writing out, for example, a typical term into which g goes r times and $m(y)$ goes $q-r$ times, we will have

$$\tilde{f}_{\tilde{s}}^{\tilde{t}}(y) = \sum_{qr\rho_1\ldots\rho_q} \frac{\partial^{\rho_1+\ldots+\rho_q}}{\partial y_1^{\rho_1}\ldots\partial y_q^{\rho_q}} \int_{\tilde{s}}^{\tilde{t}} \ldots \int_{\tilde{s}}^{\tilde{t}} \frac{1}{\mu}\tilde{g}(y_{i_1}, \sigma_{i_1}) \ldots \tag{1.13}$$
$$\ldots \frac{1}{\mu}\tilde{g}(y_{i_r}, \sigma_{i_r})\, m(y_{i_{r+1}}) \ldots m(y_{i_q})\, Q_{q\rho_1\ldots\rho_q}(\sigma_1, \ldots, \sigma_q)\, d\sigma_1 \ldots d\sigma_q.$$

We used the relations

$$Q_{q\rho_1\ldots\rho_q}\left(\frac{\sigma_1}{\mu^2}, \ldots, \frac{\sigma_q}{\mu^2}\right) = Q_{q\rho_1\ldots\rho_q}(\sigma_1, \ldots, \sigma_q).$$

We can be convinced that these are correct and that μ enters into (1.13) only in the combination g/μ by writing expressions (1.8) and (1.9) directly in time t using Eq. (1.12). We will evaluate the length of the guaranteed interval of convergence using (1.6). According to (1.10) we have $M_G=\mu M_g + O(\mu^2)$, $M_g=\sup|g|$. Thus the length of the interval of convergence on the $\tilde{t}$ axis, equal to $[M_g+O(\mu)]^{-1}\mu \min(a-y,\ a+y)$, is reduced when $\mu \to 0$, at the same time as the length on the t axis, equal to $[\mu M_g+O(\mu^2)]^{-1}\min(a-y,\ a+y)$, increases without bound. In reality the length of the actual interval of convergence is even larger. The function $g(x, t, \omega)$ as a fixed function of time has alternating values; thus the time interval of existence of the function $x(t)$ in I and the time interval of existence of all its approximations is $O(\mu^{-2})$ [or $O(1)$ in units of $\tilde{t}$]. Not having examined thoroughly the basis of this fact, we formulate the condition of convergence of the series in question as a supplementary assumption in the future.

1.2 The Fundamental Theorem

Having fixed the initial condition x_0, we examine the process $\tilde{x}(\tilde{t}) = \tilde{f}_0^{\tilde{t}}(x_0)$. The main assertion is that this process tends to the diffusion Markov process "in distribution" as $\mu \to 0$.

Theorem 1.1. Let us assume that $g(x, t, \omega)$ is a function as described above. We assume that: 1) its semi-invariants

$$\mathbf{K}[g(x_1, t_1, \omega), \ldots, g(x_r, t_r, \omega)] \equiv k_r(x_1, t_1, \ldots, x_r, t_r) \equiv \equiv k_r'(t_2 - t_1, \ldots, t_r - t_1) \tag{1.14}$$

fulfill the conditions

$$\lim_{L\to\infty} L^{-\frac{r}{2}} \int_0^L (L-\tau)\, d\tau \int_0^\tau \cdots \int_0^\tau \left| \frac{\partial^{\nu_1+\ldots+\nu_r}}{\partial x_1^{\nu_1} \ldots \partial x_r^{\nu_r}} k_r'(\tau, -\pi_1, \ldots, -\pi_{r-2}) \right| \cdot d\pi_1 \ldots d\pi_{r-2} \equiv N_r < \infty; \tag{1.15}$$

$$\lim_{L\to\infty} L^{-\frac{r}{2}} \int_0^{2L} \tau d\tau \int_0^L \cdots \int_0^L \left| \frac{\partial^{\nu_1+\ldots+\nu_r}}{\partial x_1^{\nu_1} \ldots \partial x_r^{\nu_r}} k_r'(-\zeta_1, \ldots, -\zeta_{u-1}, \tau, \tau + \pi_1, \ldots, \tau + \pi_{r-u-1}) \right| d\zeta_1 \ldots d\zeta_{u-1} d\pi_1 \ldots d\pi_{r-u-1} = 0 \tag{1.16}$$

for all $r \geqslant 2$; $u \geqslant 1$, $r - u \geqslant 1$; $\nu_1 \geqslant 0, \ldots, \nu_r \geqslant 0$; 2) the distribution of the random variables (1.23) is completely defined by its moments; and 3) that the series (1.29) converges. Then

1.1.A. Any finite distribution of the process $\tilde{x}(\tilde{t})$ defined by Eq. (1.12) converges entirely to the corresponding distribution of a certain Markov process $x_M(t)$ as $\mu \to 0$;

1.1.B. The latter is a diffusion process: $\lim \mathbf{M} \frac{\Delta x_M^q}{\Delta} = 0$, $q \geqslant 3$ and is characterized by the following parameters of drift and local variance:

$$\lim_{\Delta\to 0} \mathbf{M} \frac{\Delta x_M}{\Delta} = m(x_M) + \frac{\partial}{\partial x'} \int_{-\infty}^0 k_2'(x', x_M, \tau)\, d\tau \quad (x' = x_M);$$
$$\lim_{\Delta\to 0} \mathbf{M} \frac{\Delta x_M^2}{\Delta} = \int_{-\infty}^{\infty} k_2'(x_M, x_M, \tau)\, d\tau, \tag{1.17}$$

$$\text{if } N_r = 0 \text{ for } r \geqslant 3. \qquad (1.18)$$

In the proof of the theorem we will use

Lemma 1.1. Let two groups of random variables $\xi_\alpha = \xi_\alpha(\omega, \mu)$, $\alpha = 1, \ldots, p$ and $\xi_\beta = \xi_\beta(\omega, \mu)$, $\beta = p+1, \ldots, p+s$ be given such that all moments

$$\mathbf{M}\,\xi_{\gamma_1}\ldots\xi_{\gamma_v}\ (\gamma_1, \ldots, \gamma_v = 1, \ldots, p+s;\ v = 1, 2, \ldots),$$

and their corresponding limits

$$\lim_{\mu\to 0} \mathbf{M}\,\xi_{\gamma_1}\ldots\xi_{\gamma_v} \qquad (1.19)$$

exist and are finite. Then, if for any $k \geqslant 1$, $l \geqslant 1$ the pair correlations

$$\lim_{\mu\to 0} \mathbf{K}\,[\xi_{\alpha_1}\ldots\xi_{\alpha_k}, \xi_{\beta_1}\ldots\xi_{\beta_l}] = 0$$
$$(\alpha_i = 1, \ldots, p;\ \beta_i = p+1, \ldots, p+s), \qquad (1.20)$$

vanish, the indicated groups become independent, that is, the distribution function tends toward the creation of distribution functions

$$\mathbf{P}\,[\xi_1 < z_1, \ldots, \xi_{p+s} < z_{p+s}] \overset{\text{ent.}}{\to} F_1(z_1, \ldots, z_p)\, F_2(z_{p+1}, \ldots, z_{p+s}).$$

The convergence is "complete," or "entire" (ent.) as defined in the book by Loève [1].

Proof of Lemma 1.1. Let us take into account the known solution of the "problem of convergence of moments" (Loève [1]) which guarentees the existence of an entire limit of the distribution function $\mathbf{P}\,[\xi_1 < z_1, \ldots, \xi_{p+s} < z_{p+s}]$. This limit is determined uniquely (to within a constant) by the corresponding characteristic function and limit moments (1.19). Thus

$$\mathbf{P}\,[\xi_1 < z_1, \ldots, \xi_{p+s} < z_{p+s}] \overset{\text{ent.}}{\to} F(z_1, \ldots, z_{p+s}),$$

where $F(z_1, \ldots, z_{p+s})$ is expressed in terms of the characteristic function $\Theta(u_1, \ldots, u_{p+s})$ in the usual manner. In order to prove the lemma, it remains to be shown that this characteristic function, determined by the limits (1.19), factors into the product

$$\Theta(u_1, \ldots, u_{p+s}) = \Theta_1(u_1, \ldots, u_p)\, \Theta_2(u_{p+1}, \ldots, u_{p+s}). \qquad (1.21)$$

From (1.20) it follows that all the mixed semi-invariants tend toward zero,

$$\lim_{\mu\to 0} k_{\alpha_1\ldots\alpha_k\beta_1\ldots\beta_l} = 0,\ k \geqslant 1,\ l \geqslant 1$$
$$(k_{\alpha_1\ldots\alpha_k\beta_1\ldots\beta_l} = \mathbf{K}\,[\xi_{\alpha_1}, \ldots, \xi_{\alpha_k}, \xi_{\beta_1}, \ldots, \xi_{\beta_l}]). \qquad (1.22)$$

Let us assume the contrary and take the lowest-order semi-invariant which does not tend toward zero (having the smallest sum $k+l$), let us say, $k_{\alpha_1\ldots\alpha_\varkappa\beta_1\ldots\beta_\lambda}$. The moment $\mathbf{M}\,\xi_{\alpha_1}\ldots\xi_{\alpha_\varkappa}\xi_{\beta_1}\ldots\xi_{\beta_\lambda}$ is represented by semi-invariants according to known formulas (Stratonovich [8]). Having calculated from this expression the product of the corresponding analogous expressions for $\mathbf{M}\,\xi_{\alpha_1}\ldots\xi_{\alpha_\varkappa}$ and $\mathbf{M}\,\xi_{\beta_1}\ldots\xi_{\beta_\lambda}$, we will find the pair correlation $\mathbf{K}\,[\xi_{\alpha_1}\ldots\xi_{\alpha_\varkappa},\ \xi_{\beta_1}\ldots\xi_{\beta_\lambda}]$. It does not tend toward zero as $\mu\to 0$, if $k_{\alpha_1\ldots\alpha_\varkappa\beta_1\ldots\beta_\lambda}$ does not tend toward zero, but the lower-order semi-invariants do tend to zero. This disagrees with the formula (1.20) and proves that the given semi-invariant also tends toward zero. Expressing $\ln\Theta(u_1,\ldots,u_{p+s})$ by semi-invariants according to known formulas, we become convinced that (1.21) follows from (1.22). The lemma is proven.

Lemma 1.2. Let there be given a family of random variables $\xi(\omega,y)$, $y\in\mathcal{I}$ which satisfies the continuity condition

$$\mathbf{M}[\xi(\omega,\eta(\omega))-\xi(\omega,\eta(\omega)+\zeta_\Delta(\omega))]^2\to 0, \qquad (1.22\text{-}1)$$

as $\mathbf{M}\,\zeta_\Delta^2(\omega)\to 0$. Here $\eta(\omega)$, $\zeta_\Delta(\omega)$ are any random variables (measurable functions of ω). Then with probability 1

$$\mathbf{P}[\xi(\omega,\eta(\omega))<z\,|\,\eta(\omega)]=\lim_{\Delta\to 0}\mathbf{P}[\xi(\omega,K_\omega\Delta)<z\,|\,K_\omega\Delta] \qquad (1.22\text{-}2)$$

where $K_\omega=\left[\frac{\eta(\omega)}{\Delta}\right]$ is the integral part of $\frac{\eta(\omega)}{\Delta}$.

Proof of Lemma 1.2. Let us consider the Δ-division $\{K\Delta\}$ of the interval $\mathcal{I}$, and denote by $K_\omega\equiv K(\eta(\omega))$ the number of the elementary interval $[K\Delta, K\Delta+\Delta)$ on which $\eta(\omega)$ falls. Clearly

$$\mathbf{M}[\eta(\omega)-K_\omega\Delta]^2<\Delta^2\to 0 \text{ as } \Delta\to 0.$$

Thus to $\zeta_\Delta(\omega)=\eta(\omega)-K_\omega\Delta$ we can apply relation (1.22-1), which takes the form

$$\mathbf{M}[\xi(\omega,K_\omega\Delta)-\xi(\omega,\eta(\omega))]^2\to 0 \text{ as } \Delta\to 0.$$

From this we easily conclude that the distribution $\mu_\Delta(d\xi)$ of the random variable $\xi(\omega,K_\omega\Delta)$ and the distribution $\mu_0(d\xi)$ of the variable $\xi(\omega,\eta(\omega))$ have the continuity property

$$\mathrm{Var}_\Omega(\mu_\Delta-\mu_0)\to 0 \text{ as } \Delta\to 0. \qquad (1.22\text{-}3)$$

Using the definition of conditional probabilities, from (1.22-3) we easily find that for any σ-algebra $\mathcal{F}_1\subset\mathfrak{M}$, with probability 1

$$\mathbf{P}\{\xi(\omega,K_\omega\Delta)<z\,|\,\mathcal{F}_1\}\to\mathbf{P}\{\xi(\omega,\eta(\omega))<z\,|\,\mathcal{F}_1\}. \qquad (1.22\text{-}4)$$

As $\mathcal{F}_1$, let us take a σ-algebra derived from sets $\eta(\omega) < \mathcal{C}$. Then we will have

$$\mathbf{P}[\xi(\omega, \eta(\omega)) < z \mid \eta(\omega)] = \lim_{\Delta\to 0} \mathbf{P}[\xi(\omega, \eta(\omega)) < z \mid K_\omega \Delta]$$
$$= \lim_{\Delta\to 0} \mathbf{P}[\xi(\omega, K_\omega\Delta) < z \mid K_\omega\Delta], \tag{1.22-5}$$

almost everywhere. The proof is finished.

Proof of Theorem 1.1. We will conduct the proof of assertion 1.1.A in two stages. In the first, we will prove that Lemma 1.1 (with $s = 1$) can be applied to the random variables

$$\xi_1 = \widetilde{f}_0^{t_1}(x_0), \ldots, \xi_p = \widetilde{f}_0^{t_p}(x_0), \ \xi_{p+1} = \widetilde{f}_{t_p}^{t_{p+1}}(y), \tag{1.23}$$

$$\left[\text{where } t_1 < \ldots < t_p < t_{p+1}; \ \omega \in \Omega'\left(0, x_0, \frac{t_p}{\mu^2}, \mu\right) \cap \right.$$
$$\left. \cap\, \Omega'\left(\frac{t_p}{\mu^2}, y, \frac{t_{p+1}}{\mu^2}, \mu\right)\right]$$

and consequently prove that these variables converge to independent ones. In the second stage it will be proven that 1.1.A results from this independence.

1) Using (1.13), we get the expansion

$$\xi_{\alpha_1} \ldots \xi_{\alpha_k} \xi_{p+1}^l = \sum_{mn\lambda_1\ldots\lambda_{m+n}} \frac{\partial^{\lambda_1+\ldots+\lambda_{m+n}}}{\partial y_1^{\lambda_1} \ldots \partial y_{m+n}^{\lambda_{m+n}}} \int \cdots \int_{\sigma_1,\ldots,\sigma_m \leqslant t_p} \int \cdots \int_{[t_p, t_{p+1}]} \mu^{-m-n} \times$$
$$\times \widetilde{g}(y_1, \sigma_1) \ldots \widetilde{g}(y_{m+n}, \sigma_{m+n}) \mathbf{Q}'_{mn\lambda_1\ldots\lambda_{mn}}(\sigma_1, \ldots, \sigma_{m+n})\, d\sigma_1 \ldots d\sigma_{m+n} \tag{1.24}$$

(after differentiation it is assumed that $y_1 = \ldots = y_m = x_0$; $y_{m+1} = \ldots = y_{m+n} = y$). Here $\mathbf{Q}_{mn\lambda_1\ldots\lambda_{m+n}}$ are new functions, expressed integrally by $Q_{q\rho_1\ldots\rho_q}$ and derivatives of $m(x)$. Thus, they are dependent on x_0 and y, but not on ω and μ (nor on $y_1, \ldots, y_{m+n}$). Let us average the Eq. (1.24) and express the moments $\mathbf{M}\,\widetilde{g}(y_1, \sigma_1) \ldots \widetilde{g}(y_{m+n}, \sigma_{m+n})$

in terms of the semi-invariants (1.14):

$$\mathbf{M}\tilde{g}(y_1, \sigma_1)\ldots\tilde{g}(y_{m+n}, \sigma_{m+n}) = \sum_{\sum_i r_i = m+n}^{*} \prod \tilde{k}_{r_i}(r_i \text{ pairs from } y_1, \sigma_1, \ldots, y_{m+n}, \sigma_{m+n}), \tag{1.25}$$

where Σ^* is the known (Kuznetsov, Stratonovich, Tikhonov [1], Leonov, Shiryaev [1]) symmetric finite sum over various partitions and permutations of the arguments. If from the moment $\mathbf{M}\xi_{\alpha_1}\ldots\xi_{\alpha_k}\xi^l_{p+1}$ we go to the semi-invariant

$$\mathbf{K}[\xi_{\alpha_1}\ldots\xi_{\alpha_k}, \xi^l_{p+1}] = \mathbf{M}\xi_{\alpha_1}\ldots\xi_{\alpha_k}\xi^l_{p+1} - \mathbf{M}\xi_{\alpha_1}\ldots\xi_{\alpha_k}\mathbf{M}\xi^l_{p+1}, \tag{1.26}$$

the number of terms of the sum Σ^* in the expression for $\mathbf{M}\xi_{\alpha_1}\ldots\xi_{\alpha_k}\xi^l_{p+1}$ will decrease: there will remain only "inseparable" products (according to the terminology of Leonov and Shiryaev). A product is called "inseparable" (in this case) if it contains at least one "mixed" factor. The factor $k_r(y_{i_1}, \sigma_{i_1}, \ldots, y_{i_r}, \sigma_{i_r})$ is called "mixed" if among its arguments there is at least one from the group $\sigma_1, \ldots, \sigma_m$ and also at least one argument from $\sigma_{m+1}, \ldots \sigma_{m+n}$. With the symbol Σ^{**} we will designate the sum of the inseparable terms of the sum Σ^*. Then we will have

$$\mathbf{K}[\xi_{\alpha_1}\ldots\xi_{\alpha_k}, \xi^l_{p+1}] = \sum_{mn\lambda_1\ldots\lambda_{m+n}} \frac{\partial^{\lambda_1+\ldots+\lambda_{m+n}}}{\partial y_1^{\lambda_1}\ldots\partial y_{m+n}^{\lambda_{m+n}}}\mu^{-m-n}\times$$
$$\times \int\limits_{\sigma_1,\ldots,\sigma_m\leqslant t_p}\!\!\cdots\!\int \int\limits_{t_p}^{t_{p+1}}\!\!\cdots\!\int \sum_{\Sigma r_i = m+n}^{**}\prod_i \tilde{k}_{r_i}(r_i \text{ pairs from } y_1, \sigma_1, \ldots, y_{m+n}, \sigma_{m+n})\times \tag{1.27}$$
$$\times\, \mathbf{Q}'_{mn\lambda_1\ldots\lambda_{m+n}}(\sigma_1, \ldots, \sigma_{m+n})\, d\sigma_1\ldots d\sigma_{m+n}.$$

The dominating series

$$\sum_{mn\lambda_1\ldots\lambda_{m+n}} \overline{\mathbf{Q}}'_{mn\lambda_1\ldots\lambda_{m+n}} \sum^{**}\int\limits_0^{t_p}\!\!\cdots\!\int \int\limits_{t_p}^{t_{p+1}}\!\!\cdots\!\int \mu^{-m-n}\times$$
$$\times\left|\frac{\partial^{\lambda_1+\ldots+\lambda_{m+n}}}{\partial y_1^{\lambda_1}\ldots\partial y_{m+n}^{\lambda_{m+n}}}\prod_i \tilde{k}_{r_i}\right| d\sigma_1\ldots d\sigma_{m+n}, \tag{1.28}$$

obviously exceeds $|K[\xi_{\alpha_1} \ldots \xi_{\alpha_k}, \xi^l_{p+1}]|$. Here

$$\overline{Q}'_{mn\lambda_1\ldots\lambda_{m+n}} = \sup \{Q'_{mn\lambda_1\ldots\lambda_{m+n}}(\sigma_1, \ldots, \sigma_{m+n}) : \sigma_1, \ldots, \sigma_m \in [0, t_p]; \sigma_{m+1}, \ldots, \sigma_{m+n} \in [t_p, t_{p+1}]\} < \infty.$$

We assume the convergence of the series

$$\sum_{mn\lambda_1\ldots\lambda_{m+n}} \overline{Q}'_{mn\lambda_1\ldots\lambda_{m+n}} \sum\nolimits^{**} \sup_{\mu_1 \leqslant \mu} \int_0^{t_p} \cdots \int \int_{t_p}^{t_{p+1}} \cdots \int \mu_1^{-m-n} \left| \frac{\partial^{\lambda_1+\ldots+\lambda_{m+n}}}{\partial y_1^{\lambda_1} \ldots \partial y_{m+n}^{\lambda_{m+n}}} \prod_i \widetilde{k}_{r_i} \right| d\sigma_1 \ldots d\sigma_{m+n} < \infty. \tag{1.29}$$

Here the sums (1.27), (1.28) will tend to zero as $\mu \to 0$, if every term of the series tends to zero. In fact, it is easily shown that the sum of a converging series tends to zero as $\mu \to 0$ if all terms of this series are positive, decrease as $\mu \to 0$ and tend to zero.

We will prove that every term of the series (1.28) [and consequently (1.27)] tends to zero as $\mu \to 0$. We will examine a typical term $\overline{Q}'_{mn\lambda_1\ldots\lambda_{m+n}} S$, where

$$S = \int_0^{t_p} \cdots \int \int_{t_p}^{t_{p+1}} \cdots \int \left| \frac{\partial^{\lambda_1+\ldots+\lambda_{m+n}}}{\partial y_1^{\lambda_1} \ldots \partial y_{m+n}^{\lambda_{m+n}}} \prod_i \widetilde{k}_{r_i} \right| \mu^{-m-n} d\sigma_1 \ldots d\sigma_{m+n}.$$

This expression breaks up into a product of integrals

$$S = \prod_i S_i,$$

$$S_i = \int \cdots \int \left| \frac{\partial^{\nu_1+\ldots+\nu_{r_i}}}{\partial x_1^{\nu_1} \ldots \partial x_{r_i}^{\nu_{r_i}}} \widetilde{k}_{r_i}(x_1, \sigma'_1, \ldots, x_{r_i}, \sigma'_{r_i}) \right| \times \mu^{-r_i} d\sigma'_1 \ldots d\sigma'_{r_i}, \tag{1.30}$$

where $x_1, \sigma'_1, \ldots, x_{r_i}, \sigma'_{r_i}$ represent r_i pairs from $y_1, \sigma_1, \ldots, y_{m+n}, \sigma_{m+n}$. After differentiation with respect to x_j, it is necessary to assume $x_j = x_0$ if $x_j \in \{y_1, \ldots, y_m\}$ and $x_j = y$ if $x_j \in \{y_{m+1}, \ldots, y_{m+n}\}$. The integration is carried out over the interval $\sigma'_j \in [0, t_p]$ if $\sigma'_j \in \{\sigma_1, \ldots, \sigma_m\}$ and over the interval $[t_p, t_{p+1}]$ if $\sigma'_j \in \{\sigma_{m+1}, \ldots, \sigma_{m+n}\}$. The factor is unmixed if all its arguments $\sigma'_1, \ldots, \sigma'_r$ belong to one group $\sigma_1, \ldots, \sigma_m$ or $\sigma_{m+1}, \ldots, \sigma_{m+n}$. Let us say they belong to the first group; then the integration in (1.29) is carried out over the region $[0, t_p] \times \ldots \times [0, t_p]$.

Having made the change of variables $\tau_j = \mu^2 \sigma_j$, we have

$$S_i = \mu^{r_i} \int_0^{t_p/\mu^2} \ldots \int_0^{t_p/\mu^2} \left| \frac{\partial^{\nu_1+\ldots+\nu_{r_i}}}{\partial x_1^{\nu_1} \ldots \partial x_{r_i}^{\nu_{r_i}}} k_{r_i} \right| d\tau_1 \ldots d\tau_{r_i}.$$

We break up the region of integration $[0, \mu^{-2}t_p] \times \ldots \times [0, \mu^{-2}t_p]$ into $r_i(r_i-1)$ subregions and fix the largest and second largest of the arguments. Then

$$S_i = \sum \mu^{r_i} \int_0^{t_p/\mu^2} d\tau' \int_0^{\tau'} d\tau'' \int_0^{\tau''} \ldots \int_0^{\tau''} \left| \frac{\partial^{\nu_1+\ldots+\nu_{r_i}}}{\partial x_1^{\nu_1} \ldots \partial x_{r_i}^{\nu_{r_i}}} k_{r_i} \right| d\tau_1' \ldots d\tau_{r_i-2}',$$

where the sum contains $r_i(r_i-1)$ terms. Using the characteristic of stationarity and the identity

$$\int_0^t d\tau' \int_0^{\tau'} \varphi(\tau' - \tau'')\, d\tau'' = \int_0^t d\tau' \int_0^{\tau'} \varphi(\tau)\, d\tau = \int_0^t (t-\tau)\, \varphi(\tau)\, d\tau,$$

we obtain

$$S_i = \sum \mu^{r_i} \int_0^{t_p/\mu^2} \left(\frac{t_p}{\mu^2} - \tau \right) \times$$

$$\times \int_0^{\tau} \ldots \int_0^{\tau} \left| \frac{\partial^{\nu_1'+\ldots+\nu_{r_i}'}}{\partial x_1^{\nu_1'} \ldots \partial x_{r_i}^{\nu_{r_i}'}} k_{r_i}'(\tau, -\pi_1, \ldots, -\pi_{r_i-2}) \right| d\pi_1 \ldots d\pi_{r_i-2}. \tag{1.31}$$

$$(\tau = \tau' - \tau'', \ \pi_j = \tau'' - \tau_j').$$

According to (1.15) this expression tends to a finite limit as $\mu \to 0$.

Among the factors ΠS_i, as was noted earlier, it is known that there is at least one "mixed" factor. Among its arguments there are $u > 0$ from the group $\sigma_1, \ldots, \sigma_m$ and $r_i - u > 0$ arguments from $\sigma_{m+1}, \ldots, \sigma_{m+n}$. For this type of factor, after the change of variables $\tau_j = \mu^2 \sigma_j$, we will have

$$S_i = \mu^{r_i} \int_0^{\mu^{-2} t_p} \ldots \int \int_{\mu^{-2} t_p}^{\mu^{-2} t_{p+1}} \ldots \int \left| \frac{\partial^{\nu_1+\ldots+\nu_{r_i}}}{\partial x_1^{\nu_1} \ldots \partial x_{r_i}^{\nu_{r_i}}} k_{r_i}(x_1, \tau_1, \ldots, x_{r_i}, \tau_{r_i}) \right| \times$$

$$\times\, d\tau_1 \ldots d\tau_{r_i}$$

or if we designate $L = \mu^{-2} \max (t_p, t_{p+1} - t_p) = \mu^{-2} L_0$ and use the characteristic of stationarity

$$S_i \leqslant \mu^{r_i} \int_{-L}^{0} \cdots \int \int_{0}^{L} \cdots \int \left| \frac{\partial^{\nu_1 + \cdots}}{\partial x_1^{\nu_1} \cdots} k_{r_i} (x_1, \tau_1, \ldots, x_{r_i}, \tau_{r_i}) \right| \times \\ \times d\tau_1 \ldots d\tau_{r_i}.$$

Let

$$\tau' = \max (\tau_1, \ldots, \tau_u); \quad \tau'' = \min (\tau_{u+1}, \ldots, \tau_{r_i}),$$

then

$$S_i \leqslant \sum \mu^{r_i} \int_{-L}^{0} d\tau' \int_{-L}^{\tau'} \cdots \int d\tau_1' \ldots \\ \ldots d\tau_{u-1}' \int_{0}^{L} d\tau'' \int_{\tau''}^{L} \cdots \int \left| \frac{\partial^{\nu_1 + \cdots}}{\partial x_1^{\nu_1} \cdots} k_{r_i} \right| d\tau_1'' \ldots d\tau_{r_i - u - 1}'' \leqslant \\ \leqslant \sum \mu^{r_i} \int_{-L}^{0} d\tau' \int_{\tau' - L}^{\tau'} \cdots \int d\tau_1' \ldots \\ \ldots d\tau_{u-1}' \int_{0}^{L} d\tau'' \int_{\tau''}^{\tau'' + L} \cdots \int \left| \frac{\partial^{\nu_1 + \cdots}}{\partial x_1^{\nu_1} \cdots} k_{r_i} \right| d\tau_1'' \ldots d\tau_{r_i - u - 1}'' . \tag{1.32}$$

Here the sum contains $u(r_i - u)$ terms, corresponding to the regions $\tau' = \tau_j$, $\tau'' = \tau_k$; $j = 1, \ldots, u$; $k = u + 1, \ldots, r_i$.

It is easily seen that for any integrable nonnegative function $\varphi(\tau', \tau'')$ the inequality

$$\int_{-L}^{0} d\tau' \int_{0}^{L} \varphi(\tau', \tau'') \, d\tau'' \leqslant \int_{0}^{2L} d\tau \int_{0}^{\tau} \varphi(\tau'' - \tau, \tau'') \, d\tau'' \tag{1.33}$$

is true, inasmuch as the area of integration on the right side is greater. In our case

$$\varphi(\tau', \tau'') = \int_{\tau' - L}^{\tau'} \cdots \int d\tau_1' \ldots d\tau_{u-1}' \int_{\tau''}^{\tau'' + L} \cdots \int \left| \frac{\partial^{\nu_1 + \cdots}}{\partial x_1^{\nu_1} \cdots} k_{r_i} (\tau', \tau_1', \ldots \right. \\ \left. \ldots, \tau_{u-1}', \tau'', \tau_1'', \ldots, \tau_{r_i - u - 1}'') \right| d\tau_1'' \ldots d\tau_{r_i - u - 1}'' =$$

$$= \int_0^L \cdots \int d\zeta_1 \ldots d\zeta_{u-1} \int_0^L \cdots \int \left| \frac{\partial^{\nu_1 + \cdots}}{\partial x_1^{\nu_1} \cdots} k_{r_i}(\tau', \tau' - \zeta_1, \ldots \right.$$

$$\left. \ldots, \tau' - \zeta_{u-1}, \tau'', \tau'' + \pi_1, \ldots, \tau'' + \pi_{r_i - u - 1}) \right| d\pi_1 \ldots d\pi_{r_i - u - 1}.$$

This function depends only on the difference $\tau'' - \tau' = \tau$; thus the integration with respect to τ'' on the right side of (1.33) is reduced to multiplication by τ. Applying (1.33) to (1.32), we have

$$S_i \leqslant \sum \left(\frac{L_0}{L} \right)^{\frac{r_i}{2}} \int_0^{2L} \tau d\tau \int_0^L \cdots \int \left| \frac{\partial^{\nu_1 + \cdots}}{\partial x_1^{\nu_1} \cdots} k'_{r_i}(-\zeta_1, \ldots \right.$$

$$\left. \ldots, -\zeta_{u-1}, \tau, \tau + \pi_1, \ldots, \tau + \pi_{r_i - u - 1}) \right| d\zeta_1 \ldots$$

$$\ldots d\zeta_{u-1} d\pi_1 \ldots d\pi_{r_i - u - 1}.$$

As a consequence of (1.16) this expression tends to zero as $L \to \infty$, $\mu \to 0$.

Thus, among the factors of ΠS_i there is at least one tending to zero as $\mu \to 0$, while the remaining ones tend to a lower degree toward bounded limits. This proves that every term of the sum (1.28), and, consequently, the whole sum, tends toward zero. Thus the semi-invariant (1.26) tends toward zero. In the same way, condition (1.20) of Lemma 1.1 is proven. The application of this lemma proves that the distribution of the random variables (1.23) converges entirely to a distribution in which the variable $\xi_{p+1} = \tilde{f}_{t_p}^{t_{p+1}}(y)$ is independent of the remaining ones.

2) Until now the value y in $\tilde{x}(\tilde{t}) = \tilde{f}_{t_p}^{\tilde{t}}(y)$, $\tilde{t} > t_p$ has been an independent variable. If we are interested in the uninterrupted trajectory $\tilde{x}(\tilde{t}) = \tilde{f}_0^{\tilde{t}}(x_0)$, this value should be chosen in such a manner that $y = \tilde{f}_0^{t_p}(x_0)$.

To justify this substitution we will use Lemma 1.2 with $\xi(\omega, y) = \tilde{f}_{t_p}^{t_{p+1}}(y)$; $\eta(\omega) = \tilde{x}(t_p)$. Condition (1.22-1) is satisfied since the function $\tilde{f}_{t_p}^{t_{p+1}}(y)$ in (1.13) is differentiable with respect to y by assumption 1.A$_2$. We have

$$\mathsf{M}\left[\tilde{f}_{t_p}^{t_{p+1}}(y + \zeta_\Delta) - \tilde{f}_{t_p}^{t_{p+1}}(y) \right]^2 = \mathsf{M}\left[\frac{\partial}{\partial y} \tilde{f}_{t_p}^{t_{p+1}}(y + \Theta\zeta_\Delta) \zeta_\Delta \right] \leqslant$$

$$\leqslant \left\{ \mathrm{M}\left[\frac{\partial}{\partial y}\tilde{f}_{t_p}^{t_{p+1}}\right]^2 \mathrm{M}\zeta_\Delta^2 \right\}^{1/2} \qquad (0 \leqslant \Theta \leqslant 1). \tag{1.34}$$

To evaluate $\mathrm{M}\left[\frac{\partial}{\partial y}\tilde{f}_{t_p}^{t_{p+1}}\right]^2$, we will substitute (1.13) and after averaging use property $1.A_2$ for the moments (1.2). This yields

$$\mathrm{M}\left[\frac{\partial}{\partial y}\tilde{f}_{t_p}^{t_{p+1}}\right]^2 < \infty \tag{1.35}$$

(if the series converges). Thus condition (1.22-1) is, in fact, satisfied for these random variables. Equations (1.28) and (1.29) are retained in the limit as $\mu \to 0$ because of the assumptions in Theorem 1.1 on the boundedness of the limits (1.15), (1.16). The terms of the sum forming $\mathrm{M}\left[\frac{\partial}{\partial y}\tilde{f}_{t_p}^{t_{p+1}}\right]^2$ in this case tend to finite limits. Thus Lemma 1.2 can also be applied to the limit distributions figuring in Lemma 1.1.

Let us examine the passage to the limit as $\mu \to 0$, using Lemma 1.1 [with $\xi_{p+1} = \tilde{f}_{t_p}^{t_{p+1}}(y)$]. According to this lemma,

$$\mathrm{P}\left[\tilde{x}(t_1) < z_1, \ldots, \tilde{x}(t_p) < z_p \,;\, \tilde{f}_{t_p}^{t_{p+1}}(y) < z_{p+1}\right] \xrightarrow{\text{ent.}} F_1(z_1, \ldots, z_p) F_2(z_{p+1}|y). \tag{1.36}$$

With the notation $F_2(z_{p+1}) \equiv F_2(z_{p+1}|y)$ we stressed that the function F_2 depends on $y \in \mathfrak{I}$. If we pass to conditional probabilities, from this we will have

$$\mathrm{P}\left[\tilde{f}_{t_p}^{t_{p+1}}(y) < z_{p+1} \,|\, \tilde{x}(t_1) = z_1, \ldots, \tilde{x}(t_p) = z_p\right] \to F_2(z_{p+1} \,|\, y) \tag{1.37}$$

with probability 1.

Let us apply Lemma 1.2 to both sides of this equation. Here $\tilde{f}_{t_p}^{t_{p+1}}(\eta(\omega)) = \tilde{f}_{t_p}^{t_{p+1}}(\tilde{x}(t_p))$ coincides with $\tilde{x}(t_{p+1})$. From (1.37), assuming $y = K_\omega\Delta = \left[\frac{\tilde{x}(t_p)}{\Delta}\right]\Delta$ according to (1.22-1), we obtain with probability 1

$$\mathrm{P}\{\tilde{x}(t_{p+1}) < z_{p+1} \,|\, \tilde{x}(t_1) = z_1, \ldots, \tilde{x}(t_p) = z_p\} \xrightarrow{\text{ent.}} F_2(z_{p+1} \,|\, z_p). \tag{1.38}$$

This completes the proof of Assertion 1.1.A of the theorem. The multidimensional probability

$$\mathbf{P}\,[\tilde{x}(t_1) < z_1, \ \ldots \ , \tilde{x}(t_n) < z_n] = \int\limits_{z'_1<z_1} \ldots \int\limits_{z'_n<z_n} d\mathbf{P}\,[\tilde{x}(t_1) < z'_1] \times$$

$$\times\, d\mathbf{P}\,[\tilde{x}(t_2) < z'_2 \,|\, z'_1] \ldots d\mathbf{P}\,[\tilde{x}(t_n) < z'_n \,|\, z'_1, \ \ldots \ , z'_{n-1}]$$
$$(t_1 < \ldots . < t_n)$$

in agreement with (1.38) will tend entirely to

$$\int\limits_{z'_1<z_1} \ldots \int\limits_{z'_n<z_n} d\mathbf{P}\,[\tilde{x}(t_1) < z'_1]\, dF_2(z'_2 \,|\, z'_1) \ldots dF_2(z'_n \,|\, z'_{n-1}).$$

From this it is easy to deduce that the function $F_2(z \,|\, y)$ satisfies the Markov equation

$$F_2(z_3 \,|\, z_1) = \int dF_2(z_2 \,|\, z_1)\, F_2(z_3 \,|\, z_2).$$

For this we need to take into account that

$$\int d\mathbf{P}\,[\tilde{x}(t_2) < z_2 \,|\, \ldots , z_1]\, \mathbf{P}\,[\tilde{x}(t_3) < z_3 \,| \ \ldots \ , z_1, z_2] \xrightarrow{\text{ent.}}$$

$$\rightarrow \int dF_2(z_2 \,|\, z_1)\, F_2(z_3 \,|\, z_2),$$

when

$$\mathbf{P}\,[\tilde{x}(t_2) < z_2 \,|\, \ldots , z_1] \xrightarrow{\text{ent.}} F_2(z_2 \,|\, z_1),$$
$$\mathbf{P}\,[\tilde{x}(t_3) < z_3 \,| \ \ldots \ , z_1, z_2] \xrightarrow{\text{ent.}} F_2(z_3 \,|\, z_2).$$

3) We now turn to the proof of Assertion 1.1.B.

According to Assertion 1.1.A, for the calculation of the transition probabilities $\mathbf{P}\,[x_{\text{M}}(t_{p+1}) < z_{p+1} \,|\, z_1, \ \ldots \ , z_p] = F_2(z_{p+1} \,|\, z_p)$, it is possible to assume $p = 0$, $t_p = 0$, $y = x_0$ in (1.23), that is, to examine only one random variable $\xi_1 = \tilde{f}_0^{t_1}(x_0)$. In the calculation of its moments in formula (1.24) we assume $k = 0$, $m = 0$. Making the substitution $\mu^{-2}\sigma_i = \tau_i$, we have

$$\mathbf{M}\,\xi_1^l = \sum_{n\lambda_1 \ldots \lambda_n} \frac{\partial^{\lambda_1 + \ldots + \lambda_n}}{\partial y_1^{\lambda_1} \ldots \partial y_n^{\lambda_n}} \int\limits_0^{\mu^{-2}t_1} \ldots \int \mu^n\, \mathbf{M} g(y_1, \tau_1) \ldots g(y_n, \tau_n)$$

$$\mathbf{Q}'_{0n\lambda_1 \ldots \lambda_n}(\mu^2\tau_1, \ \ldots \ , \mu^2\tau_n)\, d\tau_1 \ldots d\tau_n.$$

Using (1.25), the terms of this expansion can be presented in the form of a product of factors (1.31). According to conditions (1.15), (1.18), the terms with $n \geqslant 3$ tend to zero as $\mu \to 0$. Since according to (1.11) the term with the first moment is absent, in the sum over n there are left only the terms with $n = 0$ and $n = 2$:

$$\lim_{\mu\to 0} \mathbf{M}\, \xi_1^s = \mathbf{Q}'_{00} + \sum_{\lambda_1\lambda_2} \frac{\partial^{\lambda_1+\lambda_2}}{\partial y_1^{\lambda_1}\,\partial y_2^{\lambda_2}} \lim_{\mu\to 0} \int_0^{\mu^{-2}t_1}\int_0^{\mu^{-2}t_1} k_2(y_1, \tau_1, y_2, \tau_2) \times$$
$$\times\, \mathbf{Q}'_{02\lambda_1\lambda_2}(\mu^2\tau_1, \mu^2\tau_2)\, d\tau_1\, d\tau_2.$$

For completion of the proof it is necessary to take into account the explicit form of the functions $\mathbf{Q}_{00}$, $\mathbf{Q}_{02\lambda_1\lambda_2}$. For this we need to turn to relations (1.7), (1.8). Substituting into them (1.10) and taking into account that only terms not containing moments of g at all and terms containing moments of the second order remain, we obtain

$$\lim_{\mu\to 0} \mathbf{M}\,[\widetilde{x}(t_1) - y] = \int (z - y)\, dF_2(z \mid y) = m(y)\, t_1 +$$
$$+ t_1 \lim_{L\to\infty} \frac{1}{L}\int_0^L d\tau \int_0^\tau \mathbf{M}\frac{\partial g(y, \tau)}{\partial y} g(y, \tau')\, d\tau' + O(t_1^2) \quad (L = \mu^{-2} t_1). \tag{1.39}$$

$O(t_1^2)$ designates the sum of other terms that remain as $\mu \to 0$. Each of them is dependent on t_1 at least quadratically, and a convergence condition for this sum is a considerably weaker condition than the condition of convergence of (1.29).

Analogously we find

$$\lim_{\mu\to 0} \mathbf{M}\,[\widetilde{x}(t_1) - y]^2 = \int (z - y)^2\, dF_2(z \mid y) =$$
$$= t_1 \lim_{L\to\infty} \frac{1}{L}\int_0^L\int_0^L \mathbf{M}\, g(y, \tau)\, g(y, \tau')\, d\tau\, d\tau' + O(t_1^2); \tag{1.40}$$

$$\lim_{\mu\to 0} \mathbf{M}\,[\widetilde{x}(t_1) - y]^q = \int (z - y)^q\, dF_2(z \mid y) = O(t_1^2), \qquad q \geqslant 3.$$

The proof is finished, since the limits (as $L \to \infty$) on the right sides of (1.39), (1.40) exist on the strength of (1.15) and are correspondingly equal to the expressions entering into (1.17).

Note. The assertion and proof of Theorem 1.1 can be generalized to the case when the function $G(x, t, \omega, \mu)$ is not stationary but limits of the type (1.17), (1.39), (1.40) exist and do not depend on time. Such a generalization is of interest because it allows the examination of periodic nonstationary functions G often encountered in the theory of fluctuations (see, for example, the monograph by Stratonovich [8]). Thus the theory of the present chapter gives a strong basis for a series of results not strictly obtained in that monograph.

1.3 Another Formulation of the Theorem

The condition in Theorem 1.1 that the series (1.29) converge is not easily checked in specific cases. In addition, condition 1.A_2, the analyticity of the functions of x, is not quite necessary. Thus, it is of interest to examine other conditions under which the original process converges to a Markov process. Aside from these deficiencies, the formulation of Theorem 1.1 presented in Sect. 1.2 has the advantage that conditions (1.14) and (1.15) for semi-invariants of finite dimension are imposed in it. If, however, we change conditions 1.A_2 and 1.A_3 and do not generate the series expansions of Sect. 1.2, we will also have to change conditions (1.14) and (1.15). In their place we will have to impose limits on the distributions. This is apparent from the formulation given below.

Theorem 1.2. Let $\tilde{x}(\tilde{t})$ be a solution of Eq. (1.12), where the functions

$$m(x)\ ,\ \ g(x,t,\omega)=\tilde{g}(x,\tilde{t},\omega)$$

(g being measurable with respect to t and ω) satisfy the following conditions:

1.2.A. The functions are differentiable and uniformly bounded:

$$|m|\ ,\ \left|\frac{\partial m}{\partial x}\right|\ ,\ \left|\frac{\partial^2 m}{\partial x^2}\right|\ ,\ |g|\ ,\ \left|\frac{\partial g}{\partial x}\right|\ ,\ \left|\frac{\partial^2 g}{\partial x^2}\right|<\mathcal{C}. \qquad (1.41)$$

1.2.B. For any given

$$k, C_1, \ldots, C_{k+3} \text{ and } B \in \mathfrak{F}(C_{k+1}T, C_{k+2}T, C_{k+3}T)$$
$$(C_i<C_{i+1})$$

with probability 1

$$|\,\mathbf{P}[B\,|\,\mathfrak{F}(C_1T,\ldots,C_kT)]-\mathbf{P}[B]\,|\leqslant\beta(C_{k+1}T-C_kT)\,\mathbf{P}[B]. \qquad (1.42)$$

Here $\beta(T)=O(T^{-2-\alpha})$, $\alpha>0$ does not depend on $K, C_1, \ldots, C_{k+3}, B$ and is a uniformly bounded function; $\mathfrak{F}(t_1, \ldots, t_r)=\bigcup\limits_{i=1}^{r-1}\mathfrak{F}_{t_i}^{t_{i+1}}$; the σ-algebras $\mathfrak{F}_s^t$ are generated by ω-sets;

$$\int\limits_s^t g(x,t',\omega)\,dt'<\mathcal{C};\quad \int\limits_s^t dt'\int\limits_s^{t'} dt''\,\frac{\partial g}{\partial x}(x,t',\omega)\,g(x,t'',\omega)<\mathcal{C}.$$

1.2.C. There exist bounded limits

$$\begin{aligned}&\lim_{T\to\infty}\frac{1}{T}\int\limits_{t_0}^{t_0+T}ds\int\limits_{t_0}^{t_0+T}dt\,\mathbf{M}\,g(x,s,\omega)\,g(x',t,\omega)=\overline{a}(x,x');\\ &\lim_{T\to\infty}\frac{1}{T}\int\limits_{t_0}^{t_0+T}ds\int\limits_{t_0-T}^{s}dt\,\mathbf{M}\,\frac{\partial g}{\partial x}(x,s,\omega)\,g(x,t,\omega)=\overline{k}(x),\end{aligned}\tag{1.43}$$

which do not depend on t_0, where $\overline{a}(x,x')$, $\overline{k}(x)$ have bounded derivatives $\partial^2\overline{a}/\partial x\partial x'$, $\partial\overline{k}/\partial x$.

Then on any finite segment $0\leqslant t\leqslant\tau_0$ the process $\widetilde{x}(\widetilde{t})$ converges (in the sense of convergence of distributions of finite dimension, or of weak convergence) to a continuous (with probability 1) Markov process, the local characteristics of which are expressed in terms of the limits (1.43) using the usual formulas (1.17).

Proof. 1) We will introduce the Δ-division of the interval $[0,\tau_0]$ by the points $\mu^2T_k=\mu^2kT=k\Delta$. As can be seen from (1.12), for any $\widetilde{s},\widetilde{t}$ we have

$$\widetilde{x}(\widetilde{t})-\widetilde{x}(\widetilde{s})=\mathcal{O}\left(\frac{\widetilde{t}-\widetilde{s}}{\mu}\right).$$

From this, using (1.41) we obtain

$$\begin{aligned}g\left(\widetilde{x}(\widetilde{s}),\frac{\widetilde{s}}{\mu^2},\omega\right)-g\left(\widetilde{x}(j\Delta-2\Delta),\frac{\widetilde{s}}{\mu^2},\omega\right)=\frac{\partial g}{\partial x}\left(\widetilde{x}(j\Delta-2\Delta),\frac{\widetilde{s}}{\mu^2},\omega\right)\left[\widetilde{x}(\widetilde{s})-\right.\\ \left.-\widetilde{x}(j\Delta-2\Delta)\right]+\mathcal{O}\left(\left(\frac{s-j\Delta+2\Delta}{\mu}\right)^2\right);\end{aligned}\tag{1.44}$$

$$m(\widetilde{x}(\widetilde{t}))-m(\widetilde{x}(j\Delta-2\Delta))=\mathcal{O}\left(\frac{s-j\Delta+2\Delta}{\mu}\right).$$

Substituting (1.44) into the obvious equation

$$\tilde{x}(j\Delta + \Delta) - \tilde{x}(j\Delta) = \int_{j\Delta}^{j\Delta+\Delta} m(\tilde{x}(\tilde{s}))\, d\tilde{s} + \frac{1}{\mu} \int_{j\Delta}^{j\Delta+\Delta} \tilde{g}(\tilde{x}(\tilde{s}), \tilde{s}, \omega)\, d\tilde{s}, \quad (1.45)$$

and taking into account that

$$\tilde{x}(\tilde{t}) - \tilde{x}(j\Delta - 2\Delta) = \frac{1}{\mu} \int_{j\Delta - 2\Delta}^{\tilde{t}} g\left(\tilde{x}(j\Delta - 2\Delta), \frac{\tilde{s}}{\mu^2}, \omega\right) d\tilde{s} + \mathcal{O}\left(\frac{\Delta^2}{\mu^2}\right)$$

for

$$\tilde{t} \in [j\Delta, j\Delta + \Delta]$$

we find for $j = 1, 2, \ldots$ the equation

$$\tilde{x}(j\Delta + \Delta) - \tilde{x}(j\Delta) = \Lambda_j(\tilde{x}(j\Delta - 2\Delta)) + R_k \Delta, \quad (1.46)$$

where

$$R_k \Delta = \mathcal{O}\left(\frac{\Delta^3}{\mu^3}\right) = \mathcal{O}(\mu^3 T^3) \quad (1.47)$$

and

$$\Lambda_j(x) = \mu \xi_j(x) + \mu^2 \eta_j(x) + \mu^2 m(x) T;$$

$$\xi_j(x) = \int_{jT}^{jT+T} g(x, s, \omega)\, ds; \quad (1.48)$$

$$\eta_j(x) = \int_{jT}^{jT+T} ds \int_{jT-T}^{s} dt \frac{\partial g}{\partial x}(x, s, \omega)\, g(x, t, \omega).$$

If we now choose a τ_1, τ_2 from $[0, \tau_0]$ and sum (1.46) over j, evaluating the differences $\tilde{x}\left(\Delta\left[\frac{\tau_i}{\Delta}\right] + \Delta\right) - \tilde{x}(\tau_i)$ $(i = 1, 2)$ using (1.44), we have

$$\tilde{x}(\tau_2) - \tilde{x}(\tau_1) = \sum_{j=l}^{m-1} \Lambda_j(\tilde{x}(j\Delta - 2\Delta)) + (\tau_2 - \tau_1)\, o(1), \quad m = \left[\frac{\tau_2}{\Delta}\right], \quad l = \left[\frac{\tau_1}{\Delta}\right] \quad (1.49)$$

(the square brackets indicate the integral part). Here it is assumed that $\Delta^2/\mu^3 = o(1)$, i.e., an appropriate dependence $T(\mu)$, $\Delta(\mu) = \mu^2 T(\mu)$ is selected, e.g.,

$$T(\mu) = \mu^{-\frac{2}{4+\alpha}}; \quad \Delta = \mu^{\frac{6+2\alpha}{4+\alpha}}. \tag{1.50}$$

For such a dependence the value of (1.47) can be estimated as

$$R_k = \mathcal{O}\left(\frac{\Delta^2}{\mu^3}\right) = \mathcal{O}\left(\mu^{\frac{\alpha}{4+\alpha}}\right) = o(1). \tag{1.51}$$

2) We will now examine a new auxiliary random process $z(\tilde{t})$, defined by a recurrence relation simpler than that in (1.46),

$$\begin{gathered} z(j\Delta + \Delta) - z(j\Delta) = \Lambda_j(z(j\Delta - 2\Delta)) \\ (j = 0, 1, \dots; \quad z(-2\Delta) = z(-\Delta) = z(0)). \end{gathered} \tag{1.52}$$

Its initial value $z(0)$ coincides with $\tilde{x}(0) = x_0$ and is nonrandom (does not depend on ω). At intermediate points $\tilde{t} \in (j\Delta, j\Delta + \Delta)$, we determine it by the formulas

$$\begin{gathered} z(\tilde{t}) = z(j\Delta) + \mu\xi_j'(z(j\Delta - 2\Delta)) + \mu^2\eta_j'(z(j\Delta - 2\Delta)) + m(z(j\Delta - 2\Delta))(\tilde{t} - j\Delta); \\ \xi_j'(x) = \int_{jT}^{\tilde{t}/\mu^2} g(x, s, \omega)\, ds; \quad \eta_j'(x) = \int_{jT}^{\tilde{t}/\mu^2} ds \int_{jT-T}^{s} dt \frac{\partial g}{\partial x}(x, t, \omega)\, g(x, t, \omega), \end{gathered} \tag{1.53}$$

analogous to (1.48). Then the value $z(\tilde{t})$ for $\tilde{t} \in (j\Delta, j\Delta + \Delta]$ will be a function of ω, measurable with respect to the σ-algebra $\mathfrak{F}(0, T, \dots, jT, \tilde{t}/\mu^2)$. The σ-algebra $\mathfrak{Y}$ formed by the sets $z(j\Delta - 2\Delta) < C$ will enter into $\mathfrak{F}(0, T, \dots, jT - 2T)$.

Let us take a particular y and examine the mathematical expectation $\mathbf{M}[\xi_j(y) \mid \mathfrak{F}(0, \dots, jT - 2T)]$ using condition (1.42). Since $\xi_j(y)$ is $\mathfrak{F}(jT, jT + T)$ measurable, from (1.42) we have (for $k = j - 2$)

$$|\xi_j(y)\mathbf{P}[d\omega \mid \mathfrak{F}(0, \dots, jT - 2T)] - \xi_j(y)\mathbf{P}[d\omega]| \leqslant \beta(T)|\xi_j(y)|\mathbf{P}[d\omega].$$

From this, integrating with respect to ω, we obtain

$$|\mathbf{M}[\xi_j(y) \mid \mathfrak{F}(0, \dots, jT - 2T)] - \mathbf{M}\xi_j(y)| \leqslant \beta(T)\mathbf{M}|\xi_j(y)|.$$

But $|\xi_j(y)| \leqslant CT$, on the strength of (1.41) and (1.48), and $\mathbf{M}\xi_j(y) = 0$

in agreement with (1.11), hence

$$\mathrm{M}[\xi_j(y)\,|\,\mathfrak{F}(0,\ldots,jT-2T)] = \beta(T)\mathcal{O}(T). \tag{1.54}$$

We will use the freedom in selecting y, and choose $y = z(j\Delta - 2\Delta)$. Here we will use Lemma 1.2 with $\xi(\omega, y) = \xi_j(y)$; $\eta(\omega) = z(j\Delta - 2\Delta)$. Condition (1.22-1) of the lemma is satisfied, since

$$|\,\xi_j(\eta + \zeta_\Delta) - \xi_j(\eta)\,| \leqslant CT\zeta_\Delta$$

on the strength of (1.41) and (1.48). In agreement with (1.22-2), from (1.54), since $\mathcal{Y} \subset \mathfrak{F}(0,\ldots,jT-2T)$, we will have

$$\mathrm{M}[\xi_j(z(j\Delta - 2\Delta))\,|\,\mathfrak{F}(0,\ldots,jT-2T)] = \beta(T)\,o(T) \tag{1.55}$$

with probability 1.

An analogous formula can also be obtained for η_j. Namely,

$$\mathrm{M}[\eta_j(z(j\Delta - 2\Delta))\,|\,\mathfrak{F}(0,\ldots,jT-2T)] = T\bar{k}(j\Delta - 2\Delta)) + \beta(T)\,o(T^2) + o(T). \tag{1.56}$$

We have now used the condition that $\eta_j(y)$ is measurable relative to the σ-algebra $\mathfrak{F}(jT-T, jT, jT+T)$, formula (1.42) with $k = j-2$, the estimate $|\eta_j| \leqslant C^2T^2$, and the relation

$$\mathrm{M}\eta_j(y) = \bar{k}(y)T + o(T),$$

which follows from (1.43).

Formulas (1.55) and (1.56), and other analogous formulas, allow us to obtain a series of preliminary results relative to the behavior of the process $z(\tilde{t})$.

a) We will examine the difference $z(\tau_2) - z(\tau_1)$, $\tau_2, \tau_1 \in [0, \tau_0]$. For it, in agreement with (1.52) and (1.53), we have

$$z(\tau_2) - z(\tau_1) = \sum_{j=l+2}^{m-1} \Lambda_j(z(j\Delta - 2\Delta)) + o(\Delta). \tag{1.56-1}$$

The conditional mathematical expectation of this can thus be written

$$\mathrm{M}[z(\tau_2) - z(\tau_1)\,|\,\mathfrak{F}] = \mathrm{M}\left\{\sum_{j=l+2}^{m-1} \mathrm{M}[\Lambda_j(z(j\Delta - 2\Delta))\,|\,\mathfrak{F}(0,\ldots,jT-2T)]\,|\,\mathfrak{F}\right\} + o(\Delta)$$

where $\mathfrak{F} \equiv \mathfrak{F}(0,\ldots,lT) \subset \mathfrak{F}(0,\ldots,jT-2T)$. Substituting the estimates (1.55) and (1.56) into this, we have

$$\mathbf{M}[z(\tau_2)-z(\tau_1)\,|\,\mathfrak{F}]=\mathbf{M}\left\{\Delta\sum_{j=l+2}^{m-1}[\bar{k}(z(j\Delta-2\Delta))+m(z(j\Delta-2\Delta))]\,|\mathfrak{F}\right\}+ \tag{1.57}$$
$$+\frac{\tau_2-\tau_1}{\mu T}\beta(T)\mathcal{O}(T)+\frac{\tau_2-\tau_1}{T}\beta(T)\mathcal{O}(T^2).$$

Taking into account (1.50), it is not difficult to see that the remaining terms $(\mu T)^{-1}\beta(T)\mathcal{O}(T)=\mathcal{O}\left(\mu^{\frac{\alpha}{4+\alpha}}\right)$; $T^{-1}\beta(T)\mathcal{O}(T^2)=\mathcal{O}(T^{-1-\alpha})$ in (1.57) are of order $o(1)$. Thus (1.57) can be written in the form

$$\mathbf{M}[z(\tau_2)-z(\tau_1)\,|\,\mathfrak{F}]=\mathbf{M}\left\{\Delta\sum_{j=l+2}^{m-1}[\bar{k}(z(j\Delta-2\Delta)+m(z(j\Delta-2\Delta))]\,|\,\mathfrak{F}\right\}+o(1). \tag{1.58}$$

b) Let us turn now to an examination of the conditional mean square $\mathbf{M}\{[z(\tau_2)-z(\tau_1)]^2\,|\,\mathfrak{F}\}$. Using (1.56-1) we will write the square of the increment in the form

$$[z(\tau_2)-z(\tau_1)]^2=\sum_{j=l+2}^{m-1}\Lambda_j^2(z(j\Delta-2\Delta))+2\sum_{j=l+3}^{m-1}\Lambda_{j-1}(z(j\Delta-3\Delta))\,\Lambda_j(z(j\Delta-$$
$$-2\Delta))+2\sum_{j=l+4}^{m-1}\Lambda_{j-2}(z(j\Delta-4\Delta))\,\Lambda_j(z(j\Delta-2\Delta))+ \tag{1.60}$$
$$+2\sum_{j=l+5}^{m-1}\sum_{k=l+2}^{j-3}\Lambda_k(z(k\Delta-2\Delta))\,\Lambda_j(z(j\Delta-2\Delta))+o(\Delta)\equiv$$
$$\equiv\mathfrak{I}_1+2\mathfrak{I}_2+2\mathfrak{I}_3+2\mathfrak{I}_4+o(\Delta)$$

and average the $\mathfrak{I}_i$ in turn. Beginning with $\mathfrak{I}_1$, and taking into account that $\Lambda_j^2=\mu^2\xi_j^2+2\mu^3\xi;\ \eta_j+\mu^4\eta_j^2+\dots$, we will write for ξ_j^2 a formula analogous to (1.55), (1.56):

$$\mathbf{M}[\xi_j^2(z(j\Delta-2\Delta))\,|\,\mathfrak{F}(0,\dots,jT-2T)]=[\mathbf{M}\,\xi_j^2(y)]_{y=z(j\Delta-2\Delta)}+\beta(T)\mathcal{O}(T^2). \tag{1.61}$$

From this, if we take into account (1.43), we obtain

$$\mathbf{M}[\xi_j^2(z(j\Delta-2\Delta))\,|\,\mathfrak{F}(0,\dots,jT-2T)]=\bar{a}(z(j\Delta-2\Delta)\,T+o(T)+\beta(T)\,O(T^2)$$
$$(\bar{a}(x)=\bar{a}(x,x')).$$

Hence

$$\mathbf{M}\left[\sum_{j=l+2}^{m-1} \mu^2 \xi_j^2 (z(j\Delta - 2\Delta)) \mid \mathfrak{F}\right] = \mathbf{M}\left\{\Delta \sum_{j=l+2}^{m-1} \bar{a}(z(j\Delta - 2\Delta)) \mid \mathfrak{F}\right\} + o(\tau_2 - \tau_1) + \\ + \frac{\tau_2 - \tau_1}{T} \beta(T) O(T^2); \tag{1.62}$$

$\beta(T)\mathcal{O}(T) = \mathcal{O}(T^{-1-\alpha}) = o(1).$

Passing to the next term, we have

$$\mathbf{M}[\xi_j \eta_j \mid \mathfrak{F}(0, \ldots, jT - 2T)] = \mathcal{O}(T^3)$$

and thus

$$\mathbf{M}\left[\sum_j \mu^3 \xi_j \eta_j \mid \mathfrak{F}\right] = \frac{\tau_2 - \tau_1}{\mu^2 T} \mu^3 \mathcal{O}(T^3) = O\left(\mu^{\frac{\alpha}{4+\alpha}}\right) = o(1).$$

Examining the remaining terms $\mu^4 \eta_j^2$, $\mu^4 m^2 T^2$, $\mu^4 \eta_j mT$, $\mu^3 \xi_j m(x) T$ in the same way, it is easy to see that their contributions to $\mathbf{M}[\Lambda_j^2 \mid \mathfrak{F}]$ are also of order $o(\Delta)$, so that

$$\mathbf{M}[\Lambda_j^2 \mid \mathfrak{F}] = \Delta \mathbf{M}[\bar{a}(z(j\Delta - 2\Delta)) \mid \mathfrak{F}] + o(\Delta);$$

$$\mathbf{M}[\mathfrak{I}_1 \mid \mathfrak{F}] = \mathbf{M}[\Delta \sum_{j=l+2}^{m-1} \bar{a}(z(j\Delta - 2\Delta)) \mid \mathfrak{F}] + o(1). \tag{1.63}$$

From the above, it is clear that in examining $\mathfrak{I}_2$ and $\mathfrak{I}_3$, we also need consider only terms $\Sigma \xi_{j-1} \xi_j$, $\Sigma \xi_{j-2} \xi_j$. The remaining terms $\xi_{j-1} \eta_j$, $\eta_{j-1} \eta_j$, etc., clearly give a contribution to $\mathbf{M}[\mathfrak{I}_{2,3} \mid \mathfrak{F}]$ of order $o(1)$.

Consider the terms

$$\xi_{j-1}(z(j\Delta - 3\Delta)) \xi_j(z(j\Delta - 2\Delta)) = \\ \int_{jT-T}^{jT} ds \int_{jT}^{jT+T} dt\, g(s, z(j\Delta - 3\Delta), \omega)\, g(t, z(j\Delta - 2\Delta), \omega).$$

We will carry out the averaging of the integrand in two stages:

$$\mathbf{M}[\xi_{j-1}(z(j\Delta - 3\Delta)) \xi_j(z(j\Delta - 2\Delta)) \mid \mathfrak{F}] = \\ = \mathbf{M}\left\{\int_{jT-T}^{jT} ds\, g(s, z(j\Delta - 3\Delta), \omega)\, \mathbf{M}[\xi_j(j\Delta - 2\Delta) \mid \mathfrak{F}(0, T, \ldots, jT - T, s)] \mid \mathfrak{F}\right\}. \tag{1.64}$$

Using condition (1.42) with

$$C_{k-1} = j - 1;\ C_k T = s < jT;\ C_{k+2} \to C_{k+1} = t/T$$

as well as (1.11), we have

$$\mathbf{M}[\xi_j(z(j\Delta - 2\Delta)) \mid \mathfrak{F}(0, T, \ldots, jT - T, s)] =$$

$$= \int_{jT}^{jT+T} \mathbf{M}[g(x, t, \omega) \mid \mathfrak{F}(0, T, \ldots, jT - T, s]\, dt =$$

$$= \int_{jT}^{jT+T} \beta(t - s)\, \mathbf{M} \mid g \mid dt \leqslant C \int_{jT}^{jT+T} \beta(t - s)\, dt.$$

Thus

$$\mathbf{M}[\xi_{j-1}(z(j\Delta - 3\Delta))\, \xi_j(z(j\Delta - 2\Delta)) \mid \mathfrak{F}] \leqslant \mathcal{C}' \int_{jT-T}^{jT} ds \int_{jT}^{jT+T} \beta(t - s)\, dt \leqslant$$
$$\leqslant \mathcal{C}' \int_0^{2T} t' \beta(t')\, dt' = O(1) \tag{1.65}$$

Summing similar expressions, we find

$$\mathbf{M}[\mathcal{I}_2 \mid \mathfrak{F}] = \frac{\tau_2 - \tau_1}{T}\, O(1) = o(1). \tag{1.66}$$

Moreover,

$$\mathbf{M}[\mathcal{I}_3 \mid \mathfrak{F}] = o(1). \tag{1.67}$$

To obtain this, it is not even necessary to carry out an integration as in (1.65); it suffices to take into account the weaker condition $\beta(T) = o(1)$.

Let us finally examine the last sum

$$\mathcal{I}_4 = \sum_{j=l+5}^{m-1} [z(j\Delta - 2\Delta) - z(l\Delta)]\, \Lambda_j(z(j\Delta - 2\Delta)).$$

We will average it in two stages:

$$\mathbf{M}[\mathcal{I}_4 \mid \mathfrak{F}] = \mathbf{M}\left\{ \sum_{j=l+5}^{m-1} [z(j\Delta - 2\Delta) - z(l\Delta)] \right.$$
$$\left. \mathbf{M}[\Lambda_j(z(j\Delta - 2\Delta)) \mid \mathfrak{F}(0, \ldots, jT - 2T)] \mid \mathfrak{F} \right\},$$

where in the first averaging it is possible to use formulas (1.55) and (1.56). This yields

$$\mathrm{M}[\mathcal{I}_4 \mid \mathcal{F}] = \mathrm{M}\left\{ \sum_{j=l+5}^{m-1} [z(j\Delta - 2\Delta) - z(l\Delta)] \right. \\ \left. [\bar{k}(z(j\Delta - 2\Delta)) + m(z(j\Delta - 2\Delta)) + o(1)]\,\Delta \mid \mathcal{F} \right\}.$$

Using the estimate $|\bar{k} + m| < C'$, from this we obtain

$$\mathrm{M}[\mathcal{I}_4 \mid \mathcal{F}] \leqslant C'\Delta\, \mathrm{M}\left\{ \sum_{j=l+5}^{m-1} | z(j\Delta - 2\Delta) - z(l\Delta) | \mid \mathcal{F} \right\} \leqslant \\ \leqslant C'\Delta \sum_{j=l+5}^{m-1} \left[\mathrm{M}\{[z(j\Delta - 2\Delta) - z(l\Delta)]^2 \mid \mathcal{F}\}\right]^{1/2}. \tag{1.68}$$

Here we used the familiar inequality

$$\mathrm{M}\{| \xi(\omega) | \mid G\} \leqslant \{\mathrm{M}[\xi^2(\omega) \mid G]\}^{1/2}$$

(almost certainly; $\xi(\omega)$, G are random). If we take into account (1.60), (1.63), (1.66), and (1.67), from (1.68) we will have

$$\mathrm{M}\{[z(\tau_2) - z(\tau_1)]^2 \mid \mathcal{F}\} \leqslant K_1(\tau_2 - \tau_1) + \\ + K_2 \sum_{j=l+5}^{m-1} \Delta\left[\mathrm{M}\{[z(j\Delta - 2\Delta) - z(l\Delta)]^2 \mid \mathcal{F}\}\right]^{1/2} \tag{1.69}$$

(K_1, K_2 are certain constants). For small Δ the sum on the right side can be changed to an integral. From the above inequality it is not difficult to obtain

$$\mathrm{M}\{[z(\tau_2) - z(\tau_1)]^2 \mid \mathcal{F}\} = K_1(\tau_2 - \tau_1) + O\left((\tau_2 - \tau_1)^{3/2}\right). \tag{1.70}$$

We will show this. Let us use the notation

$$u(\tau) = \mathrm{M}\{[z(\tau) - z(\tau_1)]^2 \mid \mathcal{F}\}$$

$$u_1(\tau) = K_1(\tau - \tau_1) + K_2 \int_{\tau_1}^{\tau} \sqrt{u(\sigma)}\, d\sigma.$$

According to (1.69), we have $u \leqslant u_1$. If further we introduce the functions

$$u_n(\tau) = K_1(\tau - \tau_1) + K_2 \int_{\tau_1}^{\tau} \sqrt{u_{n-1}(\sigma)}\, d\sigma, \quad n = 2, \ldots, \tag{1.71}$$

then on the strength of (1.69) we will have

$$u \leqslant u_1 (\leqslant u_2 \leqslant \cdots)$$

and hence

$$u \leqslant u_\infty = \lim_{n \to \infty} u_n. \tag{1.72}$$

This convergence can be supported with the help of the inequality

$$u_{n+1}^{(\tau)} - u_n(\tau) \leqslant \frac{K_2}{2} \int_{\tau_1}^{\tau} \frac{u_n^{(\sigma)} - u_{n-1}(\sigma)}{\sqrt{K_1(\sigma - \tau_1)}}\, d\sigma,$$

resulting from (1.71), which yields

$$u_{n+1}(\tau) - u_n(\tau) \leqslant \mathcal{C}_0 \frac{K_2^n}{K_1^{n/2}} \frac{(\tau - \tau_1)^{n/2}}{n!}.$$

The limit function u_∞ satisfies the equation

$$u_\infty(\tau) = K_1(\tau - \tau_1) + K_2 \int_{\tau_1}^{\tau} \sqrt{u_\infty(\sigma)}\, d\sigma$$

or

$$\frac{du_\infty}{d\tau} = K_1 + K_2 u_\infty,$$

which has the solution

$$\frac{2}{K_2}\sqrt{u_\infty} - \frac{2K_1}{K_2^2} \ln\left(1 + \frac{K_2}{K_1}\sqrt{u_\infty}\right) = \tau - \tau_1.$$

From this it is not difficult to find the terms in the expansion

$$u_\infty(\tau) = K_1(\tau - \tau_1) + \frac{2}{3}\frac{K_2}{K_1^{1/2}}(\tau - \tau_1)^{3/2} + \ldots \tag{1.73}$$

Substituting (1.73) into (1.72) we prove the required estimate (1.70), which, however, can be seen at once from the inequality $u \leqslant u_1$.

If we substitute (1.70) into (1.68), we will obtain

$$\mathbf{M}[\mathcal{J}_4 \mid \mathcal{F}] = \mathcal{O}\left((\tau_2 - \tau_1)^{3/2}\right). \tag{1.74}$$

Thus on the strength of (1.63), (1.66), (1.67), and (1.74), the conditional average of the sum (1.60) equals

$$\mathbf{M}\left\{[z(\tau_2) - z(\tau_1)]^2 \mid \mathcal{F}\right\} = \mathbf{M}\left[\sum_{j=l+r}^{m-1} \Delta\, \overline{a}(z(j\Delta - 2\Delta)) \mid \mathcal{F}\right] + \mathcal{O}\left((\tau_2 - \tau_1)^{3/2}\right). \tag{1.75}$$

c) For future use, we will also need to evaluate the conditional average $\mathbf{M}\left\{[z(\tau_2) - z(\tau_1)]^4 \mid \mathcal{F}\right\}$. Using (1.56-1) we will replace the difference $z(\tau_2) - z(\tau_1)$ by $\sum_j \Lambda_j$ and consider the sum

$$\mathcal{S} = \left(\sum_{j=l+2}^{m-1} \Lambda_j\right)^4 = \sum_s \Lambda_s^4 + \vartheta_2 \sum_{r<s} \Lambda_r \Lambda_s^3 + \vartheta_3 \sum_{r<s} \Lambda_r^2 \Lambda_s^2 + \vartheta_4 \sum_{k<r<s} \Lambda_k \Lambda_r \Lambda_s^2 +$$
$$+ \vartheta_5 \sum_{r<s} \Lambda_r^3 \Lambda_s + \vartheta_6 \sum_{k<r<s} \Lambda_k \Lambda_r^2 \Lambda_s + \vartheta_7 \sum_{k<r<s} \Lambda_k^2 \Lambda_r \Lambda_s +$$
$$+ 24 \sum_{j<k<r<s} \Lambda_j \Lambda_k \Lambda_r \Lambda_s\,, \tag{1.76}$$

where $1 \leqslant \vartheta_i \leqslant 24$. Since

$$\left(\sum_j \Lambda_j\right)^3 = \sum_r \Lambda_r^3 + 3 \sum_{k<r} \Lambda_k \Lambda_r^2 + 3 \sum_{k<r} \Lambda_k^2 \Lambda_r + 6 \sum_{j<k<r} \Lambda_j \Lambda_k \Lambda_r\,;$$
$$\left(\sum_j \Lambda_j\right)^2 = \sum_r \Lambda_r^2 + 2 \sum_{k<r} \Lambda_k \Lambda_r\,,$$

(1.76) can be written

$$\mathcal{S} = \sum_s \Lambda_s^4 + \vartheta_2 \sum_{r<s} \Lambda_r \Lambda_s^3 + \left(\vartheta_3 - \frac{\vartheta_4}{2}\right) \sum_{r<s} \Lambda_r^2 \Lambda_s^2 + \frac{\vartheta_4}{2} \sum_s \left(\sum_{j<s} \Lambda_j\right)^2 \Lambda_s^2 +$$
$$+ (\vartheta_5 - 4) \sum_{r<s} \Lambda_r^3 \Lambda_s + (\vartheta_6 - 12) \sum_{k<r<s} \Lambda_k \Lambda_r^2 \Lambda_s +$$
$$+ (\vartheta_7 - 12) \sum_{k<r<s} \Lambda_k^2 \Lambda_r \Lambda_s + 4 \sum_s \left(\sum_{j<s} \Lambda_j\right)^3 \Lambda_s \equiv \vartheta_1' \mathcal{S}_1 + \ldots + \vartheta_8' \mathcal{S}_8\,. \tag{1.77}$$

Substituting (1.77) into the relation

$$\mathbf{M}\left\{[z(\tau_2)-z(\tau_1)]^4 \mid \mathfrak{F}\right\} = \mathbf{M}[\mathcal{S} \mid \mathfrak{F}] + o(1), \tag{1.78}$$

we will estimate in turn the contributions of the various $\mathcal{S}_i$. Here the inequalities $k<r, r<s, \ldots$ will be understood in the strong sense (e.g., in the sense $k<r-2$). This can be attained by adding into (1.77) new "approximately diagonal" terms, having the same structure as those already indicated. Their order of magnitude is estimated analogously, and does not exceed that of the terms present in (1.77). Thus it is not necessary to examine them separately. An analogous situation existed earlier, when we saw that $\mathcal{O}(\mathcal{I}_2) \leqslant \mathcal{O}(\mathcal{I}_1)$; $\mathcal{O}(\mathcal{I}_3) \leqslant \mathcal{O}(\mathcal{I}_1)$. These strengthened inequalities allow the inequality (1.42) to be applied in a step-by-step averaging of factors, beginning with those on the right. We will now examine the terms one by one.

$\mathcal{S}_1$) Since $\Lambda_s = \mathcal{O}(\mu T)$, and the number of terms is $(\tau_2-\tau_1)/\mu^2 T$, we have $\mathcal{S}_1 = \mathcal{O}(\mu^2 T^3) = o(1)$.

$\mathcal{S}_2$) Writing $\mathcal{S}_2$ in the form

$$\mathcal{S}_2 = \sum_s [z(s\Delta - 2\Delta) - z(l\Delta)]\Lambda_s^3$$

and using the estimate $\Lambda_s = \mathcal{O}(\mu T)$, we have

$$|\mathbf{M}[\mathcal{S}_2 \mid \mathfrak{F}]| \leqslant \mathcal{C}\mu T^2\, \mathbf{M}[z(\tau_2) - z(\tau_1)| \mid \mathfrak{F}].$$

Thus

$$\mathbf{M}[\mathcal{S}_2 \mid \mathfrak{F}] \leqslant \mathcal{C}\mu T^2 \left[\mathbf{M}\left\{[z(\tau_2)-z(\tau_1)]^2 \mid \mathfrak{F}\right\}\right]^{1/2} = \mathcal{O}\left(\mu T^2 (\tau_2-\tau_1)^{1/2}\right) = o(1)$$

on the strength of (1.50).

$\mathcal{S}_3$) Averaging Λ_s^2 first into

$$\mathcal{S}_3 = \sum_s \left(\sum_{r<s} \Lambda_r^2\right)\Lambda_s^2$$

using (1.63) we obtain

$$\mathbf{M}[\mathcal{S}_3 \mid \mathfrak{F}] \leqslant \sum_s \mathbf{M}\left[\left(\sum_{r<s} \Lambda_r^2\right) C\Delta \mid \mathfrak{F}\right] \leqslant C^2 \int_{\tau_1}^{\tau_2} (\tau-\tau_1)\,d\tau = \frac{1}{2} C^2 (\tau_2-\tau_1)^2.$$

$\mathcal{S}_4$) Analogously

$$\mathbf{M}[\mathcal{S}_4 \mid \mathfrak{F}] \leqslant \sum_s \mathbf{M}\left[\left(\sum_{j<s} \Lambda_j\right)^2 C\Delta \mid \mathfrak{F}\right] = O\ (\tau_2-\tau_1)^2 .$$

$\mathcal{S}_5$) Taking the conditional mathematical expectation

$$\mathbf{M}[\Lambda_r | \mathcal{F}(\mathcal{O}, T, \ldots, sT - 2T)] = \mathcal{O}(\Delta)$$

and using the estimate $\Lambda_s = \mathcal{O}(\mu T)$, we have

$$|\mathbf{M}[\mathcal{S}_5 | \mathcal{F}]| \leqslant \sum_r \mathbf{M}[|\Lambda_r|^3 \Delta(m - r) | \mathcal{F}] = (\tau_2 - \tau_1)\mathcal{O}(\mu T^2) = o(1).$$

$\mathcal{S}_6$) Applying formula (1.58) to the right factor of

$$\mathcal{S}_6 = \sum_r [z(r\Delta - 2\Delta) - z(l\Delta)] \Lambda_r^2 [z(m\Delta) - z(r\Delta + 2\Delta)].$$

we will have

$$|\mathbf{M}[\mathcal{S}_6 | \mathcal{F}]| \leqslant \sum_r \mathbf{M}[| z(r\Delta - 2\Delta) - z(l\Delta) | \Lambda_r^2 \cdot \mathcal{C}_1 (\tau_2 - \tau_1) | \mathcal{F}]$$

and on the strength of (1.63),

$$|\mathbf{M}[\mathcal{S}_6 | \mathcal{F}]| \leqslant (\tau_2 - \tau_1) \mathcal{C}_1 \mathcal{C}_2 \sum_r \Delta \mathbf{M}[| z(r\Delta - 2\Delta) - z(l\Delta) | \mathcal{F}] \leqslant$$

$$\leqslant (\tau_2 - \tau_1) \mathcal{C}_1 \mathcal{C}_2 \int_{\tau_1}^{\tau_2} d\tau \left[\mathbf{M}\left\{[z(\tau) - z(\tau_1)]^2 | \mathcal{F}\right\}\right]^{1/2}.$$

Taking (1.70) into account, from this we obtain

$$|\mathbf{M}[\mathcal{S}_6 | \mathcal{F}]| \leqslant \mathcal{O}\left((\tau_2 - \tau_1)^{5/2}\right).$$

$\mathcal{S}_7$) In the examination of

$$\mathcal{S}_7 = \sum_k \Lambda_k^2 \left(\sum_{k < r < s} \Lambda_r \Lambda_s \right)$$

to the sum $\sum_{k<r<s} \Lambda_r \Lambda_s$, analogous to $\mathcal{I}_4$ in (1.60), it is expedient to apply formula (1.74). This yields

$$|\mathbf{M}[\mathcal{S}_7 | \mathcal{F}]| \leqslant \sum_k \mathbf{M}[\Lambda_k^2 O\left((m\Delta - k\Delta)^{3/2}\right) | \mathcal{F}]$$

and as a result of (1.63),

$$|\mathbf{M}[\mathcal{S}_7|\mathcal{F}]| \leqslant \sum_k \Delta \mathcal{O}\left((\tau_2-\tau_1)^{3/2}\right) = \mathcal{O}\left((\tau_2-\tau_1)^{5/2}\right).$$

The largest of the terms $\mathcal{S}_1, \ldots, \mathcal{S}_7$ is of order $\mathcal{O}\left((\tau_2-\tau_1)^2\right)$.

$\mathcal{S}_8$) We now turn to the last term $\mathcal{S}_8$. After averaging with respect to Λ_s we have

$$|\mathbf{M}[\mathcal{S}_8|\mathcal{F}]| \leqslant \sum_s \mathbf{M}\left[|z(s\Delta-2\Delta)-z(\tau_1)|^3 \mathcal{C}_2 \Delta|\mathcal{F}\right].$$

Using the inequality

$$\mathbf{M}[|\xi(\omega)|^3|G] \leqslant \left\{\mathbf{M}[\xi^4(\omega)|G]\right\}^{3/4} \text{ (almost certainly)}$$

and passing from the sum to an integral, we obtain

$$|\mathbf{M}[\mathcal{S}_8|\mathcal{F}]| \leqslant \mathcal{C}_2 \int_{\tau_1}^{\tau} \left[\mathbf{M}\left\{[z(\tau)-z(\tau_1)]^4|\mathcal{F}\right\}\right]^{3/4} d\tau.$$

Taking into account that

$$\mathbf{M}[\mathcal{S}_1+\ldots+\mathcal{S}_7] = \mathcal{O}\left((\tau_2-\tau_1)^2\right)$$

[from $\mathcal{S}_1$) — $\mathcal{S}_7$)], on the strength of (1.78) we obtain from this

$$\mathbf{M}\left\{[z(\tau_2)-z(\tau_1)]^4|\mathcal{F}\right\} \leqslant \mathcal{C}_1(\tau_2-\tau_1)^2 + \mathcal{C}_2 \int_{\tau_1}^{\tau_2} \left[\mathbf{M}\left\{[z(\tau)-z(\tau_1)]^4|\mathcal{F}\right\}\right]^{3/4} d\tau.$$

This inequality is analogous to the previously encountered inequality (1.69). From it, by the same method, we can obtain

$$\mathbf{M}\ [z(\tau_2)-z(\tau_1)]^4|\mathcal{F}\} = \mathcal{O}\left((\tau_2-\tau_1)^2\right); \tag{1.79}$$

$$\mathbf{M}[\mathcal{S}_8|\mathcal{F}] = \mathcal{O}\left((\tau_2-\tau_1)^{5/2}\right).$$

3) We will examine the consequences of the formulas (1.58), (1.75), and (1.79).

From (1.75) it follows that

$$\mathbf{M}[z(\hat{t})]^2 < \mathcal{C};\ \mathbf{M}[z(\tau_2)-z(\tau_1)]^2 < \mathcal{C}'(\tau_2-\tau_1), \tag{1.80}$$

and

$$\lim_{h \to 0} \mathbf{P}[|z(\tilde{t}+h) - z(\tilde{t})| > \varepsilon] = 0.$$

According to remark 2 on p. 17 of the book by Skorokhod [2] (A. V. Skorokhod, *Studies in the Theory of Random Processes,* Kiev University, 1961), from this it follows that from the sequence of processes $\{z_{\mu_n}, \mu_n \to 0\}$ we can select a sequence $\{z_{\mu_{n_k}}, k \to \infty\}$ such that (1°) finite dimensional distributions of the $z_{\mu_{n_k}}$ converge to limit distributions; (2°) it will be possible to construct a sequence of processes $\bar{z}_{\mu_{n_k}}$ having correspondingly the same finite dimensional distributions as $z_{\mu_{n_k}}$ converging in probability (for all τ) to a certain limit continuous separable stochastic process x_M. Its finite dimensional distributions are equal to the limits (as $k \to \infty$) of the corresponding distributions of the processes $\{\bar{z}_{\mu_{n_k}}\}$, $\{z_{\mu_{n_k}}\}$.

We will examine the properties of this limit process $x_M(\tilde{t})$. According to (1.78), for all $z_{\mu_{n_k}}$, and hence for all $\bar{z}_{\mu_{n_k}}$ and x_M, the equation

$$\mathbf{M}[z(\tau_2) - z(\tau_1)]^4 \leqslant a(\tau_2 - \tau_1)^2 \tag{1.81}$$

is satisfied.

Thus the application of the familiar theorem (e.g., Prokhorov [1]) proves that the process $x_M(\tilde{t})$ is not only stochastically continuous, but is also continuous, with probability 1.

For $x_M(\tilde{t})$ we will further use Theorem 3.3 of Chap. 6 of the monograph by Doob [1]. Conditions (a) and (b) of that theorem are satisfied [see (1.79)]. From (1.58) and (1.75), taking into account the separability and continuity of the limit process, we have

$$\mathbf{M}\{x_M(\tilde{t}+h) - x_M(\tilde{t}) | x_M(u), 0 \leqslant u \leqslant \tilde{t}\} = [\bar{k}(x_M(\tilde{t})) + m(x_M(\tilde{t}))]h + o(h);$$

$$\mathbf{M}\{[x_M(\tilde{t}+h) - x_M(\tilde{t})]^2 | x_M(u), 0 \leqslant u \leqslant \tilde{t}\} = \bar{a}(x_M(\tilde{t}))h + o(h).$$

Thus condition (c) of the theorem is satisfied (we do not need to check condition (d) since a stronger condition has been introduced). By application of the theorem we find that the process $x_M(\tau)$ is a diffusion Markov process with local parameters $\bar{k}(x) + m(x)$, $\bar{a}(x)$. These parameters do not depend on the specific sequence μ_{n_k}. Hence the limit process $x_M(\tau)$ does not depend on the particular choice of the sequence $\{z_{\mu_n}, \mu_n \to \infty\}$. Finally, using (1.80) and Lemma 2.1 from the work of Prokhorov [1], it can be proven that the convergence $z_\mu \to x_M$ as $\mu \to 0$ can be understood not only in the sense of convergence of a finite dimensional distribution, but also in the sense of a weak convergence in the space of continuous functions defined on $[0, \tau_0]$.

4) In the last stage of the proof we will show that not only is the convergence $z_\mu(\tilde{t}) \to x_M(\tilde{t})$ of the auxiliary process $z(\tilde{t})$ valid, but also convergence of the reference process $\tilde{x}(\tilde{t})$ (as $\mu \to 0$) to the same diffusion process $x_M(\tilde{t})$.

As can be seen from (1.46) and (1.52), the process $\tilde{x}(\tilde{t})$ differs from $z(\tilde{t})$ in that in place of the equation

$$z(m\Delta) = x_0 + \sum_{j=0}^{m-1} \Lambda_j(z(j\Delta - 2\Delta))$$

we use the equation

$$\tilde{x}(m\Delta) = x_0 + \sum_{j=0}^{m-1} [\Lambda_j(\tilde{x}(j\Delta - 2\Delta)) + R_j\Delta].$$

Subtracting one equation from the other, we find the difference

$$\delta_m \equiv \tilde{x}(m\Delta) - z(m\Delta) = \sum_{j=0}^{m-1} [\Lambda_j(\tilde{x}(j\Delta - 2\Delta)) - \Lambda_j(z(j\Delta - 2\Delta))] + \sum_{j=0}^{m-1} R_j\Delta. \tag{1.82}$$

Estimating the order of magnitude of its mean square, we have

$$\mathcal{O}(\mathbf{M}\,\delta_m^2) = \mathcal{O}\left(\mathbf{M}\left[\left\{\sum_{j=0}^{m-1} [\Lambda_j(\tilde{x}(j\Delta - 2\Delta)) - \Lambda_j(z(j\Delta - 2\Delta))]\right\}^2\right]\right) + \\ + \mathcal{O}\left(\mathbf{M}\left[\left(\sum_{j=0}^{m-1} \Delta R_j\right)^2\right]\right), \tag{1.83}$$

where

$$\mathcal{O}\left(\mathbf{M}\left[\left\{\sum_{j=0}^{m-1} [\Lambda_j(\tilde{x}(j\Delta - 2\Delta)) - \Lambda_j(z(j\Delta - 2\Delta))]\right\}^2\right]\right) = \\ = \mathcal{O}\left(\mathbf{M}\left[\left\{\sum_{j=0}^{m-1} \frac{\partial \Lambda_j}{\partial x}(z(j\Delta - 2\Delta)\,\delta_{j-2}\right\}^2\right]\right). \tag{1.84}$$

The mathematical expectation

$$\mathrm{M}\left\{\sum_{j=1}^{m-1} \frac{\partial \Lambda_j}{\partial x}\delta_{j-2}\right\}^2 \equiv v(m\Delta) \tag{1.85}$$

can be calculated in the same way as was the mathematical expectation (1.75) in (b). For the diagonal sum

$$\mathcal{I}_1' = \sum_{j=2}^{m-1} \delta_{j-2}^2 \left[\frac{\partial \Lambda_j}{\partial x}(z(j\Delta - 2\Delta))\right]^2,$$

taking into account (1.43) we have

$$\mathrm{M}\mathcal{I}_1' = \mathrm{M}\sum_{j=2}^{m-1} \delta_{j-2}^2\, \mathrm{M}\left\{\left[\frac{\partial \Lambda_j}{\partial x}(z(j\Delta - 2\Delta))\right]^2 \middle| \mathcal{F}(0, \ldots, jT - 2T)\right\} =$$

$$= \mathrm{M}\sum_{j=2}^{m-1} \delta_{j-2}^2 \frac{\partial^2 \overline{a}}{\partial x \partial x'}(z(j\Delta - 2\Delta), z(j\Delta - 2\Delta))(\Delta + o(\Delta)) = \tag{1.86}$$

$$= \sum_{j=2}^{m-1} \Delta \mathcal{O}(\mathrm{M}\delta_{j-2}^2).$$

The sum of the intrinsically nondiagonal terms

$$\mathcal{I}_4' = \sum_{j=5}^{m-1}\sum_{k=2}^{j-3} \delta_{k-2}\frac{\partial \Lambda_k}{\partial x}(z(k\Delta - 2\Delta))\,\delta_{j-2}\frac{\partial \Lambda_j}{\partial x}(z(j\Delta - 2\Delta))$$

in analogy with (1.68) can be estimated as

$$|\mathrm{M}\mathcal{I}_4'| = \mathrm{M}\left|\sum_{j=5}^{m-1}\left[\sum_{k=2}^{j-3}\delta_{k-2}\frac{\partial \Lambda_k}{\partial x}(z(k\Delta - 2\Delta))\right]\right.$$

$$\left.\cdot\, \delta_{j-2}\,\mathrm{M}\left\{\frac{\partial \Lambda_j}{\partial x}(z(j\Delta - 2\Delta)) \,|\, \mathcal{F}(0, \ldots, jT - 2T)\right\}\right| \leqslant$$

$$\leqslant \mathcal{C}''\Delta\sum_{j=5}^{m-1}\mathrm{M}\left|\sum_{k=2}^{j-3}\delta_{k-2}\frac{\partial \Lambda_k}{\partial x}(z(k\Delta - 2\Delta))\delta_{j-2}\right| \leqslant$$

$$\leqslant \mathcal{C}''\Delta \sum_{j=5}^{m-1} \left\{ \mathrm{M} \left[\sum_{k=2}^{j-3} \delta_{k-2} \frac{\partial \Lambda_k}{\partial x} (z(k\Delta - 2\Delta)) \right]^2 \right\}^{\frac{1}{2}} \{\mathrm{M}(\delta_{j-2}^2)\}^{\frac{1}{2}}. \tag{1.87}$$

Here the relation $\mathrm{M}\partial g(x,t,\omega)/\partial x = 0$ is used.

The sum in braces in the right side of (1.87) differs from the sum in (1.85) in that $m-1$ is replaced by $j-3$. Using the notation (1.85), in agreement with (1.86) and (1.87) we have

$$v(m\Delta) \leqslant \sum_{j=2}^{m-1} \Delta \mathcal{O}(\mathrm{M}\delta_{j-2}^2) + \mathcal{C}''\Delta \sum_{j=5}^{m-1} \sqrt{v\,(j\Delta - 2\Delta)}\ \{\mathrm{M}(\delta_{j-2}^2)\}^{\frac{1}{2}}.$$

If we substitute (1.83) and (1.84) into this and pass over to integrals, we have the inequality

$$v(\tau) \leqslant \mathcal{C}' \int_0^{\tau} v(\sigma)\,d\sigma + \frac{1}{3}\mathcal{B}^2\tau^3 + \mathcal{C}'' \int_0^{\tau} \sqrt{v(\sigma)}\,\{\mathcal{C}'v(\sigma) + \mathcal{B}^2\sigma^2\}^{\frac{1}{2}}\,d\sigma. \tag{1.88}$$

Here we replaced R_j by a larger constant $\mathcal{B}>0$, which on the strength of (1.51) is $\mathcal{O}\left(\mu^{\frac{\alpha}{4+\alpha}}\right) = o(1)$. From (1.88) we can derive results using the same method as with the inequality (1.69). Namely, we obtain

$$v(\tau) \leqslant \frac{1}{3}\mathcal{B}^2\tau^3 + \frac{2}{7\sqrt{3}}\mathcal{C}''\mathcal{B}^2\tau^{\frac{7}{2}} + \ldots$$

Substituting this into (1.83) and (1.84), we find

$$\mathrm{M}[\tilde{x}(\tau) - z(\tau)]^2 \leqslant \mathcal{O}(\tau^2\mathcal{B}^2) = \tau^2 o(1). \tag{1.89}$$

From this it follows that for all $\tilde{t} \in [0, \tau_0]$ the difference $\tilde{x}(\tilde{t}) - z(\tilde{t})$ converges in probability to zero as $\mu \to 0$. Hence the finite dimensional distributions of the process $\tilde{x}(\tilde{t})$ converge to the same limit distributions as the distributions of the process $z(\tilde{t})$, namely, to the distributions of the limit process $\tilde{x}_{\mathrm{M}}(\tilde{t})$. Thus we have proven the convergence of the process $\tilde{x}(\tilde{t})$ to a Markov process, in the sense of the convergence of finite dimensional distributions. Moreover, to the convergence $\tilde{x}(\tilde{t}) \to x_{\mathrm{M}}(\tilde{t})$ apply all the assertions in (3) relative to the convergence $z(\tilde{t}) \to x_{\mathrm{M}}(\tilde{t})$.

In fact, as a result of the convergence of the two-dimensional distribution of $\tilde{x}(\tau_1), \tilde{x}(\tau_2)$ to the distribution of the variables

$x_M(\tau_1)$, $x_M(\tau_2)$, from (1.81) we have the condition

$$\mathbf{M}[x(\tau_1) - x(\tau_2)]^4 \leqslant a(\tau_2 - \tau_1)^2, \tag{1.90}$$

as well as conditions analogous to (1.80). Inequality (1.90) allows the extension to $\tilde{x}(\tilde{t})$ of the above assertion regarding the weak convergence to $k\ x_M(\tilde{t})$ as $\mu \to 0$ in a functional space. The proof is finished.

The series of moments in the above proof was borrowed from Khas'minskiy (private communication). However, he took the condition of strong interference (1.42) in a different form:

$$\left|\mathbf{P}\left[\mathcal{B} \mid \mathcal{N}_0^t\right] - \mathbf{P}[\mathcal{B}]\right| < o(T^{-6}) \quad \text{for} \quad \mathcal{B} \in \mathcal{N}_{t+T}^{\infty}. \tag{1.91}$$

Here we have the following differences.

1) The absence of $\mathbf{P}[\mathcal{B}]$ on the right side of (1.91) makes this a weaker condition. Nevertheless, this difference is not essential; it is of a technical nature and the corresponding strengthening in (1.42) is accepted only for the sake of convenience.

2) In (1.42) it was sufficient to require that the function $\beta(T)$ decrease as $T \to \infty$ more slowly than the $o(T^{-6})$ in (1.91). This difference is related to the method used in the proof.

3) The difference is most important in that in (1.91) we use very generous σ-algebras $\mathcal{N}_s^t$ which contain all possible sets $g(x, t', \omega) < c$, $t' \in [s, t]$. This means that condition (1.91) involves infinite dimensional distributions, while condition (1.42) involves the distribution of a *finite number of random variables*. Thus it is not difficult to check the latter condition in specific examples, while the checking of condition (1.91) in a non-Markov case is no less difficult than, say, the checking of the condition that the series (1.29) must converge. Moreover, in many cases of practical importance e.g., for the Gaussian process with correlation function

$$\mathbf{M}\, \xi(t)\, \xi(t+\tau) = \sigma^2 e^{-\tau^2},$$

examined in Sect. 1.4, paragraph 1, condition (1.91) is certainly not satisfied, while (1.42) is satisfied. This is related to the fact that this process does not satisfy the Paley-Wiener regularity condition, and thus is singular. It can be precisely extended beyond the limits of the segment on which its realization is known. Condition (1.42) can, however, be satisfied with equal success for both regular and singular (in the indicated sense) processes.

Regular processes are related to processes having a rational spectral density, forming a component of a multidimensional Markov process, and compose along with them a general class of processes. Another class is composed of processes having realizations which (with probability 1) are analytic functions of time. These processes are singular and (1.91) is not satisfied for them. It is not very surprising that a Markov-type process converges to a Markov process as $\mu \to 0$. Of more depth and interest is the result we obtained that even for processes of an entirely non-Markov type, having analytic realizations, this convergence is observed.

1.4 Examples

1. Let Eq. (1.1) have the form

$$\frac{dx(t)}{dt} = \mu x^3(t)\,\xi^3(t) + \mu x(t)\,\xi(t),$$

where $\xi(t)$ is a stationary Gaussian process with zero mean value which has the correlation function $\mathbf{M}\xi(t)\xi(t+\tau) = e^{-\tau^2}$. It is easy to see here that assumptions A_1 through A_4 are fulfilled in any finite interval I. Aside from this, conditions (1.15), (1.16) are fulfilled. The convergence of the series (1.29) is more difficult to check; avoiding a detailed examination, we will assume that this is true.

For this example, conditions (1.42) and (1.43) of Theorem 1.2 are also satisfied. Condition (1.41) is, however, not satisfied, so that to apply that theorem we need to carry out a generalization.

Applying Theorem 1.1, we learn that the process $x(\mu^{-2}\tilde{t})$ as $\mu \to 0$ converges in distribution to the diffusion Markov process $x_M(\tilde{t})$, which is characterized by parameters

$$\lim_{\Delta\to 0} \frac{1}{\Delta}\mathbf{M}[\Delta x_M \mid x] \equiv a(x) =$$

$$= \int_{-\infty}^{0} \mathbf{M}[3x^2\xi^3(0) + \xi(0)][x^3\xi^3(\tau) + x\xi(\tau)]\,d\tau;$$

$$\lim_{\Delta\to 0} \frac{1}{\Delta}\mathbf{M}[\Delta x_M^2 \mid x] \equiv b(x) =$$

$$= \int_{-\infty}^{\infty} \mathbf{M}[x^3\xi^3(0) + x\xi(0)][x^3\xi^3(\tau) + x\xi(\tau)]\,d\tau;$$

$$\lim_{\Delta\to 0} \frac{1}{\Delta}\mathbf{M}[\Delta x_M^q \mid x] = 0, \quad q \geqslant 3.$$

After calculation we have

$$a(x) = \frac{\sqrt{\pi}}{2}[x + 12x^3 + 3(9 + 2\sqrt{3})x^5];$$

$$b(x) = \sqrt{\pi}\,[x^2 + 6x^4 + (9 + 2\sqrt{3})x^6].$$

2. We will take the second example from the theory of detection of random signals (Stratonovich [8]). The corresponding equation has the form

$$\frac{dx}{dt} + \alpha x = \beta e^{\xi(t) - x}, \tag{1.92}$$

where α, β are positive constants, and $\xi(t)$ is a stationary random process. We assume that it is Gaussian and has the correlation function $\sigma^2 R(\tau)$ $(R(0) = 1)$ and zero mean. Then

$$\mathbf{M}\, e^{\xi(t)} = e^{\frac{\sigma^2}{2}}.$$

Under certain conditions the process $x(t)$ is close to Markov. In order to formulate this assertion more exactly we will change Eq. (1.92) to

$$\frac{dx}{dt} = -\mu^2 \alpha_0 x + \beta_0 e^{-x} [\mu^2 \gamma_0 e^{\frac{\sigma^2}{2}} + \mu (e^{\xi(t)} - e^{\frac{\sigma^2}{2}})], \tag{1.93}$$

i.e.,

$$g(x, t) = \beta_0 e^{-x} [e^{\xi} - \mathbf{M} e^{\xi}]$$

(α_0, β_0, γ_0 do not depend on μ). Obviously, the last equation coincides with (1.92) for a particular value of the parameter $\mu = \mu_0$ if $\mu_0^2 \alpha_0 = \alpha$; $\mu_0 \beta_0 = \beta$; $\mu_0 \gamma_0 = 1$. The form of the right side of (1.93) is so selected that it satisfies (1.11).

If the correlation coefficient $R(\tau)$ vanishes sufficiently fast as $\tau \to \infty$, conditions (1.15), (1.16) will be fulfilled. The application of Theorem 1.1 to this case produces the following expressions for the parameters of drift and local variance

$$a(x) = -\alpha_0 x + \beta_0 \gamma_0 e^{\frac{\sigma^2}{2} - x} - \frac{1}{2} K e^{-2x};$$

$$b(x) = K e^{-2x};$$

$$K = 2\beta_0^2 e^{\sigma^2} \int_0^\infty [e^{\sigma^2 R(\tau)} - 1]\, d\tau$$

(it is assumed that $K < \infty$).

Having written the corresponding Fokker-Planck equation, it is possible to obtain, in particular, its stationary solution, which is the limit of the density of the probability distribution

$$p(x) = \text{const} \exp\left[-\frac{\alpha_0}{K}\left(x - \frac{1}{2}\right)e^{2x} + \frac{2\gamma_0\beta_0}{K} e^{\frac{\sigma^2}{2}+x} + x\right]. \quad (1.94)$$

In the very beginning it is convenient to carry out a substitution of $y=e^x$ in (1.93) and then to apply Theorem 1.1. Of course, this will not have an effect on the results, and in particular, not on (1.94).

In conclusion we will make several remarks in regard to possible generalizations. First, it is possible to carry out a generalization of the results to a multidimensional and nonstationary case. The first generalization is trivial. For the second it is possible, for example, to examine the function $G=\mu^2 m(x, \mu^2 t) + \mu g(x, t, \mu^2 t, \omega)$, where $g(x, t, \tilde{t}, \omega)$ is a stationary function of t for fixed $\tilde{t}$, x, ω. Second, by the selection of a more complex dependence of G on μ it is possible to obtain a limit Markov process which is not a diffusion process. Some preliminary ideas regarding the calculation of terms with higher derivatives in the operator of a Markov process are to be found in the monograph of Stratonovich [8], Sect. 4. Finally, the question of the size of the deviation of a non-Markov process from a Markov one, i.e., the question of the rate of convergence, deserves special investigation.

CHAPTER 2

A New Form of Presentation of Stochastic Integrals and Equations

Stochastic integrals and equations are important instruments of research in diffusion Markov processes and will be used here extensively. We assume that the reader is familiar with these concepts, for example, with the contents of the monographs by Doob [1] and Dynkin [3].

As is known, stochastic equations written for diffusion processes are first encountered in physical papers on Brownian motion (Langevin [1], see also Chandrasekhar [1]). A strict mathematical theory of these equations was subsequently given by Ito [1-3]. The method of determination of stochastic integrals and equations which was presented by the latter is a general and satisfactory one in many respects. Nevertheless, it does not possess one important characteristic, symmetry in time. The stochastic integral of Ito determined for direct time does not coincide with the integral determined in the same way for reverse time.

In the present chapter there will be presented another method of determining stochastic integrals and equations which is characterized by a definite symmetry with respect to past and future. This method to a certain degree is equivalent to that of Ito, but in several respects has a number of advantages. The technique of transformation of stochastic integrals is substantially simplified. As we know, the integrals in the sense of Ito need careful handling. They cannot be transformed by substitution of variables in the usual way that is suitable for smooth functions, they cannot simply be integrated by parts, etc. The matter is simpler for integrals in the new sense. They can be dealt with in the usual manner as if the diffusion processes were smooth functions. Covariant properties of the stochastic equations are associated with these. Advantages of the symmetrized stochastic integral are also found in the study of "probability functionals" (Stratonovich [5]).

Stochastic differential equations written in the new (symmetrized) form can be interpreted as the limit of equations written for non-Markov (but close to Markov) processes. From the results of Chapter 1 it follows that in this case the analytical forms of the prelimit equations and the limit equations taken in the symmetrized form coincide. In engineering realization (modeling) of stochastic equations one always has to deal not with precise, but with prelimit (approximately Markov) processes. Thus it is necessary to carry out the modeling of equations, for example, the equations of optimal nonlinear filtering, in the symmetrized form, not in the form of Ito.

The author has derived the symmetrized form of the stochastic expressions as a result of practical work with smoothed (not entirely Markov) processes [8] and with conditional Markov processes [2, 15]. In the latter articles stochastic equations are understood to be in the symmetrized sense, not in the sense of Ito. The lack of a relation between the various derivations of stochastic integrals has led to unfounded accusations of errors in the results of the indicated papers, and to confusion in their own work on the part of some authors (Kushner [1, 2]).

In some cases it is most convenient to examine the integral in the sense of Ito. For this reason we do not exclude the Ito integral from the present monograph, but use both integrals. In order to avoid confusion, integral and differential expressions in the sense of Ito will be designated by an asterisk with the differential. Where the two integrals are identical the asterisk can be used or eliminated; we chose the latter possibility.

2.1 The Symmetrized Stochastic Integral and Its Relation to the Ito Integral

1. We will begin with a one-dimensional case. Let us assume that a real diffusional process $\{x(t)\}$ is given on the interval $T = [a, b]$, for which

$$\lim_{h\downarrow 0} \mathbf{M}\left\{\frac{x(t+h)-x(t)}{h}\,\middle|\, x(t)=\xi\right\} = a(\xi, t);$$
$$\lim_{h\downarrow 0} \mathbf{M}\{h^{-1}[x(t+h)-x(t)]^2 \,|\, \xi\} = b(\xi, t); \tag{2.1}$$
$$\lim_{h\downarrow 0} \mathbf{P}\{|x(t+h)-x(t)| > \delta \,|\, \xi\} = 0, \qquad \delta > 0.$$

The functions $a(x, t)$, $b(x, t)$ are assumed to be continuous in both arguments. Aside from this, Sects. 2.2 and 2.3 require the condition of differentiability of the function $b(x, t)$.

Further, let a function $\Phi(x,t)$ be given on T, continuously differentiable in both arguments. Such a function satisfies the conditions (Dynkin [3], p. 293) for existence of a stochastic Ito integral ($\Phi \in K$ in the notation of Dynkin).

We will examine a Δ-division S_Δ of the subinterval $[s, u] \subset T$:

$$s = t_0 < t_1 < \ldots < t_N = u, \quad \max_i (t_{i+1} - t_i) = \Delta.$$

Definition 2.1. In the case in question the stochastic Ito integral is given by the formula

$$\int_s^u \Phi(x(t), t)\, d^* x(t) = \lim_{\Delta \to 0} \sum_{i=0}^{N-1} \Phi(x(t_i), t_i)[x(t_{i+1}) - x(t_i)]. \tag{2.2}$$

Here the limit is understood to be in the mean (l.i.m.) if the condition

$$\mathbf{M} \int_a^b |\Phi(x(t), t)|^2 dt < \infty \tag{2.3}$$

is fulfilled.

In the contrary case, preliminarily, in place of Φ a bounded function should be introduced and in the passage to the limit (2.2) a tendency to infinity of the level of the bound should also be included. The resulting rather complex technique is given in Dynkin's book [3]. It will not be examined, but we will rather accept condition (2.3).

Definition 2.2. The symmetrized stochastic integral is determined by the formula

$$\int_s^u \Phi(x(t), t)\, dx(t) = \lim_{\Delta \to 0} \sum_{i=0}^{N-1} \Phi\left(\frac{x(t_i) + x(t_{i+1})}{2}, \frac{t_i + t_{i+1}}{2}\right) \times \\ \times [x(t_{i+1}) - x(t_i)], \tag{2.4}$$

where the limit has the same meaning as in (2.2).

As a result of the indicated differentiability of the function Φ with respect to t, on the right side of (2.4) we can use

$$\Phi\left(\frac{x(t_i) + x(t_{i+1})}{2}, t_i\right) \quad \text{or} \quad \Phi\left(\frac{x(t_i) + x(t_{i+1})}{2}, t_{i+1}\right).$$

Theorem 2.1. With the indicated assumptions the integral (2.4) exists and is almost certainly related to the Ito integral by the formula

$$\int_s^u \Phi(x(t), t)\, dx(t) = \int_s^u \Phi(x(t), t)\, d^* x(t) + \frac{1}{2} \int_s^u \frac{\partial \Phi}{\partial x}(x(t), t)\, b(x(t), t)\, dt\,.$$

In the proof of this theorem, we will use:

Lemma 2.1. For the above diffusion process the limit

$$\lim_{\Delta\to 0}\sum_{[s,u]}[x(t_{i+1})-x(t_i)]^2=\int_s^u b(x(t),t)\,dt$$

almost certainly exists.

This lemma is a slight modification of Theorem 2.3 of Chapter VIII of the Doob monograph [1].

Proof of Theorem 2.1. Having selected a Δ-division $S_\Delta=\{t_i^{(\Delta)}\}$, we examine the difference D^Δ of the prelimit expressions in the right sides of (2.2) and (2.4). Using the differentiability of the function $\Phi(x, t)$ with respect to x, we have

$$D^\Delta\equiv\sum_i\left[\Phi\left(\frac{x_i+x_{i+1}}{2}, t_i\right)-\Phi(x_i, t_i)\right](x_{i+1}-x_i)=$$

$$=\frac{1}{2}\sum_i\frac{\partial\Phi}{\partial x}\left(\left(1-\frac{\Theta_i}{2}\right)x_i+\frac{\Theta_i}{2}x_{i+1}, t_i\right)(x_{i+1}-x_i)^2,$$

$$(0\leqslant\Theta_i\leqslant 1,\quad x_i=x(t_i)).$$

It is not difficult to see that the latter expression has as its limit as $\Delta\to 0$ the integral $\frac{1}{2}\int_s^u\partial\Phi/\partial x\, b\,dt$ with probability 1, based on Lemma 2.1. In order to be convinced of this, we will examine a large ε-division

$$\{t_k^{(\varepsilon)}\}\subset\{t_i^{(\Delta)}\},\qquad \varepsilon>\Delta$$

and substitute for $\frac{\partial\Phi(x,t)}{\partial x}$ the functions

$$\bar{f}_\varepsilon(t)=\sup\left\{\frac{\partial\Phi}{\partial x}(x(\tau),\tau),\ \tau\in[t_k^{(\varepsilon)}, t_{k+1}^{(\varepsilon)}]\right\}\quad\text{for } t\in[t_k^{(\varepsilon)}, t_{k+1}^{(\varepsilon)}],$$

$$\underline{f}_\varepsilon(t)=\inf\left\{\frac{\partial\Phi}{\partial x}(x(\tau),\tau),\ \tau\in[t_k^{(\varepsilon)}, t_{k+1}^{(\varepsilon)}]\right\}\quad\text{for } t\in[t_k^{(\varepsilon)}, t_{k+1}^{(\varepsilon)}].$$

Designating

$$\bar{D}_\varepsilon^\Delta=\frac{1}{2}\sum_i\bar{f}_\varepsilon(t_i^{(\Delta)})\,[x(t_{i+1}^{(\Delta)})-x(t_i^{(\Delta)})]^2,$$

$$\underline{D}_\varepsilon^\Delta=\frac{1}{2}\sum_i\underline{f}_\varepsilon(t_i^{(\Delta)})\,[x(t_{i+1}^{(\Delta)})-x(t_i^{(\Delta)})]^2,$$

we obviously obtain

$$\underline{D}_\varepsilon^\Delta < D^\Delta < \overline{D}_\varepsilon^\Delta. \tag{2.5}$$

In accordance with Lemma 2.1,

$$\lim_{\Delta\to 0} \sum_{[t_k^{(\varepsilon)}, t_{k+1}^{(\varepsilon)}]} [x(t_{i+1}^{(\Delta)}) - x(t_i^{(\Delta)})]^2 = \int_{t_k^{(\varepsilon)}}^{t_{k+1}^{(\varepsilon)}} b(x(t), t)\, dt,$$

and thus

$$\begin{aligned} \overline{D}_\varepsilon^0 &\equiv \lim_{\Delta\to 0} \overline{D}_\varepsilon^\Delta = \frac{1}{2}\int_s^u \bar{f}_\varepsilon (x(t), t)\, b(x(t), t)\, dt, \\ \underline{D}_\varepsilon^0 &= \frac{1}{2}\int_s^u \underline{f}_\varepsilon (x(t), t)\, b(x(t), t)\, dt \end{aligned} \tag{2.6}$$

(here ε remains fixed in the process of passage to the limit).

But as a result of the continuity of $\frac{\partial\Phi}{dx}$ and b, the differences $\bar{f}_\varepsilon - \underline{f}_\varepsilon$ and $\overline{D}_\varepsilon^0 - \underline{D}_\varepsilon^0$ can be made as small as we like by decreasing ε. Thus from (2.5), (2.6) there follows the existence of the limit with probability 1:

$$\lim_{\Delta\to 0} D^\Delta = \lim_{\varepsilon\to 0} \overline{D}_\varepsilon^0 = \lim_{\varepsilon\to 0} \underline{D}_\varepsilon^0 = \frac{1}{2}\int_s^u \frac{\partial\Phi}{\partial x}(x(t), t)\, b(x(t), t)\, dt.$$

The proof is completed.

Example. We will examine an example used by Doob ([1] on p. 398). Let $x(t)$ be the process of Brownian motion with local variance $b \equiv 1$. Then instead of the formula

$$\int_s^u [x(t) - x(s)]\, d^* x(t) = \frac{1}{2}[x(u) - x(s)]^2 - \frac{1}{2}(u - s)$$

we will have the simpler formula

$$\int_s^u [x(t) - x(s)]\, dx(t) = \frac{1}{2}[x(u) - x(s)]^2$$

for the symmetrized integral. It agrees with the rules of integration applicable for common integrals.

2. Let us turn to the multidimensional generalization. Let us assume we have a multidimensional diffusion process $x(t) = \{x_1(t), \ldots, x_m(t)\}$ described by the drift vector $\{a_\alpha(x, t)\}$ and the local variance matrix $\{b_{\alpha,\beta}(x, t), \alpha, \beta = 1, \ldots, m\}$. In addition, let the given functions $\{\Phi_\alpha(x, t), \alpha = 1, \ldots, m\}$ be continuously differentiable in all arguments.

Then it is possible to define the multidimensional stochastic integral

$$\int_s^u \Phi_\alpha(x(t), t)\, dx_\alpha(t) = \lim_{\Delta \to 0} \sum_{i=0}^{N-1} \Phi_\alpha\left(\frac{x(t_{i+1}) + x(t_i)}{2}, \frac{t_{i+1} + t_i}{2}\right)[x_\alpha(t_{i+1}) - x_\alpha(t_i)]. \tag{2.7}$$

Here and subsequently summation over repeated indices is understood.

Theorem 2.2. The limit on the right side of (2.7) almost certainly exists and is related to the Ito integral by the relation

$$\int_s^u \Phi_\alpha(x(t), t)\, dx_\alpha(t) = \int_s^u \Phi_\alpha(x(t), t)\, d^* x_\alpha(t) + \frac{1}{2}\int_s^u \frac{\partial \Phi_\alpha}{\partial x_\beta}(x(t), t)\, b_{\alpha_\beta}(x(t), t)\, dt. \tag{2.8}$$

The proof of the theorem is analogous to the proof in the one-dimensional case and we will not dwell on it. It is aided by:

Lemma 2.2. If $\psi(t)$ is a continuous function (not dependent on ω), and $x(t, \omega)$ is the above-described diffusion process, then almost certainly

$$\sum_{[s,u]} \psi(t_i)[x_\alpha(t_{i+1}) - x_\alpha(t_i)][x_\beta(t_{i+1}) - x_\beta(t_i)] \to \int_s^u \psi(t)\, b_{\alpha_\beta}(x(t), t)\, dt \quad \text{as } \Delta \to 0.$$

3. The stochastic integral can sometimes conveniently be examined as a function of a variable upper limit. Having assigned a system of functions $\Phi_{\lambda\alpha}(x, t)$; $\lambda = 1, \ldots, k$; $\alpha = 1, \ldots, m$ of the previously indicated form and continuous functions $\Psi_\lambda(x, t)$, $\lambda = 1, \ldots, k$, we examine the expression

$$z_\lambda(t) = \int_s^t \Psi_\lambda(x(t), t)\, dt + \int_s^t \Phi_{\lambda\alpha}(x(t), t)\, dx_\alpha(t). \tag{2.9}$$

The calculation of limits of the type (2.1) as functions of t for the indicated expressions is of interest. Here we will fix the condition $x(t)=\xi$.

It is easily seen that continuity conditions of the type of Eq. (2.1) are fulfilled with probability 1. In addition to this, the following theorem is true:

Theorem 2.3. Under the given assumptions the local parameters

$$\lim_{h\downarrow 0} \mathbf{M}\left\{ \frac{z_\lambda(t+h)-z_\lambda(t)}{h} \,\middle|\, x(t)=\xi \right\} =$$

$$= \Psi_\lambda(\xi,t) + \Phi_{\lambda\alpha}(\xi,t)\,a_\alpha(\xi,t) + \frac{1}{2}\,\frac{\partial\Phi_{\lambda\alpha}}{\partial x_\beta}(\xi,t)\,b_{\alpha\beta}(\xi,t);$$

$$\lim_{h\downarrow 0} \mathbf{M}\left\{ \frac{1}{h}\,[z_\lambda(t+h)-z_\lambda(t)]\,[z_\mu(t+h)-z_\mu(t)] \,|\, \xi \right\} = \tag{2.10}$$

$$= \Phi_{\lambda\alpha}(\xi,t)\,\Phi_{\mu\beta}(\xi,t)\,b_{\alpha\beta}(\xi,t);$$

$$\lim_{h\downarrow 0} \mathbf{M}\left\{ \frac{1}{h}\,[z_\lambda(t+h)-z_\lambda]\,[x_\beta(t+h)-x_\beta(t)] \,|\, \xi \right\} =$$

$$= \Phi_{\lambda\alpha}(\xi,t)\,b_{\alpha\beta}(\xi,t)$$

almost certainly characterize the functions (2.9).

These relations can be proven using the Ito theory of integrals (for example, Dynkin [3]), and then the connecting formula (2.8). As we can see from (2.10), the formula for calculating the average increase $\mathbf{M}\{dz_\lambda/dt\,|\,x\}$ is not trivial. The complicating term $\frac{1}{2}\,\frac{\partial\Phi_{\lambda\alpha}}{\partial x_\beta}b_{\alpha\beta}$ is caused by correlations between the processes $x_\alpha(t)$ which are present in a number of arguments of the function Φ, and the increases dx_α.

In an analogous way, we can prove the following simple but subsequently frequently used lemmas.

Lemma 2.3. If $v(t) = \int_s^t \varphi_\alpha(x(\tau),\tau)\,d^*x_\alpha(\tau)$ and φ_α, χ are continuously differentiable functions, then

$$\int_s^u \chi(x(t),t)\,d^*v(t) = \int_s^u \chi(x(t),t)\,\varphi_\alpha(x(t),t)\,d^*x_\alpha(t),$$

i.e.,

$$\lim_{\Delta-0} \sum_i \chi(x_i,t_i)\,[v(t_{i+1})-v(t_i)] =$$

$$= \lim_{\Delta\to 0} \sum_i \chi(x_i,t_i)\,\varphi_\alpha(x_i,t_i)\,[x_\alpha(t_{i+1})-x_\alpha(t_i)].$$

An analogous lemma is also true for the integral in the symmetrized sense.

Lemma 2.4. If $v(t) = \int_s^t \varphi_\alpha(x(\tau), \tau)\, dx_\alpha(\tau)$ and φ_α, χ are functions of the described type, then

$$\int_s^u \chi(x(t), t)\, dv(t) = \int_s^u \chi(x(t), t)\, \varphi_\alpha(x(t), t)\, dx_\alpha(t).$$

Using differential instead of integral equations, it is easily seen that, in accordance with Lemma 2.3, from $dv = \varphi_\alpha d^* x_\alpha$ there follows $\chi d^* v = \chi\varphi_\alpha\, d^* x_\alpha$, and vice versa. Analogously,

$$dv = \varphi_\alpha\, dx_\alpha \Longleftrightarrow \chi\, dv = \chi\varphi_\alpha\, dx_\alpha \quad (\chi \neq 0).$$

In this manner the differential stochastic equations can be multiplied by continuous functions, and they have, consequently, an absolute meaning without regard to one or another of the integral equations.

Subsequently, any equation involving differentials will always be understood in the sense that some corresponding equation for integrals is valid.

4. Aside from the stochastic integral

$$\int_s^u \Phi_\alpha(x(t), t)\, d^* x_\alpha(t) = \lim_{\Delta\to 0} \sum_{i=0}^{N-1} \Phi_\alpha(x(t_i), t_i)\, [x_\alpha(t_{i+1}) - x_\alpha(t_i)], \tag{2.11}$$

it is possible to introduce the Ito integral corresponding to the reverse time

$$\int_s^u d^* x_\alpha(t)\, \Phi_\alpha(x(t), t) = \lim_{\Delta\to 0} \sum_{i=0}^{N-1} [x_\alpha(t_{i+1}) - x_\alpha(t_i)]\, \Phi_\alpha(x(t_{i+1}), t_{i+1}), \tag{2.12}$$

and also the mixed integral

$$\int_s^u \Phi'_\alpha(x(t), t)\, d^* x_\alpha(t)\, \Phi''_\alpha(x(t), t) = \lim_{\Delta\to 0} \sum_{i=0}^{N-1} \Phi'_\alpha(x(t_i), t_i)\, [x_\alpha(t_{i+1}) - x_\alpha(t_i)]\, \Phi''_\alpha(x(t_{i+1}), t_{i+1}). \tag{2.13}$$

The formula connecting the integrals (2.7), (2.12), analogous to (2.8), as we can easily see, has the form

$$\int_s^u \Phi_\alpha(x(t), t)\, dx_\alpha(t) = \tag{2.14}$$
$$= \int_s^u d^* x_\alpha(t)\, \Phi_\alpha(x(t), t) - \frac{1}{2} \int_s^u \frac{\partial \Phi_\alpha}{\partial x_\beta}(x(t), t)\, b_{\alpha\beta}(x(t), t)\, dt.$$

At the same time, for integral (2.13), we have

$$\int_s^u \Phi'_\alpha\, d^* x_\alpha \Phi''_\alpha = \int_s^u \Phi'_\alpha \Phi''_\alpha\, dx_\alpha - \frac{1}{2} \int_s^u \left[\frac{\partial \Phi'_\alpha}{\partial x_\beta} \Phi''_\alpha - \Phi'_\alpha \frac{\partial \Phi''_\alpha}{\partial x_\beta} \right] b_{\alpha\beta}\, dt.$$

From (2.8) and (2.14) follows the formula connecting integrals (2.11) and (2.12)

$$\int_s^u d^* x_\alpha \Phi_\alpha - \int_s^u \Phi_\alpha\, d^* x_\alpha = \int_s^u \frac{\partial \Phi_\alpha}{\partial x_\beta} b_{\alpha\beta}\, dt. \tag{2.15}$$

In this manner, the various integrals easily transform into one another. The symmetrized integral (2.7) occupies in value an intermediate position between (2.11) and (2.12). It is equal to half their sum.

2.2 Stochastic Equations

1. In some special cases the process $\{x_\alpha(t)\}$, which we designate in this paragraph $\{\tilde{x}_\alpha\}$, and the functions $\Psi_\lambda(\tilde{x}, t)$, $\Phi_{\lambda\alpha}(\tilde{x}, t)$ are such that the processes (2.9) are identically equal to zero with probability 1: $z_\lambda(t) \equiv 0$, $t \in [s, u]$, $\lambda = 1, \ldots, k$. In this case we will say that the stochastic equations

$$\int_s^t \Psi_\lambda(\tilde{x}(\tau), \tau)\, d\tau + \int_s^t \Phi_{\lambda\alpha}(\tilde{x}(\tau), \tau)\, d\tilde{x}_\alpha(\tau) = 0, \ \lambda = 1, \ldots, k \tag{2.16}$$

are satisfied.

It is interesting to examine those relations among the processes $\tilde{x}_1(t), \ldots, \tilde{x}_m(t)$ for which this takes place. Usually it turns out that a portion of the indicated components, let us say, $\tilde{x}_1 \equiv x_1, \ldots, \tilde{x}_k \equiv x_k$ $(m-k=l>0)$, is unambiguously (to within an equivalence) determined by the remaining components $\tilde{x}_{k+1} \equiv y_1, \ldots, \tilde{x}_m \not\equiv y_{m-k}$. In this case it is said that the functions $x_1(t), \ldots, x_k(t)$ are the solution of the stochastic equations (2.16).

The theory of stochastic equations presently in existence is based on the work of Ito [2, 3] and is found in the monographs by Doob [1] and Dynkin [3]. It is concerned with stochastic equations of the more particular form

$$x_\lambda(t) = \int_s^t a_\lambda(x_1, \ldots, x_k, \tau)\, d\tau + \sum_{\rho=1}^{l} \sigma_{\lambda\rho}(x_1, \ldots, x_k, \tau)\, d^* y_\rho(\tau) \qquad (2.17)$$

($\lambda = 1, \ldots, k$; $y_\rho(t)$ are Wiener processes) and sufficient conditions for the existence of a solution for $x_1(t), \ldots, x_k(t)$ are examined. In our opinion, these conditions (especially conditions of the type $|\sigma_{\lambda\rho}(x, t) - \sigma_{\lambda\rho}(x', t)| \leqslant c|x - x'|$, etc.) can be substantially weakened. Thus we will not enumerate them nor validate them. However, whenever a stochastic equation is encountered in the text, it will be understood that the corresponding (perhaps weaker) conditions for their solution are satisfied.

2. Equation (2.17) can be obtained by a specialization of Eq. (2.16). Let us examine first the one-dimensional case when $k = 1$. Let $m = 2$ and let there be two processes $\tilde{x}_1(t) = x(t)$, $\tilde{x}_2(t) = y(t)$. Further, let the functions Φ_1, Φ_2, Ψ have the following special form:

$$\Phi_1(x, y, t) = -1; \quad \Phi_2(x, y, t) = \sigma(x, t); \quad \Psi(x, y, t) = m(x, t).$$

Then Eq. (2.16) takes the form

$$x(t) = x(s) + \int_s^t m(x(t'), t')\, dt' + \int_s^t \sigma(x(t'), t')\, dy(t'). \qquad (2.18)$$

This relation can be considered a stochastic transformation of the process $y(t)$ into $x(t)$. For the given case we will write Eq. (2.10) taking into consideration that the process $z(t)$ and consequently the limits of the left sides are equal to zero. This gives us

$$m(x, t) - a_1 + \sigma(x, t)\, a_2 + \frac{1}{2}\frac{\partial \sigma}{\partial x}(x, t)\, b_{12} = 0;$$

$$b_{11} - 2\sigma(x, t)\, b_{12} + \sigma^2(x, t)\, b_{22} = 0;$$

$$-b_{11} + \sigma(x, t)\, b_{12} = 0; \quad -b_{21} + \sigma(x, t)\, b_{22} = 0.$$

From this we find almost certainly

$$a_1 = \sigma(x, t)\, a_2 + m(x, t) + \frac{1}{2}\frac{\partial \sigma(x, t)}{\partial x}\sigma(x, t)\, b_{22};$$
$$b_{11} = \sigma^2(x, t)\, b_{22}; \quad b_{12} = \sigma(x, t)\, b_{22}\,. \qquad (2.19)$$

Turning to an even more specialized case, for $y(t)$ we take the Wiener process, i.e., we assume $a_2 = 0$; $b_{22} = 1$. Then from (2.19) we will have

$$a_1 = m(x, t) + \frac{1}{2} \frac{\partial \sigma(x, t)}{\partial x} \sigma(x, t); \qquad b_{11} = \sigma^2(x, t) \tag{2.20}$$

or, solving for m, σ,

$$m(x, t) = a_1(x, t) - \frac{1}{4} \frac{\partial b_{11}}{\partial x}(x, t);$$

$$\sigma(x, t) = \sqrt{b_{11}(x, t)}.$$

Thus, if functions $a(x, t)$, $b(x, t)$ are the drift and the local variance of a diffusion process $x(t)$ [and satisfy the previously formulated conditions of differentiability], the process $x(t)$ is described by the stochastic equation

$$dx(t) = \left[a(x, t) - \frac{1}{4} \frac{\partial b(x, t)}{\partial x} \right] dt + \sqrt{b(x, t)}\, dy(t).$$

Conversely, if the process $x(t)$ is determined by the stochastic equation (2.18), the local parameters (2.20) correspond to it.

We will show that this result correctly agrees with results of the first chapter, that (2.20) corresponds to formulas (1.17), and (2.18) to (1.12). Let us take Eqs. (1.1) and (1.12) in the form

$$\frac{dx}{dt} = \mu^2 m(x) + \mu \sigma(x) \xi(t);$$
$$\frac{d\widetilde{x}}{d\widetilde{t}} = m(\widetilde{x}) + \sigma(\widetilde{x}) \frac{1}{\mu} \xi\left(\frac{\widetilde{t}}{\mu^2}\right), \quad (g(x, t, \omega) = \sigma(x) \xi(t)), \tag{2.21}$$

where $\xi(t)$ is a Gaussian process with zero mean and finite variance satisfying the condition

$$\int_{-\infty}^{\infty} r(\tau)\, d\tau = 1 \quad (r(\tau) = \mathbf{M}\xi(t)\xi(t + \tau)). \tag{2.22}$$

Then, according to (1.14), we have

$$k_2'(x, x', \tau) = \sigma(x)\sigma(x') r(\tau); \qquad \frac{\partial}{\partial x'} \int_{-\infty}^{0} k_2'(x', x, \tau)\, d\tau =$$

$$= \frac{1}{2} \frac{\partial \sigma(x')}{\partial x'} \sigma(x); \qquad \int_{-\infty}^{\infty} k_2'(x, x, \tau)\, d\tau = \sigma^2(x),$$

and formulas (1.17) give the limit parameters

$$a(x, t) = m(x) + \frac{1}{2}\frac{\partial\sigma(x)}{\partial x}\sigma(x),$$
$$b(x, t) = \sigma^2(x).$$

This result coincides with the result of formulas (2.20) if we consider that the limit diffusion process satisfies the equation

$$dx = m(x) + \sigma(x)\,dy(t). \tag{2.23}$$

We introduce the process

$$\tilde{y}(\tilde{t}) = \int\limits_{t'<\tilde{t}} \frac{1}{\mu}\xi\left(\frac{t'}{\mu^2}\right)dt'.$$

Taking into account (2.22), it is not difficult to be convinced that as $\mu \to 0$, it tends (in distribution) to the Wiener process. With the help of $\tilde{y}(\tilde{t})$, the second equation (2.21) is written in the form

$$d\tilde{x} = m(\tilde{x})\,d\tilde{t} + \sigma(\tilde{x})\,d\,\tilde{y}(\tilde{t}). \tag{2.24}$$

The $\tilde{x}(\tilde{t})$ determined by this process, as Theorem 1.1 asserts, tends (in distribution) to a limit diffusion process as $\mu \to 0$. The latter, as we already explained, satisfies Eq. (2.23) of the exact same form.

Thus, the form of the equation connecting the prelimit processes $\tilde{x}(\tilde{t})$ and $y(\tilde{t})$ coincides with the form of the equation connecting the limit processes $x(t), y(t)$. Such an important agreement will not take place if the Ito formulation of the stochastic equations is used.

3. We turn now to the multidimensional generalization of the formulas (2.20).

Theorem 2.4. If the multidimensional process $x(t) = \{x_1(t), \ldots, x_k(t)\}$ is described by the equation

$$dx_\lambda(t) = m_\lambda(x, t)\,dt + \sum_{r=1}^{l}\sigma_{\lambda r}(x, t)\,dy_r(t), \tag{2.25}$$

where $m_\lambda(x, t)$ are continuous and $\sigma_{\lambda r}(x, t)$ are continuously differentiable functions and $y_1(t), \ldots, y_l(t)$ is a system of Wiener processes with a unit local variance matrix, then it has the following drifts and local variances:

$$\begin{aligned} a_\lambda(x, t) &= m_\lambda(x, t) + \frac{1}{2}\frac{\partial\sigma_{\lambda r}(x, t)}{\partial x_\mu}\sigma_{\mu r}(x, t); \\ b_{\lambda\mu}(x, t) &= \sigma_{\lambda r}(x, t)\,\sigma_{\mu r}(x, t). \end{aligned} \tag{2.26}$$

As in the one-dimensional case, this result can be obtained from Theorem 2.3.

In this manner, it is convenient to examine the parameters m_λ, $\sigma_{\lambda r}$, which determine the symmetrized form (2.25) as well as parameters a_λ, $b_{\lambda\mu}$, which determine the Ito form of the stochastic equation (2.17).

Parameters m_λ, $\sigma_{\lambda r}$ also have transformational advantages over a_λ, $b_{\lambda\mu}$. In the one-dimensional case these parameters transform trivially when the variable $x \to \int \varphi(x)\,dx$ is substituted

$$m \to \varphi m; \quad \sigma \to \varphi\sigma$$

($\varphi(x)$ is a continuous positive function). An analogous situation is found also in the multidimensional case.

Theorem 2.5. Under the change of variables $\tilde{x} = \tilde{x}(x)$, the vectors

$$\vec{\sigma}_1 = \{\sigma_{11}, \ldots, \sigma_{k1}\}, \ldots, \vec{\sigma}_l = \{\sigma_{1l}, \ldots, \sigma_{kl}\}, \ \vec{m} = \{m_1, \ldots, m_k\}$$

are transformed covariantly with respect to the vector $\vec{dx}$

$$\tilde{\sigma}_{\lambda r} = \frac{\partial \tilde{x}_\lambda}{\partial x_\mu} \sigma_{\mu r}; \ \tilde{m}_\lambda = \frac{\partial \tilde{x}_\lambda}{\partial x_\mu} m_\mu. \tag{2.27}$$

Consequently, Eq. (2.25) is transformed in the same way as if the processes $x_1(t), \ldots, x_k(t)$ were smooth functions of time.

The confirmation of the theorem in regard to the vectors $\vec{\sigma}_1, \ldots, \vec{\sigma}_l$ follows directly from the tensor nature of the parameters $b_{\lambda\mu}$ and the definition of these vectors. In order to prove that the vector

$$m_\lambda = a_\lambda - \frac{1}{2} \frac{\partial \sigma_{\lambda r}}{\partial x_\mu} \sigma_{\mu r} \tag{2.28}$$

is covariant, we take into account the familiar transformation formulas for the drift parameters

$$\tilde{a}_\lambda = \frac{\partial \tilde{x}_\lambda}{\partial x_\mu} a_\mu + \frac{1}{2} \frac{\partial^2 \tilde{x}_\lambda}{\partial x_\mu \partial x_\nu} b_{\mu\nu}. \tag{2.29}$$

Inserting $\tilde{\sigma}_{\mu r} = \dfrac{\partial \tilde{x}_\mu}{\partial x_\nu} \sigma_{\nu r}$, we find

$$\frac{\partial \tilde{\sigma}_{\lambda r}}{\partial \tilde{x}_\mu} \tilde{\sigma}_{\mu r} = \frac{\partial \tilde{\sigma}_{\lambda r}}{\partial \tilde{x}_\mu} \frac{\partial \tilde{x}_\mu}{\partial x_\nu} \sigma_{\nu r} = \frac{\partial \tilde{\sigma}_{\lambda r}}{\partial x_\nu} \sigma_{\nu r}.$$

Making this substitution for the second time, we obtain

$$\frac{\partial \tilde{\sigma}_{\lambda r}}{\partial x_\nu}\sigma_{\nu r} = \frac{\partial}{\partial x_\nu}\left(\frac{\partial \tilde{x}_\lambda}{\partial x_\varkappa}\sigma_{\varkappa r}\right)\sigma_{\nu r} = \frac{\partial \tilde{x}_\lambda}{\partial x_\varkappa}\frac{\partial \sigma_{\varkappa r}}{\partial x_\nu}\sigma_{\nu r} + \frac{\partial^2 \tilde{x}_\lambda}{\partial x_\nu \partial x_\varkappa}\sigma_{\varkappa r}\sigma_{\nu r}.$$

Consequently,

$$\frac{\partial \tilde{\sigma}_{\lambda r}}{\partial \tilde{x}_\mu}\tilde{\sigma}_{\mu r} = \frac{\partial \tilde{x}_\lambda}{\partial x_\varkappa}\frac{\partial \sigma_{\varkappa r}}{\partial x_\nu}\sigma_{\nu r} + \frac{\partial^2 \tilde{x}_\lambda}{\partial x_\nu \partial x_\varkappa}b_{\varkappa\nu}. \tag{2.30}$$

Calculating from (2.29) half of the expression (2.30) [in accordance with (2.28)], we are convinced of the validity of the second formula of (2.27). The proof is completed.

We will remark that as a consequence of the symmetry and nonnegative definiteness of the local variance matrix, at least one suitable system of real vectors $\vec{\sigma}_1, \ldots, \vec{\sigma}_l$ always exists. Namely, if $\|u_{\lambda r}\|$ is an orthogonal transformation bringing this matrix into diagonal form: $b_{\lambda\mu}u_{\lambda r}u_{\mu s} = b_r^0\delta_{rs}$, then $b_{\lambda\mu} = u_{\lambda r}u_{\mu r}b_r^0$ and, obviously, it is possible to assume $\sigma_{\lambda r} = u_{\lambda r}\sqrt{b_r^0}$ ($l =$ Rank $\|b_{\lambda\mu}\|$).

2.3 Invariant Formulation of the Kolmogorov Equations

The invariant formulation of the Kolmogorov equations in arbitrary curvilinear coordinates was presented in the papers of Kolmogorov [1] and Yaglom [1]. In the first the examination was limited to cases of a nonsingular local variance matrix which was used in the capacity of a metric tensor. In the second the metric tensor was assumed to be independent, but substantial limitations of a different kind were introduced. Namely, the entire phase space of the Markov process was not assumed to be a metric space, but only the space corresponding to half its variables (coordinates). The local variance matrix, on the other hand, corresponded only to the second half of the variables (velocities) and again was assumed to be nonsingular (in the space of velocities).

The vectors $\vec{m}$, $\vec{\sigma}_r$ introduced above permit an invariant formulation of the Kolmogorov equations to be obtained in the general case of an arbitrary metric phase space. In the special cases noted above, this formulation does not coincide with earlier suggested forms and appears to be simpler.

Beginning from this we will assume the phase variables to be contravariant components of a vector and will designate their differential by dx^λ. From Theorem 2.5, the vectors considered in it consequently also are contravariant; thus we will designate them m^λ, $\sigma^\lambda(r)$ [the index r is written in parentheses since it does not have a tensor character].

We will examine the Markov probability density $p(x, t; x', t')$ of transformation from x to x' in time t to t'. The Kolmogorov equation of the first kind

$$-\frac{\partial p}{\partial t} = a^{\lambda}\frac{\partial p}{\partial x^{\lambda}} + \frac{1}{2} b_{\lambda\mu}\frac{\partial^2 p}{\partial x^{\lambda}\partial x_{\mu}}$$

taking into account (2.26), transforms to the invariant form

$$-\frac{\partial p}{\partial t} = m^{\lambda}\frac{\partial p}{\partial x^{\lambda}} + \frac{1}{2}\sigma^{\lambda}(r)\frac{\partial}{\partial x^{\lambda}}\left[\sigma^{\mu}(r)\frac{\partial p}{\partial x^{\mu}}\right]. \tag{2.31}$$

In fact, the transformation probability $p(x, t; x', t')$ as a function of x is a scalar. Thus expressions $m^{\lambda}\frac{\partial p}{\partial x^{\lambda}}$, $\sigma^{\mu}\frac{\partial p}{\partial x^{\mu}} = v$, and consequently $\sigma^{\lambda}\frac{\partial v}{\partial x^{\lambda}}$, also are scalar. Thus, the right side of (2.31) as well as the left is scalar.

Analogously, by substituting formula (2.26), the equation of the second type (Fokker–Planck)

$$\frac{\partial p}{\partial t'} = -\frac{\partial}{\partial x'^{\lambda}}[a^{\lambda}p] + \frac{1}{2}\frac{\partial^2}{\partial x'^{\lambda}\partial x'^{\mu}}[b^{\lambda\mu}p]$$

changes to the form

$$\frac{\partial p}{\partial t'} = -\frac{\partial}{\partial x'^{\lambda}}[m^{\lambda}p] + \frac{1}{2}\frac{\partial}{\partial x'^{\lambda}}\left[\sigma^{\lambda}(r)\frac{\partial}{\partial x'^{\mu}}(\sigma^{\mu}(r)p)\right]. \tag{2.32}$$

Examined as a function of x', the transformation probability $p(x, t; x', t')$ is a scalar density, i.e., it is transformed as $\sqrt{g} = \det^{\frac{1}{2}}\|g_{\alpha\beta}\|$. Thus $m^{\alpha}p$, $\sigma^{\mu}p$ are vector densities. Buf if $\mathfrak{A}^{\lambda}$ is a vector density, then as we know the divergence $\frac{\partial}{\partial x'^{\lambda}}\mathfrak{A}^{\lambda}$ is again a scalar density. Thus $\frac{\partial}{\partial x'^{\lambda}}(m^{\lambda}p)$, $\frac{\partial}{\partial x'^{\mu}}(\sigma^{\mu}p) = \mathfrak{B}$, and $\frac{\partial}{\partial x'^{\lambda}}(\sigma^{\lambda}\mathfrak{B})$ are scalar densities similar to the value on the left side of (2.32).

It is possible to introduce the flow of probability

$$\mathfrak{G}^{\lambda} = m^{\lambda}p - \frac{1}{2}\sigma^{\lambda}(r)\frac{\partial}{\partial x'^{\mu}}[\sigma^{\mu}(r)p],$$

as a vector density. Then Eq. (2.32) will take on the form of a conservation equation

$$\frac{\partial p}{\partial t'} + \frac{\partial \mathfrak{G}^{\lambda}}{\partial x'^{\lambda}} = 0.$$

The cited Eqs. (2.31) and (2.32) correspond to the same invariant infinitesimal operator

$$dL = \left\{ m^{\lambda} \frac{\partial}{\partial x^{\lambda}} + \frac{1}{2} \sum_{r} \left[\sigma^{\lambda}(r) \frac{\partial}{\partial x^{\lambda}} \right]^{2} \right\} dt.$$

In Eq. (2.32) it is transposed.

2.4 Stochastic Linear Operators

We will assume here that in formula (2.16) the functions Ψ_{λ}, $\Phi_{\lambda\rho}$, $\lambda = 1, \ldots, k$; $\rho = k+1, \ldots, k+l$ are linearly dependent on $x_1, \ldots, x_k$:

$$\Psi_{\lambda} = A_{\mu\lambda}(y, t)\, x_{\mu}; \quad \Phi_{\lambda, k+\sigma} = A_{\mu\lambda\sigma}(y, t)\, x_{\mu}$$

and that

$$\Phi_{\lambda\mu} = \begin{cases} -1 \text{ for } \lambda = \mu; \\ \;\;0 \text{ for } \lambda \neq \mu; \end{cases} \quad (\lambda, \mu = 1, \ldots, k; \sigma = 1, \ldots, l).$$

Then Eq. (2.16) takes the form

$$x_{\lambda}(t) = x_{\lambda}(s) + \int_{s}^{t} [A_{\mu\lambda}(y(\tau), \tau)\, d\tau + A_{\mu\lambda\sigma}(y(\tau), \tau)\, dy_{\sigma}(\tau)]\, x_{\mu}(\tau). \quad (2.33)$$

We assume the existence of a solution of this equation. Applying Theorem 2.2, the latter equation can also be written using integrals in the sense of Ito:

$$x_{\lambda}(t) = x_{\lambda}(s) + \int_{s}^{t} x_{\mu}(\tau)\, [A^{*}_{\mu\lambda}(y(\tau), \tau)\, d\tau + A_{\mu\lambda\sigma}(y(\tau), \tau)\, d^{*}y_{\sigma}(\tau)], \quad (2.34)$$

where

$$x_{\mu} A^{*}_{\mu\lambda} = x_{\mu} A_{\mu\lambda} + \frac{1}{2} A_{\mu\lambda\sigma} b_{\mu\sigma} + \frac{1}{2} x_{\mu} \frac{\partial A_{\mu\lambda\sigma}}{\partial y_{\pi}} b_{\sigma\pi}, \; b_{\mu\sigma} = x_{\nu} A_{\nu\mu\pi} b_{\pi\sigma},$$

and, consequently,

$$A^{*}_{\mu\lambda} = A_{\mu\lambda} + \frac{1}{2} A_{\mu\nu\pi} A_{\nu\lambda\sigma} b_{\sigma\pi} + \frac{1}{2} \frac{\partial A_{\mu\lambda\sigma}}{\partial y_{\pi}} b_{\sigma\pi}. \quad (2.35)$$

We introduce two classes of operators $L(t)$, $L^*(t)$ with matrix elements

$$[L(t)]_{\mu\lambda} = [L(s)]_{\mu\lambda} + \int_s^t [A_{\mu\lambda}(y, \tau)\, d\tau + A_{\mu\lambda\sigma}(y, \tau)\, dy_\sigma(\tau)];$$
$$[L^*(t)]_{\mu\lambda} = [L^*(s)]_{\mu\lambda} + \int_s^t [A^*_{\mu\lambda}(y, \tau)\, d\tau + A_{\mu\lambda\sigma}(y, \tau)\, d^* y_\sigma(\tau)]. \tag{2.35a}$$

With their use formulas (2.33) and (2.34) are written in the form

$$x(t) - x(s) = \int_s^t x(t')\, dL(t');$$

$$x(t) - x(s) = \int_s^t x(t')\, d^* L^*(t').$$

For fixed t, the values $x(t)$ determined by the given formulas can be presented as the result of a linear transformation of the initial values $x(s)$. Designating by T_{st} the corresponding operator, we have

$$x(t) = x(s)\, T_{st}.$$

The form of the operator T_{st} is entirely determined by the operators $L(\tau)$ and $L(s)$, $\tau \in [s, t]$.

Let us find the explicit expression for the indicated operator in the case when the process $x(t)$ is one-dimensional.

Having written (2.33) with $k = 1$ in differential form

$$dx = x[A(y, t)\, dt + A_\sigma(y, t)\, dy_\sigma],$$

we divide both sides of the equation by x and integrate from s to t. We make use of the fact that in the new formulation of the stochastic integral the usual formula

$$\int_s^t \frac{dx(\tau)}{x(\tau)} = \ln \frac{x(t)}{x(s)}$$

is valid (for the Ito integral $\int d^* x/x$ it would be untrue). This gives

$$\ln \frac{x(t)}{x(s)} = \int_s^t [A(y, \tau)\, d\tau + A_\sigma(y, \tau)\, dy_\sigma], \tag{2.36}$$

i.e.,

$$x(t) = e^{L(t)-L(s)}\, x(s). \tag{2.37}$$

If we switch to the Ito integral in (2.36) and examine Eq. (2.34) with $k = 1$, then according to (2.35) and (2.8) we will have the following result:

Corollary 2.1. The equation

$$dx = x\,[A^{\bullet}(y, t)\,dt + A_{\sigma}(y, t)\,d^{\bullet}y_{\sigma}]$$

has the solution

$$x(t) = x(s)\exp\left\{\int_s^t \left(A^{\bullet} - \frac{1}{2}A_{\sigma}A_{\pi}b_{\sigma\pi}\right)d\tau + \int_s^t A_{\sigma}\,d^{\bullet}y_{\sigma}\right\}. \tag{2.38}$$

In the multidimensional case as a result of the noncommutativity of the operators $L(\tau)$ and $L(s)$, $\tau \in [s, t]$ the simple formula (2.37), generally speaking, is invalid. If, however, the indicated operators commute with each other, then the operator formula analogous to (2.37) retains its validity also in the multidimensional case. This can be proven by bringing the operators $L(\tau)$ and $L(s)$ to the diagonal form and applying the one-dimensional formula (2.37) to each component.

Stochastic linear operators of a more general form will be examined in the following chapter.

CHAPTER 3

Markov Measures and Infinitesimal Operators

The main content of the present chapter will be the definition of two families of generating operators which produce infinitesimal operators for a given unnormalized Markov system of measures and the compilation of a series of results concerning operators.

Markov measures satisfying the Chapman-Kolmogorov equation determine, in the general case, as we know, a two-parameter semigroup of operators in the combined Banach spaces of functions and the generalized measures. The study carried out in this chapter is applicable not only to *a priori* measures of the original Markov process, but also to an unnormalized (nonprobabilistic) *a posteriori* measure dependent on the observed process which is introduced in the theory of conditional Markov processes.

At present, the case of a stationary Markov process has been most thoroughly studied, corresponding to a one-parameter semigroup (Hill [1], Yoshida [1, 2], Dynkin [1, 3], see also Loève [1]). For our purposes, however, this theory is insufficient in view of the fact that *a posteriori* Markov measures are intrinsically nonstationary due to the dependence on the observed process. Moreover, in the cases of most interest to us, in which a diffusion process or a function of it is observed, the semigroup of operators T_{st} is nondifferentiable. Namely, the limit

$$\lim_{\Delta\to 0} \Delta^{-1}[T_{t,t+\Delta}g - g] = Ag$$

does not exist for a sufficiently broad class of functions g (for a set which is everywhere dense in the cited Banach space). This is caused by the fact that $T_{t,\,t+\Delta}\, g - g = O(\Delta^{1/2})$. This statement requires a substantial generalization of the theory. One of the ways in which it may be generalized is by the introduction of a one-parameter family $L^*(t)$ of generating operators. The differential $dL^*(t)$ is called an infinitesimal operator. In the particular case when the above limit exists, the simple relation $dL^*(t)=Adt$ is valid.

The indicated family entirely determines the semigroup and vice versa. By analogy to the former theory, it is also possible here to examine strong and weak closures of the area of definition, to prove uniqueness theorems, etc. Of course, in this chapter it is not possible to examine the extensive material related to this subject at any length. Our compilation will have a somewhat fragmentary and summary quality.

3.1 Operators Corresponding to Markov Measures

1. Let us assume that we are given a measurable phase space $(E, \mathscr{E})$ and a two-parameter system of measures $\mu_{st}(x, \Lambda)$, where $x\in E, \Lambda\in \mathscr{E}$; $s, t\in T$. For fixed x, s, t, the functions $\mu_{st}(x, \Lambda)$ form a measure in the indicated space, and for fixed Λ, s, t they are $\mathscr{E}$-measurable functions of x.

Let us designate by G the space of bounded Borel functions on E. It is a Banach space with natural linear operations and norm

$$\| g \| = \sup_{x\in E} | g(x) |, \quad g\in G.$$

On this space we define the operators

$$(T_{st}g)(x) = \int \mu_{st}(x, dx') g(x'), \quad s<t.$$

In addition to this, it is possible to examine the transformation of completely additive functions from the Banach space $\Phi\ni\varphi$ (with the norm $\|\varphi\|=\mathrm{Var}_E\varphi$),

$$(\varphi T_{st})(\Lambda) = \int \varphi(dx) \mu_{st}(x, \Lambda).$$

Let us assume that the system of measures in question is Markov, i.e., the Chapman-Kolmogorov equation

$$\int \mu_{st}(x, dx') \mu_{tu}(x', \Lambda) = \mu_{su}(x, \Lambda), \quad s<t<u,$$

is satisfied, or in operator form

$$T_{st}T_{tu} = T_{su}.$$

For the given Markov system of measures we introduce a one-parameter family of operators $L^*(t)$, $t\in T$ (defined to within a constant additive operator).

Definition 3.1. The family of operators $L^*(u)-L^*(s), u>s$ is formed by the passage to the limit

$$[L^*(u)-L^*(s)]g=\lim_{\Delta\to 0}[T_{t_1t_2}-I+\ldots+T_{t_{N-1},t_N}-I]g, \qquad (3.1)$$

where $t_1, \ldots, t_N$ is a Δ-division of the interval $[s, u]$ and I is the unit operator.

The space of functions $D_{L^*}\subset G$ for which (3.1) converges and for which the limits do not depend on the particular method of division is the region of definition of the indicated family of operators (it is assumed that D_{L^*} does not depend on s and u).

It is not difficult to show that in the case of a unary Markov system of measures (in the case of a one-parameter semigroup) the above operators are related to the infinitesimal operator A defined in the usual way by the relation

$$L^*(u)-L^*(s)=(u-s)A$$

and that $D_{L^*}=D_A$.

We will give without proof a series of assertions regarding the introduced operators.

Let us say that for any $g\in G_0\subset G$ the function $f(t)=T_{tu}g$ belongs to the region D_{L^*}. As a function of t it then satisfies the integral equation

$$f(t)-g=\int_t^u d^*L^*(\tau)f(\tau), \quad t<u. \qquad (3.2)$$

The integral here is understood in the sense of the limit (see Sect. 2.1)

$$\int_t^u d^*L^*(\tau)f(\tau)=\lim_{\Delta\to 0}\sum_{[t,u]}[L^*(t_{j+1})-L^*(t_j)]f(t_{j+1}).$$

An analogous equation is valid for the measure $\varphi\in\Phi$:

$$\varphi(t)-\varphi=\int_s^t \varphi(\tau)\,d^*L^*(\tau), \quad s<t, \qquad (3.3)$$

where the integral has the following significance:

$$\int_s^t \varphi(\tau)\,d^*L^*(\tau)=\lim_{\Delta\to 0}\sum_{[s,t]}\varphi(t_j)[L^*(t_{j+1})-L^*(t_j)].$$

Dropping g and φ, similar equations can also be written directly for the operators T_{su}. Several integral relations are possible here, for example,

$$T_{su} = I + \int_s^u T_{s\tau}\, d^*L^*(\tau) = T_{st} + \int_t^u T_{s\tau}\, d^*L^*(\tau);$$
$$T_{su} = I + \int_s^u d^*L^*(\tau)\, T_{\tau u} = T_{tu} + \int_s^t d^*L^*(\tau)\, T_{\tau u} \qquad (3.4)$$
$$(s < t < u),$$

and also differential relations

$$d_u T_{su} = T_{su}\, d^*L^*(u); \quad d_s T_{su} = d^*L^*(s)\, T_{su}. \qquad (3.5)$$

Thus the semigroup T_{su} determines the family of generating operators. With the help of these, integral or differential equations satisfied by the semigroup transformations are written.

The converse operation is also true: the family of generating operators determines the semigroup. If we are given a family of operators $L(t)$, we can write a differential or integral equation, for example, (3.2). Its solution $f(t)$ can be interpreted as the result of a transformation T_{tu} of the function g into the function $f(t)$. We will prove that such transformations form a semigroup. In addition to (3.2), we will examine a second equation

$$f(s) - f(t) = \int_s^t d^*L^*(\tau)\, f(\tau), \quad s < t.$$

The first, (3.2), determines $f(t)$ as the result of the transformation $T_{tu}g$, and the second determines $f(s)$ as the result of the transformation $T_{st}f(t)$. Combining these two equations we obtain

$$f(s) - g = \int_s^u d^*L^*(\tau)\, f(\tau),$$

which determines $f(s)$ as $T_{su}g$. Since in these equations $f(s)$ is the same function, we have

$$T_{st}T_{tu}g = T_{su}g.$$

In this manner the semigroup characteristic is proven.

Finding the operators $L^*(u) - L^*(s)$ for this semigroup using the formula (3.1), we obtain the original operators.

We will call the family of operators $L^*(t)$ *generating*, since it determines the semigroup. We will also use the term *infinitesimal operator* for the corresponding differential $dL^*(t)$.

The theory of the operators (3.1) is used to generalize the existing theory of a unary semigroup. For the latter semigroup the theory is simplified and Eqs. (3.2) become the familiar equations (Dynkin [3], p. 48).

Aside from the generalization to the nonunary case, for further study, one more generalization is necessary; the generalization to the case when the system of measures $\mu_{st}(x, \Lambda)$ is random, i.e., depends on a point $\omega \in \Omega$ of a probability space $(\Omega, \mathcal{M}, \mathbf{P})$. Here, all conditions and assertions of the theory (as opposed to the theory of nonrandom measures μ_{st}) need to be formulated as being fulfilled with unit probability or in the mean. From the following Theorem 3.1 it is clear that the limit (3.1) can be conveniently taken in the mean (*l. i. m*). The corresponding refinements are rather standard, and we will not discuss them each time in the following.

2. The assertions expressed in the preceding paragraph can be conveniently illustrated and substantiated with the following example.

Let E be a finite set of m points. Then the function space G will coincide with m-dimensional real space R_m, with elements g which are vectors $g = (g_1, \ldots, g_m)$. In G is is possible to define a norm

$$\|g\| = \max(g_1, \ldots, g_m).$$

The operators in this space are $m \times m$ matrices.

We now consider a family of generating operators of the diffusional form

$$L^*(t)_{\alpha\beta} = \int^t [\overset{\bullet}{A}_{\alpha\beta}(y, \tau)\, d\tau + A_{\alpha\beta\sigma}(y, \tau)\, d^*y_\sigma(\tau)], \tag{3.6}$$

analogous to (2.35a). Here $y = \{y_\sigma(t),\ \sigma = 1, 2, \ldots\}$ are diffusion processes with parameters $a_\sigma(y, t)$, $b_{\sigma\rho}(y, t)$. The functions $\overset{\bullet}{A}_{\alpha\beta}$, $A_{\alpha\beta\sigma}$, a_σ, $b_{\sigma\rho}$ are assumed to be bounded and continuous. It is convenient to consider the functions $A_{\alpha\beta\tau}$ as differentiable with respect to y_ρ.

Equation (3.2) here has the form of the system of stochastic equations

$$f_\alpha(t) - g_\alpha = \int_t^u \overset{\bullet}{A}_{\alpha\beta}(\tau) f_\beta(\tau)\, d\tau + \int_t^u A_{\alpha\beta\sigma}(\tau)\, d^*y_\sigma(\tau) f_\beta(\tau),$$

or

$$f_\alpha(f) - g_\alpha = \int_t^u {}^*A_{\alpha\beta}(\tau) f_\beta(\tau)\, d\tau + \int_t^u d^*y_\sigma(\tau)\, A_{\alpha\beta\sigma}(\tau) f_\beta(\tau)$$

$$(\alpha = 1, \ldots, M),$$

where

$$ {}^*A_{\alpha\beta} = \overset{\bullet}{A}_{\alpha\beta} - \frac{\partial A_{\alpha\beta\sigma}}{\partial y_\rho} b_{\sigma\rho} $$

according to formula (2.15) applied to the integral (3.6).

As proven in the theory of stochastic equations, the indicated equations uniquely (to within an equivalence) determine the solution $f(t)$. This solution is interpreted as $T_{tu}g$, i.e., as a result of the transformation T_{tu}. It was shown above that such transformations form a semigroup. The matrix elements $(T_{su})_{\alpha\beta}$ corresponding to this transformation, as we can easily see, satisfy

$$ (T_{tu})_{\alpha\beta} - \delta_{\alpha\beta} = \int_t^u {}^*A_{\alpha\gamma}(\tau)(T_{\tau u})_{\gamma\beta}\,d\tau + \int_t^u d^*y_\sigma(\tau)\,A_{\alpha\gamma\sigma}(\tau)(T_{\tau u})_{\gamma\beta} \quad (3.7) $$

or

$$ (T_{st})_{\alpha\beta} - \delta_{\alpha\beta} = \int_s^t (T_{s\tau})_{\alpha\gamma}\,\overset{\bullet}{A}_{\gamma\beta}(\tau)\,d\tau + \int_s^t (T_{s\tau})_{\alpha\gamma}A_{\gamma\beta\sigma}(\tau)\,d^*y_\sigma. \quad (3.8) $$

The latter are specific forms of Eqs. (3.4).

Let us examine the limit (3.1) for a semigroup constructed in such a manner.

Theorem 3.1. For the semigroup in question limit (3.1) exists in the mean and results in the operators (3.6).

The proof of this theorem uses procedures common in the theory of stochastic integrals and equations. In order to avoid cumbersome expressions, we will assume that $\overset{\bullet}{A}_{\alpha\beta} = 0$, $a_\sigma = 0$. This simplification does not involve fundamental modifications of the proof.

Let us take a Δ-division $t_1, \ldots, t_N$ of the interval $[s, u]$ and apply formula (3.8) to each elementary elementary interval $(t_i, t_{i+1}]$:

$$ (T_{t_i t_{i+1}})_{\alpha\beta} - \delta_{\alpha\beta} = \int_{t_i}^{t_{i+1}} (T_{t_i\tau})_{\alpha\gamma}\,\overset{\bullet}{A}_{\gamma\beta\sigma}(\tau)\,d^*y_\sigma(\tau). \quad (3.8a) $$

Using these equalities, we form the expression

$$ Z \equiv \sum_{i=1}^{N-1}\left[(T_{t_i t_{i+1}})_{\alpha\beta} - \delta_{\alpha\beta} - \int_{t_i}^{t_{i+1}} A_{\alpha\beta\sigma}(\tau)\,d^*y_\sigma(\tau)\right] = $$

$$ = \sum_{i=1}^{N-1}\int_{t_i}^{t_{i+1}} [(T_{t_i\tau})_{\alpha\gamma} - \delta_{\alpha\gamma}]\,A_{\gamma\beta\sigma}(\tau)\,d^*y_\sigma(\tau) \quad (3.9) $$

[the second equality is true on the strength of (3.8a)] and examine its mean square. According to the usual rule of averaging stochastic equations (for example, Doob [1], p. 400, and others), we have

$$\mathbf{M}Z^2 = \sum_{i=1}^{N-1} \int_{t_i}^{t_{i+1}} \mathbf{M}\{[(T_{t_i\tau})_{\alpha\gamma} - \delta_{\alpha\gamma}][(T_{t_i\tau})_{\alpha\gamma'} - \\ - \delta_{\alpha\gamma'}] A_{\gamma\beta\sigma}(\tau) A_{\gamma'\beta\sigma'}(\tau) b_{\sigma\sigma'}(\tau)\} d\tau. \quad (3.10)$$

Now using the formula (3.7), which corresponds to the Ito integral written for reverse time:

$$(T_{t_i\tau})_{\alpha\gamma} - \delta_{\alpha\gamma} = \int_{t_i}^{\tau} d^* y_\sigma(\tau') A_{\alpha\delta\sigma}(\tau')(T_{\tau'\tau})_{\delta\gamma}.$$

Applying the given averaging formula to the reversed time, we get

$$\mathbf{M}\{[(T_{t_i\tau})_{\alpha\gamma} - \delta_{\alpha\gamma}][(T_{t_i\tau})_{\alpha\gamma'} - \delta_{\alpha\gamma'}] A_{\gamma\beta\sigma} A_{\gamma'\beta\sigma'} b_{\sigma\sigma'}(y(\tau), \tau)\} = \\ = \int_{t_i}^{\tau} \mathbf{M}\{b_{\rho\rho'}(y(\tau'), \tau') A_{\alpha\delta\rho}(\tau') A_{\alpha\delta'\rho'}(T_{\tau'\tau})_{\delta\gamma}(T_{\tau'\tau})_{\delta'\gamma'} \times \\ \times A_{\gamma\beta\sigma}(\tau) A_{\gamma'\beta\sigma'}(\tau) b_{\sigma\sigma'}(\tau)\} d\tau'.$$

This expression, as can easily be seen, is of the order of magnitude $O(\tau - t_i)$ [i.e., $O(\Delta)$] under the assumption that the appropriate moments are bounded. It is the integrand in (3.10), and consequently

$$\lim_{\Delta\to 0} \mathbf{M}Z^2 = 0; \qquad \text{l. i. m. } Z = 0$$

for any given α and β. Taking the definition (3.9) of Z into account, we have

$$\text{l. i. m.} \sum_{i=1}^{N-1} [(T_{t_i t_{i+1}})_{\alpha\beta} - \delta_{\alpha\beta}] - \text{l. i. m.} \sum_{i=1}^{N-1} \int_{t_i}^{t_{i+1}} A_{\alpha\beta\sigma}(\tau) d^* y_\sigma(\tau) = 0.$$

But the second limit is nothing other than the stochastic integral

$$\int_s^u A_{\alpha\beta\sigma}(\tau) d^* y_\sigma(\tau) = L^*(u)_{\alpha\beta} - L^*(s)_{\alpha\beta}.$$

The proof is completed.

An analogous theorem with corresponding complications can also be formulated and proven for a more general diffusional case, examined further in Sect. 3.4.

3. The family of generating operators $L^*(t)$ introduced above seems sufficient for the construction of a theory of a nonunary semigroup and a theory of conditional Markov processes. In addition to this, nevertheless, for some purposes it is also useful to examine a second family, playing an analogous role in the theory.

We define a new family of generating operators $L(t)$, $t \in T$, using the passage to the limit

$$[L(u) - L(s)]\, g = \lim_{\Delta \to 0} [\ln T_{t_1 t_2} + \ldots + \ln T_{t_{N-1},\, t_N}]\, g \qquad (3.11)$$

$$(g \in D_L).$$

The logarithmic function of the operators should be taken in some appropriate sense. It can be defined, for example, in a natural way after bringing the operator to diagonal form (if this is possible), or by defining it using the decomposition

$$(\ln T_{t_i t_{i+1}})\, g = \sum_{n=1}^{\infty} \frac{1}{n} (-1)^{n-1} (T_{t_i t_{i+1}} - I)^n\, g. \qquad (3.12)$$

The latter can be used expediently if it is not associated with considerable limiting of the area of definition $D_L \subset G$ of the generating operators $L(t)$.

In the case of a semigroup which is homogeneous in time, the various families of generating operators coincide:

$$L(u) - L(s) = L^*(u) - L^*(s) = (u - s)\, A.$$

Extending the known theorems of this unary theory (Loève [1], Dynkin [3]) to the nonunary case, we will assume that the space D_L is everywhere dense in a Banach space $G_0 \subset G$. The generalization of the uniqueness theorem (Dynkin [3], p. 47) to this case is of interest. Without carrying out the appropriate proof, we will assume that the uniqueness is valid. If, besides, we assume that the equation

$$\lambda f - [L(u) - L(s)]\, f = g$$

has a solution $f \in D_L$ for any $g \in G_0$ and any $\lambda > 0$, $u > s$, then it is possible to conclude in analogy to the familiar theory (Dynkin [3], pp. 51-53) that the operators $L(u)-L(s)$ uniquely determine* the operators $\exp[L(u)-L(s)]$ over the space G_0. It is also possible to prove that

$$\exp[L(u)-L(s)]g \in D_L \quad \text{where} \quad g \in G_0, \ u > s.$$

For a fixed Δ-division, we will now examine the operators

$$T^{\Delta}_{tu} = \exp\left\{\frac{t_{i+1}-t}{t_{i+1}-t_i}[L(t_{i+1})-L(t_i)]\right\}\exp\{L(t_{i+2})-$$
$$-L(t_{i+1})\}\ldots\exp\{L(t_N)-L(t_{N-1})\}, \quad t \in [t_i, t_{i+1}) \tag{3.13}$$

and their corresponding functions

$$f^{\Delta}(t) = T^{\Delta}_{tu}g, \ g \in G_0. \tag{3.14}$$

From this definition it is easy to find that

$$f^{\Delta}(t_i) - f^{\Delta}(t_{i+1}) = \{\exp[L(t_{i+1})-L(t_i)] - I\} f^{\Delta}(t_{i+1})$$

and consequently

$$f^{\Delta}(t_i) - g = \sum_{j=i}^{N-1}\{e^{L(t_{j+1})-L(t_j)} - I\} f^{\Delta}(t_{j+1}). \tag{3.15}$$

We assume that for every $g \in G_0$ and every t the limit

$$f(t) = \lim_{\Delta\to 0} f^{\Delta}(t)$$

exists. This limit will be interpreted as the result of the transformation $T_{tu}g$ so that

$$T_{tu} = \lim_{\substack{\Delta\to 0\\ t_i\to t}} e^{L(t_{i+1})-L(t_i)}\ldots e^{L(t_N)-L(t_{N-1})}. \tag{3.16}$$

---

*In the cited theory, the condition

$$\|\lambda f - Bf\| \geqslant \|\lambda f\|, \ B = L(u)-L(s), \ \lambda > 0$$

related to the compressibility of the semigroup is also examined. We are not concentrating our attention on it since a generalization of the theory for noncompressible semigroups can be carried out. Specifically, the generalization for the case when $\|T_t\| < e^{Kt}$ (K being a finite constant) is trivial.

Equation (3.15) here becomes the equation*

$$f(t) - g = \int_t^u \overline{d}L(\tau) f(\tau), \tag{3.17}$$

where the integral is understood in the sense

$$\int_t^u \overline{d}L(t) f(t) = \lim_{\Delta \to 0} \sum_{[t,u]} \{e^{L(t_{j+1}) - L(t_j)} - I\} f(t_{j+1}). \tag{3.18}$$

In the above sense it is possible to assert that the family of generating operators $L(t)$ uniquely determines the function $f(t)$ as a solution of Eq. (3.17) and determines $\mathbf{T}_{tu}$ as a transformation of g into $f(t)$. From (3.16) and (3.17) follow the semigroup characteristics of these transformations.

Equation (3.17) can be written in the differential form

$$df(t) = -\overline{d}L(t) f(t).$$

An analogous equation can also be derived for $\varphi \in \Phi$; it has the form

$$\varphi(t) - \varphi(s) = \int_s^t \varphi(\tau) \overline{d}L(\tau), \quad \varphi(s) \equiv \varphi, \tag{3.19}$$

where, as above in (3.18), the integral is understood in the sense

$$\int_s^t \varphi(\tau) \overline{d}L(\tau) = \lim_{\Delta \to 0} \sum_{[s,t]} \varphi(t_j) \{e^{L(t_{j+1}) - L(t_j)} - I\}. \tag{3.19a}$$

Equations (3.17) and (3.19) are analogous to Eqs. (3.2) and (3.3), but appropriate to a different definition of the integral and to other generating operators. It is not difficult to find also the analogs of Eqs. (3.4) and (3.5). To do this, we only need to substitute into them

$$d^* L^*(t) = \overline{d}L(t). \tag{3.20}$$

4. The validity of the above assumptions can be ascertained as a result of a special investigation under more or less general

---

*In fact, from the property $\int_\alpha^\beta \overline{d}L(t) F(t) \to 0$ as $\max_{t \in [\alpha, \beta]} \|F(t)\| \to 0$ of the integral (3.18), it follows that

$$\sum [e^{L(t_i) - L(t_{i-1})} - I] f^\Delta(t_i) = \int \overline{d}L(\tau) f^\Delta(\tau) \to \int \overline{d}L(\tau) f(\tau).$$

conditions. We are not able to examine here an extensive number of questions related to this. We will limit ourselves to pointing out the fundamental importance of the condition of commutativity of the operators $L(t_{i+1})-L(t_i)$ and $L(t_i)-L(t_{i-1})$, corresponding to adjacent intervals. If on a certain interval $[a, b]$ such operators commute, the passage to the limit (3.11) need not be carried out, and the strict equation $T^{\Delta}_{tt'}=T_{tt'}$ $(t, t'\in[a,b])$ is valid, so that the passage to the limit (3.16) is unnecessary. The theory appropriate to this case is not a very substantial generalization of the theory of a unary (one-parameter) semigroup.

Often, however, strict commutativity does not occur. For the correctness of a number of the results, the somewhat weaker condition

$$[L(t_i)-L(t_{i-1})][L(t_{i+1})-L(t_i)]-[L(t_{i+1})-L(t_i)]\times$$
$$\times[L(t_i)-L(t_{i-1})]=o(\Delta)$$

is sufficient. Without examining this question in detail, we will give one important result.

Theorem 3.2. Let us assume that the operators $S_{st}=e^{L(t)-L(s)}$, $s<t$, i.e., the operators satisfying the equation

$$\ln S_{st}g=[L(t)-L(s)]g, \qquad g\in D_L, \tag{3.21}$$

are bounded:

$$\|S_{st}\|\leqslant e^{(t-s)K} \tag{3.22}$$

(K does not depend on s and t) and that the relations

$$\lim_{(t-s)\downarrow 0} S_{st}=I; \tag{3.23}$$

$$S_{t_{i-1}t_{i+1}}=S_{t_{i-1}t_i}S_{t_it_{i+1}}[1+O(\Delta^{1+\gamma})],\quad \gamma>0 \tag{3.24}$$

are satisfied (the evaluation $O(\Delta^{1+\gamma})$ is understood to be in the sense of the norm and is smooth with respect to $t_i\in T$). Then:

3.2.A. The limit (3.16) exists and does not depend on the method of division.

3.2.B. It determines the semigroup of operators.

3.2.C. This semigroup has operators (3.11) coinciding with $L(t)$.

Proof. Selecting divisions $\{t_i^{(\Delta)}\}\subset\{t_j^{\left(\frac{\Delta}{2}\right)}\}$, $j=2i,\ 2i+1$ according to (3.24) and (3.22), we have

$$\left|\prod_i S_{t_i^{(\Delta)} t_{i+1}^{(\Delta)}} - \prod_j S_{t_j^{\left(\frac{\Delta}{2}\right)} t_{j+1}^{\left(\frac{\Delta}{2}\right)}}\right| \leqslant e^{(u-s)K} \times$$
$$\times \{[1 + \Delta O(\Delta^{\gamma})]^N - 1\} = (u-s)\, e^{(u-s)K} O(\Delta^{\gamma})). \qquad (3.25)$$

We will further examine Δ_k-divisions having intervals of length $\Delta_k = \Delta \cdot 2^{-k}$, $k = 1, 2$. Summing the differences (3.25), we will have uniformly for all k

$$\left|\prod_i S_{t_i^{(\Delta)} t_{i+1}^{(\Delta)}} - \prod_l S_{t_l^{(\Delta_k)} t_{l+1}^{(\Delta_k)}}\right| \leqslant (u-s)\, e^{(u-s)}\, O(\Delta^{\gamma}), \qquad (3.26)$$

since

$$\sum_{k'=0}^{k-1} O((\Delta \cdot 2^{-k'})^{\gamma}) = O(\Delta^{\gamma}).$$

This proves the convergence of (3.16). An analogous examination can also be made for other forms of divisions.

Assertion 3.2.B obviously follows from (3.16), if 3.2.A and condition (3.23) are taken into account.

We now turn to the proof of 3.2.C. To do this, we refer to (3.11) and (3.12). These equations contain the terms ln $T_{t_i t_{i+1}}$; then the ln $S_{t_i t_{i+1}}$ (3.21) are assigned as conditions of Theorem 3.2. We find the difference between these logarithms. From (3.26) we obtain

$$\left|\prod_i S_{t_i t_{i+1}} - T_{su}\right| \leqslant (u-s)\, e^{(u-s)K} O(\Delta^{\gamma})$$

and, consequently,

$$T_{t_i t_{i+1}} = S^t_{t_i t_{i+1}} + o(\Delta). \qquad (3.27)$$

By expanding the function

$$\ln(I + A + B) \quad (A = S_{t_i t_{i+1}} - I,\ A + B = T_{t_i t_{i+1}} - I)$$

into a double series and using the familiar relations of the type $\|CD\| \leqslant \|C\|\,\|D\|$, it is easy to be convinced of the validity of the inequality

$$\|\ln(I + A + B) - \ln(I + A)\| \leqslant \ln(1 - \|A\|) -$$
$$- \ln(1 - \|A\| - \|B\|) \leqslant \frac{\|B\|}{1 - \|A\| - \|B\|}.$$

Applying it to (3.27), we get

$$\ln T_{t_i t_{i+1}} - \ln S_{t_i t_{i+1}} = \frac{o(\Delta)}{1 - \| S_{t_i t_{i+1}} - I \| - o(\Delta)} = o(\Delta).$$

Here, we used the fact that $\| S_{t_i t_{i+1}} - I \| = o(1)$ in accordance with condition (3.23). From this it follows that both operators have the same region of definition D_L, and also that the limit (3.11) exists and coincides with the original expression (3.21). The proof is finished.

3.2 A Theorem Concerning Change of the System of Measures

1. In agreement with formulas (3.16) and (3.19a), which define the differential $\overline{d}$, we understand the expression

$$\sum_q \int G_q(\tau) \overline{d} R_q(\tau) H_q(\tau) \tag{3.28}$$

in the more general case in the sense

$$\sum_q \lim_{\Delta \to 0} \sum_i G_q(t_i) \left[e^{R_q(t_{i+1}) - R_q(t_i)} - I \right] H_q(t_{i+1})$$

(if the limit exists). G_q, H_q are operators or functions. The statement also applies to the case when the operator (or operators) R_q correspond to multiplication by some function. The operators or functions R_q do not have to be of bounded variation or be continuous.

Taking the definition (3.28) into account, it is not difficult to find that this integral posesses a series of unusual characteristics. For example, the following equations are satisfied:

$$\int_s^u e^{R(\tau)} \overline{d} R(\tau) = e^{R(u)} - e^{R(s)},$$

$$\int_s^u \overline{d} R(\tau) e^{-R(\tau)} = e^{-R(s)} - e^{-R(u)}, \tag{3.29}$$

i.e.,

$$e^{R(t)} \overline{d} R(t) = d e^{R(t)}; \quad \overline{d} R(t) e^{-R(t)} = - d e^{-R(t)},$$

whereas the equations

$$\overline{d}R(t)\,e^{R(t)} = de^{R(t)};\ e^{-R(t)}\,\overline{d}R(t) = -\,de^{-R(t)};$$

$$-\,\overline{d}R(t) = \overline{d}\,[-R(t)]$$

in the general sense are untrue.

Instead of $\overline{d}R$ we can write $e^{-R}d^*e^R$, where the differential d^* is defined by the formula

$$\int G(d^*Q)H = \lim_{\Delta\to 0}\sum_i G(t_i)\,[Q(t_{i+1}) - Q(t_i)]\cdot H(t_{i+1}). \qquad (3.30)$$

The integrals in (3.2) and (3.3) are specific cases of the definition (3.30). As we can see from (3.20), it is sometimes convenient to replace the differential $\overline{d}$ of one function by the differential d^* of another.

2. Let us turn to the examination of an important theorem.

For the solution of a number of problems it is useful to carry out a change of the Markov system of measures using the formula

$$\mu'_{st}(x, \Lambda) = e^{-F_s(x)}\int_\Lambda \mu_{st}(x, dx')\,e^{F_t(x')}, \qquad (3.31)$$

where $F_t(x)$ is a function on $T\times E$, Borel measurable on $\mathscr{B}_T\times\mathscr{E}$, and is chosen correspondingly.

The question of how generating operators are transformed with such a change of measures is of interest. Let us assume that $L(t)$ are the operators of the original system $\mu_{st}(x, \Lambda)$. We introduce the operators

$$L'(t) - L'(s) = \int_s^t e^{-F_\tau}\,dL(\tau)\,e^{F_\tau} + F_t - F_s, \qquad (3.32)$$

where the integral is understood in the sense

$$\lim_{\Delta\to 0}\sum_i e^{-F_i}\,[L(t_{i+1}) - L(t_i)]\,e^{F_i}g, \qquad F_i = \frac{1}{2}\,(F_{t_i} + F_{t_{i+1}}),$$

$$g\in\widetilde{D}_L\subset D_L.$$

Here and subsequently, in the examination of a Δ-division $\{t_i\}$ of the interval $[s, t]$, we will use the notations

$$\Delta L_i = L(t_{i+1}) - L(t_i);\ \Delta F_i = F_{t_{i+1}} - F_{t_i},$$

$$\Delta L'_i = L'(t_{i+1}) - L'(t_i).$$

In addition to this, we will designate

$$\Delta L_i'' = e^{-F_i}(\Delta L_i + \Delta F_i)\, e^{F_i}; \tag{3.33}$$

then, according to (3.33) and (3.32), we will have

$$\lim_{\Delta \to 0} (\Delta L_1'' + \ldots + \Delta L_N'') = L'(t) - L'(s). \tag{3.34}$$

Condition (3.37) of the following theorem differs from this relation in its assertion of certain commutative properties of the operators $\Delta L_i''$.

Theorem 3.3. If

$$\| e^{\Delta L_i} \| \leqslant e^{K\Delta}, \tag{3.35}$$

and also the commutativity conditions

$$e^{-\frac{1}{2}\Delta F_i} e^{\Delta L_i + \Delta F_i} e^{-\frac{1}{2}\Delta F_i} = e^{\Delta L_i}[I + o(\Delta)], \tag{3.36}$$

$$\lim_{\Delta \to 0} e^{\Delta L_1''} \ldots e^{\Delta L_N''} = e^{L'(t) - L'(s)}\, [I + o(t-s)] \tag{3.37}$$

are satisfied (the evaluation $o(t-s)$ is taken according to the norm and is smooth with respect to all t), then the transformation of the generating operators (3.32) corresponds to the transformation of measures (3.31). In addition to this,

$$\overline{d}L'(t) = e^{-F_t}\overline{d}L(t)\, e^{F_t} + \overline{d}F_t = e^{-F_t}[\overline{d}L(t)\, e^{F_t} + d^* e^{F_t}] =$$
$$= [e^{-F_t}\overline{d}L(t) - d^* e^{-F_t}]\, e^{F_t}. \tag{3.38}$$

Proof. From (3.36) we have

$$e^{\Delta L_i + \Delta F_i} = e^{\frac{1}{2}\Delta F_i} e^{\Delta L_i}[1 + o(\Delta)]\, e^{\frac{1}{2}\Delta F_i}.$$

Thus, from the equation

$$\exp\{e^{-F_i}(\Delta L_i + \Delta F_i)\, e^{F_i}\} = e^{-F_i} e^{\Delta L_i + \Delta F_i} e^{F_i}$$

we obtain

$$e^{\Delta L_i''} = e^{-F_i + \frac{1}{2}\Delta F_i} e^{\Delta L_i}[1 + o(\Delta)]\, e^{F_i + \frac{1}{2}\Delta F_i} =$$
$$= e^{-F_{t_i}} e^{\Delta L_i}\, [1 + o(\Delta)]\, e^{F_{t_{i+1}}}.$$

The product of such operators, consequently, can be written

$$e^{\Delta L_1''} \ldots e^{\Delta L_{N-1}''} = e^{-F_{t_1}} e^{\Delta L_1} [1 + o(\Delta)] e^{\Delta L_2} \ldots$$
$$\ldots e^{\Delta L_{N-1}} [1 + o(\Delta)] e^{F_{t_N}}.$$

Taking into account (3.35), we have

$$e^{\Delta L_1''} \ldots e^{\Delta L_{N-1}''} = e^{-F_{t_1}} e^{\Delta L_1} e^{\Delta L_2} \ldots e^{\Delta L_{N-1}} e^{F_{t_N}} +$$
$$+ e^{(t-s)K} \{[1 + o(\Delta)]^N - 1\},$$

i.e.,

$$\lim_{\Delta \to 0} e^{\Delta L_1} \ldots e^{\Delta L_{N-1}''} = e^{-F_s} T_{st} e^{F_t}. \tag{3.39}$$

Assuming $s = t_i$, $t = t_{i+1}$ in (3.37) and (3.39), as a result of comparison of these two equations we get

$$e^{\Delta L_i'} = e^{-F_{t_i}} T_{t_i t_{i+1}} e^{F_{t_{i+1}}} [I + o(\Delta)]. \tag{3.40}$$

Consequently,

$$\lim_{\Delta \to 0} e^{\Delta L_1'} \ldots e^{\Delta L_N'} = e^{-F_s} T_{st} e^{F_t} \equiv T_{st}',$$

i.e., the operators $L'(t)$ in fact serve the semigroup T_{st}' as generating operators. In agreement with Theorem 3.2 (3.2.C), we have also

$$\lim_{\Delta \to 0} [\ln T_{t_1 t_2}' + \ldots + \ln T_{t_{N-1} t_N}'] g = [L'(t) - L'(s)] g,$$
$$g \in D_L.$$

We now turn to the proof of (3.38). The equivalence of all three Eqs. (3.38) follows from (3.29) [where $R = F$]. According to the definition of integral (3.28), the first Eq. (3.38) implies

$$\lim_{\Delta \to 0} \sum_i (e^{\Delta L_i'} - I) f(t_{i+1}) = \lim_{\Delta \to 0} \sum_i [e^{-F_{t_i}}$$
$$(e^{\Delta L_i} - I) e^{F_{t_{i+1}}} f(t_{i+1}) + (e^{\Delta F_i} - 1) f(t_{i+1})]. \tag{3.41}$$

We take into account that in agreement with (3.40) and (3.27)

$$e^{\Delta L_i'} = e^{-F_{t_i}} e^{\Delta L_i} e^{F_{t_{i+1}}} [I + o(\Delta)].$$

$$e^{\Delta L_i'} - I = [e^{-F_{t_i}} (e^{\Delta L_i} - I) e^{F_{t_{i+1}}} + e^{\Delta F_i} - I] [I + o(\Delta)],$$

from which follows (3.41). The proof is completed.

3.3 Passage to a Special Case

1. Let us assume that operators $L(t)$, $L^*(t)$ have the following special form:

$$L(t) - L(s) = \int_s^t [A(y(\tau), \tau)\, d\tau + A_\rho(y(\tau), \tau)\, dy_\rho(\tau)]; \qquad (3.42)$$

$$L^*(t) - L^*(s) = \int_s^t [d\tau \; {}^*A(y(\tau), \tau) + d^* y_\rho(\tau)\, {}^*A_\rho(y(\tau), \tau)]. \qquad (3.43)$$

Here, with fixed $\tau \in T$ and $y \equiv \{y_1, \ldots, y_l\} \in R_l$ operators A, A_ρ represent linear operators on D_L, and ${}^*A$, ${}^*A_\rho$ represent operators on $D_L{}^*$. Functions $\{y_1(t), \ldots, y_l(t)\}$ are components of a diffusion process with parameters $a_\rho(y, t)$, $b_{\rho\sigma}(y, t)$, $\rho, \sigma = 1, \ldots, l$.

The stochastic integrals (3.42) and (3.43) are understood in the sense described in Chapter 2 after the operators have acted on the function g_*. It is assumed that on A, A_ρ, ${}^*A$, ${}^*A_\rho$ (or on $Ag, \ldots, {}^*A_\rho g$), and similarly on a_ρ, $b_{\rho\sigma}$ there are imposed certain conditions necessary for the existence of the integrals (3.42) and (3.43), and also for the existence of a solution of the stochastic equations encountered subsequently.

Equation (3.2) becomes a stochastic equation of the type examined in Sect. 2.2. On the strength of (3.43) and Lemma 2.3, it has the form

$$f(t) - g = \int_t^u [dt \; {}^*A(y(\tau), \tau) f(\tau) + d^* y_\rho(\tau)\, {}^*A_\rho(y(\tau), \tau) f(\tau)] \qquad (3.44)$$

(using a reverse flow of time). In accordance with the material in Sect. 3.1, the solution of this equation, when it exists, and is unique, determines the semigroup T_{tu}.

2. Let us now examine Eq. (3.17). Taking into account that

$$e^{\Delta L_i} - I = \Delta L_i \left[I + \frac{1}{2} \Delta L_i + \frac{1}{6} \Delta L_i^2 + \ldots \right] =$$

$$= \Delta L_i \left[I + \frac{1}{24} \Delta L_i^2 + \ldots \right] e^{\frac{1}{2} \Delta L_i},$$

from (3.15) we find

$$f^\Delta(t_i) - g = \sum_{j=i}^{N-1} \left[\Delta L_j + \frac{1}{24} \Delta L_j^3 + \cdots \right] e^{\frac{1}{2} \Delta L_j} f^\Delta(t_{j+1}).$$

But on the strength of (3.13) and (3.15), we have

$$e^{\frac{1}{2}\Delta L_j} f^{\Delta}(t_{j+1}) = f^{\Delta}\left(\frac{t_j + t_{j+1}}{2}\right).$$

Thus,

$$f^{\Delta}(t_i) - g = \sum_{j=i}^{N-1}\left[\Delta L_j + \frac{1}{24}\Delta L_j^3 + \ldots\right] f^{\Delta}\left(\frac{t_j + t_{j+1}}{2}\right). \quad (3.45)$$

From (3.42) we can obtain the estimate

$$\frac{1}{24}\Delta L_j^3 + \ldots = O(\Delta^{3/2})$$

(which, generally speaking, is not uniform with respect to $\omega \in \Omega'$ and $g \in D_L$). From this it follows that the limit in (3.45) coincides with the symmetrized stochastic integral defined in Sect. 2.1. Using in addition Lemma 2.4, we have

$$f(t) - g = \int_t^u dL(\tau) f(\tau) = \int_t^u [d\tau\, A(y(\tau), \tau) f(\tau) +$$
$$+ dy_\rho(\tau) A_\rho(y(\tau), \tau) f(\tau)]. \quad (3.46)$$

An analogous examination can also be carried out for the other equations of (3.19) and (3.4). As a result, the integral expressions dL are replaced by symmetrized integrals of the same form with dL in the sense of Sect. 2.1. Specifically,

$$\varphi(t) - \varphi(s) = \int_s^t \varphi(\tau)\, dL(\tau). \quad (3.47)$$

Let us assume that operators (3.42) and (3.43) correspond to the semigroup. Then the solution of Eq. (3.44) will coincide with the solution of Eq. (3.46). Comparing the right sides of the expressions and taking the connecting formula (2.14) of the stochastic integrals into consideration, we obtain the connection between operators A and A_ρ, on the one hand, and $^*A$ and $^*A_\rho$, on the other. Namely, from (2.14) where $\{x_\alpha\} = \{y_\rho, f\}$, we have

$$^*A_\rho f\, dy_\rho = d^*y_\rho {}^*A_\rho f - \frac{1}{2}\frac{\partial^* A_\rho}{\partial y_\sigma} f b_{\rho\sigma}\, dt - \frac{1}{2}\, {}^*A_\rho b_{\rho f}\, dt,$$

where

$$b_{\rho f} = \lim_{h \downarrow 0} \frac{1}{h} [y_\rho (t+h) - y_\rho (t)] [f (t+h) - f (t)].$$

On the strength of (3.44), $b_{\rho f} = -b_{\rho\sigma} {}^*A_\sigma f$. To sum up, we get

$$A_\rho = A_\rho^*; \; A = {}^*A + \frac{1}{2} \frac{\partial {}^*A_\rho}{\partial y_\sigma} b_{\rho\sigma} - \frac{1}{2} {}^*A_\rho {}^*A_\sigma b_{\rho\sigma}. \tag{3.48}$$

Assuming that the operators ${}^*A_\rho {}^*A_\sigma$, $\frac{\partial A_\rho^*}{\partial y_\sigma}$ are defined on D_{L^*}, the operators $L(t)$, $L^*(t)$ have the same region of definition: $D_L = D_{L^*}$.

3. Let us introduce the space D_L^2 representing the space of functions g such that $\Delta L g \in D_L$. In this space we can examine the expansion

$$e^{\Delta L} g = \left(I + \Delta L + \frac{1}{2} \Delta L^2 + H \right) g, \tag{3.49}$$

in which

$$Hg = O(\Delta^{3/2}).$$

Expanding each factor of the product $e^{\Delta L_1} \ldots e^{\Delta L_{N-1}}$ in this way, we have

$$e^{\Delta L_1} \ldots e^{\Delta L_{N-1}} g = \Big[I + \sum_i \Delta L_i + \frac{1}{2} \sum_i \Delta L_i^2 + \\ + \sum_{i<j} \Delta L_i \Delta L_j \Big] g + O((u-t)^{3/2}). \tag{3.50}$$

Here if we carry out the passage to the limit (3.16), we will have

$$T_{tu} g = \Big\{ I + L(u) - L(t) + \int_t^u dL(\tau) [L(u) - L(\tau)] \Big\} g + \\ + O((u-t)^{3/2}). \tag{3.51}$$

The operators T_{tu} in the present case satisfy the equation

$$d_t T_{tu} = I + \int_t^u dL(\tau) T_{\tau u}.$$

If we seek a solution of this equation using the sequential approximations

$$d_t T_{tu}^{(n+1)} = I + \int_t^u dL(\tau) T_{\tau u}^{(n)} \quad (T^{(0)} = 1),$$

we will obtain a certain formal expansion, the first terms of which are in (3.51). We will indicate, besides, the following formal solution of the indicated equation in the form of an ordered exponential operator

$$T_{tu} = N \exp\Big[\int_{s}^{t} dL(\tau)\Big].$$

Here, the symbol N indicates that the operators following it are in chronological order.

Let us compare (3.50) with the expansion

$$e^{L(u)-L(t)}g = \Big\{I + L(u) - L(t) + \frac{1}{2}\Big[L(u) - L(t)\Big]^2\Big\} g + \\ + O((u-t)^{3/2}).$$

Their difference is

$$e^{\Delta L_1} \dots e^{\Delta L_{N-1}} - e^{L(u)-L(t)} = \frac{1}{2}\sum_{i<j}\Big[\Delta L_i \Delta L_j - \Delta L_j \Delta L_i\Big] + \\ + O((u-t)^{3/2}). \quad (3.52)$$

It is possible to show that the sum of commutators

$$\sum \equiv \sum_{i<j} [\Delta L_i \Delta L_j - \Delta L_j \Delta L_i] = \\ = \sum_j \{[L(t_j) - L(t_1)] \Delta L_j - \Delta L_j [L(t_j) - L(t_1)]\} \quad (3.53)$$

is

$$O((u-t)^{3/2}).$$

In fact, substituting (3.42) into (3.53), and using the expansion

$$A_\rho(\tau) = A_\rho(t) + \frac{\partial A_\rho}{\partial y_\sigma}(t)\,[y_\sigma(\tau) - y_\sigma(t)] + O(t-\tau), \quad (3.54)$$

we see that

$$\sum = \Big[A_\rho(t)\frac{\partial A_\pi}{\partial y_\sigma}(t) - \frac{\partial A_\pi}{\partial y_\sigma}(t)\,A_\rho(t)\Big] \times \\ \times \sum_{i,j} \operatorname{sign}(j-i)\,[y_\sigma(t_j) - y_\sigma(t)]\,\Delta y_{\rho i} \Delta y_{\pi j} + \\ + O((u-t)^{3/2}) = O((u-t)^{3/2}). \quad (3.55)$$

Consequently, from (3.52), in agreeement with (3.16), we have

$$T_{tu} = e^{L(u)-L(t)} + O((u-t)^{3/2}) = I + L(u) - L(t) + \\ + \frac{1}{2}[L(u) - L(t)]^2 + O((u-t)^{3/2}).$$

From this it is easy to obtain an expression for T_{tu} which can be conveniently used for small $u-t=\Delta$. Taking into account (3.42) and the relation (3.54), we get

$$L(u) - L(t) = A(t)\Delta + A_\rho(t)\Delta y_\rho + \\ + \frac{\partial A_\rho}{\partial y_\sigma}(t)\int_t^u [y_\sigma(\tau) - y_\sigma(t)]\,dy_\rho(\tau) + O(\Delta^{3/2}) \quad (3.56)$$

and, consequently,

$$T_{tu} = I + A(t)\Delta + A_\rho(t)\Delta y_\rho + \frac{\partial A_\rho}{\partial y_\sigma}(t) Y_{\sigma\rho} + \\ + \frac{1}{2} A_\rho(t) A_\sigma(t)\Delta y_\rho \Delta y_\sigma + O(\Delta^{3/2}), \quad (3.57)$$

where

$$\Delta y_\rho = y_\rho(u) - y_\rho(t);$$

$$Y_{\sigma\rho} = \int_t^u [y_\sigma(\tau) - y_\sigma(t)]\,dy_\rho(\tau).$$

4. Let us check in the present case whether (3.24), (3.36), and (3.37) in Sects. 3.1 and 3.2, which have a commutative character, are satisfied.

According to (3.21) and (3.49), we have

$$S_{t_i t_{i+1}} = I + \Delta L_i + \frac{1}{2}\Delta L_i^2 + O(\Delta^{3/2});$$

$$S_{t_{i-1} t_i} = I + \Delta L_{i-1} + \frac{1}{2}\Delta L_{i-1}^2 + O(\Delta^{3/2});$$

$$S_{t_{i-1} t_{i+1}} = I + \Delta L_{i-1} + \Delta L_i + \frac{1}{2}(\Delta L_{i-1} + \Delta L_i)^2 + O(\Delta^{3/2}).$$

From this we obtain

$$S_{t_{i-1} t_{i+1}} - S_{t_{i-1} t_i} S_{t_i t_{i+1}} = \frac{1}{2}[\Delta L_i \Delta L_{i-1} - \Delta L_{i-1}\Delta L_i] + O(\Delta^{3/2}).$$

Carrying out the expansion (3.54) about the same point $t=t_i$ for both operators, we can see that

$$\Delta L_i \Delta L_{i-1} - \Delta L_{i-1} \Delta L_i = O(\Delta^{3/2}).$$

Consequently,

$$S_{t_{i-1}t_{i+1}} - S_{t_{i-1}t_i} S_{t_i t_{i-1}} = O(\Delta^{3/2}). \tag{3.58}$$

We now turn to (3.36). Taking into account (3.49) and the analogous expansion of $e^{-\frac{1}{2}\Delta F_i}$ and $e^{\Delta L_i + \Delta F_i}$, we immediately get

$$e^{-\frac{1}{2}\Delta F_i} e^{\Delta L_i + \Delta F_i} e^{-\frac{1}{2}\Delta F_i} - e^{\Delta L_i} = O(\Delta^{3/2}). \tag{3.59}$$

The checking of the last condition (3.57) is somewhat more complex. For the operators $\Delta L_i''$ we form the difference

$$\begin{gathered} e^{\Delta L_1''} \ldots e^{\Delta L_{N-1}''} - [I + \Delta L_1'' + \ldots + \Delta L_{N-1}' + \\ + \frac{1}{2}(\Delta L_1'' + \ldots \Delta L_{N-1}'')^2 + \ldots] = \frac{1}{2}\sum\nolimits'' + O((u-t)^{3/2}), \end{gathered} \tag{3.60}$$

analogous to (3.52). According to (3.34), we then have

$$\sum\nolimits'' \equiv \sum_{i<j} [\Delta L_i'' \Delta L_j'' - \Delta L_j'' \Delta L_i''] =$$

$$= \sum_j \{[L'(t_j) - L'(t)]\, \Delta L_j'' - \Delta L_j'' [L'(t_j) - L'(t)]\} + o_\Delta(1).$$

We substitute into this (3.33), and the explicit expressions for the operators

$$L'(t_j) - L'(t) = \int_t^{t_j} [A'\, d\tau + A_\rho'\, dy_\rho(\tau)];$$

$$\begin{gathered} (A'(\tau) = e^{-F_\tau} A(\tau) e^{F_\tau} + f(\tau);\ A_\rho'(\tau) = e^{-F_\tau} A_\rho(\tau) e^{F_\tau} + f_\rho(\tau); \\ dF_\tau = f(\tau)\, d\tau + f_\rho(\tau)\, dy_\rho(\tau)). \end{gathered}$$

After this, by analogy to (3.55), we find that

$$\sum\nolimits'' = O((u-t)^{3/2}) + o_\Delta(1).$$

Carrying out the passage to the limit, and taking into account (3.34), we will have from (3.60)

$$\lim_{\Delta \to 0} e^{\Delta L_1''} \ldots e^{\Delta L_{N-1}''} - e^{L'(u) - L'(t)} = O((u-t)^{3/2}). \tag{3.61}$$

The derived equations (3.58), (3.59), and (3.61) agree with conditions (3.24), (3.36), and (3.37), but in contrast to those conditions, we do not prove there that the estimates $O(\Delta^{3/2})$ are satisfied uniformly for all $g \in D_L^2$, and thus from (3.58), (3.59), and (3.61) it does not necessarily follow that these relations are true for the closure of the space D_L^2. We will not carry out a more complex and complete substantiation of the indicated conditions, but will give independently of these conditions a development of the main result (used subsequently) of Theorem 3.3.

5. For a short derivation of formula (3.32), we make use of the fact that symmetrized stochastic integrals, as we noted in Sect. 2.1, permit the application of simple transformation rules.

The function

$$f(t) = \int_t^u \mu_{tu}(x, dx') g(x'),$$

as was pointed out, satisfies Eq. (3.46), i.e.,

$$-df(t) = dL(t) f(t). \tag{3.62}$$

According to the measure transformation (3.31), we have

$$f'(t) \equiv \int_t^u \mu'_{tu}(x, dx') g'(x') = e^{-F_t} f(t), \tag{3.63}$$

if

$$e^{F_u(x)} g'(x) = g(x).$$

Applying to (3.63) the usual simple rules of differentiation, we obtain

$$df'(t) = e^{-F_t} df(t) - dF_t e^{-F_t} f(t).$$

Substituting into this (3.62) and again taking into account (3.63), we find

$$df'(t) = -[e^{-F_t} dL(t) + dF_t e^{-F_t}] f(t) =$$
$$= -[e^{-F_t} dL(t) e^{F_t} + dF_t] f'(t).$$

Comparing this result with the equation

$$df'(t) = -dL'(t) f'(t),$$

we have

$$dL'(t) = e^{-F_t}\, dL(t)\, e^{F_t} + dF_t,$$

which agrees with (3.32).

We will also give a derivation of formula (3.38), which can be written

$$dL'^*(t) = e^{-F_t}\, d^*L^*(t)\, e^{F_t} - d^*(e^{-F_t})\, e^{F_t}. \tag{3.64}$$

Changing the right side of the equation

$$f'(t_i) - f'(t_{i+1}) = e^{-F_{t_i}} f(t_i) - e^{-F_{t_{i+1}}} f(t_{i+1})$$

to the form

$$e^{-F_{t_i}} [f(t_i) - f(t_{i+1})] - [e^{-F_{t_{i+1}}} - e^{-F_{t_i}}] f(t_{i+1})$$

and summing over i, we have

$$f'(t_1) - f'(t_N) = \sum_{i=1}^{N-1} \{e^{-F_{t_i}} [f(t_i) - f(t_{i+1})] -$$

$$- [e^{-F_{t_{i+1}}} - e^{-F_{t_i}}] f(t_{i+1})\}.$$

We substitute here

$$f(t_i) - f(t_{i+1}) = \int_{t_i}^{t_{i+1}} dL(\tau) f(\tau) = \int_{t_i}^{t_{i+1}} d^*L^*(\tau) f(\tau)$$

and carry out the passage to the limit $\Delta \to 0$. Using the definition of the stochastic integral of Ito and Lemma 2.3, we obtain

$$f'(t) - f'(u) = \int_t^u e^{-F_\tau} d^*L^*(\tau) f(\tau) - \int_t^u d^*(e^{-F_\tau}) f(\tau),$$

i.e., formula (3.64), since $f(\tau) = e^{F_\tau} f'(\tau)$ and

$$f'(t) - f'(u) = \int_t^u d^*L'^*(\tau) f'(\tau).$$

3.4 Diffusion Operators and Incremental Statistics

1. Let us make several more assumptions regarding especially the form of the operators $L(t)$ and the phase space E. Let us assume that E is an m-dimensional real space R_m having Borel sets

defined on it. The coordinates of this space we designate as $x=\{x_1, ..., x_m\}$. The operators $L(t)$ we assume to be diffusional, i.e., we will assume the following specific form of the operators entering into (3.42):

$$A(y, t) = c^0(x, y, t) + a^0_\alpha(x, y, t)\frac{\partial}{\partial x_\alpha} + \frac{1}{2} b^0_{\alpha\beta}(x, y, t)\frac{\partial^2}{\partial x_\alpha \partial x_\beta};$$

$$A_\rho(y, t) = c^0_\rho(x, y, t) + a^0_{\rho\alpha}(x, y, t)\frac{\partial}{\partial x_\alpha}. \tag{3.65}$$

Here summation is assumed on the indices α, β, going through $1, \ldots, m$. Functions c^0, a^0_α and the others satisfy the boundedness condition and are differentiable with respect to all arguments.

Corresponding to the connection formulas (3.48), in a similar manner, analogous expressions for the second family of operators are determined:

$$^*A(y, t) = {}^*c^0(x, y, t) + {}^*a^0_\alpha(x, y, t)\frac{\partial}{\partial x_\alpha} + \frac{1}{2}\,{}^*b^0_{\alpha\beta}(x, y, t)\frac{\partial^2}{\partial x_\alpha \partial x_\beta};$$

$$^*A_\rho(y, t) = c^0_\rho(x, y, t) + a^0_{\rho\alpha}(x, y, t)\frac{\partial}{\partial x_\alpha}, \tag{3.66}$$

where

$$^*c^0 = c^0 + \frac{1}{2}\left(c^0_\rho c^0_\sigma + a^0_{\rho\alpha}\frac{\partial c^0_\sigma}{\partial x_\alpha} - \frac{\partial c^0_\rho}{\partial y_\sigma}\right) b_{\rho\sigma};$$

$$^*a^0_\alpha = a^0_\alpha + \left(c^0_\rho a^0_{\sigma\alpha} + \frac{1}{2} a^0_{\rho\beta}\frac{\partial a^0_{\sigma\alpha}}{\partial x_\beta} - \frac{1}{2}\frac{\partial a^0_{\rho\alpha}}{\partial y_\sigma}\right) b_{\rho\sigma}; \tag{3.67}$$

$$^*b^0_{\alpha\beta} = b^0_{\alpha\beta} + a^0_{\rho\alpha} a^0_{\sigma\beta} b_{\rho\sigma}.$$

Equations (3.46) and (3.44) now take the form

$$-df = \left[c^0 f + a^0_\alpha\frac{\partial f}{\partial x_\alpha} + \frac{1}{2} b^0_{\alpha\beta}\frac{\partial^2 f}{\partial x_\alpha \partial x_\beta}\right] dt + \left[c^0_\rho f + a^0_{\rho\alpha}\frac{\partial f}{\partial x_\alpha}\right] dy_\rho;$$

$$-df = \left[{}^*c^0 f + {}^*a^0_\alpha\frac{\partial f}{\partial x_\alpha} + \frac{1}{2}\,{}^*b^0_{\alpha\beta}\frac{\partial^2 f}{\partial x_\alpha \partial x_\beta}\right] dt + \tag{3.68}$$

$$+ d^*y_\rho\left[c^0_\rho f + a^0_{\rho\alpha}\frac{\partial f}{\partial x_\alpha}\right].$$

In addition to these, it is possible in the same way to examine the equation

$$-df=\left[c^{0*}f+a_{\alpha}^{0*}\frac{\partial f}{\partial x_{\alpha}}+\frac{1}{2}b_{\alpha\beta}^{0*}\frac{\partial^{2}f}{\partial x_{\alpha}\partial x_{\beta}}\right]dt+c_{\rho}^{0}d^{*}y_{\rho}f+$$
$$+a_{\rho\alpha}^{0}d^{*}y_{\rho}\frac{\partial f}{\partial x_{\alpha}}, \tag{3.69}$$

the coefficients of which can easily be related to the coefficients (3.67). Using formula (2.15), where $\{x_{\alpha}\}$ are replaced by $\{y_{\rho}\}$, we have

$$a_{\rho\alpha}^{0}d^{*}y_{\rho}=d^{*}y_{\rho}a_{\rho\alpha}^{0}-\frac{\partial a_{\rho\alpha}^{0}}{\partial y_{\sigma}}b_{\rho\sigma}dt;$$
$$c_{\rho}^{0}d^{*}y_{\rho}=d^{*}y_{\rho}c_{\rho}^{0}-\frac{\partial c_{\rho}^{0}}{\partial y_{\sigma}}b_{\rho\sigma}dt.$$

Substituting these expressions into the right side of (3.69) and comparing it to the right side of the second equation of (3.68), we find

$$c^{0*}={}^{*}c^{0}+\frac{\partial c_{\rho}^{0}}{\partial y_{\sigma}}b_{\rho\sigma};\quad a_{\alpha}^{0*}={}^{*}a_{\alpha}^{0}+\frac{\partial a_{\rho\alpha}^{0}}{\partial y_{\sigma}}b_{\rho\sigma};\quad b_{\alpha\beta}^{0*}={}^{*}b_{\alpha\beta}^{0}$$

and on the strength of (3.67)

$$c^{0*}=c^{0}+\frac{1}{2}\left(c_{\rho}^{0}c_{\sigma}^{0}+a_{\rho\alpha}^{0}\frac{\partial c_{\sigma}^{0}}{\partial x_{\alpha}}+\frac{\partial c_{\rho}^{0}}{\partial y_{\sigma}}\right)b_{\rho\sigma}; \tag{3.70}$$
$$a_{\alpha}^{0*}=a_{\alpha}^{0}+\left(c_{\rho}^{0}a_{\sigma\alpha}^{0}+\frac{1}{2}a_{\rho\beta}^{0}\frac{\partial a_{\sigma\alpha}^{0}}{\partial x_{\beta}}+\frac{1}{2}\frac{\partial a_{\rho\alpha}^{0}}{\partial y_{\sigma}}\right)b_{\rho\sigma};$$
$$b_{\alpha\beta}^{0*}=b_{\alpha\beta}^{0}+a_{\rho\alpha}^{0}a_{\sigma\beta}^{0}b_{\rho\sigma}.$$

Analogously with (3.65) and (3.66), it is convenient to define

$$A^{*}=c^{0*}+a_{\alpha}^{0*}\frac{\partial}{\partial x_{\alpha}}+\frac{1}{2}b_{\alpha\beta}^{0*}\frac{\partial^{2}}{\partial x_{\alpha}\partial x_{\beta}}\cdot$$

Then (3.69) can be written

$$-df=A^{*}f\,dt+A_{\rho}d^{*}y_{\rho}f.$$

A comparison of this equation with (3.2) shows that

$$dL^{*}=A^{*}dt+A_{\rho}^{*}d^{*}y_{\rho}$$

[analog of (3.43)]. Equations (3.70) are equivalent to the connection formulas

$$A^{*} = A + \frac{1}{2}\left[A_{\rho}A_{\sigma} + \frac{\partial A_{\rho}}{\partial y_{\sigma}}\right] b_{\rho\sigma} \quad (A^{*}_{\rho} = A_{\rho}). \tag{3.71}$$

The latter are analogs of formulas (3.48) and, in addition to this, immediately agree with the formula (2.35).

2. In the present paragraph we will examine the relationship between the operators of the given process and the statistics of the increments $\Delta x = x(u) - x(t) = \{x_1(u) - x_1(t), \ldots, x_m(u) - x_m(t)\}$. The measure describing these increases is obtained from the measure $\mu_{tu}(x, dx')$ by a simple shift in R_m. Let us look at the function

$$\Theta(q \mid x(t)) = \int \exp\{q_{\alpha}[x_{\alpha}(u) - x_{\alpha}(t)]\} \mu_{tu}(x(t), dx(u)).$$

In view of the fact that the measure is not necessarily normalized, the indicated function does not possess the characteristic $\Theta(0 \mid x(t)) = 1$. If, however, we add the condition $x(u) \in E$, then the corresponding function

$$\Theta(q \mid x(t), x(u) \in E) = \frac{\Theta(q \mid x(t))}{\mu_{tu}(x(t), E)} \tag{3.72}$$

will already have (where $q_{\alpha} = iv_{\alpha}$) all the properties of a characteristic function.

With the help of the operators T_{tu}, Eq. (3.72) can be written

$$\Theta(q \mid x(t), E) = \frac{e^{-q_{\alpha}x_{\alpha}} T_{tu} e^{q_{\alpha}x_{\alpha}}}{T_{tu}1}. \tag{3.73}$$

Substituting here (3.57) [see also (3.56)], we obtain the following result.

Theorem 3.4. For the Markov measures examined in Sect. 3.3, the characteristic function of the increases for small $u - t = \Delta$ is determined by the formula

$$\Theta(q \mid x(t), E) = \frac{1 + e^{-q_{\alpha}x_{\alpha}}\left[\Delta L + \frac{1}{2}\Delta y_{\rho}\Delta y_{\sigma}A_{\rho}A_{\sigma}\right] e^{q_{\alpha}x_{\alpha}}}{1 + \left[\Delta L + \frac{1}{2}\Delta y_{\rho}\Delta y_{\sigma}A_{\rho}A_{\sigma}\right] 1} + O(\Delta^{3/2}) \tag{3.74}$$

$$(A_{\rho} = A_{\rho}(x, y(t)\, t)).$$

We will illustrate this formula as it applies to the operators (3.65). Substituting (3.56) and (3.65) into (3.74), and similarly into the formula

$$\mu_{tu}(x, E) = 1 + \left[\Delta L + \frac{1}{2}\Delta y_\rho \Delta y_\sigma A_\rho A_\sigma\right] 1 + O(\Delta^{3/2})$$

[see (3.57)], we find after simple calculations

$$\Theta(q \mid x, E) = 1 + \left(a^0_\alpha q_\alpha + \frac{1}{2} b^0_{\alpha\beta} q_\alpha q_\beta\right)\Delta + a^0_{\rho\alpha} q_\alpha \Delta y_\rho +$$

$$+ \frac{\partial a^0_{\rho\alpha}}{\partial y_\sigma} q_\alpha Y_{\sigma\rho} + \frac{1}{2}\Delta y_\rho \Delta y_\sigma \left[a^0_{\rho\alpha} a^0_{\sigma\beta} \cdot q_\alpha q_\beta + a^0_{\rho\alpha} \frac{\partial a^0_{\sigma\beta}}{\partial x_\alpha} q_\beta\right] + O(\Delta^{3/2});$$

$$(3.75)$$

$$\mu_{tu}(x, E) = 1 + c^0\Delta + c^0_\rho \Delta y_\rho + \frac{\partial c^0_\rho}{\partial y_\sigma} Y_{\sigma\rho} +$$

$$+ \frac{1}{2}\Delta y_\rho \Delta y_\sigma \cdot \left(c^0_\rho c^0_\sigma + a^0_{\rho\beta} \frac{\partial c^0_\sigma}{\partial x_\beta}\right) + O(\Delta^{3/2}),$$

where

$$Y_{\sigma\rho} = \int_t^u [y_\sigma(\tau) - y_\sigma(t)]\, dy_\rho(\tau); \quad Y_{\sigma\rho} + Y_{\rho\sigma} = \Delta y_\sigma \Delta y_\rho.$$

Designating in accordance with (A.1.1)*

$$\mathbf{M}_\mu [\xi \mid x] = [\mu_{tu}(x, E)]^{-1} \int \xi(x')\, \mu_{tu}(x, dx'), \tag{3.76}$$

we find the conditional moments of the increments Δx. Using the obvious formula

$$\mathbf{M}_\mu [\Delta x_\alpha \ldots \Delta x_\omega \mid x] = \left[\frac{\partial}{\partial q_\alpha} \cdots \frac{\partial}{\partial q_\omega} \Theta(q \mid x, E)\right]_{q=0},$$

from (3.75) we easily obtain

$$\mathbf{M}_\mu [\Delta x_\alpha \mid x] = a^0_\alpha \Delta + a^0_{\rho\alpha} \Delta y_\rho + \frac{\partial a^0_{\rho\alpha}}{\partial y_\sigma} Y_{\sigma\rho} +$$

$$+ \frac{1}{2}\Delta y_\rho \Delta y_\sigma a^0_{\rho\beta} \frac{\partial a^0_{\sigma\alpha}}{\partial x_\beta} + O(\Delta^{3/2});$$

$$(3.77)$$

$$\mathbf{M}_\mu [\Delta x_\alpha \Delta x_\beta \mid x] = b^0_{\alpha\beta}\Delta + \frac{1}{2}\Delta y_\rho \Delta y_\sigma a^0_{\rho\alpha} a^0_{\sigma\beta} + O(\Delta^{3/2});$$

$$\mathbf{M}_\mu [\Delta x_\alpha \Delta x_\beta \Delta x_\gamma \mid x] = O(\Delta^{3/2}).$$

---

*See Appendix I.

3. Along with the indicated approximate formulas it is possible to cite a series of precise results.

If we carry out a substitution of measures

$$\mu'_{tu}(x, dx') = e^{-q_\alpha x_\alpha}\mu_{tu}(x, dx')\, e^{q_\alpha x'_\alpha}, \tag{3.78}$$

then formula (3.73) will take the form

$$\Theta(q \mid x, E) = \frac{\mu'_{tu}(x, E)}{\mu_{tu}(x, E)} = \frac{T'_{tu}1}{T_{tu}1}. \tag{3.79}$$

Using Theorem 3.3 and taking into account (3.42), we find the infinitesimal operator of the new system of measures

$$dL' = e^{-q_\alpha x_\alpha}\, dL e^{q_\alpha x_\alpha} = A'\, dt + A'_\rho\, dy_\rho;$$

$$A' = e^{-q_\alpha x_\alpha} A e^{q_\alpha x_\alpha}; \quad A'_\rho = e^{-q_\alpha x_\alpha} A_\rho e^{q_\alpha x_\alpha},$$

i.e., on the strength of (3.65),

$$dL' = c'^0\, dt + c'^0_\rho dy_\rho + (a'^0_\alpha\, dt + a^0_{\rho\alpha}\, dy_\rho)\frac{\partial}{\partial x_\alpha} + \frac{1}{2} b^0_{\alpha\beta}\, dt \frac{\partial^2}{\partial x_\alpha\, \partial x_\beta}, \tag{3.80}$$

where

$$c'^0 = c^0 + a^0_\alpha q_\alpha + \frac{1}{2} b^0_{\alpha\beta} q_\alpha b_\beta;$$

$$c'^0_\rho = c^0_\rho + a^0_{\rho\alpha} q_\alpha; \quad a'^0_\alpha = a^0_\alpha + b^0_{\alpha\beta} q_\beta. \tag{3.81}$$

If we take into consideration the connection formulas (3.71), it is not difficult to see that the second infinitesimal operator is also transformed in an analogous fashion:

$$dL'^* = e^{-q_\alpha x_\alpha}\, dL^* e^{q_\alpha x_\alpha} = A'^*\, dt + A'_\rho\, dy_\rho; \tag{3.82}$$

$$\begin{aligned} A'^* = e^{-q_\alpha x_\alpha} A^* e^{q_\alpha x_\alpha} = c^{0*} + a^{0*}_\alpha \left(\frac{\partial}{\partial x_\alpha} + q_\alpha\right) + \\ + \frac{1}{2} b^{0*}_{\alpha\beta}\left(\frac{\partial}{\partial x_\alpha} + q_\alpha\right)\left(\frac{\partial}{\partial x_\beta} + q_\beta\right) = c'^{0*} + a'^{0*}_\alpha \frac{\partial}{\partial x_\alpha} + \\ + \frac{1}{2} b^{0*}_{\alpha\beta} \frac{\partial^2}{\partial x_\alpha\, \partial x_\beta}; \end{aligned} \tag{3.83}$$

where $$A'_\rho = c'^0_\rho + a^0_{\rho\alpha}\frac{\partial}{\partial x_\alpha},$$

$$c'^{0*} = c^{0*} + a^{0*}_{\alpha} q_{\alpha} + \frac{1}{2} b^{0*}_{\alpha\beta} q_{\alpha} q_{\beta}; \tag{3.84}$$

$$a'^{0*}_{\alpha} = a^{0*}_{\alpha} + b^{0*}_{\alpha\beta} q_{\beta}.$$

Let us turn our attention to the first formula of (3.4). Applying this operator to the unit element, we get an equation which, with the aid of the measure μ_{tu}, can be written

$$\mu_{tu}(x, E) = 1 + \int_t^u \int_E \mu_{t\tau}(x, dx')\,(d^* L^*(\tau)\, 1)(x').$$

Using the representation (3.76) of a conditional mathematical expectation, the latter equation can take the form

$$\mu_{tu}(x, E) = 1 + \int_t^u \mu_{t\tau}(x, E)\, \mathbf{M}_{\mu}[d^* L^*(\tau)\, 1 \mid x].$$

An analogous stochastic equation, of course, can also be written for the second measure

$$\mu'_{tu}(x, E) = 1 + \int_t^u \mu'_{t\tau}(x, E)\, \mathbf{M}_{\mu'}[d^* L'^*(\tau)\, 1 \mid x].$$

Substituting (3.82) and (3.83) into this, we get

$$\mu'_{tu}(x, E) = 1 + \int_t^u \mu'_{t\tau}(x, E)\, \{\mathbf{M}_{\mu'}[c'^{0*}(\tau) \mid x]\, d\tau + \mathbf{M}_{\mu'}[c'^{0}_{\rho}(\tau) \mid x]\, d^* y_{\rho}\}.$$

The resulting equation is a specific case of Eq. (2.34) with $k = 1$. Using formula (2.38), we can find its solution

$$\mu'_{tu}(x, E) = \exp\left\{\int_t^u \left\{\mathbf{M}_{\mu'}[c'^{0*}(\tau) \mid x]\, d\tau + \mathbf{M}_{\mu'}[c'^{0}_{\rho}(\tau) \mid x]\, d^* y_{\rho}(\tau) - \right.\right.$$

$$\left.\left. - \frac{1}{2} \mathbf{M}_{\mu'}[c'^{0}_{\rho}(\tau) \mid x]\, \mathbf{M}_{\mu'}[c'^{0}_{\sigma}(\tau) \mid x] . b_{\rho\sigma}\, d\tau\right\}\right\} \equiv e^{\Phi(q)}. \tag{3.85}$$

It is significant that the expression found in the exponent is a function of q. This function we designate $\Phi(q)$. Substituting (3.84) and (3.81) into (3.85), we find

$$\Phi(q) = \int_t^u \mathbf{M}_{\mu'} [c^{0*} dt + c_\rho^0 d^* y_\rho \mid x] -$$

$$- \frac{1}{2} \int_t^u \mathbf{M}_{\mu'} [c_\rho^0 \mid x] \mathbf{M}_{\mu'} [c_\sigma^0 \mid x] b_{\rho\sigma} d\tau + q_\alpha \left\{ \int_t^u \mathbf{M}_{\mu'} [a_\alpha^{0*} d\tau + a_{\rho\alpha}^0 d^* y_\rho \mid x] - \right.$$

$$\left. - \int_t^u \mathbf{M}_{\mu'} [c_\rho^0 \mid x] \cdot \mathbf{M}_{\mu'} [a_{\sigma\alpha}^0 \mid x] b_{\rho\varepsilon} d\tau \right\} + \frac{1}{2} q_\alpha q_\beta \left\{ \int_t^u \mathbf{M}_{\mu'} [b_{\alpha\beta}^{0*} \mid x] d\tau - \right.$$

$$\left. - \int_t^u \mathbf{M}_{\mu'} [a_{\rho\alpha}^0 \mid x] \mathbf{M}_{\mu'} [a_{\sigma\beta}^0 \mid x] b_{\rho\sigma} d\tau \right\}. \tag{3.86}$$

From these results, if formula (3.79) is taken into consideration, there will result, in particular, the following

Theorem 3.5. In the case under consideration, the characteristic function of the increments is

$$\Theta(q \mid x, E) = e^{\Phi(q) - \Phi(0)},$$

where the function $\Phi(q)$ is determined by formula (3.86).

In the above examination we made use of integrals and equations defined in the Ito sense. It is understood that analogous calculations using (3.80), (3.81), and (2.36) can be carried out also with integrals in the symmetrized sense. Some formulas in this case can be written more briefly. Thus, expression (3.86) will have the form

$$\Phi(q) = \int_t^u \mathbf{M}_{\mu'} [c^0 d\tau + c_\rho^0 dy_\rho \mid x] + q_\alpha \int_t^u \mathbf{M}_{\mu'} [a_\alpha^0 d\tau + a_{\rho\alpha}^0 dy_\rho \mid x] +$$

$$+ \frac{1}{2} q_\alpha q_\beta \int_t^u \mathbf{M}_{\mu'} [b_{\alpha\beta}^0 \mid x] d\tau.$$

4. In conclusion we will formulate a theorem which will subsequently be useful to us.

Theorem 3.6. Let us assume that $\mu_{tu}(x, \Lambda)$ are Markov measures connected by the relation (3.78) [the second of these depends on q and the first does not] and that for any given (complex) q the following equation is satisfied:

$$\mu'_{tu}(x, E) = 1 + \int_s^u \mu'_{t\tau}(x, E) \mathbf{M}_{\mu'} [d^* N'(\tau) 1 \mid x], \tag{3.87}$$

where $dN'(\tau)$ is a certain operator such that

$$e^{q_\alpha x_\alpha} dN'(\tau) e^{-q_\alpha x_\alpha} \equiv dN(\tau) \tag{3.88}$$

does not depend on q. Then $dN(\tau) = dL^*(\tau)$ is the infinitesimal operator of the system of measures μ_{tu}.

Proof. Taking into account (3.76), it is easily seen that (3.87) is equivalent to the equation

$$\mu'_{tu}(x, E) = 1 + \int_t^u \mu'_{t\tau}(x, dx')(d^*N'1)(x')$$

or, as a result of (3.78),

$$\int \mu_{tu}(x, dx') e^{q_\alpha x'_\alpha} = e^{q_\alpha x_\alpha} + \int_t^u \int_E \mu_{t\tau}(x, dx') e^{q_\alpha x'_\alpha}(d^*N'1)(x').$$

Taking into account the definition (3.88), we get

$$\int \mu_{tu}(x, dx') e^{q_\alpha x'_\alpha} = e^{q_\alpha x_\alpha} + \int_t^u \mu_{t\tau}(x, dx')(d^*Ne^{q_\alpha x_\alpha})(x') =$$

$$= e^{q_\alpha x_\alpha} + \int_t^u (\mu_{t\tau} d^*N)(x, dx'') e^{q_\alpha x''_\alpha}$$

for any given q. The application of the somewhat generalized (for the case of nonnormalized measure) converse theorem (Loève [1], p. 199) leads to the equation

$$\mu_{tu}(x, \Lambda) = I(x, \Lambda) + \int_t^u (\mu_{t\tau} d^*N(\tau))(x, \Lambda)$$

($I(x, \Lambda)$ is an indicator of the set Λ). This equation is equivalent to the first equation of (3.4) or (3.3) and as a result of the uniqueness of the infinitesimal operator dL^*, we have $dL^* = dN$. The proof is completed. As a result of (3.28), dN' coincides with the second infinitesimal operator dL'^* of the measures μ'_{tu}.

CHAPTER 4

Absolute Continuity of Diffusional Markov Measures and Derivatives in Function Space

The material of this chapter is necessary for the application of the general results concerning conditional Markov processes compiled in Chapter 5 to the important particular case of diffusion processes. Such a specification is carried out in Chapters 6 and 7; thus the results of the indicated chapters are based essentially on the material of the present chapter.

The question of the absolute continuity in the function space of measures of diffusion processes and of the form of the corresponding derivatives is dealt with in a large number of papers: by Cameron and Martin [1], Prokhorov [1], Skorokhod [1], and Girsanov [1]. The results of these papers were largely obtained by Wiener using a measure transformation. Theorem 4.1 of this chapter essentially repeats the indicated results. In addition, there is introduced another method of proof which is convenient as the basis of the following Theorem 4.2. The latter theorem is concerned with the derivatives in function space, corresponding to part of the components of a multidimensional diffusion process. On the remaining components, there seems to occur an averaging. The possibility of obtaining some sort of precise formulas in such a presentation of the question, as far as we know, has not yet been recognized. Theorem 4.2 is convenient for the proof of the results in Chapter 7.

The examination carried out in the present chapter would be simplified if we demanded a nonsingular local variance matrix. Nevertheless, we will not impose such a loss of generality. This somewhat complicates the formulas, which one can, however, get used to. In the expression for the derivative, the inverse of a nonsingular submatrix of local variances is used instead of the inverse of the local variance matrix. In addition to this, a necessary condition for absolute continuity of the measures is an additional condition imposed on the measure forming the drift vector in the complementary subspace. The ideas and notations connected with a singular local variance matrix are given in Sect. 4.1.

This section, to a certain extent, is a result of the general arrangement of the present chapter, as in it function spaces are not examined. Nevertheless, it is an essential one for the future, and thus we place it as the introduction.

4.1 Some Lemmas for Measures Having a Singular Variance Matrix

1. The examination of a singular variance matrix aids in extending the results of Sects. 4.3 and 4.4 and Chapters 6 and 7 to the case of a singular local variance matrix.

Lemma 4.1. Let the matrix

$$\hat{b} = \begin{Vmatrix} b & \overline{b}^{+} \\ \overline{b} & \overline{\overline{b}} \end{Vmatrix},$$

where

$$b = \| b_{\rho'\sigma'} \|; \quad \overline{b} = \| b_{\rho''\sigma'} \|; \quad \overline{b}^{+} = \| b_{\rho'\sigma''} \|; \quad \overline{\overline{b}} = \| b_{\rho''\sigma''} \|;$$
$$\rho', \sigma' = 1, \ldots, l'; \quad \rho'', \sigma'' = l' + 1, \ldots, l,$$

(the cross designates transposition) be a symmetric matrix of rank l', where the $l' \times l$ matrix $\|b, \overline{b}^{+}\|$ also has rank l'; then

$$\det b \neq 0; \tag{4.1}$$

$$\overline{\overline{b}} = \overline{b} b^{-1} \overline{b}^{+}. \tag{4.2}$$

Proof. According to the conditions of the lemma, it is possible to choose coefficients $\alpha_{\rho''\tau'}$ such that

$$b_{\rho''\sigma'} = \alpha_{\rho''\tau'} b_{\tau'\sigma'}; \quad b_{\rho''\sigma''} = \alpha_{\rho''\tau'} b_{\tau'\sigma''}, \tag{4.3}$$

or in the matrix form

$$\overline{b} = \alpha b; \quad \overline{\overline{b}} = \alpha \overline{b}^{+}$$

(indices with one prime include values $1, \ldots, l'$, and with two primes, values $l'+1, \ldots, l$). Obviously, the rank of the matrix does not change if from the columns of the matrix $\|b, \overline{b}^{+}\|$ we subtract linear combinations of its first columns, i.e., if rather than

$\|b, \underline{\bar{b}^+}\|$, we consider $\|b, \bar{b}^+ - b\alpha^+\|$, where $b\alpha^+ = \|b_{\rho'\tau'}\alpha_{\sigma''\tau'}\|$. Thus Rank $\|b, \bar{b}^+ - b\alpha^+\| = l'$, but on the strength of (4.3) and the symmetry of the matrix b we have

$$\xi_{\tau'} = \sigma^{-1}_{\tau'\rho'} (y_{\rho'} - m_{\rho'}). \tag{4.4}$$

Consequently, Rank $\|b, 0\| = l'$, which proves assertion (4.1). In order to derive (4.2), we find $\alpha^+ = \bar{b}^{-1}\bar{b}^+$ from (4.4), transpose this matrix and substitute into the second equation of (4.3). The proof is concluded.

Lemma 4.2. Let $\hat{b}$ be the matrix examined in the preceding lemma and let it be, in addition, nonnegative definite; then there exists an $l \times l'$ matrix $\hat{\sigma} = \left\| \begin{matrix} \sigma \\ - \\ \sigma \end{matrix} \right\|$ such that det $\sigma \neq 0$ and $\hat{b} = \hat{\sigma}\hat{\sigma}^+$, i.e.,

$$\sigma\sigma^+ = b \quad (4.5); \qquad \sigma\bar{\sigma}^+ = \bar{b}^+ \quad (4.6); \qquad \bar{\sigma}\bar{\sigma}^+ = \bar{\bar{b}}. \tag{4.7}$$

Proof. The formula det $\sigma \neq 0$ and (4.5) follow from (4.1), since from a nonsingular positive definite matrix it is always possible to extract a square root (it is even possible to find a symmetric matrix σ). Substituting (4.5) into (4.4) and defining $\sigma^+\alpha^+ = \bar{\sigma}^+$, we prove (4.6). Finally, the substitution of (4.5) and (4.6) into (4.2) leads to (4.7).

Lemma 4.3. Let us assume that the Gaussian random variables $(y_1, \ldots, y_l)$ have a correlation matrix $\hat{k}$ of rank l' with the properties indicated in the previous lemmas, and also a mean value m_ρ, $\rho = 1, \ldots, l$. Then the corresponding measure $\nu(\Lambda)$ in l-dimensional Euclidean space R_l is determined by the following expression:

$$\nu(\Lambda) = \int_{\Gamma\Lambda} (2\pi)^{-\frac{l'}{2}} \det^{-\frac{1}{2}} k \times \times \exp\left[-\frac{1}{2}(y_{\rho'} - m_{\rho'}) k^{-1}_{\rho'\tau'} (y_{\tau'} - m_{\tau'})\right] dy_1 \ldots dy_{l'}, \tag{4.8}$$

where

$$\Gamma = \{y : y_{\rho''} - m_{\rho''} = k_{\rho''\tau'} k^{-1}_{\tau'\pi'} (y_{\pi'} - m_{\pi'}),\ \rho'' = l' + 1, \ldots, l\}$$

is an l'-dimensional hyperplane.

For the proof, we will apply Lemma 4.2 to the matrix $\hat{k} (= \hat{b})$ and write the resulting random variables in the form

$$y_\rho = m_\rho + \sigma_{\rho\tau'} \xi_{\tau'}, \qquad \rho = 1, \ldots, l, \tag{4.9}$$

where $\xi_1, \ldots, \xi_{l'}$ are independent Gaussian random variables with zero mean and unit variance. Solving the first l' equations of (4.9) and substituting the result into the remaining $l-l'$ equations, we obtain

$$\xi_{\tau'} = \sigma^{-1}_{\tau'\rho'}(y_{\rho'} - m_{\rho'}); \tag{4.10}$$

$$y_{\rho''} - m_{\rho''} = \sigma_{\rho''\tau'}\sigma^{-1}_{\tau'\pi'}(y_{\pi'} - m_{\pi'}). \tag{4.11}$$

According to (4.5) and (4.6), we have $\bar{k}k^{-1} = \bar{\sigma}\sigma^{-1}$, hence (4.11) is equivalent to the equation

$$y_{\rho''} - m_{\rho''} = k_{\rho''\tau'}k^{-1}_{\tau'\pi'}(y_{\pi'} - m_{\pi'}). \tag{4.12}$$

This proves that the measure ν is actually concentrated on the hyperplane Γ. Equation (4.10) represents a nonsingular transformation of the random variables $\xi_1, \ldots, \xi_{l'}$, which have the distribution density

$$p(\xi_1, \ldots, \xi_{l'}) = (2\pi)^{-\frac{l'}{2}} \exp\left[-\frac{1}{2}\sum_{\rho'} \xi^2_{\rho'}\right].$$

The transformation of this density according to the usual rules and consideration of the relation $\sigma^{+-1}\sigma^{-1} = k^{-1}$ verifies the exponential expression in (4.8). The proof is completed.

2. We will introduce as the final point of this section one useful lemma regarding a more complex object, the diffusional Markov process, but closely connected with the preceding lemmas.

Lemma 4.4. Let $y(t) = \{y_1(t), \ldots, y_l(t)\}$ be a diffusion process with drift parameters $a_\rho(y, t)$ and a local variance matrix $\hat{b}(y, t) = \|b_{\sigma\rho}(y, t)\|$. It is assumed that all these functions are continuous in y and t and that for all y and t in the regions of definition the matrix $\hat{b}(y, t)$ satisfies the conditions of Lemmas 4.1 and 4.2. Then with probability 1

$$\int_\alpha^\beta (dy_{\rho''} - b_{\rho''\tau'}b^{-1}_{\tau'\pi'}d^*y_{\pi'}) = \int_\alpha^\beta (a_{\rho''} - b_{\rho''\pi'}b^{-1}_{\tau'\pi'}a_{\pi'})\,dt. \tag{4.13}$$

For proof, in essence, we can use the same process as for the proof of the previous lemma, but relations (4.10) through (4.12) should be written for differentials. We will explain this in more detail. Let us introduce matrices $\sigma, \bar{\sigma}$, defined by Lemma 4.2 ($\widehat{\sigma\sigma^+} = \hat{b}$), and examine the equations

$$y_\rho(\beta) - y_\rho(\alpha) = \int_\alpha^\beta [a_\rho\,dt + \sigma_{\rho\pi'}d^*\xi_{\pi'}(t)], \tag{4.14}$$

where $\xi_1(t), \ldots, \xi_{l'}(t)$ are independent Wiener processes.

As we know (Sect. 2.2), these equations define the diffusion process with drift parameters a_ρ and local variances $\sigma_{\rho\pi'}\sigma_{\tau\pi'} = b_{\rho\tau}$, i.e., the process defined in the conditions of Lemma 4.4.

Taking from (4.14) l'-equations

$$\int_\alpha^\beta [dy_{\rho'} - a_{\rho'}\,dt] = \int_\alpha^\beta \sigma_{\rho'\pi'}\,d^*\xi_{\pi'}$$

and using Lemma 2.3, we have

$$\int_\alpha^\beta \sigma_{\pi'\rho'}^{-1}\,[d^*y_{\rho'} - a_{\rho'}\,dt] = \xi_{\pi'}(\beta) - \xi_{\pi'}(\alpha). \tag{4.15}$$

Substituting (4.15) into the remaining equations

$$\int_\alpha^\beta [dy_{\rho''} - a_{\rho''}\,dt] = \int_\alpha^\beta \sigma_{\rho''\pi'}\,d^*\xi_{\pi'}$$

and again using Lemma 2.3, we obtain

$$\int_\alpha^\beta [dy_{\rho''} - a_{\rho''}\,dt] = \int_\alpha^\beta \sigma_{\rho''\pi'}\,\sigma_{\pi'\rho'}^{-1}\,[d^*y_{\rho'} - a_{\rho'}\,dt], \tag{4.16}$$

which proves (4.13).

Corollary 4.1. For the diffusion process examined in Lemma 4.4, the limit

$$\lim_{\Delta\to 0}\frac{1}{\Delta}\int_t^{t+\Delta} (dy_{\rho''} - b_{\rho''\tau'}\,b_{\tau'\pi'}^{-1}\,d^*y_{\pi'}) = a_{\rho''} - b_{\rho''\tau'}\,b_{\tau'\pi'}^{-1}\,a_{\pi'} \tag{4.17}$$

exists with probability 1.

4.2 Specification of σ-Algebras in Function Space

1. A two-parameter Markov measure $\mu_{st}(z, \Lambda)$ in a measurable space $(E, \mathcal{E})$ induces measures in a function space $E^T = \prod_{t\in T} E_t$, where E_t are duplicates of the space E. We will designate points in this space as $z(\cdot) = \{z(t),\ t \in T\}$.

For a unique assignment of measure in a function space it is necessary to introduce an "initial" distribution or, in place of it, to add the condition

$$z(s) = e,$$

where $e \in E$. The function space measure corresponding to this last case we will designate as $\mu_{z(s)}$.

We will introduce the notation of σ-algebras in function space. Let $\mathcal{N}_t$, $t \in T$ be a σ-algebra generated by the sets $\{z(\cdot): z(t) \in \Lambda\}$, $\Lambda \in \mathcal{E}$. More generally, let $\mathcal{N}_{\widetilde{T}}$ designate the minimal σ-algebra generated by the sets $\{z(\cdot): z(t) \in \Lambda\}$, $t \in \widetilde{T}$, $\Lambda \in \mathcal{E}$, i.e.,

$$\mathcal{N}_{\widetilde{T}} = \sigma\Big(\bigcup_{t \in \widetilde{T}} \mathcal{N}_t\Big).$$

Further, the σ-algebra generated by the sets

$$\{z(\cdot): z(t) \in \Lambda,\ t \in \widetilde{\widetilde{T}}\}, \quad \widetilde{\widetilde{T}} \subset \widetilde{T}, \quad \Lambda \in \mathcal{E}$$

we will designate as $\mathcal{M}_{\widetilde{T}}$.

As we know (for example, Dynkin [2], p. 32), under certain topological conditions (which we assume can be satisfied) the consistent measures for a finite number of time moments in the given case of measure

$$\int_{\Lambda_1} \cdots \int_{\Lambda_{n-1}} \mu_{st_1}(e, dx_1) \ldots \mu_{t_{n-1} t_n}(x_{n-1}, \Lambda_n), \quad \Lambda_1, \ldots, \Lambda_n \in \mathcal{E},$$

uniquely determine the measure $\mu_{z(s)}$ in a measurable space $(E^T, \mathcal{N}_{\widetilde{T}})$ for any given $\widetilde{T} \subset T$.

In addition to this, for a separable version of the process $z(\cdot)$ the measure $\mu_{z(s)}$ on $\mathcal{N}_T$ uniquely determines a measure on the σ-algebras $\mathcal{M}_{\widetilde{T}} \subset \mathcal{M}_T$ (for example, Loève [1], p. 529). In the future we will limit ourselves to the examination of separable processes (with reference to $\mathcal{E}$). For them there exists a denumerable set S (the set of separability) such that the set

$$\{z(\cdot): z(t) \in \Lambda,\ t \in \widetilde{T}\} \in \mathcal{M}_{\widetilde{T}}$$

differs from

$$\{z(\cdot): z(t) \in \Lambda,\ t \in \widetilde{T} S\} \in \mathcal{N}_{\widetilde{T} S}$$

at most by a subset of a set $\Gamma \in \mathcal{M}_{\widetilde{T}}$ of measure zero.

Thus, if we augment the σ-algebra $\mathcal{N}_{\widetilde{T} S}$ by the subsets of $\mathcal{M}_{\widetilde{T}}$ having zero $\mu_{z(s)}$ measure and if the resulting σ-algebra is designated $\overline{\mathcal{N}}_{\widetilde{T} S}$, we will have

$$\mathcal{M}_{\widetilde{T}} \subset \overline{\mathcal{N}}_{\widetilde{T} S}.$$

Thus, for separable processes we can consider the σ-algebra $\overline{\mathcal{N}}_{TS}$ as the widest σ-algebra. A space having the measure $(E^T, \overline{\mathcal{N}}_{TS}, \mu_{z(s)})$

can be selected as the reference. In such an approach the process $z(\cdot)$ in the terminology of Doob ([1], p. 67) is a directly specified process.

Another approach, as we know, consists in the examination of an abstract measurable space $(\Omega, \mathscr{B})$, and the process $z(\cdot)=z(\cdot, \omega)$ is introduced as a $\mathscr{B}$-measurable function over it. In this procedure it is necessary to postulate that the prototypes of all the σ-algebras described above are contained in $\mathscr{B}$. All assertions in regard to the σ-algebras $\mathscr{N}_{\widetilde{T}}$, $\mathscr{M}_{\widetilde{T}}$, $\overline{\mathscr{N}}_{\widetilde{T}}$ and others in E^T as a rule can be carried over to their prototypes in Ω. We shall not dwell on this, and will not introduce special designations for σ-algebras in Ω, designating them, if needed, by the same letters.

In the specific case when $\widetilde{T}$ is an interval $[\alpha, \beta]$, we will use the notation $\mathscr{N}_{[\alpha,\beta]}=\mathscr{N}_\alpha$ and similarly for other σ-algebras.

2. We will now examine the diffusion process $z(\cdot)=y(\cdot)$ defined by Eq. (4.14). In this case the measure $\mu_{z(s)}$ is a probability and for any s and $z(s)$ is concentrated on the set of continuous functions. To the set of the remaining functions we can assign the measure zero (or from the very beginning examine only the set of continuous functions). Then the process will be separable, and the set of separability S will be any set everywhere dense in T. (In the space of continuous functions the σ-algebras $\mathscr{N}_T$ and $\mathscr{M}_T$ will coincide.)

If the Wiener processes $\xi_{\rho'}(t)$ in (4.14) are considered $\mathscr{B}$-measurable functions of $\omega\in\Omega$, then the integral Eq. (4.14), as we know, determines the process $y(\cdot) = \{y(t,\omega)\}$ as a $\mathscr{B}$-measurable function of ω.

In the future, in order to obtain various results, we will examine a Δ-division $S_\Delta=\{t_1, \ldots, t_N\}$ of the interval $[s, t]\in T$. In this it is understood that $S_\Delta\subset S_{\Delta'}$ for $\Delta'<\Delta$. We will use the fact that the limit set $S_s^t = \lim\limits_{\Delta\to 0} S_\Delta$ is a set of separability and, consequently,

$$\overline{\mathscr{N}}_{S^t_s}\supset \mathscr{M}^t_s.$$

Along with the exact equation (4.14), it is sometimes useful to examine the corresponding finite difference equation

$$\widetilde{z}_{\rho k}-z_\rho(s)=\sum_{i=0}^{k-1}\{a_\rho(\widetilde{z}_i,\ t_i)(t_{i+1}-t_i)+$$

$$+\sigma_{\rho\pi'}(\widetilde{z}_i,\ t_i)[\xi_{\pi'}(t_{i+1})-\xi_{\pi'}(t_i)]\}. \tag{4.18}$$

$$(\widetilde{z}_{\rho i}=\widetilde{z}_\rho(t_i),\quad t_0=s).$$

The approximate process $\{\widetilde{z}(t_1), \ldots, \widetilde{z}(t_N)\}$ obtained here is in a certain sense close to the exact process $z(\cdot)$ and its corresponding measure $\widetilde{\mu}_{z(s)}$ on $\mathscr{N}_{S_\Delta}$ is close to the measure $\mu_{z(s)}$. Let us formulate the appropriate assertion in the form of a lemma which will be of use to us in the future.

We will assume that on the entire interval $[s, t]$ the rank l' of the matrix $||b_{\rho\sigma}||$ does not change and the linear independence of its first l' rows is not disturbed. Then, instead of all components of the process $z(\cdot)$, it is possible to examine the first l' of its components $z(\cdot) = \{z_{\rho'}(\cdot),\ \rho' = 1, \ldots, l'\}$. The σ-algebras on the space E^T corresponding to these components we will denote by a prime.

Lemma 4.5. The measure $\mu_{z(s)}$ of the exact process and the measure $\widetilde{\mu}_{z(s)}$ of the approximate process (4.18) are absolutely continuous on the σ-algebra $\mathscr{N}'_{S_\Delta}$, while the Radon-Nikodim derivative

$$\frac{\widetilde{\mu}_{z(s)}(dz_1' \ldots dz_N')}{\mu_{z(s)}(dz_1' \ldots dz_N')} = \widetilde{f}(z(\cdot)) \tag{4.19}$$

tends to 1 as $\Delta \to 0$ almost everywhere relative to $\mu_{z(s)}$.

Proof. Let us compare the measures $\widetilde{\mu}_{z_k}(dz'_{k+1})$ and $\mu_{z_k}(dz_{k+1})$, corresponding to one elementary interval $[t_k, t_{k+1}]$. The measure $\widetilde{\mu}_{z_k}(dz'_{k+1})$, as can be seen from (4.18), corresponds to a Gaussian distribution for the difference $\zeta_{\rho'} = z_{\rho',k+1} - z_{\rho',k}$ with mean $a_{\rho'}(z_k, t_k)(t_{k+1} - t_k)$ and variance matrix $b_{\rho'\sigma'}(z_k, t_k) \times (t_{k+1} - t_k)$. The measure $\mu_{z_k}(dz'_{k+1})$ has a distribution density $p_{z_k}(\zeta, t) \equiv p$ which satisfies the diffusion equation

$$\frac{\partial p}{\partial t} = -\frac{\partial}{\partial z_{\rho'}}[a_{\rho'}(z_k + \zeta, t)p] + \\ + \frac{1}{2}\frac{\partial^2}{\partial z_{\rho'}\partial z_{\sigma'}}[b_{\rho'\sigma'}(z_k + \zeta, t)p].$$

The approximate solution of this equation for small $t - t_k$ can conveniently be found using the Fourier transform, i.e., by examining the characteristic function

$$\Theta_{z_k}(v, t) \equiv \Theta = \int e^{iv_{\rho'}\zeta_{\rho'}} p_{z_k}(\zeta, t)\, d\zeta.$$

The diffusion equation is equivalent to the following equation for this:

$$\frac{\partial\Theta}{\partial t} = \Big[iv_{\rho'}\, a_{\rho'}\Big(z_k - i\frac{\partial}{\partial v}, t\Big) - \\ - \frac{1}{2} v_{\rho'} v_{\sigma'}\, b_{\rho'\sigma'}\Big(z_k - i\frac{\partial}{\partial v}, t\Big)\Big]\Theta \tag{4.20}$$

$$(\Theta_{z_k}(v, t_k) = 1);$$

where the operator notation

$$f\left(-i\frac{\partial}{\partial v}\right)\Theta = \frac{1}{2\pi}\int\limits_{-\infty}^{\infty} e^{iv\zeta} f(\zeta)\,d\zeta \int\limits_{-\infty}^{\infty}\frac{1-e^{-iu\zeta}}{iu}\,\Theta(u)\,du. \qquad (4.21)$$

is introduced. The functions $a_{\rho'}$, $b_{\rho'\sigma'}$ and Θ, with our assumptions, are such that the corresponding integrals in (4.21) converge.

We will solve Eq. (4.20) by the method of successive approximations:

$$\frac{\partial\varphi_n}{\partial t} = e^{-\varphi_{n-1}}\left[iv_{\rho'}\,a_{\rho'}\left(z_k - i\frac{\partial}{\partial v},\ t\right) - \right.$$
$$\left. -\frac{1}{2}\,v_{\rho'}\,v_{\sigma'}\,b_{\rho'\sigma'}\left(z_k - i\frac{\partial}{\partial v},\ t\right)\right] e^{\varphi_{n-1}}\quad (\varphi_0 = 0).$$

This gives us the result

$$\Theta(v, t) = \exp\left\{\left[iv_{\rho'}\,a_{\rho'}\,(z_k, t_k) - \right.\right.$$
$$\left.\left. -\frac{1}{2}\,v_{\rho'}\,v_{\sigma'}\,b_{\rho'\sigma'}(z_k, t_k)\right](t - t_k) + O((t - t_k)^2)\right\}. \qquad (4.22)$$

But the characteristic function

$$\exp\left\{\left[i\,v_{\rho'}\,a_{\rho'} - \frac{1}{2}\,v_{\rho'}\,v_{\sigma'}\,b_{\rho'\sigma'}\right](t - t_k)\right\} = \widetilde{\Theta}.$$

for $t = t_{k+1}$ exactly corresponds to the measure $\widetilde{\mu}_{z_k}(dz'_{k+1})$. From the equation $\Theta(v, t_{k+1}) = \widetilde{\Theta}(v, t_{k+1})\,e^{O(\Delta^2)}$ we have

$$p_{z_k}(\zeta, t_{k+1}) = \widetilde{p}_{z_k}(\zeta, t_{k+1})\,e^{O(\Delta^2)}. \qquad (4.23)$$

If we now take values z_k and $\widetilde{z}_k$ which do not coincide but which are close, then from (4.22) on the strength of the differentiability with respect to z_k of the parameters $a_{\rho'}$ and $b_{\rho'\sigma'}$, we will have

$$\Theta_{z_k}(v, t_{k+1}) = \widetilde{\Theta}_{\widetilde{z}_k}(v, t_{k+1})\exp\left[O(z_k - \widetilde{z}_k)\,\Delta + O(\Delta^2)\right].$$

Consequently, for $z_k - \widetilde{z}_k = o(1)$ we have

$$\Theta_{z_k}(v, t_{k+1}) = \widetilde{\Theta}_{\widetilde{z}_k}(v, t_{k+1})\,e^{o(\Delta)};\quad p_{z_k}(\zeta, t_{k+1}) = \widetilde{p}_{\widetilde{z}_k}(\zeta, t_{k+1})\,e^{o(\Delta)}. \qquad (4.24)$$

Let us now turn to the examination of the multidimensional distributions entering into (4.19). According to Eq. (4.16), the components $z'(\cdot) = \{z_{\rho'}\}$ uniquely determine the remaining components $z''(\cdot) = \{z_{\rho''}\}$. The same is also true for the approximate process (4.18), where $\lim\limits_{\Delta\to 0}\widetilde{z}_\rho \to z_\rho$, i.e., $z_\rho - \widetilde{z}_\rho = o(1)$. We will write (4.19) in the form

$$\frac{1}{\widetilde{f}\,(\widetilde{z}\,(\cdot))} =$$

$$= \frac{\mathbf{M}_{\mu_{z(s)}}[p_{z_0}(z_1' - z_0') \ldots p_{z_{N-1}}(z_N' - z_{N-1}') \mid z_1' = \widetilde{z}_1', \ldots, z_{N-1}' = \widetilde{z}_{N-1}']}{\widetilde{p}_{\widetilde{z}_0}(\widetilde{z}_1' - \widetilde{z}_0') \ldots \widetilde{p}_{\widetilde{z}_{N-1}}(\widetilde{z}_N' - \widetilde{z}_{N-1}')}$$

and put the denominator of the right side under the sign of mathematical expectation. Taking into consideration (4.24) here, we obtain

$$\frac{1}{\widetilde{f}(z(\cdot))} = \mathbf{M}_{\mu_{z(s)}}\{e^{\sum_{k=0}^{N-1} o(\Delta)} \mid \mathcal{N}'_{S_\Delta}\} = e^{o(1)},$$

which completes the proof.

It is obvious that the above-cited lemma is also true for the sequence of augmented σ-algebras $\{\overline{\mathcal{N}}'_{S_\Delta}\}$.

4.3 The Radon-Nikodim Derivative for a Diffusion Process

In this section we will examine a diffusional Markov measure in n-dimensional Euclidean space R_n, but of a more specific form than the measures defined by the operators (3.42) and (3.65). Namely, without introducing a supplementary diffusion process $\{y(t)\}$, we will assume

$$dL = \left(c + a_\rho \frac{\partial}{\partial z_\rho} + \frac{1}{2} b_{\rho\sigma} \frac{\partial^2}{\partial z_\rho \, \partial z_\sigma}\right) dt. \tag{4.25}$$

In comparison with (3.42) and (3.65), here the symbol x is changed to z, m to n, and it is assumed that $A_\rho \equiv 0$. The functions c, a_ρ, and $b_{\rho\sigma}$ are assumed continuous in $z_1, \ldots, z_n$, t and (if needed for changing from one stochastic integral to the other) differentiable with respect to $z_1, \ldots, z_n$.

As indicated in the preceding paragraph, the given measure determines measures $\mu_{z(s)}$ in a function space $(R_n^T, \overline{\mathcal{N}}_T)$, $R_n^T = R_n \times \ldots \times R_n$, and similarly on other, less wide σ-algebras.

In addition to the given measure μ, we will introduce another measure ν of an analogous type and examine the question of absolute continuity of these measures on $(R_n^T, \overline{\mathcal{N}}_s^u)$.

If the local variance matrix $\|b_{\rho\sigma}\|$ is nonsingular, then as we know (this follows from Lemma 2.1) for absolute continuity of the measures $\mu_{z(s)}$ and $\nu_{z(s)}$ on $\overline{\mathcal{N}}_s^u$, it is necessary and sufficient that the local variance matrices of the two measures should be equal on the entire interval $[s, u]$. The drift parameters a^{ρ} of the two processes can be different.

The situation becomes more complex for singular local variance matrices. The equality of local variance matrices in this case is insufficient for absolute continuity. As we can see from (4.17), it is also necessary to have equality of expressions (4.17) for the two processes at all interior points of the interval in question.

In the following theorem we will take as the measure $\nu_{z(s)}$ that one of all measures absolutely continuous relative to the given one which in a certain sense is simplest. Namely, let us assume it has the smallest possible number of nonzero terms in the corresponding expression

$$dL^{\nu} = \left(c^{\nu} + a_{\rho}^{\nu} \frac{\partial}{\partial z_{\rho}} + \frac{1}{2} b_{\rho\sigma}^{\nu} \frac{\partial^2}{\partial z_{\rho}\, \partial z_{\sigma}}\right) dt,$$

analogous to (4.25). Since the equation

$$a_{\rho''} - b_{\rho''\tau'} b_{\tau'\pi'}^{-1} a_{\pi'} = a_{\rho''}^{\nu} - b_{\rho''\tau'}^{\nu} b_{\tau'\pi'}^{\nu-1} a_{\pi'}^{\nu}, \quad \rho'' > l'$$

must be satisfied, obviously it is not possible to assume $a_{\rho}^{\nu} = 0$, but it is possible to assume

$$a_{\rho'}^{\nu} = 0; \quad a_{\rho''}^{\nu} = a_{\rho''} - b_{\rho''\tau'} b_{\tau'\pi'}^{-1} a_{\pi'}. \tag{4.26a}$$

Theorem 4.1. Let the measure $\mu_{z(s)}$ in space E^T be defined by the infinitesimal operator (4.25), and the measure $\nu_{z(s)}$, by the operator

$$dL^{\nu} = \left[(a_{\rho''} - b_{\rho''\tau'} b_{\tau'\pi'}^{-1} a_{\pi'}) \frac{\partial}{\partial z_{\rho''}} + \frac{1}{2} b_{\rho\sigma} \frac{\partial^2}{\partial z_{\rho}\, \partial z_{\sigma}}\right] dt. \tag{4.26}$$

Then these measures are absolutely continuous on the σ-algebra $\mathcal{N}_s^u$ or $\overline{\mathcal{N}}_s^u$, while the Radon-Nikodim derivative has the form

$$\frac{d\mu_{z(s)}}{d\nu_{z(s)}}(z(\cdot)) = \exp\left\{\int_s^u \left[c\, dt + a_{\rho'} b_{\rho'\sigma'}^{-1} d^* z_{\sigma'} - \right.\right.$$

$$\left.\left. - \frac{1}{2} a_{\rho'} b_{\rho'\sigma'}^{-1} a_{\sigma'}\, dt\right]\right\} \text{ (almost certainly)}, \tag{4.27}$$

if conditions for the existence of this stochastic integral are satisfied.

The sense of the designations $\rho', \sigma', b_{\rho',\sigma'}^{-1}$, is the same as in Lemmas 4.2 and 4.4.

The assertion of the theorem, if we neglect the terms containing c, is included in the results of the work of Girsanov [1] and others. Nevertheless, we will give a short proof here in order to illustrate the method of proof applied later (Sect. 4.4) to obtain more complex results.

We will use

Lemma 4.6. Let us say we have an expanding sequence of σ-algebras $\{\mathcal{F}_n\}$ converging to $\mathcal{F}$, and two measures μ and ν on $\mathcal{F}$. Then, if these measures are absolutely continuous on each $\mathcal{F}_n$, and if the Radon-Nikodim derivative f_n converges almost everywhere to a finite function f which is almost nowhere equal to zero, the measures μ and ν are absolutely continuous on $\mathcal{F}$ and the Radon-Nikodim derivative is equal to f.

This lemma relates to the bases of measure theory and we will not dwell on its proof.

Proof of Theorem 4.1. Let us examine the measure $\mu'_{z(s)}$ corresponding to the infinitesimal operator

$$dL' = a_\rho \frac{\partial}{\partial z_\rho} + \frac{1}{2} b_{\rho\sigma} \frac{\partial^2}{\partial z_\rho \, \partial z_\sigma},$$

i.e., to a diffusion process with parameters a_ρ, $b_{\rho\sigma}$. Lemma 4.4 applies to this process and the stochastic equations (4.14)-(4.16) are true for it. These equations can be approximately replaced by finite-difference equations and Lemma 4.5 used.

Let $S_\Delta = \{t_i\}$ be a Δ-division of the interval $[s, u]$. The limit $S_s^u = \lim_{\Delta \to 0} S_\Delta$ will be a set of separability, hence $\overline{\mathcal{N}_{S_s^u}} = \overline{\mathcal{N}}_s^u \supset \mathcal{M}_s^u$.

If we prove that the measures $\mu_{z(s)}$, $\mu'_{z(s)}$, and $\nu_{z(s)}$ are absolutely continuous on $\mathcal{N}_{S_\Delta}$ while the Radon-Nikodim derivative has a limit as $\Delta \to 0$, then according to Lemma 4.6, from this will follow the absolute continuity of these measures on $\mathcal{N}_{S_s^u}$. The absolute continuity $\mu_{z(s)} \ll \nu_{z(s)}$ obviously will not be destroyed for the σ-algebra $\mathcal{N}_{S_s^u}$ augmented by the μ-null sets. In this manner, the proof of Theorem 4.1 reduces to the proof of the convergence of Radon-Nikodim derivatives for finite divisions S_Δ, as $\Delta \to 0$.

For the division S_Δ the measure $\mu'_{z(s)}$ will be taken in the form

$$\mu'_{z(s)}(dz_1 \dots dz_N) = \tilde{f}\, \tilde{\mu}_{z(s)}(dz_1)\, \tilde{\mu}_{z_1}(dz_2) \dots \tilde{\mu}_{z_{N-1}}(dz_N), \qquad (4.28)$$

where

$$z_i = z(t_i) \quad \text{and} \quad \tilde{\mu}_{z_i}(dz_{i+1})$$

is a Gaussian measure with means $z_{\rho i} + a_\rho(z_i, t_i)(t_{i+1} - t_i)$ and variances $b_{\rho\sigma}(z_i, t_i)(t_{i+1} - t_i)$. According to the material of Lemma 4.5,

$\tilde{f}$ tends to 1 almost certainly (a.c.) as $\Delta \to 0$. It is not difficult to prove that

$$\mu_{z(s)}(dz_1 \dots dz_N) = f^{\Delta} \exp[c(z(s), s)(t_1 - s) + \dots + + c(z_{N-1}, t_{N-1})(t_N - t_{N-1})] \mu'_{z(s)}(dz_1 \dots dz_N), \tag{4.29}$$

where

$$f^{\Delta} \to 1 \text{ a.c. as } \Delta \to 0.$$

We will write for the measure $\nu_{z(s)}$ the equation analogous to (4.28):

$$\nu_{z(s)}(dz_1 \dots dz_N) = \tilde{f}^{\nu} \tilde{\nu}_{z(s)}(dz_1) \tilde{\nu}_{z_1}(dz_2) \dots \tilde{\nu}_{z_{N-1}}(dz_N). \tag{4.30}$$

Here $\tilde{\nu}_{z_i}(dz_{i+1})$ is a Gaussian measure with means $z_{\rho i} + a_{\rho}^{\nu}(z_i, t_i)(t_{i+1} - t_i)$ [see (4.26a)] and variances

$$b_{\rho\sigma}(z_i, t_i)(t_{i+1} - t_i); \quad \tilde{f}^{\nu} \to 1 \text{ a.c. as } \Delta \to 0.$$

Taking into account (4.28)–(4.30), we find that the measures (4.29) and (4.30) are absolutely continuous if the elementary Gaussian measures $\tilde{\mu}_{z_i}(dz_{i+1})$ and $\tilde{\nu}_{z_i}(dz_{i+1})$ are absolutely continuous. The application of Lemma 4.3 proves the latter and yields the corresponding derivative

$$\frac{\tilde{\mu}_{z_i}(dz_{i+1})}{\tilde{\nu}_{z_i}(dz_{i+1})} = \exp\{a_{\rho'}(z_i, t_i) b^{-1}_{\rho'\tau'}(i)[z_{\tau'}(t_{i+1}) - z_{\tau'}(t_i)] - - \frac{1}{2} a_{\rho'}(i) b^{-1}_{\rho'\tau'}(i) a_{\tau'}(i)(t_{i+1} - t_i)\}. \tag{4.31}$$

Substituting (4.28) into (4.29), dividing (4.29) by (4.30), and taking into account (4.31), we obtain

$$\frac{\mu_{z(s)}(dz_1 \dots dz_N)}{\nu_{z(s)}(dz_1 \dots dz_N)} = \frac{f^{\Delta}\tilde{f}}{\tilde{f}^{\nu}} \exp\Big\{\sum_i \Big[c(i)(t_{i+1} - t_i) + + a_{\rho'}(i) b^{-1}_{\rho'\tau'}(i)[z_{\tau'}(t_{i+1}) - z_{\tau'}(t_i)] - - \frac{1}{2} a_{\rho'}(i) b^{-1}_{\rho'\tau'}(i) a_{\tau'}(i)(t_{i+1} - t_i)\Big]\Big\}. \tag{4.32}$$

If the conditions for the existence of the stochastic integral are satisfied, the sum in (4.32) has an integral as its limit as $\Delta \to 0$. This convergence, as well as the above-mentioned convergence of f^{Δ}, $\tilde{f}$, and $\tilde{f}^{\nu}$ to 1, proves the absolute continuity of the measures on $\mathcal{N}_{s}^{Su}$ and Eq. (4.27).

4.4 The Derivative in Function Space with Partial Averaging of a Diffusion Space

Let us separate the components $z_1, \ldots, z_n$ of the diffusion process examined earlier into two groups, writing

$$z_\alpha = x_\alpha; \quad \alpha = 1, \ldots, m; \quad z_\rho = y_\rho, \quad \rho = m+1, \ldots, m+l = n.$$

The indices $\alpha, \beta, \ldots$ here and in the following run through values $1, \ldots, m$, and the indices $\rho, \sigma, \ldots$ through values $m+1, \ldots, m+l$. Let

$$l' = \text{Rank}\,\|b_{\rho\sigma}\|.$$

As in Sect. 4.1, we will use primed indices, having agreed that $\rho', \sigma', \ldots$ run through values $m+1, \ldots, m+l'$, and $\rho'', \sigma'', \ldots$ through values $m+l'+1, \ldots, m+l$. It is assumed that $\det\|b_{\rho'\sigma'}\| \neq 0$. This notation, which we will also follow in Chapter 7, makes it unnecessary to indicate each time the range of values run through.

The components $\{y_\rho\}$ taken together form a point in an l-dimensional Borel space $(R_l, \mathscr{B}_l)$. Conditions of the type $\{y_\rho(t) \in \Lambda\}, \Lambda \in \mathscr{B}_l$ (t fixed) distinguish the σ-algebra in the space R_n^T, which we will designate $\mathscr{A}_t$. In addition to this, we will use the designations $\mathscr{A}_{\widetilde{T}} = \sigma(\bigcup_{t\in\widetilde{T}} \mathscr{A}_t)$, $\overline{\mathscr{A}}_{\widetilde{T}}$. They have a meaning analogous to the meaning of the designations $\mathscr{N}_{\widetilde{T}}$, $\overline{\mathscr{N}}_{\widetilde{T}}$ explained in Sect. 4.2.

The Markov measure $\mu_{z(s)}$ on $\overline{\mathscr{N}}_s^t$ determines the measure $\mu_{z(s)}$ on $\overline{\mathscr{A}}_s^t \subset \overline{\mathscr{N}}_s^t$, but here it is essential that on $\mathscr{A}_s^t$ (i.e., for a phase space R_l) the measure should not already possess Markov characteristics. Theorem 4.1 in this case would not be applicable; however, in a certain sense, it permits a generalization to this case also.

If we take two measures μ and ν absolutely continuous on $\mathscr{F}$ and their Radon-Nikodim derivative f on $\mathscr{F}$ and examine the integral

$$\mu(\Lambda) = \int_\Lambda f\,d\nu$$

for a set $\Lambda \in \mathscr{A} \subset \mathscr{F}$, then obviously we get the result that the indicated measures are also absolutely continuous on $\mathscr{A}$. The Radon-Nikodim derivative on $\mathscr{A}$ in this situation is obtained by averaging the original derivative

$$\bar{f} = \mathbf{M}_\nu[f \mid \mathscr{A}], \tag{4.33}$$

where to the designation $\mathbf{M}_\nu[\,\cdot \mid A]$ corresponds (A.1.4), (A.1.2):

$$\mathbf{M}_\nu [f \mid \mathcal{A}] = [\nu (d\omega)]^{-1} \int_{d\omega} f \, d\nu, \; d\omega \in \mathcal{A}.$$

Of course, into the formula (4.33) it is possible to insert, let us say, (4.27) and obtain a functional derivation on $\overline{\mathcal{A}}_s^t$. Nevertheless, such a result is still not very productive. In order to obtain more useful results, we will use a different approach.

Theorem 4.2. Let us assume that the measure $\mu_{z(s)}$ on $\overline{\mathcal{N}}_s^u$ corresponds to a diffusion process in an n-dimensional space $(R_n, \mathcal{B}_n)$ having an infinitesimal operator

$$dL = \left(c + \sum_{j=1}^{n} a_j \frac{\partial}{\partial z_j} + \frac{1}{2} \sum_{j,k=1}^{n} b_{jk} \frac{\partial^2}{\partial z_j \, \partial z_k} \right) dt,$$

where $b_{\rho\sigma}$ and $a_{\rho''} - b_{\rho''\sigma'} b_{\sigma'\pi'}^{-1} a_{\pi'}$ do not depend on x_α ($\mathcal{B}_l$-measurable). Then the measure $\mu_{z(s)}$ on $\overline{\mathcal{A}}_s^u$ is absolutely continuous with respect to the measure $\nu_{y(s)}$ $(= \nu_{z(s)})$ corresponding to a diffusion process in an l-dimensional space $(R_l, \mathcal{B}_l)$ with the infinitesimal operator

$$dL^\nu = \left[(a_{\rho''} - b_{\rho''\sigma'} b_{\sigma'\pi'}^{-1} a_{\pi'}) \frac{\partial}{\partial y_{\rho''}} + \frac{1}{2} b_{\rho\sigma} \frac{\partial^2}{\partial y_\rho \partial y_\sigma} \right] dt.$$

The Radon-Nikodim derivative on $\overline{\mathcal{A}}_s^u$ has the form

$$\begin{aligned} \vartheta_s^u (x(s), y(\cdot)) \equiv \frac{\mu_{z(s)} (dy(\cdot))}{\nu_{y(s)} (dy(\cdot))} = \exp \left\{ \int_s^u \left[\mathbf{M}_\mu (c \mid \overline{\mathcal{A}}_s^t) \, dt + \right. \right. \\ + \mathbf{M}_\mu (a_{\rho'} \mid \overline{\mathcal{A}}_s^t) \, b_{\rho'\sigma'}^{-1} \, d^* y_{\sigma'} (t) - \\ \left. \left. - \frac{1}{2} \mathbf{M}_\mu (a_{\rho'} \mid \overline{\mathcal{A}}_s^t) \, b_{\rho'\sigma'}^{-1} \, \mathbf{M}_\mu (a_{\sigma'} \mid \overline{\mathcal{A}}_s^t) \, dt \right] \right\}. \end{aligned} \tag{4.34}$$

It is assumed that the conditions for the existence of these stochastic integrals are satisfied.

Proof. Choosing a Δ-division S_Δ of the interval $[s, u]$ and writing for $\mu_{z(s)}$ formulas analogous to (4.29) and (4.28), we have

$$\begin{aligned} \mu_{z(s)} (dz_1 \ldots dz_N) = f^\Delta \tilde{f} e^{c(z(s),s)(t_1 - s)} \times \\ \times \tilde{\mu}_{z(s)} (dz_1) \ldots e^{c(N-1)(t_N - t_{N-1})} \tilde{\mu}_{z_{N-1}} (dz_N), \end{aligned} \tag{4.35}$$

where $\tilde{\mu}_{z_i} (dz_{i+1})$ is a Gaussian measure with means $z_j (t_i) + a_j (z(t_i), t_i)$ $(t_{i+1} - t_i)$ and a variance matrix

$$b_{jk} (z(t_i), t_i) (t_{i+1} - t_i).$$

As a result of the Markov characteristics of the process the functions f^{Δ} and $\widetilde{f}$ entering into (4.35) separate into factors:

$$f^{\Delta} = \prod_i f_i^{\Delta}(z_i, z_{i+1}); \quad \widetilde{f} = \prod_i \widetilde{f}_i(z_i, z_{i+1}). \tag{4.36}$$

Since, as was pointed out earlier, $f^{\Delta} \to 1$ and $\widetilde{f} \to 1$ almost certainly as $\Delta \to 0$, then

$$f_i^{\Delta}(z_i, z_{i+1}) = e^{o(\Delta)}; \quad \widetilde{f}_i(z_i, z_{i+1}) = e^{o(\Delta)}. \tag{4.37}$$

Let us turn to an examination of the measure $\mu_{z(s)}(dy_1 \ldots dy_N)$ on the σ-algebra $\mathcal{A}_{S_{\Delta}}$, i.e., integrate (4.35) over $\Lambda \in \mathcal{A}_{S_{\Delta}}$.

From the definition of conditional measures (Appendix 1) follows the identity

$$\mu_{z(s)}(dy_1 \ldots dy_N) = \mu_{z(s)}(dy_1)\,\mu_{z(s)}(dy_2 \mid y_1) \ldots$$
$$\ldots \mu_{z(s)}(dy_N \mid y_1, \ldots, y_{N-1}) \tag{4.38}$$

(true almost certainly). In this, if we use the formula

$$\mu_{z(s)}(dy_{i+1} \mid y_1, \ldots, y_i) = \int \mu_{z(s)}(dy_{i+1} \mid y_1, \ldots, y_i, x_i) \times$$
$$\times\, \mu_{z(s)}(dx_i \mid y_1, \ldots, y_i)$$

and take into account the Markov property $\mu_{z(s)}(dy_{i+1} \mid y_1, \ldots y_i, x_i)$ $\mu_{x_i y_i}(dy_{i+1})$, we will get

$$\mu_{z(s)}(dy_{i+1} \mid y_1, \ldots, y_i) = \int \mu_{x_i y_i}(dy_{i+1})\,\mu_{z(s)}(dx_i \mid y_1, \ldots, y_i) \equiv$$
$$\equiv \mathbf{M}_{\mu_{z(s)}}[\mu_{x_i y_i}(dy_{i+1}) \mid y_1, \ldots, y_i] \tag{4.39}$$

[see (A.1.4)].

We take into account that, according to (4.35), (4.36), and (4.37),

$$\mu_{x_i y_i}(dy_{i+1}) = \int_{R_m} \exp\,[c(z_i, t_i)(t_{i+1} - t_i) + o(\Delta)]\,\widetilde{\mu}_{z_i}(dx_{i+1}\,dy_{i+1}), \tag{4.40}$$

and use the equation

$$\int_{R_m} e^{o(\Delta)}\,\widetilde{\mu}_{z_i}(dx_{i+1}\,dy_{i+1}) = e^{o(\Delta)} \int_{R_m} \widetilde{\mu}_{z_i}(dx_{i+1}\,dy_{i+1}) =$$
$$= e^{o(\Delta)}\,\widetilde{\mu}_{z_i}(dy_{i+1}). \tag{4.41}$$

The integration in (4.40) and (4.41) is carried out over the m-dimensional space of values x_{i+1}. As noted, $\widetilde{\mu}_{z_i}(dz_{i+1})$ is a Gaussian measure with means

$$z_j(t_i) + a_j(z_i, t_i)(t_{i+1} - t_i)$$

and variance matrix $b_{jk}(z_i, t_i)(t_{i+1} - t_i)$. Thus $\tilde{\mu}_{z_i}(dy_{i+1})$ is a Gaussian measure with means

$$y_\rho(t_i) + a_\rho(z_i, t_i)(t_{i+1} - t_i)$$

and variance matrix $b_{\rho\sigma}(z_i, t_i)(t_{i+1} - t_i)$. The form of this measure is determined by Lemma 4.3. Applying the lemma, we can easily find that the measure $\tilde{\mu}_{z_i}(dy_{i+1})$ is absolutely continuous with respect to the Gaussian measure $\tilde{\nu}_{z_i}(dy_{i+1})$, having means

$$y_\rho(t_i) + a^\nu_\rho(y_i, t_i)(t_{i+1} - t_i)$$

$$(a^\nu_{\rho'} = 0; \quad a^\nu_{\rho''} = a_{\rho''} - b_{\rho''\sigma'} b^{-1}_{\sigma'\pi'} a_{\pi'})$$

and the same variance. In this manner

$$\tilde{\mu}_{z_i}(dy_{i+1}) = \tilde{\nu}_{z_i}(dy_{i+1}) \exp\{a_{\rho'}(z_i, t_i) b^{-1}_{\rho'\sigma'}(z_i, t_i) \times$$

$$\times [y_{\sigma'}(t_{i+1}) - y_{\sigma'}(t_i)] - \frac{1}{2} a_{\rho'}(z_i, t_i) b^{-1}_{\rho'\sigma'}(z_i, t_i) \times \tag{4.42}$$

$$\times a_{\sigma'}(z_i, t_i)(t_{i+1} - t_i)\}.$$

We will now make use of the fact that, according to the conditions of Theorem 4.2, the functions $b_{\rho\sigma}(z, t) (= b_{\rho\sigma}(y, t))$, $a^\nu_\rho(z, t)$ $(= a^\nu_\rho(y, t))$ do not depend on x ($\mathscr{B}_t$-measurable). This allows us in the calculation of a conditional mathematical expression $\mathbf{M}_{\mu_{z(s)}}[\cdot \mid y_1, \ldots, y_i]$ using (4.42), to take out $\tilde{\nu}_{z_i}(dy_{j+1}) = \tilde{\nu}_{y_i}(dy_{i+1})$ from the mathematical expectation sign and, substituting (4.42) into (4.41) and (4.40), to obtain

$$\mathbf{M}_{\mu_{z(s)}}[\mu_{z_i}(dy_{i+1}) \mid y_1, \ldots, y_i] =$$

$$= \tilde{\nu}_{y_i}(dy_{i+1}) \mathbf{M}_{\mu_{z(s)}}[e^{H_i + o(\Delta)} \mid y_1, \ldots, y_i], \tag{4.43}$$

where we define

$$H_i = c(z_i, t_i)(t_{i+1} - t_i) + a_{\rho'}(z_i, t_i) b^{-1}_{\rho'\sigma'}(z_i t_i) \times$$

$$\times \left[y_{\sigma'}(t_{i+1}) - y_{\sigma'}(t_i) - \frac{1}{2} a_{\sigma'}(z_i, t_i)(t_{i+1} - t_i)\right]. \tag{4.44}$$

Now substituting (4.43) into (4.39) and (4.38), we find

$$\mu_{z(s)}(dy_1 \ldots dy_N) = \tilde{\nu}_{y(s)}(dy_1) \ldots \tilde{\nu}_{y_{N-1}}(dy_N) \mathbf{M}_{\mu_{z(s)}}[e^{H_0 + o(\Delta)}].$$

$$\mathbf{M}_{\mu_{z(s)}}[e^{H_1 + o(\Delta)} \mid y_1] \ldots \mathbf{M}_{\mu_{z(s)}}[e^{H_{N-1} + o(\Delta)} \mid y_1, \ldots, y_{N-1}]. \tag{4.45}$$

Comparison of this equation with the equation

$$\nu_{y(s)}(dy_1 \ldots dy_N) = \tilde{f}^{\nu} \tilde{\nu}_{y(s)}(dy_1) \ldots \tilde{\nu}_{y_{N-1}}(dy_N), \tag{4.46}$$

analogous to (4.30), brings us to the conclusion that the measures (4.45) and (4.46) are absolutely continuous, while the Radon-Nikodim derivative has the form

$$\frac{1}{\tilde{f}^{\nu}} \mathbf{M}_{\mu_{z(s)}} [e^{H_0 + o(\Delta)}] \mathbf{M}_{\mu_{z(s)}} [e^{H_1 + o(\Delta)} | y_1] \ldots$$
$$\ldots \mathbf{M}_{\mu_{z(s)}} [e^{H_{N-1} + o(\Delta)} | y_1, \ldots, y_{N-1}]. \tag{4.47}$$

Carrying out the passage to the limit $\Delta \to 0$, we prove the absolute continuity of these measures on $\mathcal{A}_s^u$ and the formula for the Radon-Nikodim derivative

$$\vartheta_s^u(x(s), y(\cdot)) = \lim_{\Delta \to 0} \mathbf{M}_{\mu_{z(s)}} [e^{H_0 + o(\Delta)}] \mathbf{M}_{\mu_{z(s)}} [e^{H_1 + o(\Delta)} | y_1] \ldots$$
$$\ldots \mathbf{M}_{\mu_{z(s)}} [e^{H_{N-1} + o(\Delta)} | y_1, \ldots, y_{N-1}] \tag{4.48}$$

under the condition that this limit exists almost everywhere.

In order to complete the proof of the theorem it remains to show that the indicated limit coincides with the expression on the right side of (4.34).

Let us examine a typical factor in (4.47), taking into account (4.44). From (4.44) it is easy to see that $H_i = O(\Delta^{1/2})$. Expanding the exponential and then the logarithm into a series, we obtain

$$\tilde{\mathbf{M}} e^{H_i + o(\Delta)} = 1 + \tilde{\mathbf{M}} \left[H_i + \frac{1}{2} H_i^2 + o(\Delta) \right] =$$
$$= \exp \left\{ \tilde{\mathbf{M}} \left[H_i + \frac{1}{2} H_i^2 \right] - \frac{1}{2} [\tilde{\mathbf{M}} H_i]^2 + o(\Delta) \right\}$$
$$(\tilde{\mathbf{M}} = \mathbf{M}_{\mu_{z(s)}} [\cdot | y_1, \ldots, y_i]). \tag{4.49}$$

Thus expression (4.47) is changed to the form

$$\exp \left\{ \sum_i \left[\mathbf{M}_{\mu} \left(H_i + \frac{1}{2} H_i^2 | y_1, \ldots, y_i \right) - \right.\right.$$
$$\left.\left. - \frac{1}{2} [\mathbf{M}_{\mu} (H_i | y_1, \ldots, y_i)]^2 + o(\Delta) \right] \right\}. \tag{4.50}$$

Taking into account (4.44), we get in the exponent a sum which, on the basis of Lemma 2.3, tends to the integral in the exponent of (4.34), if the conditions for its existence are satisfied. In this we take into account that a σ-algegra $\subset \mathcal{A}_{S_\Delta}$ contained in the conditional mathematical expectation in (4.50) tends in the limit to $\mathcal{A}_{S_s^t}$ (where $S_s^t = [s, t] \cap S$ is the set of separability, $s < t \leqslant u$). The Radon-Nikodim derivative turned out to be defined on $\mathcal{A}_{S_s^u}$. As a result of the separability of the process, the indicated σ-algebras can be changed to $\mathcal{A}_s^t$ and even to $\mathcal{A}_{s_0}^t$. The proof is completed.

In conclusion we will note that the functional derivatives (4.34) and (4.48) satisfy almost certainly the equation

$$d_t \vartheta_s^t = \vartheta_s^t \cdot \{\mathbf{M}_\mu [c(y(t), t) \mid \overline{\mathcal{A}}_s^t]\, dt + \mathbf{M}_\mu [a_{\rho'}(y(t), t) \mid \overline{\mathcal{A}}_s^t]\, b_{\rho'\sigma'}^{-1}(y(t), t)\, d^* y_{\sigma'}(t)\}. \tag{4.51}$$

In order to be convinced of this, it is necessary to take into account Corollary 2.1.

Since $\vartheta_s^s = 1$ [on the strength of (4.34)], the latter equation can be written in integral form

$$\vartheta_s^t = 1 + \int_s^t \vartheta_s^\tau \{\mathbf{M}_\mu [c(y(\tau), \tau) \mid \overline{\mathcal{A}}_s^\tau]\, dt + \mathbf{M}_\mu [a_{\rho'}(y(\tau), \tau) \mid \overline{\mathcal{A}}_s^\tau]\, b_{\rho'\sigma'}^{-1}(y(\tau), \tau)\, d^* y_{\sigma'}(\tau), \tag{4.52}$$

which will be used in Sect. 7.1.

PART 2

The Main Results of the Theory of Conditional Markov Processes

CHAPTER 5

Some General Results for Processes in an Arbitrary Phase Space

5.1. Presentation of the Question and the Primary Theorems

The results compiled in this chapter do not require that a phase space and the transition probabilities of the Markov process be specified. For the theory presented it seems unnecessary to have any kind of metric or even any topological concepts. The domain T of the parameter t should be an ordered set. For definiteness we will assume that this is a line segment or a subset of it. We will stop at the first case: $T=[a, b]$.

It is important that the phase space corresponding to the parameter $t \in T$ should be a measurable space $(E_t, \mathscr{E}_t)$. We will assume (although this does not appear to be necessary for the theory) that to all instants of time (values of the parameter) there corresponds one and the same phase space $(E, \mathscr{E})$.

Let there be given a probability space $(\Omega, \mathscr{B}, \mathbf{P})$ and a $\mathscr{B}$-measurable process $\{z_t(\omega), t \in T\}$ with values from $(E, \mathscr{E})$. We introduce the σ-algebras

$$\mathscr{Z}_t = \sigma(\{\omega : z_t(\omega) \in \Lambda\}, \Lambda \in \mathscr{E}) = z_t^{-1}(\mathscr{E}),$$

belonging to $\mathscr{B}$, and also an expanding family of σ-algebras $\mathscr{N}_a^t \subset \mathscr{B}$. Each σ-algebra $\mathscr{N}_a^t = \sigma(\bigcup_{\tau \in [a, t]} \mathscr{Z}_\tau)$ is the union of the events involved in the behavior of the process $\{z_t(\omega)\}$ on the interval $[a, t]$. More general σ-algebras $\mathscr{Z}_{\widetilde{T}} \equiv \mathscr{M}_{\widetilde{T}}, \widetilde{T} \subset T$ can be defined as in Sect. 4.2. Namely, $\mathscr{Z}_{\widetilde{T}}$ is the minimal σ-algebra containing all sets of the form

$$\{\omega : z_t(\omega) \in \Lambda, t \in \widetilde{\widetilde{T}}\}, \quad \widetilde{\widetilde{T}} \subset \widetilde{T}, \quad \Lambda \in \mathscr{E}.$$

Subsequently, we will examine various conditional probabilities corresponding to the cited σ-algebras, and also to the σ-algebras introduced below. It is convenient to assume once and for all that the probability space $(\Omega, \mathcal{B}, \mathbf{P})$ is *regular* in the sense that for any σ-algebra $\mathcal{Y} \subset \mathcal{B}$ the conditional probability $\mathbf{P}(\cdot \mid \mathcal{Y})$ is *regular* in the sense of Loève ([1], p. 371). This means that to within an equivalence class it is possible to choose a function $\mathbf{P}(\Lambda \mid \mathcal{Y})$ defined on $\mathcal{B} \times \Omega$ ($\mathcal{Y}$-measurable for fixed $\Lambda \in \mathcal{B}$), such that for each $\omega \in \Omega$ it is a probability measure on $\mathcal{B}$.

The fundamental conditions of the theory are the Markov conditions, which have as their essence the fact that for a fixed present the future of the process does not depend upon its past. These conditions, as we know, can be given several equivalent formulations. One of them is:

$$\mathbf{P}(\Gamma_b \mid \mathcal{F}_{pr} \mathcal{Z}_t \mathcal{F}_b) = \mathbf{P}(\Gamma_b \mid \mathcal{Z}_t \mathcal{F}_b) \quad \text{(almost certainly)} \tag{5.1}$$

where $\Gamma_b \in \mathcal{Z}_t^b$, $\mathcal{F}_b \subset \mathcal{Z}_t^b$, $\mathcal{F}_{pr} \subset \mathcal{Z}_a^t$.

The term "almost certainly" (a.c.) is necessary because the conditional possibilities themselves are only defined almost everywhere. We will not cite here the various formulations of the Markov conditions and prove their equivalence. Subsequently, in refering to this condition we will use whichever of its formulations will be the most convenient in the specific case considered.

Conditional Markov processes arise in the case when there is a certain observable process $\{y_t(\omega) = f_t(z)\}$ dependent on a reference process. We will assume (although generalizations are possible) that $t \in T$ and that for every t the function $f_t = f_t(e)$ is a known function of $e \in E$, taking a value in $(Y, \mathcal{Y}')$, and $\mathcal{E}$-measurable:

$$f_t^{-1}(\mathcal{Y}') \subset \mathcal{E}.$$

Then the σ-algebra of the process $\{y_t(\omega) = f_t(z_t(\omega))\}$ will be included in the corresponding σ-algebras of the process $\{z_t(\omega)\}$.

We will designate by $\mathcal{Y}_t$ (analog of $\mathcal{Z}_t$) the minimal σ-algebra containing the sets

$$\{\omega : y_t(\omega) \in \Lambda\}, \quad \Lambda \in \mathcal{Y}',$$

and by $\mathcal{Y}_s^t$ (analog of $\mathcal{Z}_s^t$) the σ-algebra constructed on the sets

$$\{\omega : y_t(\omega) \in \Lambda,\ t \in \tilde{\tilde{T}}\},\ \Lambda \in \mathcal{Y}',\ \tilde{\tilde{T}} \subset [s, t].$$

Then, obviously,

$$\mathcal{Y}_t \subset \mathcal{Z}_t, \quad \mathcal{Y}_s^t \subset \mathcal{Z}_s^t.$$

Definition 5.1. Let there be given

(A) a Markov process $(\Omega, \mathscr{Z}_t, t \in T, \mathbf{P})$;

(B) an observable process $(\Omega, \mathscr{Y}_t, t \in T, \mathbf{P})$ such that

$$\mathscr{Y}_t \subset \mathscr{Z}_t;$$

then the family

$$(\Omega, \mathscr{Z}_t, t \in T, \mathbf{P}(\cdot \mid \mathscr{Y}_a^u), u \in T)$$

of random variables and conditional probabilities forms a conditional Markov process (primary).

As we can see from Theorem 5.1 below, the process $(\Omega, \mathscr{Z}_t, t \in T, \mathbf{P}(\cdot \mid \mathscr{Y}_a^u))$ for fixed $u \in T$ is Markov. However, if we vary u $(\in T)$, the corresponding two-parameter family of random variables will be considerably more complex.

In the future, as in (5.1), for σ-algebras we will use the notation $\mathscr{A}\mathscr{B}$ instead of $\sigma(\mathscr{A}, \mathscr{B})$. The equations which result from the definition of conditional probabilities and conditional mathematical expectations we will usually use without any comment. From the definition these equations are true almost everywhere; however, for the sake of brevity, we will not always discuss this.

To obtain a less crowded notation for conditional probabilities and conditional mathematical expectations, we will sometimes write y_s^t in the condition instead of $\mathscr{Y}_s^t$, and, accordingly, let us say, z_u, y_s^t instead of $\sigma(\mathscr{Z}_u, \mathscr{Y}_s^t)$.

Let us first examine one preliminary theorem.

Theorem 5.1. Let us assume a Markov process and a σ-algebra $\widetilde{\mathscr{Y}} (\subset \mathscr{Z}_a^b)$, which for any $t \in T$ can be written in the form

$$\widetilde{\mathscr{Y}} = \widetilde{\mathscr{Y}}_{pr} \widetilde{\mathscr{Y}}_b,$$

where

$$\widetilde{\mathscr{Y}}_{pr} = \widetilde{\mathscr{Y}} \cap \mathscr{Z}_a^t, \quad \widetilde{\mathscr{Y}}_b = \widetilde{\mathscr{Y}} \cap \mathscr{Z}_t^b.$$

Then the conditional process described by the measure $\mathbf{P}(\cdot \mid \widetilde{\mathscr{Y}})$ is almost certainly Markov, i.e.,

$$\mathbf{P}(\Gamma_b \mid \mathscr{F}_{pr} \mathscr{Z}_t \widetilde{\mathscr{Y}}) = \mathbf{P}(\Gamma_b \mid \mathscr{Z}_t \widetilde{\mathscr{Y}}) \quad (\Gamma_b \in \mathscr{Z}_t^b, \ \mathscr{F}_{pr} \subset \mathscr{Z}_a^t). \quad \text{a.c.} \tag{5.2}$$

Proof. As a result of the Markov condition we have

$$\mathbf{P}(\Gamma_b \Lambda_{pr} \Lambda_b \mid \mathscr{F}_{pr} \mathscr{Z}_t) = \mathbf{P}(\Lambda_{pr} \mid \mathscr{F}_{pr} \mathscr{Z}_t) \mathbf{P}(\Gamma_b \Lambda_b \mid \mathscr{Z}_t) =$$
$$= \mathbf{P}(\Lambda_{pr} \mid \mathscr{F}_{pr} \mathscr{Z}_t \widetilde{\mathscr{Y}}_b) \mathbf{P}(\Gamma_b \Lambda_b \mid \widetilde{\mathscr{Y}}_{pr} \mathscr{Z}_t),$$

where $\Lambda_{pr} \in \widetilde{\mathscr{Y}}_{pr}$; $\Lambda_b \in \widetilde{\mathscr{Y}}_b$.

Having taken the Radon-Nikodim derivative of this measure with respect to the measure

$$\mathbf{P}(\Lambda_b|\mathcal{F}_{pr}\mathcal{Z}_t) = \mathbf{P}(\Lambda_b|\mathcal{Z}_t) = \mathbf{P}(\Lambda_b|\widetilde{\mathcal{Y}}_{pr}\mathcal{Z}_t)$$

(here again the Markov property is used), we find

$$\mathbf{P}(\Gamma_b\Lambda_{pr}|\mathcal{F}_{pr}\mathcal{Z}_t\widetilde{\mathcal{Y}}_b) = \mathbf{P}(\Lambda_{pr}|\mathcal{F}_{pr}\mathcal{Z}_t\widetilde{\mathcal{Y}}_b)\mathbf{P}(\Gamma_b|\mathcal{Z}_t\widetilde{\mathcal{Y}}).$$

If we now examine the derivative of the latter measure with respect to the measure $\mathbf{P}(\Lambda_{pr}|\mathcal{F}_{pr}\mathcal{Z}_t\widetilde{\mathcal{Y}}_b)$, we obtain Eq. (5.2). The proof is completed.

In the future, the main object of study will be the conditional probabilities of the form $\mathbf{P}(\Gamma_u|\mathcal{Z}_s\mathcal{Y}_s^t)$, where $\Gamma_u \in \mathcal{Z}_u$. From the Markov condition it follows immediately that almost certainly

$$\mathbf{P}(\Gamma_u|\mathcal{Z}_s\mathcal{Y}_r^t) = \mathbf{P}(\Gamma_u|\mathcal{Z}_s\mathcal{Y}_s^t) \text{ for } r < s < t, \ s < u. \tag{5.3}$$

Hence it is sufficient to consider only the probabilities on the right side. We introduce for them the special notation

$$\mathbf{P}(\Gamma_u|z_s, y_s^t) = W_s^{ut}(z_s, \Gamma_u), \quad s < t; \quad s < u \tag{5.4}$$

and establish an equation which they satisfy.

Theorem 5.2. The equation

$$W_s^{vu}(z_s, \Gamma_v) = \int W_s^{tu}(z_s, dz_t) W_t^{vu}(z_t, \Gamma_v), \tag{5.5}$$
$$s \leqslant t \leqslant v; \quad s < u; \quad t < u$$

is almost certainly satisfied.

For proof we consider the obvious equation

$$\mathbf{P}(\Gamma_v|z_s, y_s^u) = \int \mathbf{P}(\Gamma_v|z_s, z_t, y_s^u)\mathbf{P}(dz_t|z_s, y_s^u). \tag{5.6}$$

But on the strength of the Markov condition

$$\mathbf{P}(\Gamma_v|z_s, z_t, y_s^u) = \mathbf{P}(\Gamma_v|z_t, y_t^u) \text{ for } s < t < v; \ t < u,$$

thus from (5.6) follows (5.5).

5.2 Some Theorems for Processes Having Continuity of Information

In order to obtain more extensive results we will confine ourselves to the examination of conditional processes of a more limited class, namely, to processes characterized by continuity of information.*

Definition 5.2. We will say a conditional Markov process has continuity of information if the conditional measures $\mathbf{P}(\Gamma_s | y_r^s)$, $\mathbf{P}(\Gamma_s | y_r^u)$ a.c. are absolutely continuous with respect to each other for any given (if necessary, sufficiently close to each other) values $r<s\leqslant u$.

This definition asserts the continuous dependence of probabilities on the length of the information interval. Such a continuity is valid in most cases of practical interest and can be verified in specific examples.

For processes with continuity of information it is possible to introduce into the discussion the corresponding Radon-Nikodim derivative, for which we will introduce the notation

$$h_{rs}^u(z_s) = \frac{\mathbf{P}(dz_s | y_r^u)}{\mathbf{P}(dz_s | y_r^s)}, \quad r < s \leqslant u. \tag{5.7}$$

By definition it is a $\mathcal{Z}_s \, \mathcal{Y}_r^u$-measurable function.

Theorem 5.3. The measures $W_s^{tu}(z_s, \Gamma_t)$ $W_s^{tt}(t_s, \Gamma_t)$, $s<t\leqslant u$ in the case of continuity of information are absolutely continuous, while the corresponding Radon-Nikodim derivative (designated f_s^{tu}) is

$$f_s^{tu}(z_s, z_t) \equiv \frac{W_s^{tu}(z_s, dz_t)}{W_s^{tt}(z_s, dz_t)} = \frac{h_{rt}^u(z_t)\, h_{rs}^t(z_s)}{h_{rs}^u(z_s)}. \tag{5.8}$$

Proof. Taking into account (5.7), we have

$$\frac{h_{rs}^t(z_s)}{h_{rs}^u(z_s)} = \frac{\mathbf{P}(dz_s | y_r^t)}{\mathbf{P}(dz_s | y_r^u)}, \; r < s \leqslant t, \; s \leqslant u. \tag{5.9}$$

Let us examine the expression

$$B = \frac{h_{rs}^t(z_s)}{h_{rs}^u(z_s)} \mathbf{P}(\Gamma_t | z_s, y_r^t). \tag{5.10}$$

Substituting (5.9) into the right side, we find

$$B = \frac{\mathbf{P}(\Gamma_t dz_s | y_r^t)}{\mathbf{P}(dz_s | y_r^u)} = \int_{\Gamma_t} \frac{\mathbf{P}(dz_s | z_t, y_r^t)}{\mathbf{P}(dz_s | y_r^u)} \mathbf{P}(dz_t | y_r^t).$$

But on the strength of the Markov condition (in reverse time)

$$\mathbf{P}(dz_s | z_t, y_r^t) = \mathbf{P}(dz_s | z_t, y_r^u).$$

*The term "information" is not taken here in the sense of Shannon.

Thus,

$$B = \int_{\Gamma_t} \frac{\mathbf{P}(dz_s \mid z_t, y_r^u)}{\mathbf{P}(dz_s \mid y_r^u)} \mathbf{P}(dz_t \mid y_r^u) \frac{\mathbf{P}(dz_t \mid y_r^t)}{\mathbf{P}(dz_t \mid y_r^u)}$$

or, if we take into consideration (5.7),

$$B = \int_{\Gamma_t} \frac{\mathbf{P}(dz_s dz_t \mid y_r^u)}{\mathbf{P}(dz_s \mid y_r^u)} \frac{1}{h_{rt}^u(z_t)} = \int_{\Gamma_t} \frac{\mathbf{P}(dz_t \mid z_s, y_r^u)}{h_{rt}^u(z_t)}.$$

Comparing the expression on the right side of this equation with (5.10), we are convinced of the absolute continuity of the measures $\mathbf{P}(\Gamma_t \mid z_s, y_r^t)$ and $\mathbf{P}(\Gamma_t \mid z_s, y_r^u)$, i.e., on the strength of (5.3) and (5.4) of the measures examined in the theorem. This comparison also gives us the expression (5.8) for the corresponding Radon-Nikodim derivative. The proof is completed.

In the future we will use the shortened notation

$$W_s^{tt}(z_s, \Gamma_t) = W_s^t(z_s, \Gamma_t).$$

Theorem 5.4. For processes with continuity of information the equation

$$W_s^u(z_s, \Gamma_u) = \int W_s^t(z_s, dz_t)\, W_t^u(z_t, \Gamma_u)\, f_s^{tu}(z_s, z_t), \qquad (5.11)$$

$$s \leqslant t \leqslant u$$

is almost certainly true.

This result follows immediately from (5.5) if we assume $u=v$ and used Theorem 5.3.

Assuming in (5.5) $u \neq v$, again using Theorem 5.3 and comparing the result with (5.11), we are convinced of the truth of the identity

$$f_s^{tv}(z_s, z_t) = \frac{f_s^{tu}(z_s, z_t)\, f_t^{vu}(z_t, z_v)}{f_s^{vu}(z_s, z_v)},$$

which, by the way, can also be obtained from (5.8) and (5.7). It is convenient to introduce a new (nonprobabilistic) measure

$$V_{rs}^t(z_s, \Gamma_t) = h_{rs}^t(z_s)\, W_s^t(z_s, \Gamma_t) \qquad (5.12)$$

$$(r < s \leqslant t),$$

which is defined by this equation almost everywhere.

Then after substitution of (5.8) into (5.11), we will have the following result:

Theorem 5.5. For processes with continuity of information the equation

$$V_{rs}^{u}(z_s, \Gamma_u) = \int V_{rs}^{t}(z_s, dz_t)\, V_{rt}^{u}(z_t, \Gamma_u), \quad r < s \leqslant t \leqslant u \tag{5.13}$$

is almost certainly satisfied.

In view of the fact that the measure $W_s^t(z_s, \Gamma_t)$ is probabilistic ($W_s^t(z_s, \Omega) = 1$), from (5.12) we have

$$V_{ri}^{t}(z_s, \Omega) = h_{rs}^{t}(z_s). \tag{5.14}$$

Assuming $\Gamma_u = \Omega$ in (5.13), we obtain, consequently,

$$h_{rs}^{u}(z_s) = \int V_{rs}^{t}(z_s, dz_t)\, h_{rt}^{u}(z_t).$$

If the measure V_{rs}^{t} is known, then with respect to it, it is possible to find a function h_{rs}^{t} in accordance with (5.14), as well as the probability measures

$$W_s^t(z_s, \Gamma_t) = \frac{V_{rs}^{t}(z_s, \Gamma_t)}{V_{rs}^{t}(z_s, \Omega)}; \tag{5.15}$$

$$W_s^{tu}(z_s, \Gamma_t) = \frac{1}{V_{rs}^{u}(z_s, \Omega)} \int_{\Gamma_t} V_{rs}^{t}(z_s, dz_t)\, V_{rt}^{u}(z_t, \Omega). \tag{5.16}$$

In calculating the latter formulas we used (5.12), (5.14), and Theorem 5.3.

Of use to us will be

Lemma 5.1. For Markov processes the absolute dicontinuity of the measures

$$\mathbf{P}(\Gamma_s \mid y_r^t) \sim \mathbf{P}(\Gamma_s \mid y_r^s), \quad \Gamma_s \in \mathscr{Z}_s \tag{5.17}$$

implies the absolute continuity of the measures

$$\mathbf{P}(\Lambda_s^t \mid z_s) \sim \mathbf{P}(\Lambda_s^t \mid y_r^s), \quad \Lambda_s^t \in \mathscr{Y}_s^t \tag{5.18}$$

and conversely, while the Radon-Nikodim derivatives coincide.

Proof. Using (5.17) and substituting (5.7) into the equation

$$\mathbf{P}(\Gamma_s \Lambda_s^t \mid y_r^s) = \int_{\Lambda_s^t} \mathbf{P}(\Gamma_s \mid y_r^t)\, \mathbf{P}(dy_s^t \mid y_r^s),$$

according to Fubini's theorem we obtain

$$\mathbf{P}(\Gamma_s\Lambda_s^t \mid y_r^s) = \int\limits_{\Lambda_s^t}\Big[\int\limits_{\Gamma_s} h_{rs}^t(z_s)\,\mathbf{P}(dz_s \mid y_r^s)\Big]\mathbf{P}(dy_s^t \mid y_r^s) =$$

$$= \int\limits_{\Gamma_s}\Big[\int\limits_{\Lambda_s^t} h_{rs}^t(z_s)\,\mathbf{P}(dy_s^t \mid y_r^s)\Big]\mathbf{P}(dz_s \mid y_r^s). \tag{5.19}$$

At the same time the equation

$$\mathbf{P}(\Gamma_s\Lambda_s^t \mid y_r^s) = \int\limits_{\Gamma_s} \mathbf{P}(\Lambda_s^t \mid z_s,\, y_r^s)\,\mathbf{P}(dz_s \mid y_r^s)$$

is true, and on the strength of the Markov condition can be written

$$\mathbf{P}(\Gamma_s\Lambda_s^t \mid y_r^s) = \int\limits_{\Gamma_s} \mathbf{P}(\Lambda_s^t \mid z_s)\,\mathbf{P}(dz_s \mid y_r^s). \tag{5.20}$$

In the comparison of (5.19) and (5.20) we will fix Λ_s^t, and let Γ_s vary over various sets from $\mathscr{Z}_s$.

As a result of this we will have

$$\mathbf{P}(\Lambda_s^t \mid z_s) = \int\limits_{\Lambda_s^t} h_{rs}^t(z_s)\,\mathbf{P}(dy_s^t \mid y_r^s) \quad \text{a.c.} \tag{5.21}$$

From this follows (5.18) and the equation

$$h_{rs}^t(z_s) = \frac{\mathbf{P}(dy_s^t \mid z_s)}{\mathbf{P}(dy_s^t \mid y_r^s)}. \tag{5.22}$$

For proof of the converse assertion of the theorem it is necessary to examine Eqs. (5.19) and (5.21) in the reverse order. The proof is completed.

Substituting (5.22) into (5.12) we obtain

$$V_{rs}^t(z_s, \Gamma_t) = \frac{\mathbf{P}(dy_s^t \mid z_s)\,\mathbf{P}(\Gamma_t \mid z_s, y_s^t)}{\mathbf{P}(dy_s^t \mid y_r^s)} = \frac{\mathbf{P}(dy_s^t\Gamma_t \mid z_s)}{\mathbf{P}(dy_s^t \mid y_r^s)}. \tag{5.23}$$

Thus $V_{rs}^t(z_s, \Gamma_t)$ can be considered the Radon-Nikodim derivative of the measures $\mathbf{P}(\Lambda_s^t\Gamma_t \mid z_s)$, $\mathbf{P}(\Lambda_s^t \mid y_r^s)$ on the σ-algebra $\mathscr{Y}_s^t$. The continuity of information (Definition 5.2) causes the absolute continuity of these measures.

Theorem 5.6. In the case of processes having continuity of information, the ratio

$$\frac{h_{r's}^t(z_s)}{h_{rs}^t(z_s)} \equiv g_{rr'}^{st}, \quad r < s < t; \quad r' < s \tag{5.24}$$

(here for definiteness $r<r'$) is a $\mathcal{Y}_r^t$-measurable function (i.e., does not depend on z_s).

Proof. From Definition 5.2 and Lemma 5.1 follows the absolute continuity

$$\mathbf{P}(\Lambda_s^t \mid z_s) \sim \mathbf{P}(\Lambda_s^t \mid y_r^s);$$

$$\mathbf{P}(\Lambda_s^t \mid z_s) \sim \mathbf{P}(\Lambda_s^t \mid y_{r'}^s), \quad \Lambda_s^t \in \mathcal{Y}_s^t$$

and, consequently,

$$\mathbf{P}(\Lambda_s^t \mid y_r^s) \sim \mathbf{P}(\Lambda_s^t \mid y_{r'}^s).$$

Having taken the ratio of two expressions of the type (5.22), we obtain (5.24), where it is found that

$$g_{rr'}^{st} = \frac{\mathbf{P}(dy_s^t \mid y_{r'}^s)}{\mathbf{P}(dy_s^t \mid y_r^s)}.$$

The proof is completed.

According to (5.12), as a corollary to Theorem 5.6, we have the formula

$$V_{r's}^t(z_s, \Gamma_t) = g_{rr'}^{st} V_{rs}^t(z_s, \Gamma_t), \quad r<r'<s<t. \tag{5.25}$$

5.3 Introduction of the Basic A *Posteriori* Measure

As can be seen from comparison of (5.11) and (5.13), the measure V_{rs}^t (z_s, Γ_t) has the advantage over W_s^t (z_s, Γ_t) that it satisfies a simpler equation not containing any other functions. It is true that it has with respect to W_s^t (z_s, Γ_t) the disadvantage that it is not $\mathcal{Z}_s\mathcal{Y}_s^t$-measurable, since it still depends on y_r^s. From formula (5.25) it is apparent, however, that this dependence is not of a very essential quality. Namely, for a change of r the measure V_{rs}^t (z_s, Γ_t) is multiplied by a constant, i.e., a value that does not depend on z_s and Γ_t (but does depend on y_r^s). It is desirable to remove entirely the arbitrariness in the selection of r and the dependence of the measure on y_r^s.

The question arises of whether a measure (we will designate it V_s^t (z_s, Γ_t)) could be introduced, which would combine the mentioned advantages of the measures V_{rs}^t and W_s^t and would not have their disadvantages. We will give a more precise description of the characteristics of this measure:

1°. $V_s^t(z_s, \Gamma_t)$ is $\mathscr{Z}_s\mathscr{Y}_s^t$-measurable;

2°. $V_s^t(z_s, \Gamma_t) = g_{rs}^t V_{rs}^t(z_s, \Gamma_t)$, (5.26)

i.e., differs from V_{rs}^t by a factor g_{rs}^t which does not depend on z_s and Γ_t;

3°. it satisfies the equation

$$V_s^u(z_s, \Gamma_u) = \int V_s^t(z_s, dz_t)\, V_t^u(z_t, \Gamma_u),\ s \leqslant t \leqslant u. \tag{5.27}$$

The characteristics enumerated give a descriptive definition of the basic system of measures $V_s^t(z_s, \Gamma_t)$.

It is not difficult to see that from (5.26) and Eqs. (5.15) and (5.16) [taking into account (5.13)] the analogous equations for the basic measures are necessarily true, namely:

$$W_s^t(z_s, \Gamma_t) = \frac{V_s^t(z_s, \Gamma_t)}{V_s^t(z_s, \Omega)}; \tag{5.28}$$

$$W_s^{tu}(z_s, \Gamma_t) = \frac{1}{V_s^u(z_s, \Omega)} \int_{\Gamma_t} V_s^t(z_s, dz_t)\, V_t^u(z_t, \Omega). \tag{5.29}$$

Characteristic 2° can be considered equivalent to Eq. (5.28).

The above characteristics 1°–3° do not define the system of measures $V_s^t(z_s, \Gamma_t)$ entirely unambiguously. In fact, if $V_s^t(z_s, \Gamma_t)$ is a measure with the indicated characteristics, then these characteristics, as can easily be seen, will be possessed by the measure

$$V_s'^t(z_s, \Gamma_t) = \vartheta_s^t V_s^t(z_s, \Gamma_t), \tag{5.30}$$

where ϑ_s^t is a $\mathscr{Y}_s^t$-measurable multiplicative functional, i.e., a family of functions satisfying the equation

$$\vartheta_s^u = \vartheta_s^t \vartheta_t^u, \quad s \leqslant t \leqslant u.$$

If the basic *a posteriori* measure described above exists, then evidently it can be obtained by means of the passage to the limit

$$V_s^t(z_s, \Gamma_t) = \lim_{r \uparrow s} G_r V_{rs}^t(z_s, \Gamma_t)$$

with a suitable choice of the $\mathscr{Y}_r^t$-measurable factor G_r.

Let us here give one specific constructional method of introducing the basic measure. We will examine a Δ-division $S_\Delta = \{t_1, \ldots, t_N\}$ of the set T, such that for decreasing Δ the set S_Δ expands and has as its limit (as $\Delta \to 0$) a set S everywhere dense in T. We form the step function

$$\varphi(t) = \max\{t_i : t_i < t\}$$

(hence $\varphi(t_j)=t_{j-1}$). For a fixed Δ we will define the family of measures $\overline{V}_s^t(z_s, \Gamma_t)$ in the following manner. If s and $t>s$ belong to the same interval $(t_i, t_{i+1}]$, then we assume

$$\overline{V}_s^t(z_s, \Gamma_t) = V_{\varphi(s),s}^t(z_s, \Gamma_t).$$

If they belong to neighboring intervals $t_i < s \leqslant t_{i+1} < t \leqslant t_{i+2}$, let

$$\overline{V}_s^t(z_s, \Gamma_t) = \int V_{t_i s}^{t_{i+1}}(z_s, dz_{t_{i+1}}) V_{t_i t_{i+1}}^t(z_{t_{i+1}}, \Gamma_t) = V_{t_i s}^t(z_s, \Gamma_t). \tag{5.31}$$

If $t_i < s \leqslant t_{i+1},\ t_{i+2} < t \leqslant t_{i+3}$, then we assume

$$\overline{V}_s^t(z_s, \Gamma_t) = \int \overline{V}_s^{t_{i+2}}(z_s, dz_{t_{i+2}}) V_{t_{i+1} t_{i+2}}^t(z_{t_{i+2}}, \Gamma_t).$$

Using (5.31), (5.25), and (5.13), we can express this measure in terms of $V_{\varphi(s),s}^t$:

$$\overline{V}_s^t(z_s, \Gamma_t) = g_{\varphi(s),t_{i+1}}^{t_{i+2},t} \int V_{\varphi(s),s}^{t_{i+2}}(z_s, dz_{t_{i+2}}) V_{\varphi(s),t_{i+2}}^t(z_{t_{i+2}}, \Gamma_t) =$$
$$= g_{\varphi(s),t_{i+1}}^{t_{i+2},t} V_{\varphi(s),s}^t(z_s, \Gamma_t). \tag{5.32}$$

For the following interval, where $t_{i+3} < t \leqslant t_{i+4}$, let

$$\overline{V}_s^t(z_s, \Gamma_t) = \int \overline{V}_s^{\varphi(t)}(z_s, dz_{\varphi(t)}) V_{t_{i+2},\varphi(t)}^t(z_{\varphi(t)}, \Gamma_t).$$

Using (5.32), and also the equation

$$V_{t_{i+2},\varphi(t)}^t(z_{\varphi(t)}, \Gamma_t) = g_{\varphi(s),t_{i+2}}^{\varphi(t),t} V_{\varphi(s),\varphi(t)}^t(z_{\varphi(t)}, \Gamma_t),$$

and (5.13), we have

$$\overline{V}_s^t(z_s, \Gamma_t) = g_{\varphi(s),t_{i+1}}^{t_{i+2},t_{i+3}} g_{\varphi(s),t_{i+2}}^{t_{i+3},t} V_{\varphi(s),s}^t(z_s, \Gamma_t). \tag{5.33}$$

In an analogous manner the process of defining the measures $\overline{V}_s^t$ is continued for values s and t more distant from each other. It corresponds to the recursion formula

$$\overline{V}_s^t(z_s, \Gamma_t) = \int \overline{V}_s^{\varphi(t)}(z_s, dz_{\varphi(t)}) V_{\varphi(\varphi(t)),\varphi(t)}^t(z_{\varphi(t)}, \Gamma_t).$$

In a way analogous to how Eqs. (5.32) and (5.33) were derived, from this, using (5.25) and (5.13), we can obtain

$$\overline{V}_s^t(z_s, \Gamma_t) = \prod_{t_{j-1}=\varphi(s)}^{t_{j+2}=\varphi(t)} g_{\varphi(s),t_j}^{t_{j+1},t_{j+2}} g_{\varphi(s),\varphi(\varphi(t))}^{\varphi(t),t} V_{\varphi(s),s}^t(z_s, \Gamma_t).$$

If in addition we take into account that

$$V^t_{\varphi(s),;s}(z_s, \Gamma_t) = g^{st}_{r,\varphi(t)} V^t_{rs}(z_s, \Gamma_t),$$

we will have

$$\overline{V}^t_s(z_s, \Gamma_t) = g^{st}_{r,\varphi(t)} g^{t_{i+2},t_{i+3}}_{\varphi(s),t_{i+1}} \dots g^{\varphi(t),t}_{\varphi(s),\varphi(\varphi(t))} V^t_{rs}(z_s, \Gamma_t). \tag{5.34}$$

This equation is the analog for $\overline{V}^t_s(z_s, \Gamma_t)$ of Eq. (5.26). From the definition of the measures $\overline{V}^t_s$ it follows that they satisfy Eq. (5.27), if $t \in S_\Delta$. In addition to this, it is evident that $\overline{V}^t_s(z_s, \Gamma_t)$ is a $\mathscr{Z}_s\mathscr{Y}^t_{\varphi(s)}$-measurable function, where $s-\varphi(s) \leqslant \Delta$.

We will now complete the passage to the limit $\Delta \to 0$. If the σ-algebras $\mathscr{Y}^t_s$ are continuous from the left with respect to s,

$$\lim_{\tau \uparrow s} \mathscr{Y}^t_\tau = \mathscr{Y}^t_s,$$

then the limit

$$\lim_{\Delta \to 0} \overline{V}^t_s(z_s, \Gamma_t) = V^t_s(z_s, \Gamma_t), \tag{5.35}$$

if it exists, is a $\mathscr{Z}_s\mathscr{Y}^t_s$-measurable function. By the same token, condition 1° is satisfied for the limit measures. Further, Eq. (5.34) with the existence of (5.35) changes in the limit to (5.26). It remains to check the last condition 3°. As was noted, the prelimit measures satisfy Eq. (5.27) for $t \in S_\Delta$. The limit measures (5.35) will thus satisfy the indicated equation on the limit set S, everywhere dense in T. From this follows the validity of Eq. (5.27) on the entire set T with certain supplementary assumptions of continuity.

5.4 Another Method of Introducing the Basic *A Posteriori* Measure

For practical purposes a more useful method of introducing the basic measures may be found, which we will describe here. We will use this method in the two succeeding chapters.

The new method does not explicitly depend upon the assumption of continuity of information, but, on the other hand, requires that another assumption, which we formulate below, be satisfied.

Hypothesis 5.1. There exists a probabilistic Markov measure $\mathbf{Q}(\Lambda)$ in the space $(\Omega, \mathscr{Y}_T)$ such that the measures

$$\mathbf{P}(\Lambda^t_s \Gamma_t \mid z_s), \ \Lambda^t_s \in \mathscr{Y}^t_s$$

are almost everywhere absolutely continuous with respect to the measure $\mathbf{Q}(\Lambda_s^t | y_s)$ on the σ-algebra $\mathcal{Y}_s^t$. Here s, $t(>s)$, and Γ_t are arbitrary (from T and from $\mathcal{X}_t$, respectively), but are fixed.

The Radon-Nikodim derivative corresponding to the indicated measures

$$V_s^t(z_s, \Gamma_t) = \frac{\mathbf{P}(dy_s^t \Gamma_t | z_s)}{\mathbf{Q}(dy_s^t | y_s)} \tag{5.36}$$

forms the desired measure (unnormalized) in the space $(\Omega, \mathcal{X}_t)$. Varying s and t, we obtain a two-parameter family of measures. We will cite two theorems.

Theorem 5.7. From Hypothesis 5.1 follows the continuity of information of the conditional process.

Theorem 5.8. The family of measures (5.36) satisfies the requirements 1°–3°, i.e., it represents one of the forms of the basic *a posteriori* measure.

Proof of Theorem 5.7. According to Lemma 5.1, it is sufficient to prove the absolute continuity

$$\mathbf{P}(\Lambda_s^t | z_s) \sim \mathbf{P}(\Lambda_s^t | y_r^s), \quad \Lambda_s^t \in \mathcal{Y}_s^t.$$

Since on the strength of Hypothesis 5.1

$$\mathbf{P}(\Lambda_s^t | z_s) \sim \mathbf{Q}(\Lambda_s^t | y_s),$$

for the proof of Theorem 5.7, it is sufficient to prove the absolute continuity

$$\mathbf{P}(\Lambda_s^t | y_r^s) \sim \mathbf{Q}(\Lambda_s^t | y_s). \tag{5.37}$$

From the equation

$$\mathbf{P}(\Lambda_s^t | y_r^s) = \int \mathbf{P}(\Lambda_s^t | z_s, y_r^s)\, \mathbf{P}(dz_s | y_r^s)$$

as a result of the Markov condition we have

$$\mathbf{P}(\Lambda_s^t | y_r^s) = \int \mathbf{P}(\Lambda_s^t | z_s)\, \mathbf{P}(dz_s | y_r^s).$$

From this, using Hypothesis 5.1 and (5.36), we find

$$\mathbf{P}(\Lambda_s^t | y_r^s) = \int \Big[\int_{\Lambda_s^t} V_s^t(z_s, \Omega)\, \mathbf{Q}(dy_s^t | y_s) \Big] \mathbf{P}(dz_s | y_r^s).$$

Changing the order of integration (Fubini's theorem), we obtain

$$\mathbf{P}(\Lambda_s^t \mid y_r^s) = \int_{\Lambda_s^t} \left[\int V_s^t(z_s, \Omega)\,\mathbf{P}(dz_s \mid y_r^s)\right] \mathbf{Q}(dy_s^t \mid y_s). \tag{5.38}$$

The function $V_s^t(z_s, \Omega)$ is bounded and nonzero on $\mathscr{Z}_t \mathscr{Y}_s^t$ almost everywhere with respect to the measure $\mathbf{P}$ as a result of Hypothesis 5.1. Thus the integral

$$\int V_s^t(z_s, \Omega)\,\mathbf{P}(dz_s \mid y_r^s)$$

entering into (5.38) is bounded and nonzero almost everywhere. From this results the absolute continuity (5.37), which, as was noted, is sufficient for the proof of Theorem 5.7.

Proof of Theorem 5.8. The fulfillment of 1° obviously follows from (5.36) and does not require further elaboration. In order to prove 2° we need to compare the expressions (5.36) and (5.23) and prove that they differ only by a factor which is independent of z_s and Γ_t. But on the strength of Hypothesis 5.1 and the absolute continuity (5.37), we have

$$\frac{\mathbf{P}(dy_s^t\Gamma_t \mid z_s)}{\mathbf{P}(dy_s^t \mid y_r^s)} = \frac{\mathbf{P}(dy_s^t\Gamma_t \mid z_s)}{\mathbf{Q}(dy_s^t \mid y_s)}\,\frac{\mathbf{Q}(dy_s^t \mid y_s)}{\mathbf{P}(dy_s^t \mid y_r^s)}.$$

From this the assertion follows, as well as the form of the factor in question,

$$g_{rs}^t = \frac{\mathbf{P}(dy_s^t \mid y_r^s)}{\mathbf{Q}(dy_s^t \mid y_s)}.$$

Let us turn now to the verification of requirement 3°, where we use the Markov characteristics of both measures.

Let us consider the sets $\Lambda_s^t \in \mathscr{Y}_s^t$, $\Lambda_t^u \in \mathscr{Y}_t^u$ and $\Gamma_u \in \mathscr{Z}_u$, $(s<t<u)$, and examine the equation

$$\mathbf{P}(\Lambda_s^t\Lambda_t^u\Gamma_u \mid z_s) = \int_{\Lambda_s^t} \mathbf{P}(\Lambda_t^u\Gamma_u \mid z_s, z_t, y_s^t)\,\mathbf{P}(dy_s^t\, dz_t \mid z_s),$$

which, on the strength of the Markov condition, can be written

$$\mathbf{P}(\Lambda_s^t\Lambda_t^u\Gamma_u \mid z_s) = \int_{\Lambda_s^t} \mathbf{P}(\Lambda_t^u\Gamma_u \mid z_t)\,\mathbf{P}(dy_s^t\, dz_t \mid z_s). \tag{5.39}$$

Analogously, on the strength of the Markov characteristics of the second measure,

$$\mathbf{Q}(\Lambda_s^t \Lambda_t^u \mid y_s) = \int_{\Lambda_s^t} \mathbf{Q}(\Lambda_t^u \mid y_t)\, \mathbf{Q}(dy_s^t \mid y_s). \tag{5.40}$$

We write all three measures entering into (5.39) in terms of the measures V_σ^τ, for example,

$$\mathbf{P}(\Lambda_t^u \Gamma_u \mid z_t) = \int_{\Lambda_t^u} V_t^u(z_t, \Gamma_u)\, \mathbf{Q}(dy_t^u \mid y_t).$$

After this, (5.39) takes the form

$$\int_{\Lambda_s^t \Lambda_t^u} V_s^u(z_s, \Gamma_u)\, \mathbf{Q}(dy_s^u \mid y_s) =$$

$$= \int_{\Lambda_s^t} \Big[\int_{\Lambda_t^u} V_t^u(z_t, \Gamma_u)\, \mathbf{Q}(dy_t^u \mid y_t) \Big] V_s^t(z_s, dz_t)\, \mathbf{Q}(dy_s^t \mid y_s).$$

Using Fubini's theorem, we change the order of integration on the right side and take into account (5.40). This gives us the equation

$$\int_{\Lambda_s^t \Lambda_t^u} V_s^t(z_s, \Gamma_u)\, \mathbf{Q}(dy_s^u \mid y_s) = \int_{\Lambda_s^t \Lambda_t^u} \Big[\int V_s^t(z_s, dz_t)\, V_t^u(z_t, \Gamma_u) \Big]\, \mathbf{Q}(dy_s^u \mid y_s).$$

According to the Radon-Nikodim theorem, we obtain from this (5.27). The proof is completed.

5.5 *A Posteriori* Measures Corresponding to an Initial Distribution

It is possible to express some *a posteriori* probabilities in terms of the basic *a posteriori* measure V_s^t, but not all. In the general case the indicated measure is insufficient for determination of the *a posteriori* probabilities, and it is necessary to assign in addition some initial distribution. In this section we will give formulas which enable us to find various *a posteriori* probabilities when we know the basic *a posteriori* measure and the initial distribution.

1. Using (5.7), and then (5.14), we have

$$\mathbf{P}(\Gamma_s \mid y_r^t) = \int_{\Gamma_s} h_{rs}^t(z_s)\, \mathbf{P}(dz_s \mid y_r^s) = \int_{\Gamma_s} V_{rs}^t(z_s, \Omega)\, \mathbf{P}(dz_s \mid y_r^s) \quad (r < s < t)$$

and as a result of (5.26)

$$\mathbf{P}(\Gamma_s \mid y_r^t) = \frac{1}{g_{rs}^t} \int_{\Gamma_s} \mathbf{P}(dz_s \mid y_r^s)\, V_s^t(z_s, \Omega). \tag{5.41}$$

We introduce the symbol

$$V_{rst}(\Gamma_t) = \int \mathbf{P}(dz_s \mid y_r^s)\, V_s^t(z_s, \Gamma_t). \tag{5.42}$$

Since the conditional measure $\mathbf{P}(\Gamma_s \mid y_r^t)$ is a probability ($\mathbf{P}(\Omega \mid y_r^t) = 1$), from (5.41) and (5.42) we have

$$g_{rs}^t = V_{rst}(\Omega); \tag{5.43}$$

$$\mathbf{P}(\Gamma_s \mid y_r^t) = \frac{1}{V_{rst}(\Omega)} \int_{\Gamma_s} \mathbf{P}(dz_s \mid y_r^s)\, V_s^t(z_s, \Omega). \tag{5.44}$$

Substituting (5.43) into (5.26) and taking into account (5.14), we can also express the function h_{rs}^t in terms of V_s^t and $\mathbf{P}(\Gamma_s \mid y_r^s)$:

$$h_{rs}^t(z_s) = \frac{V_s^t(z_s, \Omega)}{V_{rst}(\Omega)}.$$

2. Let us introduce another time instant r', intermediate to r and s, and express the probabilities and functions examined above in terms of V_s^t and $V_{rr's}$.

On the strength of the Markov condition we have

$$\mathbf{P}(\Gamma_s \mid y_r^t) = \int \mathbf{P}(\Gamma_s \mid z_{r'}, y_r^t)\, \mathbf{P}(dz_{r'} \mid y_r^t) = \int W_{r'}^{st}(z_{r'}, \Gamma_s)\, \mathbf{P}(dz_{r'} \mid y_r^t).$$

Substituting (5.29) and (5.44) into this, we obtain

$$\mathbf{P}(\Gamma_s \mid y_r^t) = \frac{1}{V_{rr't}(\Omega)} \int_{\Omega} \int_{\Gamma_s} \mathbf{P}(dz_{r'} \mid y_r^{r'})\, V_{r'}^s(z_{r'}, dz_s)\, V_s^t(z_s, \Omega)$$

or, if we take into account (5.42),

$$\mathbf{P}(\Gamma_s \mid y_r^t) = \frac{1}{V_{rr't}(\Omega)} \int_{\Gamma_s} V_{rr's}(dz_s)\, V_s^t(z_s, \Omega). \tag{5.45}$$

In particular, if in this equation we assume $s=t$, we will have

$$\mathbf{P}(\Gamma_s \mid y_r^s) = \frac{V_{rr's}(\Gamma_s)}{V_{rr's}(\Omega)}. \tag{5.46}$$

The application of the last two equations in conjunction with (5.7) gives the result

$$h_{rs}^t(z_s) = \frac{V_{rr's}(\Omega)}{V_{rr't}(\Omega)}\, V_s^t(z_s, \Omega).$$

3. Let us assume that the region of definition of the process is the interval $T=[a, b]$, where $a<0$; $b=T_0$. We will assume in the

preceding formulas that $r=a$, $r'=0$, and will take points s, t, etc., from the interval $[0, T_0]$. We introduce the shortened notation

$$V_{a0t}(\Gamma_t) \equiv V_t(\Gamma_t); \quad \mathbf{P}(\Gamma_t \mid y_a^t) \equiv W_t(\Gamma_t).$$

Then, obviously, formulas (5.46) and (5.45) take the form

$$W_t(\Gamma_t) = \frac{V_t(\Gamma_t)}{V_t(\Omega)}; \tag{5.47}$$

$$\mathbf{P}(\Gamma_s \mid y_a^t) = \frac{1}{V_t(\Omega)} \int\limits_{\Gamma_s} V_s(dz_s) V_s^t(z_s, \Omega), \; s < t. \tag{5.48}$$

If we carry out the measure transformation

$$\widetilde{V}_s^t(z_s, \Gamma_t) = V_s(\Omega) V_s^t(z_s, \Gamma_t) \frac{1}{V_t(\Omega)}, \tag{5.49}$$

then, in accordance with (5.47), the formula (5.48) using the new measure can be written thus:

$$\mathbf{P}(\Gamma_s \mid y_a^t) = \int\limits_{\Gamma_s} W_s(dz_s) \widetilde{V}_s^t(z_s, \Omega), \; s < t. \tag{5.50}$$

Using (5.27) and the definition of the family of measures V_t, we easily find that these measures satisfy the equation

$$V_t(\Gamma_t) = \int V_s(dz_s) V_s^t(z_s, \Gamma_t), \quad s \leqslant t. \tag{5.51}$$

Changing to the measures (5.47) and (5.49), this equation can be written

$$W_t(\Gamma_t) = \int W_s(dz_s) \widetilde{V}_s^t(z_s, \Gamma_t). \tag{5.52}$$

Let us examine the time instants $0 \leqslant t_1 \leqslant \ldots t_n \leqslant u \leqslant b$ and the multidimensional *a posteriori* distribution $\mathbf{P}(\Gamma_{t_1} \ldots \Gamma_{t_n} \mid y_a^u)$, $\Gamma_{t_i} \in \mathscr{Z}_{t_i}$ corresponding to them. As a result of Theorem 5.1 (for $\widetilde{\mathscr{Y}} = \mathscr{Y}_a^u$) the conditional process is a Markov process. To it evidently correspond the transition probabilities $\mathbf{P}(\Gamma_t \mid z_s, y_a^u) = W_s^{tu}(z_s, \Gamma_t)$ and the initial distribution $\mathbf{P}(\Gamma_{t_1} \mid y_a^u)$, hence

$$\mathbf{P}(\Gamma_{t_1} \ldots \Gamma_{t_n} \mid y_a^u) = \int\limits_{\Gamma_{t_1}} \ldots \int\limits_{\Gamma_{t_n}} \mathbf{P}(dz_1 \mid y_a^u) W_{t_1}^{t_2 u}(z_1, dz_2) \ldots \ldots W_{t_{n-1}}^{t_n, u}(z_{n-1}, dz_n). \tag{5.53}$$

If we substitute here (5.29) and (5.48), this expression is transformed to the form

$$\mathbf{P}(\Gamma_{t_1}\ldots\Gamma_{t_n}\mid y_a^u)=\frac{1}{V_u(\Omega)}\int\limits_{\Gamma_{t_1}}\ldots\int\limits_{\Gamma_{t_n}}V_{t_1}(dz_1)\,V_{t_1}^{t_2}(z_1,dz_2)\ldots$$

$$\ldots V_{t_{n-1}}^{t_n}(z_{n-1},dz_n)\,V_{t_n}^{u}(z_n,\Omega). \tag{5.54}$$

We turn finally to the measures (5.49). Substituting

$$V_s^t(z_s,\Gamma_t)=\frac{1}{V_s(\Omega)}\widetilde{V}_s^t(z_s,\Gamma_t)\,V_t(\Omega)$$

into (5.54), we obtain

$$\mathbf{P}(\Gamma_{t_1}\ldots\Gamma_{t_n}\mid y_a^u)=\int\limits_{\Gamma_{t_1}}\ldots\int\limits_{\Gamma_{t_n}}W_{t_1}(dz_1)\,\widetilde{V}_{t_1}^{t_2}(z_1,dz_2)\ldots$$

$$\ldots\widetilde{V}_{t_{n-1}}^{t_n}(z_{n-1},dz_n)\,\widetilde{V}_{t_n}^{u}(z_n,\Omega). \tag{5.55}$$

4. Formulas (5.29) and (5.49) can be considered as a replacement for the Markov system of measures (3.31). The family of measures $\widetilde{V}_s^t$ or the family W_s^{tu} (u being fixed), considered as a Markov system of measures in accordance with (5.55) and (5.53), has with respect to the basic system V_s^t the disadvantage that a measure $\widetilde{V}_s^t(z_s,\Gamma_t)$ or $W_s^{tu}(z_s,\Gamma_t)$ is not $\mathscr{X}_s\mathscr{Y}_s^t$-measurable (in contrast to V_s^t). In addition to this, $\widetilde{V}_s^t$ depends on the initial distribution, and W_s^{tu} on the arbitrariness in the selection of the end point u.

The indicated family of measures, like any Markov system of measures, is described by infinitesimal operators (Chapter 3). Let $L(t)$ be the operators of the family of measures V_s^t, $\widetilde{L}(t)$ the operators of the family $\widetilde{V}_s^t$, and $\widetilde{\widetilde{L}}(t)$ the operators of the family W_s^{tu}.

As a result of property 1° of the measures V_s^t, the operators $L(t)$ have the property that the difference $L(t)-L(s)$ is $\mathscr{Y}_s^t$-measurable. The operators $\widetilde{L}(t)$ and $\widetilde{\widetilde{L}}(t)$, of course, do not have such a property.

As was shown in Sect. 3.1, if Eqs. (5.27) and (5.51) are satisfied the following differential equation is satisfied:

$$dV_t=V_t\overline{d}L(t). \tag{5.56}$$

Analogously from (5.52) there follows the equation

$$dW_t=W_t\overline{d}\widetilde{L}(t). \tag{5.57}$$

The function $V_t^u(z_t,\Omega)$ which enters into (5.48), (5.49) and (5.54), having the meaning of a probability function, as we can easily understand, satisfies the equation

$$d_t V_t^u (z, \Omega) = -(\bar{d}L(t) V_t^u)(z, \Omega), \tag{5.58}$$

while the other function $\tilde{V}_t^u (z, \Omega)$, entering into (5.50) and (5.55), satisfies an analogous equation with another infinitesimal operator

$$d_t \tilde{V}_t^u (z, \Omega) = -(\bar{d}\tilde{L}(t) \tilde{V}_t^u)(z, \Omega). \tag{5.59}$$

The infinitesimal operator $d\tilde{L}$ can be expressed in terms of the basic operator dL, using Theorem 3.3. Applying formula (3.38) to the change of measures (5.49), we obtain

$$\bar{d}\tilde{L}(t) = [V_t(\Omega)\bar{d}L(t) - d^*V_t(\Omega)] \frac{1}{V_t(\Omega)}. \tag{5.60}$$

But on the strength of (5.56) and (5.47)

$$dV_t(\Omega) = (V_t \bar{d}L(t))(\Omega) = V_t(\Omega)(W_t \bar{d}L(t))(\Omega).$$

Thus (5.60) can be written

$$\bar{d}\tilde{L}(t) = V_t(\Omega)[\bar{d}L(t) - (W_t \bar{d}L(t))(\Omega)] \frac{1}{V_t(\Omega)} =$$

$$= dL_1(t) - (W_t d^*L_1(t))(\Omega), \tag{5.60a}$$

where

$$dL_1(t) = V_t(\Omega)\bar{d}L(t) \frac{1}{V_t(\Omega)} = V_t(\Omega) d^*L^*(t) \frac{1}{V_t(\Omega)} \tag{5.60b}$$

[using (3.20)]. Equations (5.57) and (5.59) thus will take on the form

$$dW_t(\Gamma) = (W_t d^*L_1(t))(\Gamma) - W_t(\Gamma)(W_t d^*L_1(t))(\Omega), \tag{5.61}$$

$$-d\tilde{V}_t^u(z, \Omega) = (d^*L_1(t)\tilde{V}_t^u)(z, \Omega) - (W_t d^*L_1(t))(\Omega)\tilde{V}_t^u(z, \Omega). \tag{5.62}$$

In an analogous manner it is possible to express the operator $d\tilde{\tilde{L}}(t)$ in terms of $dL(t)$. The application of formula (3.38) to the transformation (5.29) gives

$$\bar{d}\tilde{\tilde{L}}(t) = \frac{1}{V_t^u(z, \Omega)} [\bar{d}L(t) V_t^u(z, \Omega) + d^*V_t^u(z, \Omega)]$$

and on the strength of (5.58)

$$\bar{d}\tilde{\tilde{L}}(t) = \frac{1}{V_t^u(z, \Omega)} [\bar{d}L(t) V_t^u(z, \Omega) - (\bar{d}L(t) V_t^u)(z, \Omega)]. \tag{5.63}$$

As we can easily see from (5.61) and (5.63), the relations

$$dW_t(\Omega) = 0; \quad \overline{d}\tilde{\tilde{L}}(t)\,1 = 0,$$

are satisfied, which, of course, is necessary for the retention of the normalization of the probabilistic measures (for example, from $W_t(\Omega) = 1$ follows $dW_t(\Omega) = 0$).

As a result of (5.49) it is easily seen that in (5.63) instead of V_t^u it is possible to write $\tilde{V}_t^u$.

The infinitesimal operator (5.63) determines the equation

$$d\mathbf{P}(dz_t|y_a^u) = \mathbf{P}(dz_t|y_a^u)\,\overline{d}\tilde{\tilde{L}}(t) \tag{5.63a}$$

which is analogous to Eqs. (5.56) and (5.57). We will designate $\mathbf{P}(dz_t|y_a^u) = P_t(dz_t)$. Substituting in (5.63) we thus have

$$dP_t(dz_t) = \left[\frac{P_t(dz_t)}{\tilde{V}_t^u(z_t, \Omega)}\,\overline{d}L(t)\right]\tilde{V}_t^u(z, \Omega) - \frac{P_t(dz_t)}{\tilde{V}_t^u(z_t, \Omega)}\,(\overline{d}L(t)\,\tilde{V}_t^u)(z, \Omega).$$

The last equation, if (5.50) is taken into account, can be transformed to the form

$$dP_t(dz_t) = (W_t(dz_t)\,\overline{d}L(t))\,\frac{P_t(dz_t)}{W_t(dz_t)} - W_t(dz_t)\left(\overline{d}L(t)\,\frac{P_t(dz_t)}{W_t(dz_t)}\right). \tag{5.63b}$$

Equation (5.63b), as opposed to the preceding equation (5.63a), is appropriate for the interpretation of an *a posteriori* process $(\Omega\mathscr{Z}_t,\, t \in T,\, \mathbf{P}(\cdot|y_a^u))$ [u being fixed] as a Markov process occurring in reverse time. The infinitesimal operator

$$W_t(dz)\,\overline{d}L(t)\,\frac{1}{W_t(dz)} - \frac{(W_t'(dz)\,\overline{d}L(\overline{t}))}{W_t(dz)}$$

corresponding to (5.63b), can be obtained from (5.63a) by the inversion of time.

In conclusion, let us stop at that special case when the system of measures V_s^u possesses the properties of the measures examined in Sect. 3.3. In this case, as a supplement to (5.56) and (5.63), it is possible to give a series of simpler formulas. Thus, in accordance with (3.47), besides (5.56) and (5.58) it is possible to consider the equations

$$dV_t = V_t\,dL(t); \quad -d_tV_t^u(z, \Omega) = (dL(t)\,V_t^u)(z, \Omega) \tag{5.64}$$

where the stochastic expressions are understood in the symmetrized sense (Sect. 2.1). Analogously it is possible to remove the dash above the differential in formulas (5.57) and (5.59).

Let us apply the simple rules for transformation of stochastic expressions in the symmetrized sense in order to derive analogs of Eqs. (5.61) and (5.62). According to (3.32), for the change of measures (5.49) we have

$$d\widetilde{L}(t) = V_t(\Omega)\, dL(t) \frac{1}{V_t(\Omega)} - d \ln V_t(\Omega) = dL(t) - \frac{dV_t(\Omega)}{V_t(\Omega)}.$$

Substituting in this the first equation of (5.64), we obtain

$$d\widetilde{L}(t) = dL(t) - (W_t\, dL)(\Omega). \tag{5.65}$$

Consequently,

$$dW_t(\Gamma) = (W_t\, dL(t))(\Gamma) - W_t(\Gamma)(W_t\, dL(t))(\Omega); \tag{5.66}$$

$$-d\widetilde{V}_t^u(z, \Omega) = (dL(t)\widetilde{V}_t^u)(z, \Omega) - (W_t\, dL(t))(\Omega)\widetilde{V}_t^u)(z, \Omega). \tag{5.67}$$

Further, if we apply (3.32) to (5.29), we will get

$$d\widetilde{\widetilde{L}}(t) = \frac{1}{V_t^u(z, \Omega)} [dL(t) V_t^u(z, \Omega) - (dL(t) V_t^u)(z, \Omega)]. \tag{5.68}$$

Formula (5.63b) here has the form

$$dP_t(dz) = \left(W_t(dz)\, dL(t)\right) \frac{P_t(dz)}{W_t(dz)} - W_t(dz)\left(dL(t) \frac{P_t(dz)}{W_t(dz)}\right). \tag{5.68a}$$

Examples of the cited formulas will be examined subsequently.

5.6 Some General Properties of *A Posteriori* Measures

1. Let us examine first the properties of *a posteriori* measures associated with averaging with respect to values of the observed process $\{y_t\}$ on one or another interval. Directly from the definition of the conditional probabilities there follows a series of relations of the type

$$\mathbf{M}[\mathbf{P}(\Gamma_s \mid y_a^t) \mid y_a^s] = \mathbf{P}(\Gamma_s \mid y_a^s); \tag{5.69}$$

$$\mathbf{M}[W_s^{tu}(z_s, \Gamma_t) \mid z_s] = \mathbf{P}(\Gamma_t \mid z_s), \quad s < t \leqslant u. \tag{5.70}$$

If we assume $u=t$ in the last equation and insert (5.28), we get

$$\mathbf{M}\left[\frac{V_s^t(z_s, \Gamma_t)}{V_s^t(z_s, \Omega)} \,\Big|\, z_s\right] = \mathbf{P}(\Gamma_t \mid z_s), \quad s < t. \tag{5.71}$$

TABLE 5.1. Summary of *a posteriori* measures and their infinitesimal operators

$(a<s<t<u)$

Measure	Operator
Basic *a posteriori* measure:	
$V_s^t(z_s, dz_t)$	$dL(s),\ dL(t)$
$V_t(dz_t)$	$dL(t)$
Auxiliary *a posteriori* measure:	
$\widetilde{V}_s^t(z_s, dz_t) = \dfrac{V_s(\Omega)}{V_t(\Omega)} V_s^t(z_s, dz_t)$	$d\widetilde{L}(s),\ d\widetilde{L}(t)$
Final *a posteriori* probability:	
$W_t(dz_t) = \mathbf{P}(dz_t \mid y_a^t) = \dfrac{V_t(dz_t)}{V_t(\Omega)}$	$d\widetilde{L}(t)$
Inner *a posteriori* probability:	
$W_s^{tu}(z_s, dz_t) = \mathbf{P}(dz_t \mid z_s, y_a^u) = \dfrac{V_t^u(z_t, \Omega)}{V_s^u(z_s, \Omega)} V_s^t(z_s, dz_t)$	$d\widetilde{\widetilde{L}}(s),\ d\widetilde{\widetilde{L}}(t)$
$\mathbf{P}(dz_t \mid y_a^u) = \dfrac{V_t^u(z_t, \Omega)}{V_u(\Omega)} V_t(dz_t)$	$d\widetilde{\widetilde{L}}(t)$

Further, inserting (5.50) into (5.69) and taking into account that $W_s(\Gamma_s)$, for fixed Γ_s, is a $\mathcal{Y}_a^s$-measurable function such that it is possible to remove it from under the sign of mathematical expectation, we find

$$\int_{\Gamma_s} W_s(dz_s)\, \mathbf{M}[\widetilde{V}_s^t(z_s, \Omega) \mid y_a^s] = W_s(\Gamma_s). \tag{5.72}$$

From this it follows that

$$\mathbf{M}[\widetilde{V}_s^t(z_s, \Omega) \mid y_a^s] = 1, \quad a<s<t.$$

It is possible to make a larger assertion. As a result of the Markov condition, we have

$$\mathbf{M}[\mathbf{P}(\Gamma_s\Gamma_t \mid y_a^t) \mid y_a^s] = \mathbf{P}(\Gamma_s\Gamma_t \mid y_a^s) = \int_{\Gamma_s} \mathbf{P}(dz_s \mid y_a^s)\, \mathbf{P}(\Gamma_t \mid z_s).$$

We will express $\mathbf{P}(\Gamma_s\Gamma_t \mid y_a^t)$ in terms of W_s and $\widetilde{V}_s^t$, using formula (5.55); then

$$\mathbf{M}\Big[\int_{\Gamma_s} W_s(dz_s)\, \widetilde{V}_s^t(z_s, \Gamma_t) \mid y_a^s\Big] = \int_{\Gamma_s} W_s(dz_s)\, \mathbf{P}(\Gamma_t \mid z_s).$$

Removing $W_s(dz_s)$ from under the sign of mathematical expectation as in (5.72) and using the arbitrariness of $\Gamma_s \in \mathscr{Z}_s$ (according to the Radon-Nikodim theorem), we obtain

$$\mathbf{M}\,[\widetilde{V}_s^t(z_s, \Gamma_t) \mid y_a^s] = \mathbf{P}(\Gamma_t \mid z_s). \tag{5.73}$$

From the resulting formulas (5.71), (5.73) and (5.70) it is apparent that *a posteriori* transition probabilities under averaging turn into *a priori* transition probabilities. The corresponding assertion can be made also for the infinitesimal operators of the indicated transition probabilities. Without particular argument we will cite here the relation

$$\mathbf{M}\,[d\widetilde{L}^*(t)]\, y_a^s] = dL_{pr}^*(t) \tag{5.74}$$

(L_{pr} being an *a priori* infinitesimal operator), which results from (5.73). These relations will be supported in the particular cases examined in Chapters 6 and 7.

2. A second group of properties of *a posteriori* measures is their Markov properties, if these measures are considered as a random process occurring in time. Let us consider the process $\{V_t(\Gamma_t),\ \Gamma_t \in \mathscr{Z}_t\}$. The interval $[0, T_0]$ is the region of definition of the parameter, and the phase space is the set of all measures on $\mathscr{Z}_t$ (t is fixed). The conditions imposed on V_t define, where t is fixed, a certain σ-algebra $\mathscr{V}_t$ in the space Ω. Since $V_t(\Gamma)$ for any given $\Gamma \in \mathscr{Z}_t$ is a $\mathscr{Y}_a^t$-measurable function, $\mathscr{V}_t \subset \mathscr{Y}_a^t$.

Definition 5.3. Let there be given

(A) a Markov process $(\Omega, \mathscr{Z}_t, t \in T, \mathbf{P})$;

(B) an observed process $(\Omega, \mathscr{Y}_t, t \in T, \mathbf{P})$, such that

$$\mathscr{Y}_t \subset \mathscr{Z}_t,$$

and (C) any desired variant of the basic *a posteriori* measure V_t and hence its corresponding σ-algebras $\mathscr{V}_t$. Then the process $(\Omega, \mathscr{V}_t, t \in T, \mathbf{P})$ is called a secondary *a posteriori* V-process.

Aside from the indicated process, the process W_t appears as a secondary process. The set of probabilistic measures on $\mathscr{Z}_t$ serves as the phase space of the latter. For this reason, to the time instant t there corresponds a σ-algebra $\mathscr{W}_t \subset \mathscr{Y}_a^t$, which is analogous to $\mathscr{V}_t$ and defines the conditions on W_t.

Definition 5.4. Let there be given

(A) a Markov process $(\Omega, \mathscr{Z}_t, t \in T, \mathbf{P})$;

(B) an observed process $(\Omega, \mathscr{Y}_t, t \in T, \mathbf{P})$, $\mathscr{Y}_t \subset \mathscr{Z}_t$;

(C) the conditional probabilities $W_t(\cdot) = \mathbf{P}(\cdot \mid \mathscr{Y}_a^t)$

and their corresponding σ-algebras $\mathcal{W}_t$. Then the process $(\Omega, \mathcal{W}_t, t \in T, \mathbf{P})$ is called a secondary *a posteriori* W-process.

Theorem 5.8. The secondary *a posteriori* V-process $\{V_t\}$ is almost certainly Markov.

Proof. We will prove that for any given $t_1 < \ldots < t_{n+1}$ (from $[0, T_0]$), the equation

$$\mathbf{P}(B \mid \mathcal{V}_{t_1} \ldots \mathcal{V}_{t_n}) = \mathbf{P}(B \mid \mathcal{V}_{t_n}), \quad B \in \mathcal{V}_{t_{n+1}} \tag{5.75}$$

is almost certainly satisfied. In accordance with (5.51) we have

$$V_{t_{n+1}}(\Gamma) = \int V_{t_n}(dz)\, V_{t_n}^{t_{n+1}}(z, \Gamma), \tag{5.76}$$

where $V_{t_n}^{t_{n+1}}$ on the strength of 1° is a $\mathcal{Z}_{t_n} \mathcal{Y}_{t_n}^{t_{n+1}}$-measurable function. From this it follows that $V_{t_{n+1}}(\Gamma)$ is a $\mathcal{V}_{t_n} \mathcal{Y}_{t_n}^{t_{n+1}}$-measurable function for any given $\Gamma \in \mathcal{Z}_t$. The characteristic function of the set $B \in \mathcal{V}_{t_{n+1}}$ is also a $\mathcal{V}_{t_n} \mathcal{Y}_{t_n}^{t_{n+1}}$-measurable function, and

$$\mathbf{P}(B \mid \mathcal{V}_{t_1} \ldots \mathcal{V}_{t_n} \mathcal{Y}_{t_n}^{t_{n+1}}) = \mathbf{P}(B \mid \mathcal{V}_{t_n} \mathcal{Y}_{t_n}^{t_{n+1}}) = \mathcal{I}_B(\omega) \tag{5.77}$$

Let us consider the equation

$$\mathbf{P}(dy_{t_n}^{t_{n+1}} \mid \mathcal{V}_{t_1} \ldots \mathcal{V}_{t_n}) = \int \mathbf{P}(dy_{t_n}^{t_{n+1}} \mid \mathcal{V}_{t_1} \ldots \mathcal{V}_{t_n} \mathcal{Z}_{t_n})\, \mathbf{P}(dz_{t_n} \mid \mathcal{V}_{t_1} \ldots \mathcal{V}_{t_n}) \tag{5.78}$$

and examine the probabilities contained in its right side. With respect to the "present" $\mathcal{Z}_{t_n}$ the events $dy_{t_n}^{t_{n+1}} \in \mathcal{Y}_{t_n}^{t_{n+1}}$ are "future," and the events $C \in \mathcal{V}_{t_1} \ldots \mathcal{V}_{t_n}$ are "past." As a result of the Markov property, we have

$$\mathbf{P}\left(dy_{t_n}^{t_{n+1}} \mid \mathcal{V}_{t_1} \ldots \mathcal{V}_{t_n} \mathcal{Z}_{t_n}\right) = \mathbf{P}\left(dy_{t_n}^{t_{n+1}} \mid \mathcal{Z}_{t_n}\right). \tag{5.79}$$

Let us turn to the other probability $\mathbf{P}(dz_{t_n} \mid \mathcal{V}_{t_1} \ldots \mathcal{V}_{t_n})$ entering into (5.78). Since $\mathcal{V}_{t_i} \subset \mathcal{Y}_a^{t_n}$, $i = 1, \ldots, n$, then

$$\mathbf{P}(\Gamma_{t_n} \mid \mathcal{V}_{t_1} \ldots \mathcal{V}_{t_n}) = \mathbf{M}[\mathbf{P}(\Gamma_{t_n} \mid \mathcal{Y}_a^{t_n}) \mid \mathcal{V}_{t_1} \ldots \mathcal{V}_{t_n}].$$

But according to (5.47)

$$\mathbf{P}(\Gamma_{t_n} \mid \mathcal{Y}_a^{t_n}) = \frac{V_{t_n}(\Gamma_{t_n})}{V_{t_n}(\Omega)}, \quad \Gamma_{t_n} \in \mathcal{Z}_{t_n},$$

where V_{t_n} is a $\mathcal{V}_{t_n}$-measurable function. Thus

$$\mathbf{P}(\Gamma_{t_n}|\mathcal{V}_{t_1}\ldots\mathcal{V}_{t_n}) = \mathbf{M}\left[\frac{V_{t_n}(\Gamma_{t_n})}{V_{t_n}(\Omega)}\,|\mathcal{V}_{t_1}\ldots\mathcal{V}_{t_n}\right] = \frac{V_{t_n}(\Gamma_{t_n})}{V_{t_n}(\Omega)}. \tag{5.80}$$

Equation (5.78), according to (5.79) and (5.80), takes the form

$$\mathbf{P}(dy_{t_n}^{t_{n+1}}|\mathcal{V}_{t_1}\ldots\mathcal{V}_{t_n}) = \int \mathbf{P}(dy_{t_n}^{t_{n+1}}|\mathcal{V}_{t_n}\mathcal{Z}_{t_n})\,\frac{V_{t_n}(dz_{t_n})}{V_{t_n}(\Omega)}.$$

This proves that $\mathbf{P}(dy_{t_n}^{t_{n+1}}|\mathcal{V}_{t_1}\ldots\mathcal{V}_{t_n})$ is a $\mathcal{V}_{t_n}$-measurable function:

$$\mathbf{P}\left(dy_{t_n}^{t_{n+1}}\,\middle|\,\mathcal{V}_{t_1}\ldots\mathcal{V}_{t_n}\right) = \mathbf{P}\left(dy_{t_n}^{t_{n+1}}\,\middle|\,\mathcal{V}_{t_n}\right). \tag{5.81}$$

Let $B \in \mathcal{V}_{t_{n+1}}$. Obviously,

$$\mathbf{P}(B|\mathcal{V}_{t_1}\ldots\mathcal{V}_{t_n}) = \int \mathbf{P}\left(B|\mathcal{V}_{t_1}\ldots\mathcal{V}_{t_n}\mathcal{Y}_{t_n}^{t_{n+1}}\right)\mathbf{P}\left(dy_{t_1}^{t_n}\middle|\mathcal{V}_{t_1}\ldots\mathcal{V}_{t_n}\right).$$

Substituting (5.77) and (5.81) into this, we obtain

$$\mathbf{P}(B|\mathcal{V}_{t_1}\ldots\mathcal{V}_{t_n}) = \int \mathbf{P}\left(B|\mathcal{V}_{t_n}\mathcal{Y}_{t_n}^{t_{n+1}}\right)\mathbf{P}\left(dy_{t_1}^{t_n}\middle|\mathcal{V}_{t_n}\right). \tag{5.82}$$

This proves (5.75) and completes the proof.

An analogous theorem is valid for the other secondary *a posteriori* process.

Theorem 5.9. The process $\{W_t\}$ is almost certainly Markov.

The proof is analogous to the preceding one. The difference lies in the fact that now it is impossible to use (5.76) for the proof of the inclusion $\mathcal{W}_{t_{n+1}} \subset \mathcal{W}_{t_n}\mathcal{Y}_{t_n}^{t_{n+1}}$. Instead it is necessary to turn to the equation

$$W_{t_{n+1}}(\Gamma) = \left[\int W_{t_n}(dz)\,V_{t_n}^{t_{n+1}}(z,\Omega)\right]^{-1}\int W_{t_n}(dz)\,V_{t_n}^{t_{n+1}}(z,\Gamma), \tag{5.83}$$

resulting from (5.52), (5.49), and the normalizing condition $W_t(\Omega) = 1$. In addition to this, instead of (5.80) it is now sufficient to use the simpler equation $\mathbf{P}(\Gamma_{t_n}|\mathcal{W}_{t_1}\ldots\mathcal{W}_{t_n}) = W_{t_n}(\Gamma_{t_n})$. Other changes do not require explanations.

The fact that the transition probabilities of the secondary processes satisfy the Chapman–Kolmogorov equation is a consequence of the cited theorems. We will call these secondary *a posteriori* transition probabilities, as opposed to the (primary) *a posteriori* measures $V_s^t, \widetilde{V}_s^t$ and W_s^{tu}. The infinitesimal operators corresponding to the secondary *a posteriori* probabilities we will call secondary *a posteriori* operators, and designate them by $\mathcal{L}(t)$.

3. We will now consider the question of whether a Markov process is created by the inner *a posteriori* probabilities.

Definition 5.5. Let there be given

(A) a Markov process $(\Omega, \mathcal{Z}_t, t \in T, \mathbf{P})$;

(B) an observed process $(\Omega, \mathcal{Y}_t, t \in T, \mathbf{P})$, $\mathcal{Y}_t \subset \mathcal{Z}_t$;

(C) conditional probabilities $P_t(\Gamma_t) = \mathbf{P}(\Gamma_t | y_a^u)$ and their corresponding σ-algebras $\mathcal{P}_t$. The process $(\Omega, \mathcal{P}_t, t \in T, \mathbf{P})$ we will call a secondary inner *a posteriori* $\mathcal{P}$-process.

It is also possible to examine the combination of an inner *a posteriori* $\mathcal{P}$-process with a final secondary process $\mathcal{W}$ or $\mathcal{V}$.

Definition 5.6. The combined process $(\Omega, \mathcal{W}_t, \mathcal{P}_t, t \in T, \mathbf{P})$ composed of a secondary W-process (Definition 5.4) and an inner P-process (Definition 5.5) we will call a secondary inner *a posteriori* WP-process.

Theorem 5.10. The secondary inner *a posteriori* WP-process is Markov.

Proof. We will show that

$$\mathbf{P}(B | \mathcal{W}_{t_1} \mathcal{P}_{t_1} \ldots \mathcal{W}_{t_n} \mathcal{P}_{t_n}) = \mathbf{P}(B | \mathcal{W}_{t_n} \mathcal{P}_{t_n}) \tag{5.84}$$

where

$$B \in \mathcal{W}_{t_{n+1}} \mathcal{P}_{t_{n+1}} \quad (t_1 \leqslant \cdots \leqslant t_n \leqslant t_{n+1}).$$

The probabilities $P_{t_{n+1}} = \mathbf{P}(\Gamma_{t_{n+1}} | y_a^u)$ can be obtained from P_{t_n} by solving Eq. (5.63b) in the interval $(t_n, t_{n+1}]$. Hence they are functions of W measurable with respect to $\mathcal{P}_{t_n} \mathcal{W}_{t_n}^{t_{n+1}} \mathcal{Y}_{t_n}^{t_{n+1}}$, that is,

$$\mathcal{P}_{t_{n+1}} \subset \mathcal{P}_{t_n} \mathcal{W}_{t_n}^{t_{n+1}} \mathcal{Y}_{t_n}^{t_{n+1}}. \tag{5.85}$$

Examining further the equation of the type (5.83), we have

$$\mathcal{W}_t \subset \mathcal{W}_{t_n} \mathcal{Y}_{t_n}^t \quad (t_n < t \leqslant t_{n+1}).$$

This in conjunction with (5.85) gives us

$$\mathcal{P}_{t_{n+1}} \subset \mathcal{W}_{t_n} \mathcal{P}_{t_n} \mathcal{Y}_{t_n}^{t_{n+1}}; \; \mathcal{W}_{t_{n+1}} \mathcal{P}_{t_{n+1}} \subset \mathcal{W}_{t_n} \mathcal{P}_{t_n} \mathcal{Y}_{t_n}^{t_{n+1}}. \tag{5.86}$$

Let us consider the probabilities

$$\mathbf{P}\left(dy_{t_n}^{t_{n+1}} \middle| \mathcal{W}_{t_1}\mathcal{P}_{t_1}\ldots\mathcal{W}_{t_n}\mathcal{P}_{t_n}\right)=\int \mathbf{P}\left(dy_{t_n}^{t_{n+1}} \middle| \mathcal{Z}_{t_n}\mathcal{W}_{t_1}\mathcal{P}_{t_1}\ldots \ldots\mathcal{W}_{t_n}\mathcal{P}_{t_n}\right)\mathbf{P}\left(dz_{t_n}|\mathcal{W}_{t_1}\mathcal{P}_{t_1}\ldots\mathcal{W}_{t_n}\mathcal{P}_{t_n}\right). \tag{5.87}$$

As a result of the Markov property of the initial process we have

$$\mathbf{P}\left(dy_{t_n}^{t_{n+1}} \middle| \mathcal{Z}_{t_n}\mathcal{W}_{t_1}\mathcal{P}_{t_1}\ldots\mathcal{W}_{t_n}\mathcal{P}_{t_n}\right)=\mathbf{P}\left(dy_{t_n}^{t_{n+1}} \middle| \mathcal{Z}_{t_n}\mathcal{P}_{t_1}\ldots\mathcal{P}_{t_n}\right) \tag{5.88}$$

since $\mathcal{W}_{t_1}\ldots\mathcal{W}_{t_n}\subset\mathcal{Y}_a^{t_n}$ relate to the past, and $dy_{t_n}^{t_{n+1}}$ to the future, with respect to the "present" $\mathcal{Z}_{t_n}$.

If Eq. (5.63b) is solved with the reverse flow of time, then by analogy to (5.85) we will have

$$\mathcal{P}_{t_i}\subset\mathcal{P}_{t_n}\mathcal{W}_{t_i}^{t_n}\mathcal{Y}_{t_i}^{t_n}\subset\mathcal{P}_{t_n}\mathcal{Y}_a^{t_n}\quad(t_i\leqslant t_n). \tag{5.89}$$

Thus the right side of (5.88) can be written

$$\mathbf{P}\left(dy_{t_n}^{t_{n+1}} \middle| \mathcal{Z}_{t_n}\mathcal{P}_{t_1}\ldots\mathcal{P}_{t_n}\right)=\mathbf{M}\left[\mathbf{P}\left(dy_{t_n}^{t_{n+1}} \middle| \mathcal{Z}_{t_n}\mathcal{P}_{t_n}\mathcal{Y}_a^{t_n}\right) \middle| \mathcal{Z}_{t_1}\mathcal{P}_{t_1}\ldots\mathcal{P}_{t_n}\right].$$

But

$$\mathbf{P}\left(dy_{t_n}^{t_{n+1}} \middle| \mathcal{Z}_{t_n}\mathcal{P}_{t_n}\mathcal{Y}_a^{t_n}\right)=\mathbf{P}\left(dy_{t_n}^{t_{n+1}} \middle| \mathcal{Z}_{t_n}\mathcal{P}_{t_n}\right)$$

on the strength of the Markov condition, hence

$$\begin{aligned}\mathbf{P}\left(dy_{t_n}^{t_{n+1}} \middle| \mathcal{Z}_{t_n}\mathcal{P}_{t_1}\ldots\mathcal{P}_{t_n}\right)&=\mathbf{M}\left[\mathbf{P}\left(dy_{t_n}^{t_{n+1}} \middle| \mathcal{Z}_{t_n}\mathcal{P}_{t_n}\right)|\mathcal{Z}_{t_1}\mathcal{P}_{t_1}\ldots\mathcal{P}_{t_n}\right]\\&=\mathbf{P}\left(dy_{t_n}^{t_{n+1}} \middle| \mathcal{Z}_{t_n}\mathcal{P}_{t_n}\right).\end{aligned} \tag{5.90}$$

In this way the probability (5.88) entering into the right side of (5.87) is $\mathcal{Z}_{t_n}\mathcal{P}_{t_n}$-measurable. We will examine the other probability. Since $\mathcal{W}_{t_1}\mathcal{P}_{t_1}\ldots\mathcal{W}_{t_n}\mathcal{P}_{t_n}\subset\mathcal{Y}_a^u$, it can be written

$$\begin{aligned}\mathbf{P}(dz_{t_n}|\mathcal{W}_{t_1}\mathcal{P}_{t_1}\ldots\mathcal{W}_{t_n}\mathcal{P}_{t_n})&=\mathbf{M}[\mathbf{P}(dz_{t_n}|\mathcal{Y}_a^u)\,|\,\mathcal{W}_{t_1}\mathcal{P}_{t_1}\ldots\mathcal{W}_{t_n}\mathcal{P}_{t_n}]\\&=\mathbf{M}[P_{t_n}(dz_{t_n})\,|\,\mathcal{W}_{t_1}\mathcal{P}_{t_1}\ldots\mathcal{W}_{t_n}\mathcal{P}_{t_n}].\end{aligned}$$

From this

$$\mathbf{P}(dz_{t_n}|\mathcal{W}_{t_1}\mathcal{P}_{t_1}\ldots\mathcal{W}_{t_n}\mathcal{P}_{t_n})=P_{t_n}(dz_{t_n})=\mathbf{M}[P_{t_n}(dz_{t_n})|\mathcal{P}_{t_n}]. \tag{5.91}$$

Substituting (5.90) and (5.91) into (5.87), we prove that

$$\mathbf{P}\left(dy_{t_n}^{t_{n+1}} \middle| \mathcal{W}_{t_1}\mathcal{P}_{t_1}\dots\mathcal{W}_{t_n}\mathcal{P}_{t_n}\right) = \int_{Z_{t_n}} \mathbf{P}\left(dy_{t_n}^{t_{n+1}} \middle| \mathcal{Z}_{t_n}\mathcal{P}_{t_n}\right) P_{t_n}(dz_{t_n})$$

$$= \mathbf{P}\left(dy_{t_n}^{t_{n+1}} \middle| \mathcal{P}_{t_n}\right). \tag{5.92}$$

For completion of the proof one need only use the equation

$$\mathbf{P}\left(B \middle| \mathcal{W}_{t_1}\mathcal{P}_{t_1}\dots\mathcal{W}_{t_n}\mathcal{P}_{t_n}\mathcal{Y}_{t_n}^{t_{n+1}}\right) = \mathbf{P}\left(B \middle| \mathcal{W}_{t_n}\mathcal{P}_{t_n}\mathcal{Y}_{t_n}^{t_{n+1}}\right) = \mathcal{I}_B(\omega)$$
$$B \in \mathcal{W}_{t_{n+1}}\mathcal{P}_{t_{n+1}} \subset \mathcal{W}_{t_n}\mathcal{P}_{t_n}\mathcal{Y}_{t_n}^{t_{n+1}} \tag{5.93}$$

resulting from the second of relations (5.86). In fact, substituting (5.92) and (5.93) into the obvious relation

$$\mathbf{P}(B|\mathcal{W}_{t_1}\mathcal{P}_{t_1}\dots\mathcal{W}_{t_n}\mathcal{P}_{t_n}) =$$
$$\int \mathbf{P}\left(B \middle| \mathcal{W}_{t_1}\mathcal{P}_{t_1}\dots\mathcal{W}_{t_n}\mathcal{P}_{t_n}\mathcal{Y}_{t_n}^{t_{n+1}}\right) \mathbf{P}\left(dy_{t_n}^{t_{n+1}} \middle| \mathcal{W}_{t_1}\mathcal{P}_{t_1}\dots\mathcal{W}_{t_n}\mathcal{P}_{t_n}\right),$$

we obtain (5.84). The proof is completed.

In an analogous manner we can prove the Markov properties of the secondary *a posteriori* PV-process formed by the processes P_t and V_t^u (u being fixed). More unexpected is the following theorem about the Markov property of the P-process by itself.

Theorem 5.11. The secondary inner *a posteriori* P-process almost certainly is Markov.

Proof. Since the Markov property is reversible in time, we will prove it for reverse time, namely, we will show that

$$\mathbf{P}(B|\mathcal{P}_{t_2}\dots\mathcal{P}_{t_n}) = \mathbf{P}(B|\mathcal{P}_{t_2})$$
$$B \in \mathcal{P}_{t_1} \quad (t_1 \leqslant \dots < t_n). \tag{5.94}$$

As noted in the proof of the preceding theorem, from Eq. (5.63b) follows the inclusion

$$\mathcal{P}_{t_1} \subset \mathcal{P}_{t_2}\mathcal{Y}_a^{t_2} \tag{5.95}$$

[see (5.89)]. Further, from the equation

$$dP_t = P_t \bar{d}\,\overset{\approx}{\mathrm{L}}(t)$$

with the operator (5.63), it follows that

$$\mathcal{P}_t \subset \mathcal{P}_{t_2}\mathcal{Y}_{t_2}^u, \quad t > t_2 \tag{5.96}$$

Using (5.96), we obtain

$$\mathrm{P}(dy_a^{t_2}|\mathcal{Z}_{t_2}\mathcal{P}_{t_2}\dots\mathcal{P}_{t_n}) = \mathrm{M}\left[\mathrm{P}(dy_a^{t_2}|\mathcal{Z}_{t_2}\mathcal{P}_{t_2}\mathcal{Y}_{t_2}^{u})|\mathcal{Z}_{t_2}\mathcal{P}_{t_2}\dots\mathcal{P}_{t_n}\right],$$

from which, as a result of the Markov property

$$\mathrm{P}\left(dy_a^{t_2}|\mathcal{Z}_{t_2}\mathcal{P}_{t_2}\mathcal{Y}_{t_2}^{u}\right) = \mathrm{P}\left(dy_a^{t_2}|\mathcal{Z}_{t_2}\mathcal{P}_{t_2}\right)$$

we have

$$\mathrm{P}\left(dy_a^{t_2}|\mathcal{Z}_{t_2}\mathcal{P}_{t_2}\dots\mathcal{P}_{t_n}\right) = \mathrm{P}\left(dy_a^{t_2}|\mathcal{Z}_{t_2}\mathcal{P}_{t_2}\right). \tag{5.97}$$

Further,

$$\mathrm{P}(dz_{t_2}|\mathcal{P}_{t_2}\dots\mathcal{P}_{t_n}) = \mathrm{M}\left[\mathrm{P}(dz_{t_2}|\mathcal{Y}_a^{u})|\mathcal{P}_{t_2}\dots\mathcal{P}_{t_n}\right] = P_{t_2}(dz_{t_2}) \tag{5.98}$$

since $\mathcal{P}_{t_2}\dots\mathcal{P}_{t_n}\subset\mathcal{Y}_a^{u}$. Substituting (5.97) and (5.98) into the equation

$$\mathrm{P}\left(dy_a^{t_2}|\mathcal{P}_{t_2}\dots\mathcal{P}_{t_n}\right) = \int \mathrm{P}\left(dy_a^{t_2}|\mathcal{Z}_{t_2}\mathcal{P}_{t_2}\dots\mathcal{P}_{t_n}\right)\mathrm{P}(dz_{t_2}|\mathcal{P}_{t_2}\dots\mathcal{P}_{t_n}),$$

we will have

$$\mathrm{P}\left(dy_a^{t_2}|\mathcal{P}_{t_2}\dots\mathcal{P}_{t_n}\right) = \mathrm{P}\left(dy_a^{t_2}|\mathcal{P}_{t_2}\right). \tag{5.99}$$

Using (5.95), from which we have

$$\mathrm{P}\left(B|\mathcal{P}_{t_2}\dots\mathcal{P}_{t_n}\mathcal{Y}_a^{t_2}\right) = \mathrm{P}\left(B|\mathcal{P}_{t_2}\mathcal{Y}_a^{t_2}\right) = \mathcal{I}_B(\omega)$$

we will write the conditional probability of the set $B\in\mathcal{P}_{t_1}$ in the form

$$\mathrm{P}(B|\mathcal{P}_{t_2}\dots\mathcal{P}_{t_n}) = \int \mathrm{P}\left(B|\mathcal{P}_{t_2}\mathcal{Y}_a^{t_2}\right)\mathrm{P}\left(dy_a^{t_2}|\mathcal{P}_{t_2}\dots\mathcal{P}_{t_n}\right). \tag{5.100}$$

After substituting (5.99) into the relation (5.100), we obtain (5.94). The proof is completed.

As a result of the above-mentioned Markov properties of inner secondary *a posteriori* processes there exist inner secondary *a posteriori* infinitesimal operators corresponding to these processes. We will designatė them thus: $d\mathcal{L}^P$ is the operator for the P-process, $d\mathcal{L}^{WP}$ the operator for the WP-process, etc. Examples of these operators will be given subsequently.

* * *

The proofs of the latter theorems, as well as the other results compiled in this chapter, are based on the assumption of the existence of a system of measures V_s^t which satisfy the requirements 1°–3°. Intuitive insight does not permit us to doubt the fact that this system of measures, defined in one way or another (perhaps in the generalized sense), exists without exception in all cases of conditional Markov processes. Its existence does not necessarily require assumptions of the type "continuity of information" or of the type of Hypothesis 5.1. It is true that in more complex cases the indicated measures can have a more "exotic" form, possibly going outside the framework of the existing theory of measure. A generalization of the usual concepts may be needed for their examination.

Let us turn, for example, to formula (5.7). If the measure $\mathbf{P}(\Gamma_s | y_r^u)$ is not absolutely continuous with respect to $\mathbf{P}(\Gamma_s | y_r^s)$, it is impossible to use the Radon-Nikodim theorem to define the function (5.7). Nevertheless, if we include generalized functions in the examination, then the measures $\mathbf{P}(\Gamma_s | y_r^u)$ and $\mathbf{P}(\Gamma_s | y_r^s)$ will define the function (5.7) as a generalized function to a sufficient degree of uniqueness. The other objects of the theory can also be defined in the generalized sense. The main assertions of the theory regarding the relations between them and the question of their measurability after the appropriate generalization of these objects will remain true as formerly. Of course, a strict proof of these assertions will be much more complicated.

CHAPTER 6

Discontinuous Changes of an Observed Diffusion Process

In this chapter we will examine one of the important specific cases of conditional Markov processes. It will be assumed that we have a finite number m of different diffusion processes between which Markov transitions are possible *a priori*. The observer has at his disposal a realization of a diffusion process, but does not know to which of the diffusion processes it refers. Hence the reference Markov process in this case is a combination of a process with m states and a diffusion process, and the *a posteriori* process is a process with m states (in combination with the observed process). This problem is a natural generalization of known problems in mathematical statistics in which *a priori* transitions between states are assumed impossible (see supplement).

Among the problems examined here is the problem of estimation of a Markov process having several states observed with additive white noise. It was solved by the author in papers [1, 2]. The process with two states used as an example in Sect. 6.5 was thoroughly examined by the author [1, 2, 15, 19]. The equation of this process is written in two forms: in the form of Ito, and in the symmetrical form. The equations for the specific case of additive white noise, not in final simplified for, were also later deduced by Kushner [1, 2], in which various forms of the equation and associated possibilities for its simulation remained unexplained.

6.1 The Markov Process with m States

1. Let us begin with the specific form of a series of formulas from Chapter 3 as they apply to a Markov process with m states. The phase space $E = E_m$ of such a process consists of m points. With no loss of generality these points can be considered as numbers

1, ..., m. The measure μ in such a space is determined entirely by the values $\mu(1), \ldots, \mu(m)$. Thus μ can be taken as a point in an m-dimensional space, and the space of the measures can be taken as a region of this space. In the role of the Markov system of measures $\{\mu_{st}(x, \Lambda)\}$ we can take $\{\mu_{st}(\alpha, \beta)\}$, where $\mu_{st}(\alpha, \beta)$ has fixed $s, t \in T$, and $\alpha, \beta \in E_m$ represents an $m \times m$ matrix. The operator T_{st} in $T_{st}g$ and in φT_{st} (Sect. 3.1) we will take in this case to be operators in an m-dimensional linear space. We will understand every operator equation to be an element-by-element equation of the corresponding $m \times m$ matrices.

Let us assume we are given a Markov system of measures $\{\mu_{st}(\alpha, \beta)\}$ such that the limits (3.1) and (3.11) exist:

$$L(t) - L(s) = \lim_{\Delta \to 0} [\ln \mu_{t_1 t_2} + \ldots + \ln \mu_{t_{N-1} t_N}]; \tag{6.1}$$

$$[L^*(t) - L^*(s)]_{\alpha\beta} = \lim_{\Delta \to 0} [\mu_{t_1 t_2}(\alpha, \beta) - \delta_{\alpha\beta} + \ldots$$
$$\ldots + \mu_{t_{N-1}, t_N}(\alpha, \beta) - \delta_{\alpha\beta}] \tag{6.2}$$

($\|\delta_{\alpha\beta}\| = I$; $\{t_i\}$ is a Δ-division of the interval $[s, t]$; $\ln \mu_{t_i t_{i+1}}$ is the matrix logarithm).

We will assume that the elements of the indicated matrices represent diffusion processes, that is, that the operator defined by Eq. (6.2) has the form

$$L^*(t) - L^*(s) = \int_s^t [A^*(y(\tau), \tau)\, d\tau + A_\sigma(y(\tau), \tau)\, d^* y_\sigma]. \tag{6.3}$$

Here A^* and A_σ are matrices with elements $\overset{*}{A}_{\alpha\beta}(y, \tau)$ and $A_{\alpha\beta\sigma}(y, \tau)$ which we consider to be bounded and continuous functions of $y_1, \ldots, y_l, t$ (in addition to this, they satisfy a differentiability condition). Further, $\{y(t)\} = \{y_1(t), \ldots, y_l(t)\}$ is a diffusion process with drift parameters $a_\sigma(y, t)$ and a local variance matrix $b_{\sigma\rho}(y, t)$. These parameters are functions of y and t with the same properties as $\overset{*}{A}_{\alpha\beta}, A_{\alpha\beta\sigma}$.

The first formula (3.4) in this case takes on the form

$$\mu_{st}(\alpha, \beta) = \delta_{\alpha\beta} + \int_s^t \mu_{s\tau}(\alpha, \gamma) [\overset{*}{A}_{\gamma\beta}(y(\tau), \tau)\, d\tau +$$
$$+ A_{\gamma\beta\sigma}(y(\tau), \tau)\, d^* y_\sigma(\tau), \tag{6.4}$$

analogous to (2.34). This equation is a stochastic equation (see Chapter 2) and determines the system of measures $\mu_{st}(\alpha, \beta)$ as a function of $y(t, \omega)$ (and hence of ω), i.e., as a diffusional random process.

If we use the symmetrized stochastic integral defined in Sect. 2.1, then in accordance with (2.33) and (2.35) we will have

$$\mu_{st}(\alpha, \beta) = \delta_{\alpha\beta} + \int_s^t \mu_{s\tau}(\alpha, \gamma)\,[A_{\gamma\beta}(y(\tau), \tau)\,d\tau +$$

$$+ A_{\gamma\beta\sigma}(y(\tau), \tau)\,dy_\sigma(\tau)], \tag{6.5}$$

$$A_{\alpha\beta} = \overset{*}{A}_{\alpha\beta} - \frac{1}{2}\left[A_{\alpha\gamma\sigma}A_{\gamma\beta\rho} + \frac{\partial A_{\alpha\beta\sigma}}{\partial y_\rho}\right]b_{\sigma\rho}. \tag{6.6}$$

Let us assume that Eq. (6.4) or (6.5) determines the system of measures μ_{st}. It is possible to prove that it satisfies Eqs. (6.1) and (6.2), and conversely that (6.4) follows from (6.2) and the Chapman-Kolmogorov equation. Thus the measure (6.4) is determined by the operator (6.3) with that degree of uniqueness with which the solution of a stochastic equation is determined (the reference measure belongs to the same class of uniqueness).

For the proof it is convenient to introduce the norm of the $m \times m$ matrices, for example,

$$\|B\| = m \max\{|B_{\alpha\beta}|,\ \alpha, \beta = 1, \ldots, m\}.$$

Then the space of the matrices will be a Banach space, in which the inequality

$$\|BC\| \leqslant \|B\|\ \|C\|$$

will be satisfied. Applying formulas (3.57) and (3.56), we have

$$\mu_{st}(\alpha, \beta) = \delta_{\alpha\beta} + \int_s^t [A_{\alpha\beta}d\tau + A_{\alpha\beta\sigma}dy_\sigma] +$$

$$+ \frac{1}{2}A_{\alpha\gamma\rho}(y(s), s)\,A_{\gamma\beta\sigma}(y(s), s)\,[y_\rho(t) -$$

$$- y_\rho(s)]\,[y_\sigma(t) - y_\sigma(s)] + O((t-s)^{3/2}). \tag{6.7}$$

Here the estimate $O((t-s)^{3/2})$ is taken in the sense of the norm.

Using Eq. (6.7) and the equation

$$(\ln \mu_{st})_{\alpha\beta} = \int_s^t [A_{\alpha\beta}(y(\tau), \tau)\,d\tau +$$

$$+ A_{\alpha\beta\sigma}(y(\tau), \tau)\,dy_\sigma(\tau)] + O((t-s)^{3/2}),$$

derived from it, it is not difficult to prove the convergence of (6.1) and (6.2) if we take into account Lemma 2.2. We will not dwell on this in more detail, but will go on to the examination of the random process $\{x(t)\}$ in E_m, described by the indicated system of measures.

2. As was noted in Sect. 4.2, the system of measures $\{\mu_{st}(\alpha, \beta)\}$ assigns a measure in a function space. Its elements in the present case are discontinuously changing functions $x(\cdot)$ with values on E_m. We will consider the separable variant of the process. Let S be the set defining separability (everywhere dense in T), and S_Δ a Δ-division of the interval $[s, u] \subset T$, monotonically converging to $[s, u] \cap S$. As indicated in Sect. 4.2, for the examination of functional Radon-Nikodim derivatives, it is sufficient to consider the σ-algebras

$$\mathcal{N}_s^u = \lim_{\Delta \to 0} \mathcal{N}_{S_\Delta} \text{ and } \overline{\mathcal{N}}_s^u. \tag{6.8}$$

We will assume that the measure is concentrated on a set X of functions having a finite number of discontinuities in any finite interval (the remaining functions form a subset of a set of measure zero). Then each function from X which is of interest to us is characterized by the points $\tau_1 < \tau_2 < \ldots < \tau_n$ (from $T = [a, b]$), at which discontinuities occur, and by the values of the function before (β_j) and after (β_{j+1}) the discontinuity. A function $x(\cdot) \in X$ can be replaced by the parameters $n, \beta_1, \tau_1, \beta_2, \ldots, \beta_n, \tau_n, \beta_{n+1}$, and the conditions $\tau_1' \leqslant \tau_1 \leqslant \tau_1'', \ldots, \tau_n' \leqslant \tau_n \leqslant \tau_n''$ characterize the subsets

$$\Lambda = \{x(\cdot) : \beta_1, \tau_1' \leqslant \tau_1 \leqslant \tau_1'', \ldots, \beta_n, \tau_n' \leqslant \tau_n \leqslant \tau_n'', \beta_{n+1}\}$$

in X.

Let us take the interval $[s, u]$ and find the measure of the set Λ_α of functions identically equal to α on this interval:

$$\Lambda_\alpha = \{x(\cdot) : x(t) = \alpha, \ t \in [s, u] \cap S\}.$$

This set belongs to $\mathcal{N}_s^u$ and on the strength of the convergence (6.8) its measure can be written

$$\begin{aligned}\mu(\Lambda_\alpha \mid x(s) = \alpha) &= \lim_{\Delta \to 0} \mu\{x(t_1) = \alpha, \ldots, x(t_N) = \alpha \mid x(s) = \alpha\} = \\ &= \lim_{\Delta \to 0} \mu_{st_1}(\alpha, \alpha)\, \mu_{t_1 t_2}(\alpha, \alpha) \ldots \mu_{t_N u}(\alpha, \alpha).\end{aligned} \tag{6.9}$$

In order to calculate this measure explicitly, we will substitute (6.7) into (6.9). Taking into account that

$$\begin{aligned}\ln[\mu_{t_i t_{i+1}}(\alpha, \alpha)] = \int_{t_i}^{t_{i+1}} [A_{\alpha\alpha} d\tau + A_{\alpha\alpha\sigma} dy_\sigma] + \frac{1}{2} A_{\alpha\gamma\rho}(i)\, A_{\gamma\alpha\sigma}(i)\, \Delta y_\rho \Delta y_\sigma - \\ - \frac{1}{2}[A_{\alpha\alpha\sigma}(i)\, \Delta y_\sigma]^2 + O(\Delta^{3/2}),\end{aligned}$$

$$(A_{\alpha\gamma\rho}(i) = A_{\alpha\gamma\rho}(y(t_i), t_i);\ \Delta y_\sigma = y_\sigma(t_{i+1}) - y_\sigma(t_i)),$$

on the strength of Lemma 2.2 we obtain

$$\mu(\Lambda_\alpha \mid x(s) = \alpha) = \varphi_s^u(\alpha),$$

where

$$\ln \varphi_s^u(\alpha) = \int_s^u [A_{\alpha\alpha} d\tau + A_{\alpha\alpha\sigma} dy_\sigma] +$$

$$\frac{1}{2}\int_s^u [A_{\alpha\gamma\rho} A_{\gamma\alpha\sigma} - A_{\alpha\alpha\rho} A_{\alpha\alpha\sigma}]\, b_{\rho\sigma} d\tau =$$

$$= \int_s^u [A^*_{\alpha\alpha} d\tau + A_{\alpha\alpha\sigma} d^* y_\sigma] - \frac{1}{2}\int_s^u A_{\alpha\alpha\rho} A_{\alpha\alpha\sigma} b_{\rho\sigma} d\tau \tag{6.10}$$

(formulas (2.8) and (6.6) are used). We will note that $\varphi_s^t(\alpha)$ satisfies the simple stochastic equation

$$d_t \varphi_s^t(\alpha) = \varphi_s^t(\alpha)\,[A^*_{\alpha\alpha} dt + A_{\alpha\alpha\sigma} d^* y_\sigma] \equiv \varphi_s^t(\alpha)\, d^* L^*(t)_{\alpha\alpha}, \tag{6.11}$$

which is equivalent to (6.10) according to Corollary 2.1.

Now we will examine functions ($\in \Lambda_{\alpha\beta}$) which have a single discontinuity at a point τ in the interval $[\tau_1', \tau_1''] \subset [s, u]$, and are equal to α on the interval $[s, \tau)$ and to β on $(\tau, u]$. In analogy with (6.9) the measure of these functions can be written

$$\mu(\Lambda_{\alpha\beta} \mid x(s) = \alpha) = \lim_{\Delta\to 0} \sum_{\tau_1' \leqslant t_k < \tau_1''} \mu\{x(t_1) = \alpha, \ldots$$

$$\ldots, x(t_k) = \alpha,\ x(t_{k+1}) = \beta, \ldots, x(t_N) = \beta \mid x(s) = \alpha\}.$$

As a result of the Markov condition,

$$\mu(\Lambda_{\alpha\beta} \mid x(s) = \alpha) = \lim_{\Delta\to 0} \sum_{\tau_1' \leqslant t_k < \tau_1''} \mu_{st_1}(\alpha, \alpha) \ldots$$

$$\ldots \mu_{t_k, t_{k+1}}(\alpha, \beta) \ldots \mu_{t_{N-1}, t_N}(\beta, \beta).$$

As before, we will substitute here (6.7) and pass to the limit $\Delta \to 0$. Again using Lemma 2.2, we obtain a formula which can be written particularly compactly if using formula (6.6) we pass over to the operator (6.3). This result has the form

$$\mu(\Lambda_{\alpha\beta} \mid x(s) = \alpha) = \int_{\tau_1'}^{\tau_1''} \varphi_s^\tau(\alpha)\, d^* L^*(\tau)_{\alpha\beta}\, \varphi_\tau^u(\beta).$$

3. An analogous development can also be carried out for a larger number of discontinuities. Ultimately we will obtain the following result:

Theorem 6.1. Let us assume $\Lambda = \Lambda(\nu, \alpha, \tau_1', \tau_1'', \beta_1, \ldots, \beta_{\nu-1}, \tau_\nu', \tau_\nu'', \beta_\nu)$ is the set of functions:

$$x(t) = \begin{cases} \alpha \text{ for } s < t < \tau_1; \\ \beta_1 \text{ for } \tau_1 < t < \tau_2; \\ \cdots\cdots \\ \beta_\nu \text{ for } \tau_\nu < t < u, \end{cases}$$

where

$$\tau_1 \in [\tau_1', \tau_1''], \ldots, \tau_\nu \in [\tau_\nu', \tau_\nu''] \; (s \leqslant \tau_1' < \tau_1'' < \ldots < \tau_\nu' < \tau_\nu'' \leqslant u).$$

The measure of this set is determined by the formula

$$\mu(\Lambda | x(s) = \alpha) = \int_{\tau_1'}^{\tau_1''} \ldots \int_{\tau_\nu'}^{\tau_\nu''} \varphi_s^{\tau_1}(\alpha)\, d^*L^*(\tau_1)_{\alpha\beta_1} \varphi_{\tau_1}^{\tau_2}(\beta_1)\, d^*L^*(\tau_2)_{\beta_1\beta_2} \varphi_{\tau_2}^{\tau_3}(\beta_2) \ldots$$

$$\ldots d^*L^*(\tau_\nu)_{\beta_{\nu-1}\beta_\nu} \varphi_{\tau_\nu}^{u}(\beta_\nu), \tag{6.12}$$

where $\varphi_\tau^\sigma(\beta)$ is determined from (6.10) or (6.11).
A corollary of this theorem is:

Theorem 6.2. Let us assume we have two measures μ and ν, the infinitesimal operators of which are connected by the relation

$$dL^*(t)_{\alpha\beta} - dL^*(t)_{\alpha\beta}^{\nu} = [g_\alpha^*(y(t), t)\, dt + g_{\alpha\sigma}(y(t), t)\, d^*y_\sigma(t)]\, \delta_{\alpha\beta}.$$

$$(t \in [s, u]). \tag{6.13}$$

Then these measures are absolutely continuous in the space $(X, \mathcal{N}_s^u)$ and the Radon-Nikodim derivative is equal to

$$\frac{\mu(dx(\cdot) | x(s) = \alpha)}{\nu(dx(\cdot) | x(s) = \alpha)} = \chi_s^u(x(\cdot)) = \exp\left\{\int_s^u [g_{x(t)}^*(y(t), t)\, dt + \right.$$

$$\left. + g_{x(t)\sigma} d^*y_\sigma] - \frac{1}{2}\int_s^u g_{x(t)\sigma} g_{x(t)\rho} b_{\sigma\rho}\, dt\right\}, \tag{6.14}$$

i.e., $\chi_s^u(x(\cdot))$ is the solution of the equation

$$d_t\chi_s^t = \chi_s^t [g_{x(t)}^*(y(t), t)\, dt + g_{x(t)\sigma}(y(t), t)\, d^*y_\sigma(t)] \equiv$$

$$\equiv \chi_s^t (dL^* - dL^{*\nu})_{x(t), x(t)}.$$

For the proof of the theorem we first need to prove the analogous assertions for the space $(X_n, \mathcal{N}_s^u \cap X_n)$, where $X_n \subset X$ is a set of functions having exactly n discontinuities on the interval $[s, u]$. Considering the integral

$$\int_\Lambda \chi_s^u \, \nu(dx(\cdot) \mid x(s) = \alpha), \quad \Lambda \in \mathcal{N}_s^t \cap X_n, \tag{6.15}$$

where $\nu(\Lambda)$ is determined by formula (6.12), and using the continuity of the function χ_s^u and properties of stochastic integrals of the type formulated in Lemma 2.3, we obtain an expression similar to (6.12), but for a different operator dL^*. Hence the integral (6.15) is equal to $\mu(\Lambda \mid x(s) = \alpha)$, which proves the assertion for $(X_n, \mathcal{N}_s^u \cap X_n)$. In order to complete the proof it remains to construct a union of these subsets coincident with $(X, \mathcal{N}_s^u)$.

Further we will need the converse theorem:

Theorem 6.3. Let us assume we have two Markov measures absolutely continuous on $(X, \mathcal{N}_s^u)$, where the derivative has the form (6.14). Then on $[s, u]$ the infinitesimal operators of these measures are related by (6.13).

For the proof we need to examine the infinitesimal operator

$$dL^*(t)^{\bar{\mu}}_{\alpha\beta} = dL^*(t)^{\nu}_{\alpha\beta} + [\overset{*}{g}_\alpha dt + g_{\alpha\sigma} d^* y_\sigma] \, \delta_{\alpha\beta}$$

and its corresponding measure $\bar{\mu}$. Using the direct theorem, we have $\bar{\mu} = \mu$. But an infinitesimal operator is uniquely determined by the system of measures [see formula (6.2)], hence $dL^{*\bar{\mu}} = dL^*$.

6.2 Several Diffusion Processes and Markov Transitions Among Them

1. Let us assume we have m diffusion processes $\{y(t)\}$ in an l-dimensional space R_l, and that each of them is described by an infinitesimal operator

$$dL_\alpha(t) = d\overset{*}{L}_\alpha(t) = \Big[c(\alpha, y, t) + a_\rho(\alpha, y, t) \frac{\partial}{\partial y_\rho} + \\ + \frac{1}{2} b_{\rho\sigma}(\alpha, y, t) \frac{\partial^2}{\partial y_\rho \partial y_\sigma} \Big] dt, \quad \alpha = 1, \ldots, m. \tag{6.16}$$

Here $c(\alpha, y, t)$, $a_\rho(\alpha, y, t)$, ... are functions of y and t, with the properties described at the beginning of the preceding section. They depend, in addition to this, on the number $\alpha \in E_m = \{1, \ldots, m\}$. To each number corresponds a measure $\mathbf{P}_\alpha$ in a function space $(Y, \mathcal{Y})$. The functions $y(t)$ with values in R_l are elements of the latter. Similar function spaces, σ-algebras in them, and measures were examined in Sects. 4.2 and 4.3. We will use those results here.

Let us assume that we are observing the process $\{y(t)\}$ in the interval $[s, u]$. To this observation corresponds the σ-algebra $\mathcal{Y}_s^u$ (coinciding with $\mathcal{N}_s^u$ or $\mathcal{M}_s^u$ in the notation of Sect. 4.2). The observer is interested in the question of which process of the m possible ones was actually realized. In general, he cannot answer this question precisely, but can only indicate an *allowable set* $H \subset E_m$, to which the observed process necessarily belongs. This set is the set of those processes with measures on $\mathcal{Y}_s^u$ which are mutually absolutely continuous with the measure of the true process. This set is not empty with probability 1 since the true process necessarily belongs to it. If the allowable set contains only one element, the statistical problem is solved completely: the observer correctly (with probability 1) indicates the number of the true process. With a larger number of elements in the allowable set there arises a typical problem of mathematical statistics.

As we can see from the above material, the question of absolute continuity of the measures of the diffusion process examined in Chapter 4 is of fundamental importance for this question. As a result of Lemmas 2.2 and 4.4, we can consider that in addition to the process $\{y(t)\}$ on the interval $[s, u]$, we also observe the processes

$$q_{\rho\sigma}(t) = b_{\rho\sigma}(\alpha, y(t), t); \quad r_{\rho''}(t) = a_{\rho''}(\alpha, y(t), t) - \\ - b_{\rho''\sigma'}(\alpha, y(t), t)\, \overset{-1}{b}_{\sigma'\pi'}(\alpha, y(t), t)\, a_{\pi'}(\alpha, y(t), t) \tag{6.17} \\ (\rho, \sigma = 1, \dots l; \ \rho'' = l' + 1, \dots l).$$

The allowable set is thus the set of processes having functions (6.17) similar to those of the true process:

$$H = \{\alpha : b_{\rho\sigma}(\alpha, y(t), t) = q_{\rho\sigma}(t); \ a_{\rho''}(\alpha, y(t), t) - \\ - b_{\rho''\sigma'} \overset{-1}{b}_{\sigma'\pi'}\, a_{\pi'} = r_{\rho''}(t); \\ t \in [s, u]; \ \rho, \sigma = 1, \dots, l; \ \rho'' = l' + 1, \dots, l\}.$$

Thus the statistical problem is nontrivial if there are at least two processes for which the identity

$$b_{\rho\sigma}(\alpha, y(t), t) \equiv b_{\rho\sigma}(\alpha', y(t), t), \ \dots \quad \text{for } t \in [s, u].$$

is valid. Theorem 4.1 gives the expression for the Radon-Nikodim derivative of the measures of the allowable set.

2. Let us turn to the consideration of discontinuous changes of the diffusion process number. The number of the process is now a

function of time $x(t)$ with values in E_m. Let $x(\cdot)$ have a finite number of discontinuities in the interval $[s, t]$. The observed diffusion process $\{ y(t) \}$ now corresponds to the infinitesimal operator

$$dL_{x(\cdot)}(t) = \Big[c(x(t), y, t) + a_\rho(x(t), y, t) \frac{\partial}{\partial y_\rho} + \\ + \frac{1}{2} b_{\rho\sigma}(x(t), y, t) \frac{\partial^2}{\partial y_\rho \partial y_\sigma} \Big] dt,$$

instead of (6.16). The measure of this process in the function space $(Y, \mathcal{Y})$ can conveniently be designated $\mathbf{P}(\Lambda \mid x(\cdot)), \Lambda \in \mathcal{Y}$.

Instead of the number α, the function $x(\cdot)$ is now the independent variable. Everything stated above regarding solution of a statistical problem immediately applies to this case. The allowable set H is the set $H \subset X$ of functions which can compete with the function in fact being realized. That is,

$$H = \{ x(\cdot) : b_{\rho\sigma}(x(t), y(t), t) = q_{\rho\sigma}(t),\ a_{\rho''}(x(t), y(t), t) - \\ - b_{\rho''\sigma'} b^{-1}_{\sigma'\pi'} a_{\pi'} = r_{\rho''}(t); \\ t \in [s, u];\ \rho, \sigma = 1, \ldots, l;\ \rho'' = l' + 1, \ldots, l \}. \tag{6.18}$$

We apply Theorem 4.1 to the measure $\mathbf{P}(\Lambda \mid x(\cdot))$ corresponding to the allowable set. As a result of (6.18) the infinitesimal operator (4.26) [where we assume $\nu = \mathbf{Q}$] can be replaced by the operator

$$dL^{\mathbf{Q}}(t) = \Big[r_{\rho''}(t) \frac{\partial}{\partial y_{\rho''}} + \frac{1}{2} q_{\rho\sigma}(t) \frac{\partial^2}{\partial y_\rho \partial y_\sigma} \Big] dt.$$

The measure corresponding to this operator will be designated $\mathbf{Q}(\Lambda), \Lambda \in \mathcal{Y}$. Theorem 4.1 yields the following expression for the Radon-Nikodim derivative of the measures $\mathbf{P}(\Lambda \mid x(\cdot))$ and $\mathbf{Q}(\Lambda)$ with respect to the σ-algebra $\mathcal{Y}_s^u$:

$$\frac{\mathbf{P}(dy(\cdot) \mid x(\cdot), y(s))}{\mathbf{Q}(dy(\cdot) \mid y(s))} = \chi_s^u(x(\cdot), y(\cdot)), \tag{6.19}$$

where

$$\chi_s^u = \exp \Big\{ \int_s^u \Big[c(x(t), y(t), t)\, dt + \\ + a_{\rho'}(x(t), y(t), t)\, q^{-1}_{\rho'\sigma'}(t)\, d^* y_{\sigma'}(t) - \\ - \frac{1}{2} a_{\rho'}(x(t), y(t), t)\, q^{-1}_{\rho'\sigma'}(t)\, a_{\sigma'}(x(t), y(t), t)\, dt \Big] \Big\}. \tag{6.20}$$

Turning to the Bayesian statistical problem, we assign a measure $\mathbf{R}(\Gamma)$, $\Gamma \in \mathcal{X}$ in the function space $X \ni x(\cdot)$. Let this measure be

Markov and be described by an *a priori* infinitesimal operator: $d\overset{*}{L}_{pr}(t)_{\alpha\beta}$.

The combination of the measures $\mathbf{R}$ and $\mathbf{P}(\cdot|x(\cdot))$ determines the measure in the combined space $(Z,\mathscr{Z})=(X\times Y,\ \mathscr{X}\times\mathscr{Y})$. In fact, it can be assumed that

$$\mathbf{P}(\Gamma\Lambda)=\int_{\Gamma}\mathbf{P}(\Lambda\,|\,x(\cdot))\,\mathbf{R}(dx(\cdot)),\quad \Gamma\in\mathscr{X},\ \Lambda\in\mathscr{Y}. \tag{6.21}$$

It is easy to understand that the measure in the combined space will be Markov as a result of the Markov properties of the reference measures $\mathbf{R}$ and $\mathbf{P}(\cdot|x(\cdot))$.

6.3 *A Posteriori* Infinitesimal Operators

1. Let us take the equation

$$\mathbf{P}(\Lambda\,|\,x(\cdot),\,y(s))=\int_{\Lambda}\chi_s^u\,\mathbf{Q}(dy(\cdot)\,|\,y(s)),$$

equivalent to (6.19), and integrate it over the set $\Gamma\in\mathscr{X}$ using the measure $\mathbf{R}(\cdot|x(s))$. According to (6.21) we will have

$$\mathbf{P}(\Gamma\Lambda\,|\,x(s),\,y(s))=\int_{\Gamma}\Big[\int_{\Lambda}\chi_s^u\,\mathbf{Q}(dy(\cdot)\,|\,y(s))\Big]\,\mathbf{R}(dx(\cdot)\,|\,x(s)).$$

Using Fubini's theorem, we obtain from this

$$\mathbf{P}(\Gamma\Lambda\,|\,x(s),\,y(s))=\int_{\Lambda}\Big[\int_{\Gamma}\chi_s^u\,\mathbf{R}(dx(\cdot)\,|\,x(s))\Big]\,\mathbf{Q}(dy(\cdot)\,|\,y(s)).$$

Hence for fixed $\Gamma\in\mathscr{X}$ the measure $\mathbf{P}(\Gamma\Lambda|x(s),\,y(s))$ is absolutely continuous with respect to $\mathbf{Q}(\Lambda|y(s))$ on $\mathscr{Y}_s^u\ni\Lambda$ and the corresponding derivative is

$$\frac{\mathbf{P}(\Gamma dy(\cdot)\,|\,x(s),\,y(s))}{\mathbf{Q}(dy(\cdot)\,|\,y(s))}=\int_{\Gamma}\chi_s^u\,\mathbf{R}(dx(\cdot)\,|\,x(s)). \tag{6.22}$$

We assume here $\Gamma=\Gamma_u\in\mathscr{X}_u,\ u>s$ and define

$$V_s^u(x(s),\,y(s),\,\Gamma_u)\equiv V_s^u(x(s),\,\Gamma_u)=\frac{\mathbf{P}(\Gamma_u dy(\cdot)\,|\,x(s),\,y(s))}{\mathbf{Q}(dy(\cdot)\,|\,y(s))}. \tag{6.23}$$

Let us compare the above with Hypothesis 5.1. In such a comparison, naturally, it must be assumed that

$$E=E_m\times R_l;\quad \mathscr{Z}_t=\mathscr{X}_t\times\mathscr{Y}_t;$$
$$\mathscr{X}_t=\mathscr{X}_t\times\mathscr{Y}^\circ;\quad \mathscr{Y}_t=\mathscr{X}^\circ\times\mathscr{Y}_t,$$

where $\mathscr{X}^\circ$, $\mathscr{Y}^\circ$ are trivial σ-algebras consisting of the entire space X or Y and the empty set. Hypothesis 5.1 is satisfied, while the measure (6.23) serves as the basic *a posteriori* measure (5.36).

Let us find the infinitesimal operator corresponding to this *a posteriori* measure.

In Sect. 5.4 it was proven [Theorem 5.8, property 3°, and the formula (5.27)] that the system of measures (6.23), and hence also the measure (6.22), i.e., the measure $V(\Gamma \mid x(s)) = \frac{\mathbf{P}(\Gamma\, dy(\cdot) \mid x(s),\ y(s))}{\mathbf{Q}(dy(\cdot) \mid y(s))}$, $\Gamma \in \mathscr{X}^u_s$, is Markov. The measures $V(\Gamma|x(s))$ and $\mathbf{R}(\Gamma|x(s))$, as can be seen from (6.22), are absolutely continuous on $\mathscr{X}^u_s$, where the corresponding derivative χ^u_s has a form analogous to (6.14). Thus to these measures we can apply Theorem 6.3. As can be seen from comparison of (6.14) and (6.20), we have

$$g^*_{x(t)}(y,t)\,dt + g_{x(t)\sigma'}(y,t)\,d^*y_{\sigma'} = c(x(t),y,t)\,dt + a_{\rho'}(x(t),y,t)\,q^{-1}_{\rho'\sigma'}(t)\,d^*y_{\sigma'},$$

so that formula (6.13) takes on the form

$$dL^*(t)_{\alpha\beta} = dL^*(t)^R_{\alpha\beta} + [c(\alpha, y(t), t)\,dt + a_{\rho'}(\alpha, y(t), t)\,q^{-1}_{\rho'\sigma'}(t)\,d^*y_{\sigma'}(t)]\,\delta_{\alpha\beta}. \tag{6.24}$$

Thus we obtained the following result:

Theorem 6.4. In the case under consideration the basic *a posteriori* measure (6.22) and (6.23) is concentrated on the allowable set (6.18) and has the infinitesimal operators (6.24), where $dL^{*R} = dL^*_{pr}$ is the *a priori* infinitesimal operator corresponding to the *a priori* transitions between states.

Usually for such *a priori* transitions, $(dL^*_{pr})_{\alpha\beta} = p_{\alpha\beta}(t)\,dt$. Thus comparison of (6.24) with (6.3) gives us

$$A^*_{\alpha\beta}(y,t) = p_{\alpha\beta}(t) + c(\alpha,y,t)\,\delta_{\alpha\beta};$$
$$A_{\alpha\beta\sigma'}(y,t) = a_{\rho'}(\alpha,y,t)\,q^{-1}_{\rho'\sigma'}(t)\,\delta_{\alpha\beta};\quad A_{\alpha\beta\sigma''} = 0. \tag{6.25}$$

2. Let us now find the other infinitesimal operator $dL(t)$, defined by (6.2), for the *a posteriori* system of measures V^t_s. Applying the connection formula (6.6) to (6.24), we easily obtain

$$A_{\alpha\beta} = p_{\alpha\beta} + \left\{c(\alpha) - \frac{1}{2}\,a_\rho(\alpha)\,b^{-1}_{\rho'\sigma'}a_{\sigma'}(\alpha) - \frac{1}{2}\,\frac{\partial[a_{\rho'}(\alpha)\,b^{-1}_{\rho'\sigma'}]}{\partial y_\pi(t)}\,b_{\sigma'\pi}\right\}\delta_{\alpha\beta},$$

i.e.,

$$dL(t)_{\alpha\beta} = p_{\alpha\beta}dt + \Big\{c(\alpha)\,dt + a_{\rho'}(\alpha)\,b^{-1}_{\rho'\sigma'}\Big[dy_{\sigma'} - \\ - \frac{1}{2}a_{\sigma'}(\alpha)\,dt\Big] - \frac{1}{2}\frac{\partial}{\partial y_\pi}[a_{\rho'}(\alpha)\,b^{-1}_{\rho'\sigma'}]\,b_{\sigma'\pi}dt\Big\}\,\delta_{\alpha\beta}, \qquad (6.26)$$

where

$$a_{\rho'}(\alpha) = a_{\rho'}(\alpha, y(t), t);\;\; b_{\rho'\sigma'} = b_{\rho'\sigma'}(\alpha, y(t), t) = q_{\rho'\sigma'}(t).$$

The last term can also be written in the form

$$\frac{\partial}{\partial y_\pi}[a_{\rho'}(\alpha)\,b^{-1}_{\rho'\sigma'}]\,b_{\sigma'\pi} = \frac{\partial a_{\rho'}(\alpha)}{\partial y_\pi}\,b^{-1}_{\rho'\sigma'}b_{\sigma'\pi} + a_{\rho'}(\alpha)\,\frac{\partial b^{-1}_{\rho'\sigma'}}{\partial y_\pi}\,b_{\sigma'\pi} = \\ = \frac{\partial a_{\rho'}(\alpha)}{\partial y_\pi}\,b^{-1}_{\rho'\sigma'}b_{\sigma'\pi} - a_{\rho'}(\alpha)\,b^{-1}_{\rho'\tau'}\,\frac{\partial b_{\tau'\pi'}}{\partial y_\pi}\,b^{-1}_{\pi'\sigma'}b_{\sigma'\pi}. \qquad (6.27)$$

We will prove that the expression

$$\frac{\partial b^{-1}_{\rho'\sigma'}}{\partial y_\pi}\,b_{\pi\sigma'} = -\,b^{-1}_{\rho'\tau'}\left(\frac{\partial b_{\tau'\pi'}}{\partial y_\pi}\,b_{\pi\sigma'}\right)b^{-1}_{\sigma'\pi'} \qquad (6.28)$$

does not depend on α in the allowable set (6.18). To do this we will consider the increment

$$\Delta q_{\rho\sigma}(t) = \Delta b_{\rho\sigma}(x(t), y(t), t) \quad (\Delta f \equiv f(t+\Delta) - f(t)).$$

If in the neighborhood of the point t the function $x(t)$ does not have a discontinuity, then

$$\Delta q_{\rho\sigma}(t) = \frac{\partial b_{\rho\sigma}}{\partial y_\pi}(x(t), y(t), t)\,\Delta y_\pi + O(\Delta).$$

Multiplying both sides of this equation by Δy_τ and using Lemma 2.2, we have

$$\lim_{\Delta\to 0}\sum \Delta q_{\rho\sigma}\Delta y_\tau = \int \frac{\partial b_{\rho\sigma}}{\partial y_\pi}\,b_{\pi\tau}dt. \qquad (6.29)$$

But the left side does not depend on α on the allowable set (6.18). Thus the expression $\frac{\partial b_{\rho\sigma}}{\partial y_\pi}\,b_{\pi\tau}$ (for any ρ, σ, τ) on the right side also does not depend on α. Thus (6.28) also has this property. In a word, all functions entering into (6.26) and (6.27), aside from $c(\alpha)$, $a_{\rho'}(\alpha)$, and $\frac{\partial a_{\rho'}(\alpha)}{\partial y_\pi}$ are independent of α.

3. We will express the operator (6.26) in terms of the parameters m_ρ, $\sigma_{\rho r'}$ ($\rho=1, \ldots, l$; $r'=1, \ldots, l'$) which have a tensor-invariant

character (Theorem 2.5). For this we will use formulas (2.26). Since $b_{\rho\sigma}$ is independent of α on the allowable set (6.18), then it is clearly possible to select $\sigma_{\rho r'}$, such that they also will be independent of α. In addition to this, taking an increment

$$\Delta\sigma_{\rho r'} = \frac{\partial\sigma_{\rho r'}}{\partial y_\pi}\Delta y_\pi + O(\Delta)$$

and writing the equation analogous to (6.29), it is easy to see that $\frac{\partial\sigma_{\rho r'}}{\partial y_\pi} b_{\pi\tau'} = \frac{\partial\sigma_{\rho r'}}{\partial y_\pi}\sigma_{\pi s'}\sigma_{\tau' s'}$ does not depend on α. Applying the transformation $\sigma^{-1}_{q'\tau'}$ to these quantities, we find that $\frac{\partial\sigma_{\rho r'}}{\partial y_\pi}\sigma_{\pi q'}$ and $\frac{\partial\sigma_{\rho r'}}{\partial y_\pi}\sigma_{\pi r'} = 2a_\circ - 2m_\rho$ do not depend on α. From this we have

$$a_{\rho'}b^{-1}_{\rho'\tau'}dy_{\tau'} = m_{\rho'}\sigma^{-1}_{\rho' r'}\sigma^{-1}_{\tau' r'}dy_{\tau'} + \ldots;$$

$$a_{\rho'}b^{-1}_{\rho'\tau'}a_{\tau'} = m_{\rho'}\sigma^{-1}_{\rho' r'}\sigma^{-1}_{\tau' r'}m_{\tau'} + m_{\rho'}\sigma^{-1}_{\rho' r'}\sigma^{-1}_{\tau' r'}\frac{\partial\sigma_{\tau' s'}}{\partial y_\pi}\sigma_{\pi s'} + \ldots;$$

$$\frac{\partial}{\partial y_\pi}[a_{\rho'}b^{-1}_{\rho'\tau'}]\,b_{\tau'\pi} = \frac{\partial}{\partial y_\pi}[m_{\rho'}\sigma^{-1}_{\rho' r'}\sigma^{-1}_{\tau' r'}]\,\sigma_{\tau' s'}\sigma_{\pi s'} + \ldots,$$

where the dots indicate terms independent of α. If we substitute these equations into (6.26) and take into account the identity

$$\frac{\partial}{\partial y_\pi}[m_{\rho'}\sigma^{-1}_{\rho' r'}\sigma^{-1}_{\tau' r'}\sigma_{\tau' s'}] = \frac{\partial}{\partial y_\pi}[m_{\rho'}\sigma^{-1}_{\rho' s'}],$$

we will have

$$dL(t)_{\alpha\beta} = p_{\alpha\beta}dt + \Big\{c(\alpha)\,dt + m_{\rho'}(\alpha)\,\sigma^{-1}_{r'\rho'}\sigma^{-1}_{r'\tau'}\Big[dy_{\tau'} - \frac{1}{2}m_{\tau'}(\alpha)\,dt\Big] - \frac{1}{2}\frac{\partial}{\partial y_\pi}[m_{\rho'}(\alpha)\,\sigma^{-1}_{r'\rho'}]\,\sigma_{\pi r'}dt\Big\}\delta_{\alpha\beta}. \tag{6.30}$$

Here we dropped terms independent of α, which is related to the equivalence transformation (5.30). The operators (6.26) and (6.30) coincide to within an equivalence.

4. Aside from the infinitesimal operators found above, it is possible to obtain expressions for the operators $d\tilde{L}(t)$ and $d\tilde{\tilde{L}}(t)$ of the systems of measures (5.49) and (5.29). The formulas transforming to these measures from V^t_s are particular cases of the measure transformation (3.31). Theorem 3.3 can be applied to calculate the corresponding infinitesimal operators. As was indicated in Chapter 5, this leads to formulas (5.65) and (5.68).

In order to apply expression (5.65) to this case, we will take into account the form of the operator (6.26). For brevity, we introduce the notation

$$w_\alpha(t) = W_t[x(t) = \alpha]; \; v_\alpha(t) = V_t[x(t) = \alpha];$$

$$\mathbf{M}_{ps}\psi = \sum \psi(\alpha)\,\mathbf{P}[x(t) = \alpha \mid y_a^t] = \sum_{\alpha=1}^{m} \psi(\alpha)\, w_\alpha(t).$$

Then (5.65) will have the form

$$d\widetilde{L}(t)_{\alpha\beta} = p_{\alpha\beta}dt + \Big\{[a_{\rho'}(\alpha) - \mathbf{M}_{ps}a_{\rho'}]\, b^{-1}_{\rho'\sigma'} dy_{\sigma'} -$$

$$- \frac{dt}{2}[a_{\rho'}(\alpha)\, a_{\sigma'}(\alpha) - \mathbf{M}_{ps}a_{\rho'}a_{\sigma'}]\, b^{-1}_{\rho'\sigma'} -$$

$$- \frac{dt}{2}\left[\frac{\partial a_{\rho'}(\alpha)}{\partial y_\pi} - \mathbf{M}_{ps}\frac{\partial a_{\rho'}}{\partial y_\pi}\right] b^{-1}_{\rho'\sigma'} b_{\sigma'\pi} -$$

$$- \frac{dt}{2}[a_{\rho'}(\alpha) - \mathbf{M}_{ps}a_{\rho'}]\frac{\partial b^{-1}_{\rho'\sigma'}}{\partial y_\pi} b_{\sigma'\pi}\Big\}\, \delta_{\alpha\beta}$$

(here and henceforth assume $c=0$; $\sum_\beta p_{\alpha\beta}=0$). In accordance with this, the basic equation (5.66) for the *a posteriori* probabilities will have the form

$$dw_\alpha = w_\gamma p_{\gamma\alpha}dt + w_\alpha[a_{\rho'}(\alpha) - \mathbf{M}_{ps}a_{\rho'}]\, b^{-1}_{\rho'\sigma'} dy_{\sigma'} -$$

$$- \frac{1}{2} w_\alpha \Big\{[a_{\rho'}(\alpha)\, a_{\sigma'}(\alpha) - \mathbf{M}_{ps}a_{\rho'}a_{\sigma'}]\, b^{-1}_{\rho'\sigma'} +$$

$$+ \left[\frac{\partial a_{\rho'}}{\partial y_\pi}(\alpha) - \mathbf{M}_{ps}\frac{\partial a_{\rho'}}{\partial y_\pi}\right] b^{-1}_{\rho'\sigma'} b_{\sigma'\pi} +$$

$$+ [a_{\rho'}(\alpha) - \mathbf{M}_{ps}a_{\rho'}]\frac{\partial b^{-1}_{\rho'\sigma'}}{\partial y_\pi} b_{\sigma'\pi}\Big\}\, dt. \quad (6.31)$$

This equation will look somewhat simpler if we change the notation of the equation to that of the Ito sense. In order to do this, it is possible to use Eq. (5.61) which is given by the infinitesimal operator

$$d\widetilde{L}^*(t) = dL_1(t) - [W_t d^* L_1(t)](\Omega) \quad (6.32)$$

[see (5.60a) or (3.64)]. Here, in agreement with (5.60a),

$$dL_1(t) = V_t(\Omega)\, d^*L^*(t)\frac{1}{V_t(\Omega)} \qquad \left(V_t(\Omega) = \sum_\alpha v_\alpha(t)\right).$$

Substituting here (6.24), we have

$$dL_1(t)_{\alpha\beta} = V_t(\Omega)\{p_{\alpha\beta}dt + [a_{\rho'}(\alpha)\, b^{-1}_{\rho'\sigma'} d^* y_{\sigma'}]\, \delta_{\alpha\beta}\}\frac{1}{V_t(\Omega)}. \quad (6.33)$$

This equation allows the final form of the operator dL_1 to be found in the case in question. Applying formula (2.15), we complete the transformation

$$d^* y_{\sigma'} \frac{1}{V_t(\Omega)} = \frac{1}{V_t(\Omega)} d^* y_{\sigma'} - \frac{1}{[V_t(\Omega)]^2} b_{V\sigma'} dt. \tag{6.34}$$

Here

$$b_{V\sigma'} = \lim_{\Delta\to 0} \frac{1}{\Delta} \mathbf{M} \Delta V_t(\Omega) \Delta y_{\sigma'} = \sum_\alpha b_{\alpha\sigma'};$$

$$b_{\alpha\sigma'} = \lim_{\Delta\to 0} \frac{1}{\Delta} \mathbf{M}\, \Delta v_\alpha \Delta y_{\sigma'}$$

are parameters which can easily be calculated using the equation $dV_t = V_t d^* L^*$(5.56), i.e., the equation

$$dv_\alpha = v_\gamma p_{\gamma\alpha} dt + v_\alpha a_{\rho'}(\alpha) b^{-1}_{\rho'\tau'} d^* y_{\tau'}. \tag{6.35}$$

They turn out to be

$$b_{\alpha\sigma'} = v_\alpha a_{\sigma'}(\alpha);\; b_{V\sigma'} = \sum_\alpha v_\alpha a_{\sigma'}(\alpha) = V_t(\Omega) \mathbf{M}_{ps} a_{\sigma'}. \tag{6.36}$$

Inserting (6.34) and (6.36) into (6.33) we obtain

$$dL_1(t)_{\alpha\beta} = p_{\alpha\beta} dt + a_{\rho'}(\alpha) b^{-1}_{\rho'\sigma'} (d^* y_{\sigma'} - \mathbf{M}_{ps} a_{\sigma'} dt)\, \delta_{\alpha\beta}.$$

Furthermore, the insertion of this result into (6.32) yields

$$d\widetilde{L}^*(t)_{\alpha\beta} = p_{\alpha\beta} dt + [a_{\rho'}(\alpha) - \mathbf{M}_{ps} a_{\rho'}]\, b^{-1}_{\rho'\sigma'} (d^* y_{\sigma'} - \mathbf{M}_{ps} a_{\sigma'} dt)\, \delta_{\alpha\beta}. \tag{6.37}$$

Equation (5.61) thus takes the form

$$dw_\alpha = w_\gamma p_{\gamma\alpha} + w_\alpha [a_{\rho'}(\alpha) - \mathbf{M}_{ps} a_{\rho'}]\, b^{-1}_{\rho'\sigma'} (d^* y_{\sigma'} - \mathbf{M}_{ps} a_{\sigma'} dt). \tag{6.38}$$

It is equivalent to Eq. (6.31).

Using formula (6.37) found above, it is not difficult to verify that the relation (5.74) is satisfied.

Continuing this examination, it is also possible to specialize Eq. (5.62) which would be applicable to this case. In addition, it is possible to find the other infinitesimal operator $d\widetilde{\widetilde{L}}$ and to write the formulas corresponding to it. Not stopping to do this in detail, we will give the expression for this operator:

$$d\widetilde{\widetilde{L}}(t)_{\alpha\beta} = d^* \widetilde{\widetilde{L}}(t)_{\alpha\beta} = dt \begin{cases} p_{\alpha\beta} \dfrac{V_t^u(\beta, \Omega)}{V_t^u(\alpha, \Omega)} & \text{for } \alpha \neq \beta; \\ -\sum\limits_{\gamma\neq\alpha} p_{\alpha\gamma} \dfrac{V_t^u(\gamma, \Omega)}{V_t^u(\alpha, \Omega)}, & \text{for } \alpha = \beta. \end{cases} \tag{6.39}$$

In this, terms involving $dy_{\sigma'}$ turn out to be absent. The reason for this is the fact that in this particular case the terms involving $d^*y_{\sigma'}$ in expression (6.24) for dL^* are located only on the main diagonal. In other examples (let us say, in the example of Chapter 7), the situation can turn out to be different.

Equations (5.63b) and (5.68a) in the case under consideration take the form

$$dp_\beta = \left[\sum_\alpha w_\alpha p_{\alpha\beta} \frac{p_\beta}{w_\beta} - w_\beta \sum_\gamma p_{\beta\gamma} \frac{p_\gamma}{w_\gamma}\right] dt. \qquad (6.39a)$$

A particular case of this equation is given in Sects. 6.5 and 9.6.

6.4 The Secondary *A Posteriori* Operator

Any measure V in the space E_m is determined by the values $v_\alpha = V(\alpha)$, $\alpha = 1, ..., m$. Thus, the process $\{V_t(\Gamma), \Gamma \subset E_m\}$, formed by the *a posteriori* measure V_t on E_m, reduces in this case to the m-component process $\{v_1(t), ..., v_m(t)\}$. The same can be said of the other secondary process $\{W_t\} = \{w_\alpha(t)\}$; in addition to this, its components are connected by the relation $\sum_\alpha w_\alpha = 1$. Equations (6.31) and (6.38) are stochastic equations (see Sect. 2.2), and determine the process $\{w_\alpha(t)\}$. Analogous equations, for example, (6.35), are obtained for $\{v_\alpha(t)\}$ if we specialize Eqs. (5.58) and (5.64).

Applying Theorem 2.3, in which it is necessary to assume $\{x_\alpha\} = \{w_\alpha, y_{\sigma'}\}$ $z_\lambda = 0$, to Eq. (6.31), or (even more briefly) using (6.38), we obtain the following result:

Theorem 6.5. In the case under consideration, the process $\{w_\alpha(t)\}$ as a diffusion process is characterized by drift parameters and local variances:

$$\begin{aligned}
&\lim_{\Delta\downarrow 0} \frac{1}{\Delta} \mathbf{M} \{w_\alpha(t+\Delta) - w_\alpha(t) \mid w(t) = w,\ y(t) = y\} = w_\gamma p_{\gamma\alpha};\\
&\lim_{\Delta\downarrow 0} \frac{1}{\Delta} \mathbf{M} \{[w_\alpha(t+\Delta) - w_\alpha(t)][w_\beta(t+\Delta) - w_\beta(t)] \mid w, y\} =\\
&\qquad = w_\alpha [a_{\rho'}(\alpha) - \mathbf{M}_{ps} a_{\rho'}] b^{-1}_{\rho'\sigma'} [a_{\sigma'}(\beta) - \mathbf{M}_{ps} a_{\sigma'}] w_\beta;\\
&\lim_{\Delta\downarrow 0} \frac{1}{\Delta} \mathbf{M} \{[w_\alpha(t+\Delta) - w_\alpha(t)][y_{\rho'}(t+\Delta) - y_{\rho'}(t)] \mid w, y\} =\\
&\qquad = w_\alpha [a_{\rho'}(\alpha) - \mathbf{M}_{ps} a_{\rho'}];\\
&\lim_{\Delta\downarrow 0} \frac{1}{\Delta} \mathbf{M} \{[w_\alpha(t+\Delta) - w_\alpha(t)][y_{\rho''}(t+\Delta) - y_{\rho''}(t)] \mid w, y\} =\\
&\qquad = w_\alpha [a_{\rho'}(\alpha) - \mathbf{M}_{ps} a_{\rho'}] b^{-1}_{\rho'\sigma'} b_{\sigma'\rho''} = w_\alpha [a_{\rho''}(\alpha) - \mathbf{M}_{ps} a_{\rho''}].
\end{aligned} \qquad (6.40)$$

We can be convinced of the correspondence of the expressions $[a_{\rho'}(\alpha) - \mathbf{M}_{ps}a_{\rho'}(\alpha)]\, b^{-1}_{\rho'\sigma'} b_{\sigma'\rho''}$ and $a_{\rho''}(\alpha) - \mathbf{M}_{ps}a_{\rho''}$ if we take into account that the difference $a_{\rho''} - a_{\rho'}\, b^{-1}_{\rho'\sigma'}\, b_{\sigma'\rho''} = r_{\rho''}$ does not depend on α on the allowable set (6.18), so that $r_{\rho''} - \mathbf{M}_{ps}r_{\rho''} = 0$.

The secondary *a posteriori* process $\{W_t(\Gamma),\ \Gamma \in \mathscr{Z}_t\}$ defined in Sect. 5.6 (see Definition 5.4), in the case under consideration, reduces to the combined process $\{w_\alpha,\ y_\rho\}$. In fact, the *a posteriori* measure W_t in the combined phase space $E = E_m \times R_l$ will be fully defined, given the measure W_t on E_m (i.e., on the σ-algebra $\mathscr{X}_t \times \mathscr{Y}^\circ$) and a point $y \in R_l$. In accordance with Theorem 5.9, the process $\{w_\alpha,\ y_\rho\}$ is Markov. From Eqs. (6.31) and (6.38) and from Theorem 6.5 it follows in addition that it is diffusional and is described by the secondary infinitesimal operator

$$d\mathscr{L}(t) = \Big\{ w_\beta p_{\beta\alpha} \frac{\partial}{\partial w_\alpha} + \mathbf{M}_{ps} a_\rho \frac{\partial}{\partial y_\rho} +$$

$$+ \frac{1}{2} w_\alpha [a_{\rho'}(\alpha) - \mathbf{M}_{ps}a_{\rho'}]\, b^{-1}_{\rho'\sigma'}\, [a_{\sigma'}(\beta) - \mathbf{M}_{ps}a_{\sigma'}]\, w_\beta \frac{\partial^2}{\partial w_\alpha \partial w_\beta} +$$

$$+ w_\alpha [a_\rho(\alpha) - \mathbf{M}_{ps}a_\rho] \frac{\partial^2}{\partial w_\alpha \partial y_\rho} + \frac{1}{2} \mathbf{M}_{ps}\, b_{\rho\sigma} \frac{\partial^2}{\partial y_\rho \partial y_\sigma} \Big\} dt. \qquad (6.41)$$

The *a posteriori* process $\{v_\alpha,\ y_\rho\}$ in its turn is also diffusional and for it, in an analogous manner, there can be found a secondary infinitesimal operator, for example, by using formula (6.35).

We will write the infinitesimal operator of a secondary *a posteriori* WP-process. To do this we need to take into consideration Eqs. (6.38) and (6.39a). In averaging the differential dy_ρ we now need to use not the probabilities w_α, but rather the probabilities p_α:

$$\mathbf{M}[y_\rho(t+\Delta) - y_\rho(t) \mid y_t, w_t, p_t] = a_\rho(\alpha) p_\alpha \Delta + o(\Delta)\,.$$

Finally, we will have

$$d\mathscr{L}(t)^{WP} = \Big\{ a_\rho(\alpha) p_\alpha \frac{\partial}{\partial y_\rho} + \frac{1}{2} b_{\rho\sigma}(\alpha) p_\alpha \frac{\partial^2}{\partial y_\rho \partial y_\sigma} + [w_\beta p_{\beta\alpha} + w_\alpha (a_{\rho'}(\alpha) -$$

$$- a_{\rho'}(\epsilon) w_\epsilon)(b_{\rho'\sigma'}(\gamma) w_\gamma)^{-1} a_{\sigma'}(\delta)(p_\delta - w_\delta)] \frac{\partial}{\partial w_\alpha} + \frac{1}{2} w_\alpha (a_{\rho'}(\alpha) -$$

$$- a_{\rho'}(\epsilon) w_\epsilon)(b_{\rho'\sigma'}(\gamma) w_\gamma)^{-1} (a_{\sigma'}(\beta) - a_{\sigma'}(\delta) w_\delta) w_\beta \frac{\partial^2}{\partial w_\alpha \partial w_\beta} +$$

$$+ w_\alpha (a_\rho(\alpha) - a_\rho(\epsilon) w_\epsilon) \frac{\partial^2}{\partial w_\alpha \partial y_\rho} + \Big(w_\alpha p_{\alpha\beta} \frac{p_\beta}{w_\beta} -$$

$$- w_\beta p_{\beta\gamma} \frac{p_\gamma}{w_\gamma} \Big) \frac{\partial}{\partial p_\beta} \Big\} dt\,. \qquad (6.41a)$$

This operator gives the equation

$$d\pi_t(y,w,p) = (d\mathcal{L}(t)^{WP}\pi_t)(y,w,p) \tag{6.41b}$$

for the joint distribution density $\pi_t(y,w,p)$. By integrating over $w_1, \ldots, w_m$ it is possible to convert to the distribution $\pi_t(y,p)$, corresponding to the inner secondary *a posteriori* P-process. The latter is Markov on the strength of Theorem 5.11 and, hence, in its turn has an infinitesimal operator. Integrating Eq. (6.41b) over $w_1, \ldots, w_m$, taking into account (6.41a), we obtain the equation

$$\frac{d\pi_t(y,p)}{dt} = -\frac{\partial}{\partial y_\rho}[a_\rho(\alpha)p_\alpha\pi_t(y,p)] + \frac{1}{2}\frac{\partial^2}{\partial y_\rho \partial y_\sigma}[b_{\rho\sigma}(\alpha)p_\alpha\pi_t(y,p)] -$$

$$-\frac{\partial}{\partial p_\beta}\left[\int\left(w_\alpha p_{\alpha\beta}\frac{p_\beta}{w_\beta} - w_\beta p_{\beta\gamma}\frac{p_\gamma}{w_\gamma}\right)\pi_t(y,w,p)\,dw\right]$$

$$(dw = dw_1 \ldots dw_m).$$

From this we conclude that the operator of a secondary P-process has the form

$$d\mathcal{L}^P = \left\{a_\rho(\alpha)p_\alpha\frac{\partial}{\partial y_\rho} + \frac{1}{2}b_{\rho\sigma}(\alpha)p_\alpha\frac{\partial^2}{\partial y_\sigma \partial y_\rho} + \right.$$

$$\left. + \int\left(w_\alpha p_{\alpha\beta}\frac{p_\beta}{w_\beta} - w_\beta p_{\beta\gamma}\frac{p_\gamma}{w_\gamma}\right)\pi_t(w \mid y,p)\,dw\,\frac{\partial}{\partial p_\beta}\right\}dt.$$

Here $\pi_t(w \mid y,p) = \pi_t(y,w,p)/\pi_t(y,p)$ is a conditional probability distribution density.

If Eq. (6.41b) is integrated not over w but rather over p, then we naturally come again to the operator (6.41), since

$$p_\alpha \pi_t(p \mid y,w)\,dp = w_\alpha,$$

as can be seen from the relation $\mathbf{M}[\mathbf{P}(x_t \mid y_a^u) \mid y_a^t] = \mathbf{P}(x_t \mid y_a^t)$.

Since the normalizing relations

$$\sum_\alpha w_\alpha = 1; \quad \sum_\alpha p_\alpha = 1,$$

are satisfied, the probability densities $\pi_t(y,w,p)$, $\pi_t(y,p)$, and $\pi_t(y,w)$ are concentrated on these hyperplanes, that is, they have delta singularities. In place of these densities it is possible to consider probability densities depending on a smaller number of independent variables and not having delta singularities. In such a substitution the form of the above secondary operators will not change essentially.

6.5 Example. A Process with Two States

We will consider the particular case of two diffusion processes ($m=2$). The *a posteriori* Markov transitions between them can be described by the operator $p_{\alpha\beta}dt$, where

$$\| p_{\alpha\beta} \| = \begin{Vmatrix} -\mu & \mu \\ \nu & -\nu \end{Vmatrix}$$

($\mu = \mu(t)$, $\nu = \nu(t)$ are continuous time functions). For simplicity, we will assume that both diffusion processes have the same nonsingular local variance matrix of the following simple form:

$$b_{\rho\sigma} = N\delta_{\rho\sigma};$$

where N is a constant (then $l'=l$ and indices with one prime can be made identical with unprimed indices).

According to formulas (6.26) and (6.37), in this case the *a posteriori* infinitesimal operators have the form

$$dL(t)_{\alpha\beta} = p_{\alpha\beta}\,dt + \frac{1}{N}\left\{a_\rho(\alpha)\left[dy_\rho - \frac{1}{2}a_\rho(\alpha)\,dt\right] - \right.$$
$$\left. -\frac{1}{2}\frac{\partial a_\rho(\alpha)}{\partial y_\rho}\,dt\right\}\delta_{\alpha\beta}; \qquad (6.42)$$

$$d\widetilde{L}^*(t)_{\alpha\beta} = p_{\alpha\beta}\,dt + \frac{1}{N}\left[a_\rho(\alpha) - \mathbf{M}_{ps}\,a_\rho\right]\left[d^*y_\rho - \mathbf{M}_{ps}\,a_\rho\,dt\right]\delta_{\alpha\beta}.$$

Since

$$f(1) - \mathbf{M}_{ps} f = w_2\left[f(1) - f(2)\right],$$

the basic equations (5.61) and (5.66) can be written in either of the two forms

$$dw_1 = -dw_2 = (-\mu w_1 + \nu w_2)\,dt + \frac{w_1 w_2}{N}\left[a_\rho(1) - a_\rho(2)\right] \times$$
$$\times\left[dy_\rho - \frac{a_\rho(1) + a_\rho(2)}{2}\,dt\right] - \frac{w_1 w_2}{2N}\left[\frac{\partial a_\rho(1)}{\partial y_\rho} - \frac{\partial a_\rho(2)}{\partial y_\rho}\right]dt; \qquad (6.43)$$

$$dw_1 = (-\mu w_1 + \nu w_2)\,dt + \frac{w_1 w_2}{N}\left[a_\rho(1) - a_\rho(2)\right] \times$$
$$\times\left[d^*y_\rho - w_1 a_\rho(1) - w_2 a_\rho(2)\right],$$

resulting from (6.31) and (6.38).

Further, Eqs. (5.67) for $\widetilde{V}_t^u(\alpha, \Omega)$ $(\equiv \widetilde{V}(\alpha))$ as functions of t and α take the form

$$-d\widetilde{V}(1) = -\mu[\widetilde{V}(1) - \widetilde{V}(2)]\,dt +$$
$$+\frac{1}{N}\widetilde{V}(1)w_2\left\{[a_\rho(1) - a_\rho(2)]\left[dy_\rho - \frac{a_\rho(1) + a_\rho(2)}{2}\,dt\right] -\right.$$
$$\left.-\frac{dt}{2}\left[\frac{\partial a_\rho(1)}{\partial y_\rho} - \frac{\partial a_\rho(2)}{\partial y_\rho}\right]\right\};$$
$$-d\widetilde{V}(2) = \nu[\widetilde{V}(1) - \widetilde{V}(2)]\,dt - \tag{6.44}$$
$$-\frac{1}{N}\widetilde{V}(2)w_1\left\{[a_\rho(1) - a_\rho(2)]\left[dy_\rho - \frac{a_\rho(1) + a_\rho(2)}{2}\,dt\right] -\right.$$
$$\left.-\frac{dt}{2}\left[\frac{\partial a_\rho(1)}{\partial y_\rho} - \frac{\partial a_\rho(2)}{\partial y_\rho}\right]\right\}.$$

We will also give the infinitesimal operator $d\widetilde{\widetilde{L}}(t)$ corresponding to this case. Substituting (6.42) into (5.68) we find

$$\|d\widetilde{\widetilde{L}}\| = \left\|\begin{matrix} -\mu\dfrac{V(2,\Omega)}{V(1,\Omega)} & \mu\dfrac{V(2,\Omega)}{V(1,\Omega)} \\ \nu\dfrac{V(1,\Omega)}{V(2,\Omega)} & -\nu\dfrac{V(1,\Omega)}{V(2,\Omega)} \end{matrix}\right\|\,dt$$

in accordance with (6.39). Here, in agreement with (5.58), the function $V(\alpha,\Omega) \equiv V_t^u(\alpha,\Omega)$ as a function of t satisfies the equation

$$-dV(1,\Omega) = -\mu[V(1,\Omega) - V(2,\Omega)]\,dt +$$
$$+\frac{1}{N}V(1,\Omega)\left\{a_\rho(1)\left[dy_\rho - \frac{1}{2}a_\rho(1)\,dt\right] - \frac{dt}{2}\frac{\partial a_\rho(1)}{\partial y_\rho}\right\};$$
$$-dV(2,\Omega) = \nu[V(1,\Omega) - V(2,\Omega)]\,dt + \tag{6.45}$$
$$+\frac{1}{N}V(2,\Omega)\left\{a_\rho(2)\left[dy_\rho - \frac{1}{2}a_\rho(2)\,dt\right] - \frac{dt}{2}\frac{\partial a_\rho(2)}{\partial y_\rho}\right\}.$$

The inner probabilities $\mathbf{P}(x_t \mid y_a^u) = P_t(x_t)$ can be calculated with the aid of Eqs. (6.43) and (6.44), and formula (5.50), or, in place of this, with the aid of Eq. (6.39a), which for a process having two states is written in the form

$$dp_1 = -dp_2 = \left(-\mu\frac{p_2 w_1}{w_2} + \nu y\frac{w_2 p_1}{w_1}\right)dt. \tag{6.45a}$$

In conclusion we will turn our attention to the secondary process and its infinitesimal operator. As a result of the relation $w_1 + w_2 = 1$ it is possible to limit ourselves in the case $m=2$ to an examination of only one probability, let us say, w_1. The process $\{w_1, y_\rho\}$ represents a diffusional Markov process and, according to (6.41), its operator has the form

$$d\mathscr{L}(t) = \Big\{(-\mu w_1 + \nu w_2)\frac{\partial}{\partial w_1} + \mathbf{M}_{ps} a_\rho \frac{\partial}{\partial y_\rho} + \\ + \frac{1}{2N} w_1^2 w_2^2 \sum_\rho [a_\rho(1) - a_\rho(2)]^2 \frac{\partial^2}{\partial w_1^2} + \\ + w_1 w_2 [a_\rho(1) - a_\rho(2)] \frac{\partial^2}{\partial w_1 \partial y_\rho} + \frac{1}{2N}\sum_\rho \frac{\partial^2}{\partial y_\rho^2}\Big\} dt. \tag{6.46}$$

Finally, the inner secondary *a posteriori* operator of the joint process (w_1, p_2, y_ρ) includes, according to (6.41a), in addition to the terms entering into (6.46), the terms

$$d\mathscr{L}(t)^{WP} = \Big\{[a_\rho(1)p_1 + a_\rho(2)p_2]\frac{\partial}{\partial y_\rho} + \frac{1}{2N}\sum_\rho \frac{\partial^2}{\partial y_\rho^2} + \\ + \Big[-\mu w_1 + \nu w_2 + \frac{w_1 w_2}{N}[a_\rho(1) - a_\rho(2)][a_\rho(1)(p_1 - w_1) + \\ + a_\rho(2)(p_2 - w_2)]\Big]\frac{\partial}{\partial w_1} + \frac{w_1^2 w_2^2}{2N}[a_\rho(1) - a_\rho(2)]^2 \frac{\partial^2}{\partial w_1^2} + \\ + w_1 w_2 [a_\rho(1) - a_\rho(2)]\frac{\partial^2}{\partial w_1 \partial y_\rho} + \left(-\mu\frac{p_1 w_1}{w_2} + \nu\frac{w_2 p_1}{w_1}\right)\frac{\partial}{\partial p_1}\Big\} dt.$$

The results of this chapter may be generalized to the case where the number of the various diffusion processes is not finite, i.e., where the parameter α (with Markov variation) of a diffusion process takes values from a more complex set E^x rather than from E_m. A simple generalization of Eq. (6.24) has the form

$$dL^*(t) = dL^*_{pr}(t) + df(\alpha, t), \tag{6.47}$$

where $dL^*(t)$ is the operator of the *a posteriori* process in E^x, dL^*_{pr} is the operator of the *a priori* process, and $df(\alpha, t)$ is the operator corresponding to multiplication by a function,

$$df(\alpha, t) = c(\alpha, y(t), t)\,dt + a_{\rho'}(\alpha, y(t), t)\, b^{-1}_{\rho'\sigma'}(t)\, d^* y_{\sigma'}(t), \\ \alpha \in E^x. \tag{6.48}$$

For validity of this result it is essential only that the *a priori* process E^x be Markov and that the measure of the process in the combined space $E = E^x \times R_l$ be determined by formula (6.21). Having limited ourselves by this remark, we will not further examine this generalization here.

CHAPTER 7

Incomplete Observation of a Multidimensional Diffusion Process

7.1 Presentation of the Question and the Basic Results

In this chapter we will examine another particular case of conditional Markov processes. The unique feature of this case is the fact that it is not combined. If in the preceding chapter the reference process was a combined process in a product space, here the reference will be a single process in $(m+l)$-dimensional space R_{m+l}; l coordinates of this space will be observed. We will concentrate here on the case of a diffusion process in R_{m+l} because this case is important from a practical point of view. It is also of indisputable theoretical interest since diffusion processes are the most important Markov processes and are closely related to differential equations. It is natural to expect that *a posteriori* infinitesimal operators, like the *a priori*, will have the form of differential operators. In the chapters of the first part we prepared material which can be used to obtain the basic results.

Since in the preceding chapter the diffusion process was also a part of the combined Markov process, the case under examination here is not very distant from the preceding one, from the point of view of the mathematical apparatus. If the parameter α of Chapter 6 undergoes *a priori* changes in a diffusional manner, i.e., if $\{\alpha(t)\}$ is a diffusion process, the results obtained on the basis of the theory of Chapter 6 will be a special case of the results of this chapter. A second specific case of the general theory of the present chapter is the simple case examined by Wentzel [1]. In this case the observed components of the combined process form in themselves a Markov process, which, it is true, rarely occurs in practical problems.

1. Let z_j, $j=1, ..., m+l$ be the coordinates of a point in the $(m+l)$-dimensional space R_{m+l}, and let $m+l=n$. The reference diffusion process in this space, corresponding to the measure **P**, is described by the parameters $c(z,t)$, $a_j(z,t)$, and $b_{jk}(z,t)$, i.e., it has the infinitesimal operator

$$dL_{pr}(t) = \left(c + a_j \frac{\partial}{\partial z_j} + \frac{1}{2} b_{jk} \frac{\partial}{\partial z_j \, \partial z_k}\right) dt. \tag{7.1}$$

The functions c, a_j, and b_{jk} are as usual assumed continuous with respect to all arguments and are continuously differentiable with respect to all arguments except time.

Let us observe part of the components in the reference process, say, $z_{m+1}(t), ..., z_{m+l}(t)$. For clarity, as in Sect. 4.4, the observed components will be designated by a different letter: $y_\rho(t) = z_\rho(t)$, $\rho = m+1, ..., m+l$, while the remaining unobserved components will be designated: $x_\alpha(t) = z_\alpha(t)$, $\alpha = 1, ..., m$. The choice of index indicates the range of its variation: $j, k, ...$ run through values 1, ..., $m+l$; α, β, ... through values 1, ... m; ρ, σ,, ... through values $m+1$, ..., $m+l$; ρ', σ', ... through values $m+1$, ..., $m+l'$; and, finally, ρ'', σ'', ... through values $m+l'+1$, ..., $m+l$.

The process $\{x_\alpha(t), y_\rho(t)\}$, or, what is essentially the same, the process $\{x_\alpha(t)\}$ with the conditional measures $\mathbf{P}(\cdot \mid y_s^u)$, is in this case a conditional Markov process, and subject to study. The application of Theorem 4.1 yields the following assertion.

Theorem 7.1. If $b_{\rho\sigma}$ and $a_{\rho''} - b_{\rho''\tau'} b_{\tau'\pi'}^{-1} a_{\pi'}$ are independent of x, then the process in question satisfies Hypothesis 5.1, where the measure **Q** is determined by the infinitesimal operator

$$dL^{\mathbf{Q}}(t) = \left[(a_{\rho''} - b_{\rho''\tau'} b_{\tau'\pi''}^{-1} a_{\pi''}) \frac{\partial}{\partial y_{\rho''}} + \frac{1}{2} b_{\rho\sigma} \frac{\partial^2}{\partial y_\rho \partial y_\sigma}\right] dt. \tag{7.2}$$

In fact, as a result of Theorem 4.1, the Radon-Nikodim derivative (5.36) can be obtained by averaging (4.33) of the derivative (4.27):

$$\frac{\mathbf{P}(dy_s^t \Gamma_t \mid z_s)}{\mathbf{Q}(dy_s^t \mid y_s)} = \frac{\mathbf{P}(dy_s^t \Gamma_t \mid z_s)}{\mathbf{Q}(dy_s^t \mid z_s)} =$$

$$= \mathbf{M}_{\mathbf{Q}}\left[\exp\left\{\int_s^t \left[c\, d\tau + a_{j'} b_{j'k'}^{-1} d^* z_{k'} - \frac{1}{2} a_{j'} b_{j'k'}^{-1} a_{k'}\, d\tau\right]\right\} \Big| \, z_s, y_s^t\right].$$

We used the relation $\mathcal{Y}_s^t \subset \mathcal{N}_s^t$ and the equation $\mathbf{Q}(dy_s^t \mid x_s, y_s) = \mathbf{Q}(dy_s^t \mid y_s)$, arising from the fact that the operator (7.2) does not depend on x_α, from the condition of the theorem. For this reason the measure $\mathbf{Q}$ is Markov on the σ-algebras $\{\mathcal{Y}_t\}$. In the future, by σ-algebras $\mathcal{Y}_t$ are to be understood not only σ-algebras in the space R_{m+l}, but also σ-algebras in the space R_l.

Theorem 7.2. In fulfilling the conditions of Theorem 7.1, the Markov system of measures

$$V_s^t(z_s, \Gamma_t) = \frac{\mathbf{P}(dy_s^t \Gamma_t \mid z_s)}{\mathbf{Q}(dy_s^t \mid y_s)} \tag{7.3}$$

has the infinitesimal operator

$$dL^*(t) = c\,dt + a_{\rho'} b^{-1}_{\rho'\sigma'} d^* y_{\sigma'} + (a_\alpha\,dt + b_{\alpha\rho'} b^{-1}_{\rho'\sigma'} d^* y_{\sigma'}) \frac{\partial}{\partial x_\alpha} + \frac{1}{2} b_{\alpha\beta}\,dt \frac{\partial^2}{\partial x_\alpha \partial x_\beta}. \tag{7.4}$$

Proof. Besides the measure $\mathbf{P}$, with the infinitesimal operator (7.1), we will consider the measure $\mathbf{P}'$ defined by the measure transformation

$$\mathbf{P}'(\Gamma_t \mid z(s)) = e^{-q_\alpha x_\alpha(s)} \int_{\Gamma_t} \mathbf{P}(dz \mid z(s))\, e^{q_\alpha x_\alpha}. \tag{7.5}$$

In accordance with Theorem 3.3, all conditions of which are satisfied in this case, the infinitesimal operator

$$dL'_{pr} = e^{-q_\alpha x_\alpha} dL_{pr}\, e^{q_\alpha x_\alpha} = \left(c' + a'_j \frac{\partial}{\partial z_j} + \frac{1}{2} b_{jk} \frac{\partial^2}{\partial z_j \partial z_k}\right) dt;$$

$$c' = c + a_\alpha q_\alpha + \frac{1}{2} b_{\alpha\beta} q_\alpha q_\beta; \quad a'_j = a_j + b_{j\alpha} q_\alpha \tag{7.6}$$

corresponds to the measure in question.

Let us now apply Theorem 4.2 to the measures $\mathbf{P}'$ and $\mathbf{Q}$. This is possible since $b_{\rho\sigma}$ and $a_{\rho''} - b_{\rho''\tau'} b^{-1}_{\tau'\pi'} a_{\pi'}$ do not depend on x_α. In agreement with formulas (4.34), (4.51), and (4.52) we have

$$\frac{\mathbf{P}'(dy_s^t \mid z_s)}{\mathbf{Q}(dy_s^t \mid y_s)} = \Theta_s^t(z_s, y_s^t), \tag{7.7}$$

where Θ_s^t is the solution of the equation

$$\Theta_s^t = 1 + \int_s^t \Theta_s^\tau \{\mathbf{M}_{\mathbf{P}'}[c'(z_\tau, \tau) \mid z_s, y_s^\tau] + \mathbf{M}_{\mathbf{P}'}[a'_{\rho'}(z_\tau, \tau) \mid z_s, y_s^\tau]\, b^{-1}_{\rho'\sigma'}(y_\tau, \tau)\, d^* y_{\sigma'}(\tau)\}. \tag{7.8}$$

Taking into account (7.5), it is easy to find the connecting formula

$$V_s'^t(z, \Gamma_t) = e^{-q_\alpha x_\alpha} \int_{\Gamma_t} V_s^t(z, dz') \, e^{q_\alpha x'_\alpha} \tag{7.9}$$

between the derivative (7.3) and the derivative

$$V_s'^t(z_s, \Gamma_t) \equiv \frac{\mathbf{P}'(dy_s^t \Gamma_t \mid z_s)}{\mathbf{Q}(dy_s^t \mid y_s)} \tag{7.10}$$

Formula (7.7) clearly can be written

$$V_s'^t(z_s, \Omega) = \Theta_s^t. \tag{7.11}$$

Let us turn to Theorem 3.6. It is not difficult to see that as a result of (7.11), Eq. (7.8) coincides with (3.87) if we assume $\mu'_{st} = V_s'^t$. According to (A.1.4) and (A.1.2), the conditional mathematical expectation in (7.8) is an integral with respect to the measure

$$\mathbf{P}'(dz_t \mid z_s, y_s^t) = \frac{\mathbf{P}'(dz_t \, dy_s^t \mid z_s)}{\mathbf{P}'(dy_s^t \mid z_s)}. \tag{7.12}$$

The mathematical expectation $\mathbf{M}_{V_s'^t}[\,\cdot \mid z_s\,]$, on the strength of (A.1.1), is an integral with respect to the measure $V_s'^t(z_s, dz_t)/V_s'^t(z_s, \Omega)$. As a result of (7.10) the latter coincides with (7.12), so that

$$\mathbf{M}_{\mathbf{P}'}[\,\cdot \mid z_s \, y_s^t\,] = \mathbf{M}_{V_s'^t}[\,\cdot \mid z_s].$$

Finally, this convinces us of the coincidence of Eqs. (7.8) and (3.87), where

$$dN'1 = c'\,dt + a'_{\rho'} b^{-1}_{\rho'\sigma'} d^* y_{\sigma'} = \left(c + a_\alpha q_\alpha + \frac{1}{2} b_{\alpha\beta} q_\alpha q_\beta\right) dt + \\ + (a_{\rho'} + b_{\rho'\alpha} q_\alpha) \, b^{-1}_{\rho'\sigma'} d^* y_{\sigma'} \tag{7.13}$$

[using (7.6)]. Let us assume

$$dN' = \left(c + a_\alpha q_\alpha + \frac{1}{2} b_{\alpha\beta} q_\alpha q_\beta\right) dt + (a_{\rho'} + b_{\rho'\alpha} q_\alpha) \, b^{-1}_{\rho'\sigma'} d^* y_{\sigma'} + \\ + (a_\alpha \, dt + b_{\alpha\beta} q_\beta \, dt + b_{\alpha\rho'} b^{-1}_{\rho'\sigma'} d^* y_{\sigma'}) \frac{\partial}{\partial x_\alpha} + \frac{1}{2} b_{\alpha\beta} \, dt \frac{\partial^2}{\partial x_\alpha \partial x_\beta};$$

then clearly (7.13) will be satisfied and, in addition, operator (3.88),

$$e^{q_\alpha x_\alpha} dN' e^{-q_\alpha x_\alpha} = c\,dt + a_{\rho'} b^{-1}_{\rho'\sigma'} d^* y_{\sigma'} + \\ + (a_\alpha \, dt + b_{\alpha\rho'} b^{-1}_{\rho'\sigma'} d^* y_{\sigma'}) \frac{\partial}{\partial x_\alpha} + \frac{1}{2} b_{\alpha\beta} \, dt \frac{\partial^2}{\partial x_\alpha \partial x_\beta} \tag{7.14}$$

will not depend on q_α, in agreement with the condition of Theorem 3.6.

Relation (7.9) between the measures V_s^t and $V_s'^t$, considered (for a fixed process y_s^t) as measures in R_m, coincides with (3.78). In the same way, all conditions of Theorem 3.6 are satisfied; applying it, we find that (7.14) is the infinitesimal operator of the system of measures (7.3). This completes the proof of the theorem.

2. The operator (7.4) found above relates to the type of operators studied in Sects. 3.3 and 3.4; thus the results obtained in those sections necessarily apply to this case. In order to find the symmetrized *a posteriori* operator dL, we need to use formula (3.70) or (3.71). In the present case

$$c^{0*} = c; \quad \overset{0*}{a_\alpha} = a_\alpha; \quad \overset{0*}{b_{\alpha\beta}} = b_{\alpha\beta};$$

$$\overset{0}{c_{\sigma'}} = b^{-1}_{\rho'\sigma'} a_{\rho'}; \quad \overset{0}{a_{\sigma'\alpha}} = b^{-1}_{\sigma'\rho'} b_{\rho'\alpha}; \; \overset{0}{c_{\sigma''}} = 0; \quad \overset{0}{a_{\sigma''\alpha}} = 0;$$

thus, in agreement with (3.70),

$$c^0 = c - \frac{1}{2}\left[a_{\rho'}\, b^{-1}_{\rho'\sigma'} a_{\sigma'} + b_{\alpha\rho'}\, b^{-1}_{\rho'\sigma'} \frac{\partial a_{\sigma'}}{\partial x_\alpha} + b_{\pi\rho'} \frac{\partial (b^{-1}_{\rho'\sigma'} a_{\sigma'})}{\partial y_\pi}\right];$$

$$\overset{0}{a_\alpha} = a_\alpha - \left[a_{\rho'}\, b^{-1}_{\rho'\sigma'} b_{\sigma'\alpha} + \frac{1}{2} b_{\beta\rho'}\, b^{-1}_{\rho'\sigma'} \frac{\partial b_{\sigma'\alpha}}{\partial x_\beta} + \frac{1}{2} b_{\pi\rho'} \frac{\partial (b^{-1}_{\rho'\sigma'} b_{\sigma'\alpha})}{\partial y_\pi}\right];$$

$$\overset{0}{b_{\alpha\beta}} = b_{\alpha\beta} - b_{\alpha\sigma'}\, b^{-1}_{\sigma'\rho'}\, b_{\rho'\beta}. \tag{7.15}$$

Thus, in accordance with (3.42) and (3.65), we have

$$dL = c\,dt + a_{\rho'}\, b^{-1}_{\rho'\sigma'}\left(dy_{\sigma'} - \frac{1}{2} a_{\sigma'}\,dt\right) - \frac{1}{2} b_{j\rho'} \frac{\partial (b^{-1}_{\rho'\sigma'} a_{\sigma'})}{\partial z_j}\,dt +$$
$$+ \left[a_\alpha\,dt + b_{\alpha\rho'}\, b^{-1}_{\rho'\sigma'} (dy_{\sigma'} - a_{\sigma'}\,dt) - \frac{1}{2} b_{j\rho'} \frac{\partial (b^{-1}_{\rho'\sigma'} b_{\sigma'\alpha})}{\partial z_j}\,dt\right] \frac{\partial}{\partial x_\alpha} +$$
$$+ \frac{1}{2}(b_{\alpha\beta} - b_{\alpha\sigma'}\, b^{-1}_{\sigma'\rho'}\, b_{\rho'\beta})\,dt \frac{\partial^2}{\partial x_\alpha\,\partial x_\beta}. \tag{7.16}$$

It is not difficult to obtain expressions also for the other infinitesimal operators (5.65) and (5.68). They have the form

$$d\widetilde{L} = (c - \mathbf{M}_{ps}\, c)\,dt + (a_{\rho'} - \mathbf{M}_{ps}\, a_{\rho'})\, b^{-1}_{\rho'\sigma'}\, dy_{\sigma'} -$$
$$- \frac{1}{2}(a_{\rho'}\, a_{\sigma'} - \mathbf{M}_{ps}\, a_{\rho'}\, a_{\sigma'})\, b^{-1}_{\rho'\sigma'}\, dt -$$
$$- \frac{1}{2}\left[b_{j\rho'} \frac{\partial (b^{-1}_{\rho'\sigma'} a_{\sigma'})}{\partial z_j} - \mathbf{M}_{ps}\, b_{j\rho'} \frac{\partial (b^{-1}_{\rho'\sigma'} a_{\sigma'})}{\partial z_j}\right] dt +$$
$$+ \left[a_\alpha\,dt + b_{\alpha\rho'}\, b^{-1}_{\rho'\sigma'} (dy_{\sigma'} - a_{\sigma'}\,dt) - \frac{1}{2} b_{j\rho'} \frac{\partial (b^{-1}_{\rho'\sigma'} b_{\sigma'\alpha})}{\partial z_j}\,dt\right] \frac{\partial}{\partial x_\alpha} +$$
$$+ \frac{1}{2} \widetilde{b}_{\alpha\beta}\,dt \frac{\partial^2}{\partial x_\alpha\,\partial x_\beta}, \tag{7.17}$$

where

$$\mathbf{M}_{ps} \ldots = \int \ldots W_t(dx); \quad \widetilde{b}_{\alpha\beta} = b_{\alpha\beta} - b_{\alpha\rho'} b^{-1}_{\rho'\sigma'} b_{\sigma'\beta},$$

and

$$d\widetilde{\widetilde{L}}(t) = \left[a_\alpha\, dt + b_{\alpha\rho'} b^{-1}_{\rho'\sigma'} (dy_{\sigma'} - a_{\sigma'}\, dt) - \frac{1}{2} b_{j\rho'} \frac{\partial (b^{-1}_{\rho'\sigma'} b_{\sigma'\alpha})}{\partial z_j} dt + \right.$$
$$\left. + \widetilde{b}_{\alpha\beta} \frac{\partial \ln V^u_t(z_t, \Omega)}{\partial x_\beta} dt \right] \frac{\partial}{\partial x_\alpha} + \frac{1}{2} \widetilde{b}_{\alpha\beta}\, dt \frac{\partial^2}{\partial x_\alpha\, \partial x_\beta}. \tag{7.18}$$

In agreement with (7.17) the basic equation (5.66) is written for the density $w_t(x) = W_t(dx)/dx$ in the form

$$dw_t = \left\{ (c - \mathbf{M}_{ps} c)\, dt + (a_{\rho'} - \mathbf{M}_{ps} a_{\rho'})\, b^{-1}_{\rho'\sigma'} dy_{\sigma'} - \right.$$
$$- \frac{1}{2} (a_{\rho'} a_{\sigma'} - \mathbf{M}_{ps} a_{\rho'} a_{\sigma'})\, b^{-1}_{\rho'\sigma'} dt - \frac{1}{2} \left[b_{j\rho'} \frac{\partial (b^{-1}_{\rho'\sigma'} a_{\sigma'})}{\partial z_j} - \right.$$
$$\left. \left. - \mathbf{M}_{ps} b_{j\rho'} \frac{\partial (b^{-1}_{\rho'\sigma'} a_{\sigma'})}{\partial z_j} \right] dt \right\} w_t - \frac{\partial}{\partial x_\alpha} \left\{ \left[a_\alpha\, dt + \right. \right.$$
$$\left. \left. + b_{\alpha\rho'} b^{-1}_{\rho'\sigma'} (dy_{\sigma'} - a_{\sigma'}\, dt) - \frac{1}{2} b_{j\rho'} \frac{\partial (b^{-1}_{\rho'\sigma'} b_{\sigma'\alpha})}{\partial z_j} dt \right] w_t \right\} +$$
$$+ \frac{1}{2} \frac{\partial^2}{\partial x_\alpha\, \partial x_\beta} [\widetilde{b}_{\alpha\beta} w_t]. \tag{7.19}$$

Expressions (7.17) through (7.19) take on a somewhat shorter form if we consider nonsymmetrized differential expressions defined in the Ito sense (Sect. 2.1).

In analogy with the way in which formula (6.37) was introduced in Sect. 6.3, in the present case we can get

$$d\widetilde{L}^* = (c - \mathbf{M}_{ps} c)\, dt + (d^* y_{\rho'} - \mathbf{M}_{ps} a_{\rho'}\, dt)\, b^{-1}_{\rho'\sigma'} \times$$
$$\times \left[a_{\sigma'} - \mathbf{M}_{ps} a_{\sigma'} + b_{\sigma'\alpha} \frac{\partial}{\partial x_\alpha} \right] + \left[a_\alpha \frac{\partial}{\partial x_\alpha} + \frac{1}{2} b_{\alpha\beta} \frac{\partial^2}{\partial x_\alpha\, \partial x_\beta} \right] dt. \tag{7.20}$$

We will similarly find the corresponding analog of formula (7.18). According to (5.63) we have

$$d\widetilde{\widetilde{L}}^*(t) = \frac{1}{V^u_t(z, \Omega)} [d^* L^*(t)\, V^u_t(z, \Omega) - (d^* L^*(t)\, V^u_t)(z, \Omega)]$$

or, if we substitute (7.4),

$$d\widetilde{\widetilde{L}}^*(t) = \frac{1}{V_t^u(z,\Omega)}\left[\left(a_\alpha \frac{\partial}{\partial x_\alpha} + \frac{1}{2} b_{\alpha\beta} \frac{\partial^2}{\partial x_\alpha \partial x_\beta}\right) V_t^u(z,\Omega) - \right.$$

$$\left. - a_\alpha \frac{\partial V_t^u(z,\Omega)}{\partial x_\alpha} - \frac{1}{2} b_{\alpha\beta} \frac{\partial V_t^u(z,\Omega)}{\partial x_\alpha \partial x_\beta}\right] dt +$$

$$+ b_{\alpha\rho'} b^{-1}_{\rho'\sigma'} \frac{1}{V_t^u(z,\Omega)} d^* y_{\sigma'} V_t^u(z,\Omega) \frac{\partial}{\partial x_\alpha}.$$

Using the equation $d_t V_t^u = -d^* L^* V_t^u$ (5.58), it is not difficult to obtain

$$d^* y_{\sigma'} V_t^u = V_t^u d^* y_{\sigma'} + b_{V\sigma'}\, dt = V_t^u d^* y_{\sigma'} - V_t^u a_{\sigma'}\, dt - b_{\alpha\sigma'} \frac{\partial V_t^u}{\partial x_\alpha}\, dt.$$

Due to this the formula in question takes the form

$$d\widetilde{\widetilde{L}}^*(t) = \left[a_\alpha\, dt + b_{\alpha\rho'} b^{-1}_{\rho'\sigma'} (d^* y_{\sigma'} - a_{\sigma'}\, dt) + \right.$$

$$\left. + \widetilde{b}_{\alpha\beta} \frac{\partial \ln V_t^u(z_t,\Omega)}{\partial x_\beta}\, dt\right] \frac{\partial}{\partial x_\alpha} + \frac{1}{2} b_{\alpha\beta}\, dt \frac{\partial^2}{\partial x_\alpha \partial x_\beta}$$

[compare with (7.18)].

We will finally write Eq. (5.68a) taken in the symmetrized form, that is, corresponding to the operator (7.18). Inserting (7.18) into the equation

$$dp_t = p_t d\widetilde{\widetilde{L}}(t) \quad (p_t(x_t) = P(dx_t \mid y_a^u)/dx_t),$$

we take into account that $\widetilde{V}_t^u(z_t,\Omega) = \dfrac{p_t(x_t)}{w_t(x_t)}$ on the strength of (5.50) and that hence

$$\frac{\partial \ln V_t^u}{\partial x_\beta} = \frac{\partial \ln \widetilde{V}_t^u}{\partial x_\beta} = \frac{1}{p_t} \frac{\partial p_t}{\partial x_\beta} - \frac{1}{w_t} \frac{\partial w_t}{\partial x_\beta}.$$

As a result we obtain the equation

$$dp_t = -\frac{\partial}{\partial x_\alpha}\left\{\left[a_\alpha\, dt + b_{\alpha\rho'} b^{-1}_{\rho'\sigma'} (dy_{\sigma'} - a_{\sigma'}\, dt) - \frac{1}{2} b_{j\sigma'} \frac{\partial (b^{-1}_{\rho'\sigma'} b_{\sigma'\alpha})}{\partial z_j}\, dt - \right.\right.$$

$$\left.\left. - \widetilde{b}_{\alpha\beta} \frac{\partial \ln w_t}{\partial x_\beta}\, dt - \frac{\partial \widetilde{b}_{\alpha\beta}}{\partial x_\beta}\, dt\right] p_t\right\} - \frac{1}{2}\, dt \frac{\partial^2}{\partial x_\alpha \partial x_\beta}\left[\widetilde{b}_{\alpha\beta} p_t\right]. \tag{7.18a}$$

Here we carried out the following transformation:

$$-\frac{\partial}{\partial x_\alpha}\left[\widetilde{b}_{\alpha\beta} \frac{\partial p_t}{\partial x_\beta}\right] = -\frac{\partial^2}{\partial x_\alpha \partial x_\beta}\left[\widetilde{b}_{\alpha\beta} p_t\right] + \frac{\partial}{\partial x_\alpha}\left[\frac{\widetilde{b}_{\alpha\beta}}{\partial x_\beta} p_t\right].$$

It is also not difficult to find Eq. (7.18a) in various variants of the Ito form; however, we will not stop to do this.

3. We will cite another consequence of the results derived in this section. Namely, we will find the *a posteriori* statistics of the increments $\Delta x_\alpha = x_\alpha(t+\Delta) - x_\alpha(t)$ considered in Sect. 3.4. Inserting expressions (7.15) into (3.75) and (3.77), we obtain in this case

$$\mathbf{M_P}[\Delta x_\alpha | x_t, y_\alpha^{t+\Delta}] = a_\alpha(z_t, t)\Delta + b_{\alpha\rho'}(z_t, t) \times$$
$$\times\, b^{-1}_{\rho'\sigma'}(\Delta y_{\sigma'} - a_{\sigma'}\Delta) + b_{j\rho'} b^{-1}_{\rho'\pi'}\left(Y_{\pi'\tau'} - \frac{1}{2} b_{\pi'\tau'}\Delta\right) \times$$
$$\times \frac{\partial(b^{-1}_{\tau'\sigma'} b_{\sigma'\alpha})}{\partial z_j} + O(\Delta^{3/2}); \tag{7.21}$$
$$\mathbf{M_P}[\Delta x_\alpha \Delta x_\beta | x_t, y_\alpha^{t+\Delta}] = b_{\alpha\beta}\Delta + b_{\alpha\rho'}(b^{-1}_{\rho'\pi'}\Delta y_{\pi'}\Delta y_{\tau'} b^{-1}_{\tau'\sigma'} -$$
$$- b^{-1}_{\rho'\sigma'}\Delta) b_{\sigma'\beta} + O(\Delta^{3/2});$$

and also

$$V_t^{t+\Delta}(x_t, R_m) = 1 + a_{\rho'}(z_t, t) b^{-1}_{\rho'\sigma'}\Delta y_{\sigma'} + c\Delta +$$
$$+ a_{\rho'}\left(b^{-1}_{\rho'\pi'} Y_{\pi'\tau'} b^{-1}_{\tau'\sigma'} - \frac{1}{2} b^{-1}_{\rho'\sigma'}\Delta\right) a_{\sigma'} +$$
$$+ b_{j\rho'} b^{-1}_{\rho'\pi'}\left(Y_{\pi'\tau'} - \frac{\Delta}{2} b_{\pi'\tau'}\right)\frac{\partial(b^{-1}_{\tau'\sigma'} a_{\sigma'})}{\partial z_j} + O(\Delta^{3/2}).$$

In concluding this section we will note that a special verification shows that the equations found above are invariant with respect to transformations of the form

$$x' = x'(x, y); \quad y' = y.$$

The need for such transformations can arise in the consideration of practical problems. Nevertheless, we will not give the calculations supporting this invariance.

7.2 Some Generalizations

The results in the preceding section were obtained under one substantial limitation. Namely, it was assumed that $b_{\rho\sigma}$ and $a_{\rho''} - b_{\rho''\tau'} b^{-1}_{\tau'\pi'} a_{\pi'}$ do not depend on x_α. In the present section, we will indicate the means for solving problems in the more general case that this assumption is not satisfied. It turns out that for the solution of the more general problem there is no need to calculate new formulas and expressions, but there is a need to expand sufficiently (add new components to) the reference Markov process and the observed process.

Along with this we will carry out here another less essential generalization: we will assume that we are studying not components of the reference Markov process, but certain functions defined on its phase space.

The difficulties connected with these generalizations are overcome by increasing the number of functions actually observed. In the process of observation in the general case the observer learns with certainty not only the observed functions indicated in the condition of the problem, but also their local variances (and similarly the local variances of these variances, etc.). Thus, the number of functions actually observed turns out to be greater than initially indicated. In Sect. 6.2 we already noted that as a supplement to the process $\{y(t)\}$, we can also consider the functions (6.17) as observations. They can be included in the number of observed components. In such an increase of the number of observed functions it is of great use that the basic formulas are insensitive to degeneracy of the local variance matrices, so that any number of functions can be adjoined to the reference process and considered as components of a combined diffusion process. This is the value of the efforts expended earlier in Chapter 4 on the consideration of the case of a singular local variance matrix.

Let $z=\{z_\alpha,\ \alpha=1,\dots,m\}$ be a diffusion process in R_m and let there be given observed functions

$$y_\rho = F_\rho(z, t), \quad \rho = 1, \dots, l. \tag{7.22}$$

These functions and also the parameters of the reference process we can assume to be differentiable a sufficiently large number of times. The processes $\{z_\alpha\}$ and $\{y_\rho\}$ can be combined into a single diffusional Markov process defined in R_{m+l}. We will find the parameters of this single process. It is not difficult to see that the local variance matrix will have the form

$$\begin{pmatrix} b_{\alpha\beta} & b_{\alpha\sigma} \\ b_{\rho\beta} & b_{\rho\sigma} \end{pmatrix},$$

where

$$b_{\rho\sigma} = \frac{\partial F_\rho}{\partial z_\gamma}\frac{\partial F_\sigma}{\partial z_\delta} b_{\gamma\delta}; \qquad b_{\rho\alpha} = b_{\alpha\rho} = \frac{\partial F_\rho}{\partial z_\beta} b_{\alpha\beta}.$$

Further, the drift vector will be $(a_\alpha,\ a_\rho)$, where

$$a_\rho = \frac{\partial F_\rho}{\partial t} + \frac{\partial F_\rho}{\partial z_\alpha} a_\alpha + \frac{1}{2}\,\frac{\partial^2 F_\rho}{\partial z_\alpha\,\partial z_\beta} b_{\alpha\beta}.$$

The parameter c (if it is necessary to consider it) remains unchanged. With this combining of the processes z_α and y_ρ, the problem being considered reduces to the problem examined in the preceding paragraph (with the obvious substitution of x_α for z_α, n for $m+l$, etc.). Separating out from $\|b_{\rho\sigma}\|$ the nonsingular $\|b_{\rho'\sigma'}\|$, we will consider the $(l-l')$-component subvector $g_{\rho''}=a_{\rho''}-b_{\rho''\rho'}b^{-1}_{\rho'\sigma'}a_{\sigma'}$.

In order to apply the results of Sect. 7.1 it is necessary to verify that the functions $b_{\rho\sigma}(z, t)$ and $a_{\rho''}(z, t)-b_{\rho''\rho'}(z, t)b^{-1}_{\rho'\sigma'}(z, t)a_{\sigma'}(z, t)$ are independent of z. If this condition is not satisfied, we must carry out a further expansion of the process $\{z_\alpha, y_\rho\}$, attaching to its components those of the indicated functions which depend on z. We will designate such functions $F_{\tilde\rho}(z, t)$, $\tilde\rho=l+1, \ldots, l+\tilde l\ (\tilde l\leqslant l^2+l-l')$. As noted, the functions $F_{\tilde\rho}$ can be combined with the observed functions (7.22), considering the processes

$$y_{\tilde\rho}=F_{\tilde\rho}(z, t) \tag{7.23}$$

also as observables.

In a manner similar to that in which we earlier enlarged the process $\{z_\alpha\}$ by the components $\{y_\rho\}$, we will now enlarge it by the components $\{y_\rho, y_{\tilde\rho}\}$. For the process $\{z_\alpha, y_\rho, y_{\tilde\rho}\}$ we will again check that the (new) parameters $b_{\tilde\rho\tilde\sigma}$, $b_{\tilde\rho\sigma}$ and $g_{\tilde\rho''}$ are independent of z. If earlier, let us say, the function $b_{\rho_1\sigma_1}(z, t)$ had depended on z, it has now been converted into $y_{\tilde\rho_1}$ and in the process has lost the explicit dependence on z. In the case when all necessary parameters depend only on $\{y_\rho, y_{\tilde\rho}, t\}$, the results of Sect. 7.1 can be applied to the problem; otherwise we need to carry out a further expansion of the observed process $\{y_\rho, y_{\tilde\rho}\}$ and of the basic Markov process.

It is apparent that this process of supplementation either terminates (in which case we will have finite observable and basic processes), or does not terminate (in which case we will have denumerable observable and basic processes). In both cases the *a posteriori* measure will be concentrated on the allowable set

$$\{z(\cdot): F_\rho(z(t), t)\equiv y_\rho(t), \quad F_{\tilde\rho}(z(t), t)\equiv y_{\tilde\rho}(t), \ \ldots\},$$

which with probability 1 is not empty (it is understood that a nontrivial problem exists only in the case when the allowable set contains more than one point).

In the case of a finite process when the expansion terminates in a finite number of steps, the results of the preceding paragraph can be applied immediately to the problem. With an infinite process the results of Sect. 7.1 need to be generalized to the case of a denumerable diffusion process. We will not examine this generalization, but will limit ourselves to the remark that for cases of practical interest all main formulas from Sect. 7.1 will retain their form also in this case and will not contain infinite sums. The reason for this is that only nonsingular components $y_{\rho'}$ go into the formulas, and in the process $\{y_\rho, y_{\tilde{\rho}}, \ldots\}$ there is only a finite number of nonsingular components (the rank of the local variance matrix cannot exceed m). Thus the formulas of the preceding section give a solution of the general problem although the justification becomes more complex in the infinite case.

In the following section an example for which the described expansion of the process is quickly completed will be examined.

7.3 Two Examples

1. We will examine first an example to which we can immediately apply the results of Sect. 7.1. Let us observe the sum $y(t) = x(t) + \xi(t)$ of two independent single-component diffusion processes $x(t)$ and $\xi(t)$. Let the first of them be characterized by parameters $a(x, t)$, $b(x, t)$, and the second by $a'(\xi, t)$, $b'(\xi, t)$. (Let these functions be continuous and differentiable with respect to x and ξ, respectively.) We are required to examine the *a posteriori* process $x(t)$.

We will consider the two-dimensional diffusion process $\{x(t), y(t)\}$. It is characterized by drift parameters $a_\alpha = a_1 = a(x, t)$, $a_\rho = a_2 = a(x, t) + a'(y-x, t)$ and the local variance matrix

$$\| b_{jk} \| = \begin{Vmatrix} b_{11} & b_{12} \\ b_{21} & b_{22} \end{Vmatrix} = \begin{Vmatrix} b(x, t) & b(x, t) \\ b(x, t) & b(x, t) + b'(y-x, t) \end{Vmatrix}.$$

We will assume that $b + b' \neq 0$ and $\frac{\partial b}{\partial x}(x, t) \equiv 0$; $\frac{\partial b'}{\partial \xi}(\xi, t) = 0$. Then the conditions of Theorems 7.1 and 7.2 are satisfied ($l = l' = 1$, and the parameters $a_{\rho''} - b_{\rho''\sigma'} b^{-1}_{\sigma'\pi'} a_{\pi'}$ need not be considered). Applying Theorem 7.2 and specializing (7.4), we obtain the *a posteriori* infinitesimal operator

$$dL^* = \frac{a + a'}{b + b'} d^*y + \left(a\,dt + \frac{b}{b + b'} d^*y\right) \frac{\partial}{\partial x} + \frac{1}{2} b \;\; t \frac{\partial^2}{\partial x^2}. \quad (7.24)$$

The symmetrized operator (7.16) has the form

$$\begin{aligned} dL = {} & \frac{a + a'}{b + b'} \left[dy - \frac{1}{2} (a + a')\,dt \right] - \\ & - \frac{1}{2} \left[\frac{b}{b + b'} \frac{\partial (a + a')}{\partial x} + \frac{\partial a'}{\partial y} \right] dt + \\ & + \left\{ a\,dt + \frac{b}{b + b'} [dy - (a + a')\,dt] \right\} \frac{\partial}{\partial x} + \\ & + \frac{1}{2} \tilde{b}\,dt \frac{\partial^2}{\partial x^2}, \quad \tilde{b} = \frac{bb'}{b + b'}. \end{aligned}$$

Further, formulas (7.17) and (7.18) are written in the form

$$d\widetilde{L} = \frac{dy}{b+b'}\left[a+a' - \mathbf{M}_{ps}(a+a')\right] -$$

$$-\frac{1}{2}\,\frac{dt}{b+b'}\left[(a+a')^2 - \mathbf{M}_{ps}(a+a')^2\right] -$$

$$-\frac{dt}{2}\left\{\frac{b}{b+b'}\left[\frac{\partial(a+a')}{\partial x} - \mathbf{M}_{ps}\frac{\partial(a+a')}{\partial x}\right] +\right.$$

$$\left. + \frac{\partial a'}{\partial y} - M_{ps}\frac{\partial a'}{\partial y}\right\} + \left[\frac{b}{b+b'}\,dy + \frac{ab'-ba'}{b+b'}\,dt\right]\frac{\partial}{\partial x} +$$

$$+\frac{1}{2}\,\widetilde{b}dt\,\frac{\partial^2}{\partial x^2}; \tag{7.25}$$

$$d\widetilde{\widetilde{L}} = \left[\frac{b}{b+b'}\,dy + \frac{ab'-ba'}{b+b'}\,dt + \widetilde{b}\,\frac{\partial \ln V_t^u(x, R_1)}{\partial x}\,dt\right]\frac{\partial}{\partial x_\alpha} +$$

$$+\frac{1}{2}\,\widetilde{b}dt\,\frac{\partial^2}{\partial x^2}. \tag{7.26}$$

In (7.25)

$$\mathbf{M}_{ps}\ldots = \int \ldots W_t(dx) = \int \ldots w_t(x)\,dx,$$

if the *a posteriori* probability $W_t(dx)$ has the density $w_t(x)$. Taking into account (7.25), we write Eq. (7.19) for the *a posteriori* distribution density

$$dw_t = \frac{1}{2}\,\widetilde{b}dt\,\frac{\partial^2 w_t}{\partial x^2} - \frac{\partial}{\partial x}\left\{\left[\frac{b}{b+b'}\,dy +\right.\right.$$

$$\left.\left. + \frac{ab'-ba'}{b+b'}\,dt\right]w_t\right\} + w_t\left[dF - \mathbf{M}_{ps}\,dF\right],$$

$$dF = \frac{a+a'}{b+b'}\left[dy - \frac{1}{2}(a+a')\,dt\right] -$$

$$-\frac{1}{2}\left[\frac{b}{b+b'}\,\frac{\partial(a+a')}{\partial x} + \frac{\partial a'}{\partial y}\right]dt.$$

Finally, we will cite Eqs. (5.58) and (5.64) which are satisfied by the function $V_t^u(x, R_1)$ entering into (7.26). They have the form

$$-d_t V_t^u(x, R_1) = \frac{1}{2}\,\widetilde{b}dt\,\frac{\partial^2 V_t^u(x, R_1)}{\partial x^2} +$$

$$+\left[\frac{b}{b+b'}\,dy - \frac{ab'-ba'}{b+b'}\,dt\right]\frac{\partial V_t^u(x, R_1)}{\partial x} + dF\cdot V_t^u(x, R_1).$$

If necessary, other equations appropriate to this case can also be written out.

2. For the second example we will consider isotropic diffusion in a three-dimensional space with coordinates x_1, x_2, x_3, where there is a central force field described by a potential function $U(r)$, $r=\sqrt{x_1^2+x_2^2+x_3^2}$. Expressing this differently, we accept the following form of the *a priori* infinitesimal operator:

$$dL_{pr}=\sum_{i=1}^{3}\left[-\frac{\partial U}{\partial x_i}\frac{\partial}{\partial x_i}+\frac{D}{2}\frac{\partial^2}{\partial x_i^2}\right]. \tag{7.27}$$

Let the observed function be the polar angle

$$y_3(t)=\arctan\frac{x_2(t)}{x_3(t)}. \tag{7.28}$$

We wish to examine the *a posteriori* process.

This problem can conveniently be examined in the coordinates

$$(z_1, z_2, z_3)=(r, \rho, y_3), \text{ where } \rho=\sqrt{x_2^2+x_3^2}, \text{ so that}$$
$$x_1=\sqrt{r^2-\rho^2};\quad x_2=\rho\sin y_3;\quad x_3=\rho\cos y_3.$$

It is easy to obtain the drift parameters in terms of these variables:

$$(a_1, a_2, a_3)=\left(-U'+\frac{D}{r},\quad -\frac{\rho}{r}U', 0\right),\quad U'=\frac{dU(r)}{dr},$$

and the local variance matrix

$$\| b_{jk} \| = D\begin{Vmatrix} 1 & \frac{\rho}{r} & 0 \\ \frac{\rho}{r} & 1 & 0 \\ 0 & 0 & \frac{1}{\rho^2} \end{Vmatrix}. \tag{7.29}$$

When the coordinate $y_3(t)$ is observed, the condition of Theorem 7.1 is not satisfied, since the local variance $b_{33}=\rho^{-2}$ depends on other coordinates (namely, on the coordinate $z_2=\rho$). According to what we have said in Sect. 7.2, we can expand the observed process, adding to y_3 the function b_{33}or, equivalently, the function $y_2(t)=\rho$. Thus the observation of one coordinate $y_3(t)$ is equivalent to the observation of two coordinates $\{y_2(t), y_3(t)\}$. The local variance matrix

$$D\begin{Vmatrix} 1 & 0 \\ 0 & \rho^{-2} \end{Vmatrix}$$

corresponding to these observed processes is nonsingular and its elements do not depend on other (unobserved) coordinates. For this reason a further extension of the observed process need not be considered.

There remains only one unobserved coordinate $z_1 = r$ and the *a posteriori* operators hence will correspond to a one-component process.

The application of Theorem 7.2 and formula (7.4) to the two-component observed process $\{\rho, y_3\}$ yields the following expression for the *a posteriori* infinitesimal operator:

$$dL^* = -\frac{1}{D}\frac{\rho}{r}U' d^*\rho + \left[\left(-U' + \frac{D}{r}\right)dt + \frac{\rho}{r}d^*\rho\right]\frac{\partial}{\partial r} + \\ + \frac{D}{2}dt\frac{\partial^2}{\partial r^2}. \tag{7.29a}$$

Further, in agreement with (7.16) we have

$$dL(t) = dF + \left[\left(-U' + \frac{D}{r}\right)dt + \right. \\ \left. + \frac{\rho}{r}\left(d\rho + \frac{\rho}{r}U'\,dt\right) - \frac{D}{2}\frac{r^2-\rho^2}{r^3}dt\right]\frac{\partial}{\partial r} + \\ + \frac{D}{2}\frac{r^2-\rho^2}{r^2}dt\frac{\partial^2}{\partial r^2}, \tag{7.30}$$

where

$$dF = -\frac{1}{D}\frac{\rho}{r}U'\left(d\rho + \frac{1}{2}\frac{\rho}{r}U'\,dt\right) + \\ + \frac{1}{2}\frac{\rho^2}{r}\frac{\partial}{\partial r}\left(\frac{1}{r}U'\right) + \frac{1}{2r}U'\,dt.$$

Hence Eq. (7.19) for the *a posteriori* probability distribution density $w_t(r)$ takes the form

$$dw_t(r) = \frac{D}{2}\frac{\partial^2}{\partial r^2}\left(\frac{r^2-\rho^2}{r^2}w_t\right) - \frac{\partial}{\partial r}\left\{\left[\left(-U' + \frac{D}{r}\right)dt + \right.\right. \\ \left.\left. + \frac{\rho}{r}\left(d\rho + \frac{\rho}{r}U'\,dt\right) - \frac{D}{2}\frac{r^2-\rho^2}{r^3}dt\right]w_t\right\} + [dF - \mathbf{M}_{ps}\,dF]\,w_t.$$

It is interesting to note that if we were observing both spherical angles, the statistical problem would be singular, since in terms of them it would be possible to determine the radius $r(t)$ without error. The allowable set would reduce to a single point.

* * *

In concluding this chapter we will take note of one particular case in which the results obtained are related to the results of

Chapter 6. Assume that in the formulas of Sect. 7.1 the covariances vanish ($b_{\alpha\rho} \equiv 0$) and a_α, $b_{\alpha\beta}$ do not depend on y_ρ. Then from (7.4) we have

$$dL^* = c\,dt + a_{\rho'} b^{-1}_{\rho'\sigma'} d^* y_{\sigma'} + \left(a_\alpha \frac{\partial}{\partial x_\alpha} + \frac{1}{2} b_{\alpha\beta} \frac{\partial^2}{\partial x_\alpha \partial x_\beta}\right) dt. \quad (7.31)$$

But

$$\left(a_\alpha \frac{\partial}{\partial x_\alpha} + \frac{1}{2} b_{\alpha\beta} \frac{\partial^2}{\partial x_\alpha \partial x_\beta}\right) dt$$

is nothing other than the *a priori* infinitesimal operator dL^*_{pr} in the space $R_m \ni x$. Thus the formula (7.31) coincides with (6.47) and (6.48) if we identify α and x ($=\{x_1, \ldots, x_m\} \in R_m$) with each other.

PART 3

Application of the Theory of Conditional Markov Processes to the Theory of Optimal Control

CHAPTER 8

Some General Results of the Theory of Optimal Control

Before we consider the application of the theory of conditional Markov processes, we will compile a series of statements regarding the general theory of optimal control. This theory is not strictly necessary for the understanding of the specific results of the particular problems solved subsequently. Nevertheless, it allows various problems in which it is necessary to find one or another optimal solution to be considered from a single point of view. Of course, the general formulation of the optimal control problem given here, regardless of its generality, is not the most general. Its limitations are related to the Bayesian approach and also to the condition that the information available to the observer-operator receiving the solution should not decrease with the passage of time. All particular examples considered are specific cases of this general problem, although interesting examples are possible beyond the framework of this theory. Non-Bayesian problems can be solved, as we know, by reducing them to Bayesian ones. Problems containing decreasing information at the present time are little studied and we will not dwell on them.

The essence of the theory is that we consider a chain of alternate conditional minimizations and averages in a unified abstract measurable space in which a family of monotonic σ-algebras is defined. The alternating minimizations and averages were used by the author in [13], and the monotonic σ-algebras were related to the theory of optimal control in [14]. This chain of minimizations and averages and its corresponding recursive transformations in reality form in the most abstract sense the familiar "principle of optimality" of Bellman [1]. However, whereas in the work of Bellman a function of a finite number of certain state variables is considered and subjected to minimization, here we have to deal with a function defined in the abstract in a general case of a function space. The conversion to a finite number of variables is carried out in subsequent sections (beginning with Sect. 8.5) as a result of the introduction of sufficient coordinates.

In this approach, not only do we not need metric concepts to obtain the main results, but also we need not introduce a topology in a reference measurable space.

Aside from Bellman, recursive relations for risks applicable to statistical problems (predominantly of the sequential analysis type) were examined by: Wald and Wolfowitz [1], Blackwell and Girshik [1], and Mikhalevich [2]. The latter, after a passage to the limit, also examined the case of continuous time, for which the recursive relations go over into differential equations.

The majority of the work in dynamic programming corresponds to discrete time. However, there is a series of papers (Bellman [1], Glicksberg and Gross [1], Stratonovich and Shmal'gauzen [1], Stratonovich [18], [19], and others) in which recursive relations (differential equations) for continuous time are examined. The corresponding passage to the limit is carried out without particular substantiation.

The substantiation of the passage to continuous time can be carried out in the framework of the general theory presented in Chapter 8.

The study of these questions turns out to be closely connected with the study of the infinitesimal commutativity of the operations of conditional averaging and minimization.

It is characteristic of the theory presented in this chapter that clearly one need not consider decision rules (strategies), but can concentrate attention immediately on the optimal strategies. It is assumed that no limitations on the choice of strategies are imposed by the conditions of the problem (we should not confuse such limitations with limitations imposed on the control functions considered by the theory).

A second characteristic property of the theory is the absence of any requirements of positiveness or convexity imposed on the penalty functions. It is not excluded that such requirements might be useful for obtaining certain other specific results.

We will touch on the question of randomized solutions. In the present theory randomizing is not very essential. If the lower bound is attained at one or more points, then with equal success we can find any of these points, and also any randomized selection rule can be found among these. Thus, among the optimal solutions there exists an equally good nonrandomized solution. If the lower bound is not attained on the set under examination, then we can find a nonrandomized solution arbitrarily near the optimal which is no worse than the randomized one. This situation is typical of the theory. For convenience and generality of the treatment in the text of this chapter we will, nevertheless, consider the randomized solution resulting from selecting one particular consistent method of randomization generated by a certain supplementary measure, the "basis of the randomization" $\nu(\cdot)$. We should keep in mind that the quality of the solution (the size of the average risk) does not depend on the selection of the basis of the randomization. It remains the same even if it is limited to nonrandomized solutions.

Randomization becomes important with the generalization of the theory to a game situation (Sect. 8.8). The extension of the theory to the case of antagonistic games does not involve any great difficulties and does not require the introduction of new ideas. The only change lies in the fact that a single control is changed to a pair, and conditional minimization, to the minimax. Ultimately, we obtain a far-reaching development of one segment of game theory.

For the actual solution of problems in optimal control, the concept of sufficient coordinates, which allows the transition from an abstract (function) space to a finite space in which we consider functions and recursive transformations, is important. This concept is a change in form (applicable to the theory of optimal control) of the concept of sufficient statistics familiar in mathematics (see, for example, Van der Waerden [1]). The importance of this concept for the development of the theory of dynamic programming was noted by Bellman and Kalaba [1]. The general definition of sufficient coordinates is given by the author in [16, 17, 14]. In the case when the basic controlled process is a Markov process, among sufficient coordinates the most important are *a posteriori* probabilities or the parameters replacing them, i.e., the "secondary *a posteriori* process." For this reason, the theory of conditional Markov processes plays an important role in such problems. It gives an analytic basis for the formulation and solution of the recursive equations, i.e., the basic equations of the theories of optimal control. The form of these equations is in the main determined by the "secondary" infinitesimal operator which was studied above (in Sects. 5.6 and 6.4).

In some specific cases the "secondary *a posteriori* process" represents a diffusion process with its parameters and infinitesimal operator dependent on the control. In such cases the determination of the risk (as a function of the coordinates of the diffusion process) is carried out (with a reverse time flow) coincident with its minimization, i.e., with the selection of the optimal control. Such problems were examined as independent problems by Dynkin [4] and Girsanov [2]. The diffusion process is their reference, while for us this process is secondary, representing the sufficient coordinates (*a posteriori* probabilities) of some more complicated problem of optimal control with incomplete observation. In passing we will remark that substitution of the penalty functions recommended in the cited work by Dynkin is usually inapplicable in the case of nonterminating processes (since the condition $\mathbf{M}_x \overset{\circ}{\varphi}_\zeta < \infty$ is violated). Thus, the results of that paper are immediately inapplicable even to the simplest problems of the sequential analysis of Wald.

A series of results on conditional Markov processes as applied to nonlinear filtering was given by the author [3] at the Sixth All-Union Conference on the Theory of Probability and Mathematical Statistics (Vilnios, 1960) and at the First Congress of the International Federation on Automic Control (IFAC) (Moscow, 1960). After this the author carried on work on the application of the theory to problems in radio engineering [6, 7, 10-12] and on the extension of its area of application. A series of problems in mathematical statistics and dynamic programming was solved (Stratonovich [15-19]). In the process of working on these problems the basic formulations and results of the general theory of optimal control presented in Chapter 8 crystallized. These questions were reflected in the author's presentation at the Fourth All-Union Mathematical Meeting (Leningrad, 1961), and also in articles [13-17]. The results obtained by the author in 1960 and partially reviewed in [15] make up the contents of the Supplement (p. 318).

8.1 General Presentation of the Problem. The Risk Function in a Measurable Space

1. The theory of optimal control compiled below has a time-sequential character. Let the set of values of the parameter (time) t represent the interval $T=[a, b]$, or a subset of it; for definiteness we will use the first case.

The control process. Let the control process u form a point in a measurable space $(U, \mathcal{U}')$. A monotonic family of σ-algebras $\mathcal{U}'^t, t \in T$ $(\mathcal{U}'^s \subset \mathcal{U}'^t \subset \mathcal{U}'^b \equiv \mathcal{U}', s \leqslant t)$ is contained in it. For clarity, it is convenient to assume that u is a function $u(\cdot) = \{u(t), t \in T\}$, and that the σ-algebra $\mathcal{U}'^t$ is determined by conditions imposed on its "previous" values, i.e., on $u_a^t = \{u(\tau), \tau \in [a, t]\}$. In this interpretation, aside from U it is possible to consider the space $U^s \ni u_a^s$, $s \in T$ and the space $U_s^t(u_a^s)$, $s < t$ of all possible $u_s^t = \{u(\tau), \tau \in [s, t]\}$. The latter spaces are taken with fixed u_a^s; thus in the general case they are dependent on u_a^s. In these spaces it is possible to define σ-algebras in a natural way: $\mathcal{U}''^s$ in U^s and $\mathcal{U}_s''^t(u_a^s)$ in $U_s^t(u_a^t)$. The prototypes of these σ-algebras in the general space $(U, \mathcal{U}')$ we will indicate by $\mathcal{U}'^s, \mathcal{U}_s'^t(u_a^s) \equiv \mathcal{U}_s'^t(\mathcal{U}'^s)$ [the latter can be considered to be $\mathcal{U}'^s$-measurable functions of u].

In some specific cases the spaces $(U_s^t(u_a^s), \mathcal{U}_s''^t(u_a^s))$ do not depend on u_a^s. Then, obviously,

$$U^t = U^s \times U^t_s,\ \mathcal{U}''^t = \mathcal{U}''^s \times \mathcal{U}''^t_s;\ \mathcal{U}'^t = \sigma(\mathcal{U}'^s \cup \mathcal{U}'^t_s);$$
$$U^t_r = U^s_r \times U^t_s,\ \mathcal{U}''^t_r = \mathcal{U}''^s_r \times \mathcal{U}''^t_s \quad (r < s < t).$$

These cases we will call cases of independent choice of control or cases of *uncoupled control.*

In the general case in which $U^t_s(u^s_a)$ and $\mathcal{U}'^t_s(u^s_a)$ depend on $\overset{s}{u}_a$, the matter is more complex. Nevertheless, in this case we will also assume

$$U^t = U^s \times U^t_s(u^s_a);\ \mathcal{U}''^t = \mathcal{U}''^s \times \mathcal{U}''^t_s(\mathcal{U}''^s),$$

as well as

$$\mathcal{U}'^t = \sigma(\mathcal{U}'^s \cup \mathcal{U}'^t_s(\mathcal{U}'^s)). \tag{8.1}$$

In the general case these relations can be understood as definitions of the Cartesian product "$\times$" and the conditional σ-algebra* $\mathcal{U}'^t_s(\mathcal{U}'^s)$. In place of (8.1), we will also use the shorter notation

$$\mathcal{U}'^t = \mathcal{U}'^s \mathcal{U}'^t_s(\mathcal{U}'^s),\ s < t.$$

More general than the case of uncoupled control is the case of *Markov coupled control.*

Definition 8.1. A control is called Markov coupled if there exist functions $\tilde{u}_s = \tilde{u}_s(\overset{s}{u}_a)$, $s \in T$, such that

$$U^t_s(u^s_a) = U^t_s(\tilde{u}_s),\ \mathcal{U}'^t_s(u^s_a) = \mathcal{U}'^t_s(\tilde{u}_s).$$

Here we will call $\tilde{u}_s$ the ***Markov coordinate of the process.*** If $\tilde{\mathcal{U}}'_s(\subset \mathcal{U}'^s)$ is a σ-algebra defined by conditions imposed on $\tilde{u}_s(\overset{s}{u}_a)$, then obviously

$$\mathcal{U}'^t_s(\mathcal{U}'^s) = \mathcal{U}'^t_s(\tilde{\mathcal{U}}'_s).$$

*We will briefly explain the concept of a conditional σ-algebra. Assume we have a measurable space $(\Omega, \mathcal{B})$ and $\mathcal{F} \subset \mathcal{B}$. The family of σ-algebras $\mathcal{G}(\mathcal{F}) = \mathcal{G}(\omega)\ (\subset \mathcal{B})$, dependent on $\omega \in \Omega$, which as a function of ω is $\mathcal{F}$-measurable (if $\mathcal{G}_0$ is a fixed σ-algebra, then $\{\omega : \mathcal{G}(\omega) = \mathcal{G}_0\} \in \mathcal{F}$), is called a conditional σ-algebra.

We select a set $\Lambda \in \mathcal{F}$, a point $\omega_0 \in \Lambda$, and a set $\Gamma \in \mathcal{G}(\omega_0)$ and take the intersection $\Gamma\Lambda$. The minimal σ-algebra containing all such sets $\Gamma\Lambda$ for all possible Λ, ω_0, Γ, we designate

$$\sigma(\mathcal{F} \cup \mathcal{G}(\mathcal{F})) \equiv \mathcal{F}\mathcal{G}(\mathcal{F}).$$

If $(\mathcal{B} \supset)\ \mathcal{H} \supset \mathcal{F}$, there exists a conditional σ-algebra $\mathcal{G}(\mathcal{F})$ such that $\mathcal{F}\mathcal{G}(\mathcal{F}) = \mathcal{H}$.

The conditional measure $\mathbf{P}(A \mid \mathcal{F})$ assigned on $\mathcal{H} \ni A$, can equally well be considered as defined on the conditional σ-algebra $\mathcal{G}(\mathcal{F})$, and conversely.

Although this is not very important, the σ-algebras $\mathcal{U}'^a$ will be assumed trivial, i.e., consisting of the empty set and the entire space.

2. **The basic process.** The selection of a control indicates the probabilistic behavior of some basic process. More precisely, fixing the control u_a^t prior to the instant t assigns a probabilistic measure $\mathbf{P}(\cdot|u_a^t)$*on a certain σ-algebra $\mathcal{A}''^t(u_a^t)$ of a certain space $\Omega^t(u_a^t) \ni \zeta$ (in the general case this space and the σ-algebra depend on u_a^t). The pair (u_a^t, ζ) forms a point of the space $U^t \times \Omega^t(u_a^t)$ in which the σ-algebra

$$\mathcal{B}''^t = \mathcal{U}''^t \times \mathcal{A}''^t(\mathcal{U}''^t)$$

is defined. We will assume that $\Omega^t(u_a^t) = \Omega^s(u_a^s) \times \Omega_s^t$ where $s < t$, where Ω_s^t is a certain supplementary space.

It is convenient to introduce a single measurable space of elementary events,

$$(\Omega, \mathcal{B}) = (U^b \times \Omega^b(u_a^b), \mathcal{U}''^b \times \mathcal{A}''^b(\mathcal{U}''^b))$$

(i.e., $\mathcal{B} = \mathcal{B}''^b$), and instead of the σ-algebras (for example, $\mathcal{U}'^t$, $\mathcal{A}''^t(u_a^t)$, $\mathcal{B}''^t$) in various spaces, to consider the corresponding σ-algebras in $(\Omega, \mathcal{B})$. Thus, imposing the condition $u \in \Lambda \in \mathcal{U}'^t$ on the first point of the pair (u, ζ), $u \in U$, $\zeta \in \Omega^b(u)$, we define the σ-algebra $\mathcal{U}^t \subset \mathcal{B}$, which is the prototype of the σ-algebra $\mathcal{U}'^t$ (σ-algebras in $(\Omega, \mathcal{B})$ we designate with the same letter, but without the prime).

In the same way as in the preceding notation the point $\mathcal{U}''^b$ coincides with $\mathcal{U}'^b$, we designate $\mathcal{A}'^b = \mathcal{A}''^b$. In the space $\Omega^b(u)$, to the σ-algebras $\mathcal{A}''^t(u_a^t)$ there correspond σ-algebras $\mathcal{A}'^t(u_a^t) \subset \mathcal{A}'^b(u)$. This family is monotonic:

$$\mathcal{A}'^s(u_a^s) \subset \mathcal{A}'^t(u_a^t). \tag{8.2}$$

In the combined space $\Omega = U \times \Omega^b(u)$ it is possible to consider the family of σ-algebras $\mathcal{B}^t = \mathcal{U}'^t \times \mathcal{A}'^t(\mathcal{U}'^t)$. Using $\mathcal{U}^t (\subset \mathcal{B})$ the latter can be written: $\mathcal{B}^t = \mathcal{U}^t \mathcal{A}^t(\mathcal{U}^t)$. As a result of (8.2) the conditional σ-algebras entering into this are monotonic: $\mathcal{A}^s(u_a^s) \subset \mathcal{A}^t(u_a^t)$, $s \leqslant t$.

Thus in the space of elementary events, besides the monotonic family of σ-algebras of the control $\mathcal{U}^t$, there is the monotonic family $\mathcal{B}^t$, $(\mathcal{B}^s \subset \mathcal{B}^t, \ s \leqslant t)$, where

$$\mathcal{B}^t \supset \mathcal{U}^t, \quad t \in T.$$

For each $t \in T$ there is assigned the probabilistic measure $\mathbf{P}(\Lambda|\mathcal{U}^t)$, $\Lambda \in \mathcal{A}^t(\mathcal{U}^t)$. It is (for fixed Λ) a $\mathcal{U}^t$-measurable function of the point $\omega \in \Omega$. It is also possible to consider that the measure

*The use of the measures $\mathbf{P}(\cdot|u_a^t)$ as conditional probabilities assumes that they satisfy the usual consistency conditions for conditional probabilities.

$\mathbf{P}(\cdot|\mathcal{U}^t)$ is assigned on $\mathcal{B}^t$. The σ-algebra $\mathcal{B}^t$ has the sense of a combination of events the probabilities of which are already defined by the control u_a^t.

Sometimes, depending on the conditions of the problem, there is a sequentially developing random process $z=\{z_t, t\in T\}$. By analogy to u, for such a process it is possible to introduce spaces and σ-algebras Z^t, $Z_s^t(z_a^s)$, $\mathcal{Z}''^t$, $\mathcal{Z}'^t$, $\mathcal{Z}_s'^t(z_a^s)$ etc. (the difference in notation in comparison with paragraph 1 lies only in that the letter u is replaced by z). Usually, the process $\{z_t\}$ is such that its past and present are defined in a probabilistic sense if the past and present control are fixed. According to the concepts introduced above, this can briefly be written

$$\mathcal{Z}^t(u_a^t)\subset\mathcal{A}^t(u_a^t),\ \mathcal{U}^t\mathcal{Z}^t(\mathcal{U}^t)\subset\mathcal{B}^t.$$

Thus we do not exclude those cases in which the state space of the process z is determined by the control.

For a fixed control u_a^t, of course, the measure on $\mathcal{Z}^t$ is defined as soon as the measure $\mathbf{P}(\cdot|\mathcal{U}^t)$ is assigned on $\mathcal{B}^t$.

3. **The observed process.** At each instant of time t the observer-operator has at its disposal certain observed data l^t which do not decrease as time goes on. The conditions imposed on these data (for a fixed instant t) define a σ-algebra in the space of elementary events which we will designate $\mathcal{L}^t$. The observed data at the instant t should be defined in a probabilistic sense by the control u_a^t, i.e.,

$$\mathcal{L}^t\subset\mathcal{B}^t. \tag{8.3}$$

We will assume that the observer-operator remembers the preceding control it selected:

$$\mathcal{U}^t\subset\mathcal{L}^t.$$

We will designate by $y^{\varphi(t)}$ those data which enter into l^t but are not contained in u_a^t. The corresponding conditional σ-algebra we will designate $\mathcal{Y}^{\varphi(t)}(\mathcal{U}^t)$. In other words, $\mathcal{Y}^{\varphi(t)}(\mathcal{U}^t)$ is the σ-algebra defined by the relation

$$\mathcal{L}^t=\mathcal{U}^t\mathcal{Y}^{\varphi(t)}(\mathcal{U}^t).$$

From (8.3) we clearly have

$$\mathcal{Y}^{\varphi(t)}(\mathcal{U}^t)\subset\mathcal{A}^t(\mathcal{U}^t). \tag{8.4}$$

The "informational" σ-algebras introduced above possess monotonic characteristics

$$\mathcal{L}^s \subset \mathcal{L}^t; \ \mathcal{Y}^{\varphi(s)}(u) \subset \mathcal{Y}^{\varphi(t)}(u) \quad \text{for} \quad s < t \tag{8.5}$$

in accordance with the condition of no decrease of information noted earlier.

It is convenient to assume that the observed data l^t are composed of the sequentially chosen control and some sequentially observable process $\{ y_t(\omega) \}$, $\omega \in \Omega$. Let the values of this process on the interval $[a, \varphi(t)]$ be known at the instant t, so that

$$l^t = (u_a^t, y_a^{\varphi(t)}).$$

We will assume that $\mathcal{Y}^t(\mathcal{U}^t) \subset \mathcal{A}^t(\mathcal{U}^t)$, where $\mathcal{Y}^t(\mathcal{U}^t)$ is the σ-algebra assigned by the conditions imposed on y_a^t. Then condition (8.4) will be satisfied, if $\varphi(t) \leqslant t$. In order for the monotonic relation (8.5) to be satisfied, the function $\varphi(t)$ should be nondecreasing. For convenience in further work we will assume it to be continuous from the right. A function $\varphi(t)$ with the described properties, and defined on T and having values on T, we will call a ***solution index.***

In the majority of problems with continuous time it is possible to assume $\varphi(t) = t$.

The problem of selecting the optimal control will be solved by the methods of inverse probability (Bayes rule). In this the basic role will be played by the ***a posteriori*** probability $\mathbf{P}(\cdot \mid \mathcal{L}^t)$, corresponding to the data l^t at the instant $t \in T$. This probability we obtain from the earlier introduced $\mathbf{P}(\cdot \mid \mathcal{U}^t)$, since $\mathcal{L}^t \supset \mathcal{U}^t$.

4. The solution measure. Relying on the available data, the observer-operator sequentially chooses the control. The theoretical problem is to indicate the optimal rule for choosing this control. In the general case this rule has a probabilistic character (randomized solution), i.e., only the probabilities of sets of control processes are indicated.

A two-parameter family of conditional probabilistic measures

$$\mu_s^t(\Lambda \mid \mathcal{L}^s), \ s < t; \ s, t \in T,$$

i.e., the measure $\mu_s^t(\Lambda \mid u_a^s, y_a^{\varphi(s)}) \equiv \mu_s^t(\Lambda \mid \mathcal{U}^s \mathcal{Y}^{\varphi(s)})$

on the σ-algebra $\mathcal{U}_s^{"t}(\mathcal{U}^s)$ or (equivalently) on the σ-algebras $\mathcal{U}_s^t(\mathcal{U}^s)$ or $\mathcal{U}^t$ we will call a ***solution*** δ. Each measure δ of the family we will call a ***solution measure.***

The solution measure $\mu_s^t(\Lambda \in \mathcal{U}_s^t \mid \mathcal{U}^s \mathcal{Y}^{\varphi(s)})$ in combination with the measure $\mathbf{P}(\Gamma \in \mathcal{B}^t \mid \mathcal{U}^t)$ determines the conditional measure $\mathbf{Q}(\Gamma \mid \mathcal{L}^s)$ on the σ-algebra $\mathcal{B}^t \ni \Gamma$ by the formula

$$\mathbf{Q}(\Gamma \mid \mathcal{L}^s) = \int \mathbf{P}(\Gamma \mid \mathcal{L}^s \mathcal{U}_s^t(\mathcal{U}^s)) \, \mu_s^t(d\omega \in \mathcal{U}_s^t(\mathcal{U}^s) \mid \mathcal{L}^s), \ s < t,$$

or, using a different notation,

$$\mathbf{Q}(\Gamma \mid \mathscr{L}^s) = \int \mathbf{P}(\Gamma \mid \mathcal{U}^t \mathscr{L}^s)\, \mu_s^t (d\omega \in \mathcal{U}_s^t \mid \mathscr{L}^s).$$

The solution measures should satisfy the consistency relations

$$\mu_r^t(\Gamma_1 \Gamma_2 \mid \mathcal{U}^r \mathcal{Y}^{\varphi(r)}) = \int_{du_r^s \subset \Gamma_1} \mu_s^t(\Gamma_2 \mid \mathcal{U}^s \mathcal{Y}^{\varphi(s)})\, \mathbf{Q}(du_r^s\, dy_{\varphi(r)}^{\varphi(s)} \mid \mathcal{U}^r \mathcal{Y}^{\varphi(r)}),$$

$(\Gamma_1 \in \mathcal{U}_r^s,\ \Gamma_2 \in \mathcal{U}_s^t,\ r < s < t)$ or, more briefly,

$$\mu_r^t(\Gamma \in \mathcal{U}^t \mid \mathscr{L}^r) = \int \mu_s^t(\Gamma \mid \mathscr{L}^s)\, \mathbf{Q}(d\omega \in \mathscr{L}^s \mid \mathscr{L}^r).$$

The solution measures can be considered as conditional probabilities $\mu_s^t(\Gamma \mid \mathscr{L}^s) = \mu(\Gamma \mid \mathscr{L}^s)$, $\Gamma \in \mathcal{U}^t$, formed in the usual way from a single solution measure $\mu(\Delta) = \mu_a^b(\Delta \mid \mathcal{U}^a)$, $\Delta \in \mathcal{U}^b$. Further, all measures $\mu_s^t(\Gamma \in \mathcal{U}^t \mid \mathscr{L}^s)$, $\mathbf{P}(A \in \mathscr{B}^t \mid \mathcal{U}^t)$, $\mathbf{Q}(A \in \mathscr{B}^t \mid \mathscr{L}^s)$ can be considered as conditional probabilities formed from a single combined probabilistic measure $\mathbf{Q}(\Lambda \mid \mathscr{L}^a) \equiv \mathbf{Q}(\Lambda)$, $\Lambda \in \mathscr{B}^b \equiv \mathscr{B}$ in accordance with the formula

$$\mu_s^t(\Gamma \in \mathcal{U}^t \mid \mathscr{L}^s) = \mathbf{Q}(\Gamma \mid \mathscr{L}^s);\ \mathbf{P}(A \in \mathscr{B}^t \mid \mathcal{U}^t) = \mathbf{Q}(A \mid \mathcal{U}^t);$$
$$\mathbf{Q}(A \in \mathscr{B}^t \mid \mathscr{L}^s) = \mathbf{Q}(A \mid \mathscr{L}^s),\ s < t \quad (\text{a.c. } \mathbf{Q}).$$

A solution δ thus defines a unique measure $\mathbf{Q}$ in the space $(\Omega, \mathscr{B})$, and conversely.

5. **The penalty function and conditional risks.** The quality of the solution is determined by the size of the risk. By the latter we mean the mathematical expectation of a *penalty function* $c(\omega)$, $\omega \in \Omega$. This function, which we assume to be $\mathscr{B}$-measurable and $\mathbf{Q}$-summable, is assigned in the conditions of the problem. Since the measure $\mathbf{Q}$ is defined by a solution δ, the risk

$$R^\delta = \int c(\omega)\, \mathbf{Q}(d\omega) \tag{8.6}$$

is a characteristic of the solution δ. Along with the indicated risk it is possible to consider the conditional risks

$$R^\delta(\mathscr{L}^t) \equiv R^\delta(\omega \mid \mathscr{L}^t) = \int c(\omega)\, \mathbf{Q}(d\omega \mid \mathscr{L}^t). \tag{8.7}$$

These risks form a one-parameter family with the consistency condition

$$R^\delta(\mathscr{L}^s) = \int R^\delta(\mathscr{L}^t)\, \mathbf{Q}(d\omega \mid \mathscr{L}^s),\ s < t.$$

The last element of the family coincides with (8.6): $R^\delta(\mathscr{L}^a) = R^\delta$, since the σ-algebra $\mathscr{L}^a$ is assumed to be trivial.

8.2 The Case of a Stepped Index. Optimal Conditional Risks

1. Let us assume that the index $\varphi(t)$ is a step function having a finite number of jumps at the points $a=t_0<t_1<\ldots<t_N<b$. Thus

$$\varphi(t)=\varphi_k \quad \text{for} \quad t\in[t_k, t_{k+1}),\ k=0, 1, \ldots, N-1,$$
$$(\varphi_k \leqslant t_k;\ t_i<t_k \quad \text{for} \quad i<k)$$

if we write $\varphi(t_k)=\varphi_k$.

In this case the family of δ solution measures, and thus also the measure $\mathbf{Q}$, is completely defined by a finite system of measures:

$$\mu_{t_k}^{t_{k+1}}(\Lambda\in\mathcal{U}^{t_{k+1}}\,|\,\mathcal{U}^{t_k}\mathcal{Y}^{\varphi_k}), \quad k=0, 1, \ldots, N.$$

We will show this. Using $\mathbf{P}(\Lambda\in\mathcal{B}^b\,|\,\mathcal{U}^b)$, we can find $\mathbf{P}(\Lambda\,|\,\mathcal{U}^b\mathcal{Y}^{\varphi_N})$. Using, in addition, the measure $\mu_{t_N}^{b}(\Gamma\,|\,\mathcal{U}^{t_N}\mathcal{Y}^{\varphi_N})$, we can calculate the measure

$$\mathbf{Q}(\Lambda\,|\,\mathcal{U}^{N}\mathcal{Y}^{\varphi_N})=\int\mathbf{P}(\Lambda\,|\,\mathcal{U}^b\mathcal{Y}^{\varphi_N})\,\mu_{t_N}^{b}(d\omega\in\mathcal{U}^b\,|\,\mathcal{U}^{t_N}\mathcal{Y}^{\varphi_N}),$$
$$\Lambda\in\mathcal{B}^b.$$

Further, since

$$\mathcal{U}^{t_N}\mathcal{Y}^{\varphi_N}\subset\mathcal{B}^{t_N},$$

it is possible to determine $\mathbf{Q}(\Lambda\,|\,\mathcal{U}^{t_N}\mathcal{Y}^{\varphi_{N-1}})$ using the integral

$$\mathbf{Q}(\Lambda\,|\,\mathcal{U}^{t_N}\mathcal{Y}^{\varphi_{N-1}})=\int\mathbf{Q}(\Lambda\,|\,\mathcal{U}^{t_N}\mathcal{Y}^{\varphi_N})\,\mathbf{P}(d\omega\in\mathcal{U}^{t_N}\mathcal{Y}^{\varphi_N}\,|\,\mathcal{U}^{t_N}\mathcal{Y}^{\varphi_{N-1}}). \quad (8.8)$$

The measure $\mathbf{Q}(\Lambda\,|\,\mathcal{U}^{t_N}\mathcal{Y}^{\varphi_N})$ has already been defined, and $\mathbf{P}(d\omega\subset\mathcal{B}^{t_N}\,|\,\mathcal{U}^{t_N}\mathcal{Y}^{\varphi_{N-1}})$ is assigned by the condition of paragraph 2, Sect. 8.1. Analogously, using the solution measure $\mu_{t_{N-1}}^{t_N}(\Gamma\,|\,\mathcal{U}^{t_{N-1}}\mathcal{Y}^{\varphi_{N-1}})$, we calculate

$$\mathbf{Q}(\Lambda\,|\,\mathcal{U}^{t_{N-1}}\mathcal{Y}^{\varphi_{N-1}})=\int\mathbf{Q}(\Lambda\,|\,\mathcal{U}^{t_N}\mathcal{Y}^{\varphi_{N-1}})\,\mu_{t_{N-1}}^{t_N}(d\omega\,|\,\mathcal{U}^{t_{N-1}}\mathcal{Y}^{\varphi_{N-1}}). \quad (8.9)$$

Continuing this process of integration, alternately using weight $\mathbf{P}(\cdot\,|\,\mathcal{U}^{t_{k+1}}\mathcal{Y}^{\varphi_k})$ and weight $\mu_{t_k}^{t_{k+1}}(\cdot\,|\,\mathcal{U}^{t_k}\mathcal{Y}^{\varphi_k})$, we determine the various measures $\mathbf{Q}(\Lambda\,|\,\mathcal{U}^{t_k}\mathcal{Y}^{\varphi_k})$, $\Lambda\in\mathcal{B}$. The latter will be used to calculate the single combined measure $\mathbf{Q}(\Lambda\,|\,\mathcal{L}^a)=\mathbf{Q}(\Lambda)$.

A direct verification will show that all assertions of paragraph 4, Sect. 8.1 hold for it.

Taking into account formulas of the type (8.8) and (8.9), we find that the conditional risks (8.7) satisfy in this case the recurrence relations

$$R^{\delta}(\mathcal{U}^{t_{k+1}}\mathcal{Y}^{\varphi_k}) = \int R^{\delta}(\mathcal{U}^{t_{k+1}}\mathcal{Y}^{\varphi_{k+1}})\,\mathbf{P}(d\omega\,|\,\mathcal{U}^{t_{k+1}}\mathcal{Y}^{\varphi_k}); \qquad (8.10)$$

$$R^{\delta}(\mathcal{U}^{t_k}\mathcal{Y}^{\varphi_k}) = \int R^{\delta}(\mathcal{U}^{t_{k+1}}\mathcal{Y}^{\varphi_k})\,\mu_{t_k}^{t_{k+1}}(d\omega\,|\,\mathcal{U}^{t_k}\mathcal{Y}^{\varphi_k}). \qquad (8.11)$$

In these relations the role of "initial" condition is played by the function $R^{\delta}(\mathcal{U}^{b}\mathcal{Y}^{\varphi(b)})$ and the final function $R^{\delta}(\mathcal{U}^{a}\mathcal{Y}^{\varphi(a)})$ coincides with the risk (8.6).

2. Let us introduce into consideration the *optimal conditional risks* $R(\mathcal{U}^{t_k}\mathcal{Y}^{\varphi_k})$. Let them be defined by recurrence relations analogous to (8.10) and (8.11), with the same "initial" condition, but in contrast to these preceding recurrence relations, the averaging (8.11) with weight $\mu_{t_k}^{t_{k+1}}(\cdot\,|\,\mathcal{U}^{t_k}\mathcal{Y}^{\varphi_k})$ is replaced by a conditional minimization:

$$R(\mathcal{U}^{t_k}\mathcal{Y}^{\varphi_k}) = \inf_{\omega\,|\,\mathcal{U}^{t_k}\mathcal{Y}^{\varphi_k}} R(\mathcal{U}^{t_{k+1}}\mathcal{Y}^{\varphi_k}). \qquad (8.12)$$

The conditional minimum

$$\inf_{\omega\,|\,\mathcal{F}_1} f(\omega)$$

of the $\mathcal{F}_2$-measurable function $f(\omega)$ relative to the σ-algebra $\mathcal{F}_1 \subset \mathcal{F}_2$ as defined in Appendix 2 is an $\mathcal{F}_1$-measurable function satisfying conditions A.2.1.A—B. In Appendix 2 it is proven that the conditional minimum has the following characteristic (Theorem A.2.3): for any probabilistic measure $\mu(\Lambda \in \mathcal{F}_2\,|\,\mathcal{F}_1)$ [defined on $\mathcal{F}_2 \times \Omega$ and $\mathcal{F}_1$-measurable with respect to the second argument] the inequality

$$\inf_{\omega\,|\,\mathcal{F}_1} f(\omega) \leqslant \int f(\omega)\,\mu(d\omega\,|\,\mathcal{F}_1).$$

is satisfied.

Comparison of the transformations (8.11) and (8.12) at each stage of the recursive transformations, using this, shows that a smaller (more precisely, at most an equal) resulting function corresponds to transformation (8.12). Comparing the functions at the last stage of the transformations we have $R^{\delta} \geqslant R$.

In this manner we obtain the following result:

Theorem 8.1. The optimal risks do not exceed the risks of any solution δ having the same stepped index $\varphi(t)$:

$$R(\mathcal{U}^{t_k}\mathcal{Y}^{\varphi_k}) \leqslant R^{\delta}(\mathcal{U}^{t_k}\mathcal{Y}^{\varphi_k}), \quad k=0,\ 1,\ \ldots,\ N.$$

In the next theorem the optimal risks corresponding to different stepped indices are compared.

Theorem 8.2. The optimal risk R_φ for a stepped index $\varphi(t)$ does not exceed the optimal risk corresponding to an at most equal stepped index $\varphi'(t) \leqslant \varphi(t)$.

Proof. From any step function having a finite number of steps it is possible to convert to any other step function by means of a finite sequence of step functions in which the neighboring functions differ in only one step. Thus it is sufficient to prove Theorem 8.2 for a function $\varphi(\cdot)$ having one differing step as compared with $\varphi'(\cdot)$, and with the remaining steps coinciding. Let us assume, for example, $\varphi'(t)=\varphi(t)$ for $t<t_k$ and $t>t_{k+1}$, and $\varphi(t)=\varphi_k$, $\varphi'(t)=\varphi'_k<\varphi_k$ for $t_k<t<t_{k+1}$.

According to (8.10) and (8.12), for $\varphi(t)$ we have

$$R_\varphi(\mathcal{U}^{t_k}\mathcal{Y}^{\varphi'_k}) = \int [\inf_{\omega|\mathcal{U}^{t_k}\mathcal{Y}^{\varphi_k}} g(\omega)]\, \mathbf{P}(d\omega\,|\,\mathcal{U}^{t_k}\mathcal{Y}^{\varphi'_k}).$$

For $\varphi'(t)$ at the same time

$$R_{\varphi'}(\mathcal{U}^{t_k}\mathcal{Y}^{\varphi'_k}) = \inf_{\omega|\mathcal{U}^{t_k}\mathcal{Y}^{\varphi'_k}} \int g(\omega)\, \mathbf{P}(d\omega\,|\,\mathcal{U}^{t_{k+1}}\mathcal{Y}^{\varphi'_k}),$$

where

$$g(\omega) = R_\varphi(\mathcal{U}^{t_{k+1}}\mathcal{Y}^{\varphi_k}) = R_{\varphi'}(\mathcal{U}^{t_{k+1}}\mathcal{Y}^{\varphi_k}).$$

Since

$$\inf_{\omega|\mathcal{U}^{t_k}\mathcal{Y}^{\varphi_k}} g(\omega) \leqslant g(\omega)$$

(see Theorem A.2.2), then, obviously,

$$\mathbf{M}[\inf_{\omega|\mathcal{U}^{t_k}\mathcal{Y}^{\varphi_k}} g(\omega)\,|\,\mathcal{U}^{t_{k+1}}\mathcal{Y}^{\varphi'_k}] \leqslant \mathbf{M}[g(\omega)\,|\,\mathcal{U}^{t_{k+1}}\mathcal{Y}^{\varphi'_k}]. \tag{8.13}$$

The expression on the left side coincides with $\mathbf{M}\left[\inf_{\omega|\mathcal{U}^{t_k}\mathcal{Y}^{\varphi_k}} g(\omega)\,|\,\mathcal{U}^{t_k}\mathcal{Y}^{\varphi'_k}\right]$ as a result of the $\mathcal{U}^{t_k}\mathcal{Y}^{\varphi_k}$-measurability of the functions $\inf_{\omega|\mathcal{U}^{t_k}\mathcal{Y}^{\varphi_k}} g(\omega)$.

Taking the lower bound with respect to $\omega\,|\,\mathcal{U}^{t_k}\mathcal{Y}^{\varphi'_k}$ in (8.13), we get

$$\inf_{\omega|\mathcal{U}^{t_k}\mathcal{Y}^{\varphi'_k}} \mathbf{M}\left[\inf_{\omega|\mathcal{U}^{t_k}\mathcal{Y}^{\varphi_k}} g(\omega)\,|\,\mathcal{U}^{t_k}\mathcal{Y}^{\varphi'_k}\right] \leqslant \inf_{\omega|\mathcal{U}^{t_k}\mathcal{Y}^{\varphi'_k}} \mathbf{M}\left[g(\omega)\,|\,\mathcal{U}^{t_{k+1}}\mathcal{Y}^{\varphi'_k}\right].$$

The multiple minimization on the left side is superfluous since the function subjected to minimization is already $\mathcal{U}^{t_k}\mathcal{Y}^{\varphi'_k}$-measurable. Thus,

$$\mathbf{M}\left[\inf_{\omega|\mathcal{U}^{t_k}\mathcal{Y}^{\varphi_k}} g(\omega)\,|\,\mathcal{U}^{t_k}\mathcal{Y}^{\varphi'_k}\right] \leqslant \inf_{\omega|\mathcal{U}^{t_k}\mathcal{Y}^{\varphi'_k}} \mathbf{M}\left[g(\omega)\,|\,\mathcal{U}^{t_{k+1}}\mathcal{Y}^{\varphi'_k}\right],$$

i.e.,

$$R_\varphi(\mathcal{U}^{t_k}\mathcal{Y}^{\varphi'_k}) \leqslant R_{\varphi'}(\mathcal{U}^{t_k}\mathcal{Y}^{\varphi'_k}).$$

Subsequent recursive transformations coincide for both indices because of the coincidence of $\varphi(t)$ and $\varphi'(t)$ for $t<t_k$. Thus the resulting inequality is preserved for all $t_i<t_k$, including $t_0=a$. The proof is completed.

Combining Theorems 8.1 and 8.2, it is easily seen that the optimal risk for a stepped index $\varphi(t)$ does not exceed the risk for any solution corresponding to a lesser or equal stepped index $\varphi'(t)\leqslant\varphi(t)$.

3. We shall turn now to the examination of risks for a continuous index. In order to define these we will consider a sequence of stepped indices $\{\varphi^N(t)\}$, everywhere converging to $\varphi(t)$ as $N\to\infty$. For a stepped index it is possible to use the facts determined above. If the limit of the corresponding risks exists as $N\to\infty$, then we will accept it as the definition of the risk in the case of a continuous index.

Definition 8.2. Let a certain sequence of stepped indices $\{\varphi^N(t)\}$ converge to $\varphi(t)$ from below and to each N let there correspond a solution δ^N, with $\delta^N\to\delta$ as $N\to\infty$, i.e., $\mu_{t_k}^{t_l}(\cdot\,|\,\mathcal{L}^{t_k})\to\mu_s^t(\cdot\,|\,\mathcal{L}^s)$ as $N\to\infty$, $t_k\to s$, $t_l\to t$. Then, if $\lim_{N\to\infty,\,t_k\to t} R^{\delta^N}(\mathcal{U}^{t_k}\mathcal{Y}^{\varphi^N(t_k)}) = R^\delta(\mathcal{U}^t\mathcal{Y}^{\varphi(t)})$, the solution δ is called regular.

In this definition we assume the existence of at least one specific sequence of prelimit indices φ^N and solutions δ^N.

Let us also define the optimal risks for a continuous index. Let $S_N=\{\tau_1,\dots,\tau_N\}$ be a set of points from T. Arranging these points in a nondecreasing sequence ($t_i=\tau_{k_i}$, $t_i<t_j$ for $i<j$), we obtain a certain division of the interval T. For this division we form an approximation $\varphi(S_N)$ of the index φ. Namely, we assume

$$\varphi(t, S_N)=\varphi(t_i) \text{ for } t_i \leqslant t < t_{i+1}.$$

Obviously, with such a definition $\varphi(t, S_N) \leqslant \varphi(t)$ and $\varphi(t, S') \leqslant \varphi(t, S'')$, if $S' \subset S''$.

Definition 8.3. Let $R_{\varphi(S_N)}$ be the optimal risk of the approximation $\varphi(S_N)$. The optimal risk of the continuous index $\varphi(t)$ we define as the lower bound

$$R_\varphi = \inf_{N, S_N} R_{\varphi(S_N)} \tag{8.14}$$

over all possible finite divisions of the interval T.

Theorem 8.3. There exists a sequence S (we will call it the risk-defining sequence) such that

$$R_\varphi = \lim_{N\to\infty} R_{\varphi(S_N)}, \tag{8.15}$$

where S_N is the set of the N first elements of the sequence S.

We will prove the theorem for the case of greatest interest, when the lower bound (8.14) is finite. According to (8.14), for any given $\varepsilon_1>0$ there exists a set S^1 such that

$$R_{\varphi(S^1)} - R_\varphi < \varepsilon_1.$$

Taking $\varepsilon_2=\varepsilon_1/2$, in the same way there exists a set S^2, such that $R_{\varphi(S^2)}-R_\varphi<\varepsilon_2$. Similar sets can be found also for $\varepsilon_3=\varepsilon_1/4$, etc. If we form the sequence $S=(S^1, S^2, \ldots)$, then from Theorem 8.2 we will have

$$R_{\varphi(S^k)} \geqslant R_{\varphi(S^1,\ldots,S^k)} \;(\geqslant R_\varphi).$$

Thus from the convergences $R_{\varphi(S^k)} \to R_\varphi$ results the convergence $R_{\varphi(S^1,\ldots,S^k)} \to R_\varphi$ as $k\to\infty$. The proof is completed.

In agreement with Theorem 8.2 the risk-defining sequence S will remain the same if at any place we join to it any points from T.

Along with the risk (8.15) it is possible to define the conditional optimal risks

$$R_\varphi(\mathcal{U}^t\mathcal{Y}^{\varphi(t)}) = \lim_{N\to\infty}(R_{\varphi(S_N)}(\mathcal{U}^t\mathcal{Y}^{\varphi(t,S_N)}),$$

where the approximation $\varphi(t, S_N)$ is the same as in Theorem 8.3.

The limit always exists because of the monotonic dependence on N of the risk on the right side (Theorem 8.2).

Usually a risk-defining sequence is any set including points of a jump index and everywhere dense on segments of continuous increase (see Sect. 8.4).

4. Let us continue the comparison of risks for various indices begun in paragraph 2.

Theorem 8.4. The optimal risk R_φ for any index $\varphi(t)$ is not greater than the risk of any solution (optimal or nonoptimal) corresponding to a lesser or equal stepped index $\varphi'(t) \leqslant \varphi(t)$.

This theorem is a result of Theorems 8.1 and 8.2, and of Definition 8.3 (if the index $\varphi(t)$ is not stepped).

In the next theorem, nonstepped indices $\varphi'(t)$ $(\leqslant \varphi(t))$ are also included in the indices being compared.

Theorem 8.5. The optimal risk R_φ for the index $\varphi(t)$ does not exceed any other risk of a regular solution corresponding to any lesser or equal index $\varphi'(t) \leqslant \varphi(t)$.

This theorem includes as special cases Theorems 8.1, 8.2, and 8.4. The new assertion applies to the case when the index $\varphi'(t)$ is not stepped.

Let $R_{\varphi'}$ be the optimal risk for the index $\varphi'(t)$. Using Definition 8.3 and Theorem 8.3, we take the risk-defining set S' of $R_{\varphi'}$. It is obvious that as a result of the condition $\varphi'(t) \leqslant \varphi(t)$ for each $S'_N \subset S'$ we will have

$$\varphi'(t, S'_N) \leqslant \varphi(t, S'_N).$$

Applying Theorem 8.2, we get

$$R_{\varphi(S'_N)} \leqslant R_{\varphi'(S'_N)}.$$

But the left side does not exceed $\inf\limits_{S_N} R_{\varphi(S_N)} = R_\varphi$, hence

$$R_\varphi \leqslant R_{\varphi'(S'_N)}.$$

Passing to the limit as $N \to \infty$, we get $R_\varphi \leqslant R_{\varphi'}$.

Let us now examine the nonoptimal risk $R^\delta_{\varphi'}$ for the index φ'. We take into account Definition 8.2. From Theorems 8.1 and 8.2 we have

$$R_{\varphi'(S_N)} \leqslant R_{\varphi' N} \leqslant R^{\delta N}_{\varphi' N},$$

where S_N are the points of discontinuity of the prelimit index $\varphi'^N(t)$ ($\leqslant \varphi'(t)$) which enters into Definition 8.2 [thus $\varphi'^N(t) \leqslant \varphi'(t, S_N)$]. Passing to the limit as $N \to \infty$ and taking into account Definition 8.3, we have $R_{\varphi'} \leqslant R^{\delta}_{\varphi'}$. But, as already shown, $R_{\varphi} \leqslant R_{\varphi'}$. Consequently, $R_{\varphi} \leqslant R^{\delta}_{\varphi'}$, which completes the proof of Theorem 8.5.

According to the above, the optimal solution is the best of all regular solutions of no larger index.

8.3 Optimal Solutions

1. In the preceding section, in considering the optimal risks $R_{\varphi}(\mathcal{U}^t \mathcal{Y}^{\varphi(t)})$ nothing was said about the solutions to which these risks correspond. If there exists a solution, the risk of which coincides with the optimal risk, then such a solution is naturally called optimal.

The examination carried out above shows that there always exist optimal risks. The question arises as to whether an optimal solution always exists. An affirmative answer to this question can apparently not be given in general. In order to prove rigorously the existence of an optimal solution, certain limitations are needed, topological assumptions, for example.

It is easier (there is no need for supplementary assumptions) to prove the existence of solutions arbitrarily close to the optimal, the risk of which can be arbitrarily close to R_{φ}.

We will first consider the case of a discontinuous index $\varphi^N(t)$ having N jumps and construct for it a solution δ_{ε}, the risk $R^{\delta_{\varepsilon}}_{\varphi N}$ of which differs from the optimal R_{φ^N} by less than ε ($\varepsilon > 0$ is arbitrary). The calculation of the optimal risk R_{φ^N} is carried out using the recurrence relations (8.10) and (8.12), the conditional minimization (8.12) being needed $N + 1$ times. The first time we calculate the conditional minimum

$$R_{\varphi^N}(\mathcal{U}^{t_N} \mathcal{Y}^{\varphi_N}) = \inf_{\omega \mid \mathcal{U}^{t_N} \mathcal{Y}^{\varphi_N}} R_{\varphi^N}(\mathcal{U}^b \mathcal{Y}^{\varphi_N}).$$

As shown in the Appendix (Theorem A.2.4), for an arbitrary $\varepsilon_0 \left(= \frac{\varepsilon}{N+1}\right)$ for every point it is possible to find a point $\omega^*(\omega)$, such that

$$R_{\varphi^N}(\omega^*(\omega) \mid \mathcal{U}^b \mathcal{Y}^{\varphi_N}) - R_{\varphi^N}(\omega \mid \mathcal{U}^{t_N} \mathcal{Y}^{\varphi_N}) < \varepsilon_0.$$

Let Γ_{ω} be the set

$$\Gamma_{\omega} = \{\omega' \colon u^b_{t_N}(\omega') = u^b_{t_N}(\omega^*(\omega))\} \in \mathcal{U}^b_{t_N}(\mathcal{U}^{t_N} \mathcal{Y}^{\varphi_N}),$$

and $\mu^b_{t_N}(\Gamma \in \mathcal{U}^b_{t_N} | \mathcal{U}^{t_N}\mathcal{Y}^{\varphi_N})$ be a measure concentrated on this set. Then obviously

$$R_{\varphi^N}(\omega^*(\omega) | \mathcal{U}^b\mathcal{Y}^{\varphi_N}) = \int R_{\varphi^N}(\omega' | \mathcal{U}^b\mathcal{Y}^{\varphi_N}) \mu^b_{t_N}(d\omega' | \mathcal{U}^{t_N}\mathcal{Y}^{\varphi_N}),$$

i.e., $R_{\varphi^N}(\omega^* | \mathcal{U}^b\mathcal{Y}^{\varphi_N})$ is the conditional risk $R^\delta_{\varphi^N}(\mathcal{U}^{t_N}\mathcal{Y}^{\varphi_N})$ corresponding to the solution measure $\mu^b_{t_N}$. Thus, the solution measure $\mu^b_{t_N}(\Gamma | \mathcal{U}^{t_N}\mathcal{Y}^{\varphi_N})$ so constructed, which produces the conditional risk, differs from the optimal by less than $\frac{\varepsilon}{N+1}$.

According to (8.10), we carry out the conditional averaging $\mathbf{M}[\cdot | \mathcal{U}^{t_N}\mathcal{Y}^{\varphi_{N-1}}]$ of these risks, and at the second step look for the conditional minimum

$$\inf_{\omega | \mathcal{U}^{t_{N-1}}\mathcal{Y}^{\varphi_{N-1}}} R^\delta_{\varphi^N}(\omega | \mathcal{U}^{t_N}\mathcal{Y}^{\varphi_{N-1}}) =$$

$$= \inf_{\omega | \mathcal{U}^{t_{N-1}}\mathcal{Y}^{\varphi_{N-1}}} R_{\varphi^N}(\omega | \mathcal{U}^{t_N}\mathcal{Y}^{\varphi_{N-1}}) + O\left(\frac{\varepsilon}{N+1}\right). \tag{8.16}$$

Theorem A.2.4 guarantees the existence of a point $\omega^*(\omega)$ such that

$$R_{\varphi^N}(\omega^*(\omega) | \mathcal{U}^{t_N}\mathcal{Y}^{\varphi_{N-1}}) - R_{\varphi^N}(\omega | \mathcal{U}^{t_{N-1}}\mathcal{Y}^{\varphi_{N-1}}) < \frac{\varepsilon}{N+1}. \tag{8.17}$$

For the solution measure $\mu^{t_N}_{t_{N-1}}(\Gamma \in \mathcal{U}^{t_N}_{t_{N-1}} | \mathcal{U}^{t_{N-1}}\mathcal{Y}^{\varphi_{N-1}})$ we will take a measure concentrated on the set

$$\Gamma_\omega = \{\omega' : u^{t_N}_{t_{N-1}}(\omega') = u^{t_N}_{t_{N-1}}(\omega^*(\omega))\} \in \mathcal{U}^{t_N}_{t_{N-1}}(\mathcal{U}^{t_{N-1}}\mathcal{Y}^{\varphi_{N-1}}).$$

Then, in agreement with (8.16) and (8.17), to the solution measures $\mu^{t_N}_{t_{N-1}}$, $\mu^b_{t_N}$ will correspond a conditional risk differing from the optimal by less than $2\varepsilon/(N+1)$.

Continuing this process, using Theorem A.2.5, we construct the solution measures $\mu^{t_1}_a$, $\mu^{t_2}_{t_1}, \ldots \mu^b_{t_N}$. Each of them corresponds to the approximate [to within $\varepsilon/(N+1)$] minimization of an optimal conditional risk. The risk of this solution ultimately will differ from the optimal risk by not more than ε. This proves the existence of a solution arbitrarily close to optimal in the case of a discontinuous risk.

For an arbitrary index $\varphi(t)$ it is possible to consider its step approximation $\varphi^N(t) \leqslant \varphi(t)$ such that $R_{\varphi^N} - R_\varphi > \frac{\varepsilon_1}{2}$. Further, using the previous reasoning, we need to find a solution δ for which $R_\varphi^{\delta N} - R_\varphi{}^N < \frac{\varepsilon_1}{2} = \varepsilon$. Finally, $R_\varphi^{\delta N}$ will differ from R_φ by not more than ε_1. This proves the assertion for an arbitrary indix.

Thus, the proof of the existence of a solution arbitrarily close to optimality reduces to the application of Theorem A.2.5 (Appendix 2) at each stage.

2. The solutions close to the optimal constructed in the preceding section do not necessarily have a randomized character. We will now consider randomized solutions. It is convenient to introduce a new concept, a measure ν in the space $(\Omega, \mathcal{U}^b)$, which helps to carry out the randomization. Thus we will call it the ***basis of randomization***. In contrast with the theory presented in the preceding paragraph, the present examination will be called ***variant II***.

Combining the measure $\nu(\Lambda)$ assigned on $\mathcal{U}^b \ni \Lambda$ with the measure $\mathbf{P}(\Gamma \in \mathcal{B} \mid \mathcal{U}^b)$, it is possible to find a measure (we will also designate it by ν) in the measurable space $(\Omega, \mathcal{B})$ by means of the formula

$$\nu(\Gamma) = \int \mathbf{P}(\Gamma \mid \mathcal{U}^b)\, \nu(d\omega \in \mathcal{U}^b), \quad \Gamma \in \mathcal{B}.$$

The theory gains in certain respects if in its exposition we systematically use the existence of the measure ν in the space $(\Omega, \mathcal{B})$ assigned by the conditions of the problem. In this process the series of concepts defined above is naturally subjected to modification. Thus, it is possible to assume that the probabilistic measures $\mathbf{P}(\cdot \mid \mathcal{U}^t)$ are defined and $\mathcal{U}^t$-measurable almost everywhere (to within a set of ν measure zero). Similarly, the solution measures $\mu_s^t(\cdot \mid \mathcal{L}^t)$ can be assumed defined to within a ν-equivalence. Further, the conditional minimum in formulas (8.12), (8.13), and others should, of course, be replaced by the absolute minimum (relative to ν) [see Appendix 2, variant II]. Thus, (8.12) takes on the form

$$R(\omega \mid \mathcal{U}^{t_k} \mathcal{Y}^{\varphi_k}) = \underset{\omega \mid \mathcal{U}^{t_k} \mathcal{Y}^{\varphi_k}}{\text{vrai inf}}\ R(\omega \mid \mathcal{U}^{t_k+1} \mathcal{Y}^{\varphi_k}).$$

It is important that in variant II, with appropriate modifications (replacement of equalities "everywhere" by equalities "almost everywhere" with respect to ν) all the results compiled above (Sect. 8.2) retain their validity.

In the new variant of the theory it is also possible to carry out arguments analogous to those of the preceding paragraph and prove the existence of an ε-optimal solution. As a supplement to this it is now convenient to consider one particular randomized ε-optimal solution, which will be mentioned below.

In the proof of Theorem A.2.5, it is shown that there exists a nonempty set

$$A_k = \{\omega : \inf_{\omega|\mathcal{F}_1} f(\omega) \in [c_k, c_{k+1})\} \cap \{\omega : f(\omega) \in [c_k, c_{k+1})\} \in \mathcal{F}_2,$$

if $\Gamma_k = \{\omega : \inf_{\omega|\mathcal{F}_1} f(\omega) \in [c_k, c_{k+1})\}$ is nonempty $(c_{k+1} - c_k < \varepsilon)$. The selection of any probabilistic measure concentrated on A_k gives an ε-optimal solution measure. The particular choice of this measure, nevertheless, is not mentioned. In the new variant it is guaranteed that the analogous set has nonzero measure:

$$\nu(A_k) > 0, \quad \text{if} \quad \nu(\Gamma_k) > 0$$

$$(A_k = \{\omega : f(\omega) \in [c_k, c_{k+1}), \ \operatorname*{vrai\,inf}_{\omega|\mathcal{F}_1} f(\omega) \in [c_k, c_{k+1})\}).$$

Thus for solution measure $\mu(\Lambda \in \mathcal{F}_2 | \mathcal{F}_1)$ we can now choose the measure

$$\mu(\Lambda | \mathcal{F}_1) = \mu(\Lambda | \sigma(\ldots, \Gamma_1, \Gamma_2, \ldots)) = \frac{\nu(\Lambda A_k)}{\nu(A_k)} = \nu(\Lambda | A_k)$$

$$\text{for} \quad \omega \in \Gamma_k.$$

It is obvious that the particular measure under consideration relates to a number of suitable measures, such as

$$0 \leqslant \int f(\omega') \mu(d\omega' | \mathcal{F}_1) - \operatorname*{vrai\,inf}_{\omega'|\mathcal{F}_1} f(\omega') < \varepsilon$$

corresponding to Theorems A.2.8 and A.2.9.

A similar particular choice should be made at each stage of the recursive transformations.

Let the index $\varphi(t)$ be stepped, with jumps at the points $a = t_0 < t_1 < \ldots, < t_N$, and let the points c_j, $j = \ldots, 1, 2, \ldots$ $(c_{j+1} > c_j)$ represent an ε_0-division of the real axis $\left(\varepsilon_0 = \frac{\varepsilon}{N+1}\right)$. According to the above, we choose the following solution measure:

$$\mu^b_{t_N}(\Lambda \in \mathcal{U}^b_{t_N} | \mathcal{U}^{t_N} \mathcal{Y}^{\varphi_N}) = \frac{\nu(\Lambda A^N_{k(\omega)} | \mathcal{U}^{t_N} \mathcal{Y}^{\varphi_N})}{\nu(A^N_{k(\omega)} | \mathcal{U}^{t_N} \mathcal{Y}^{\varphi_N})} = \nu(\Lambda | \mathcal{U}^{t_N} \mathcal{Y}^{\varphi_N} A^N_{k(\omega)}).$$

Here

$$A^N_k = \{\omega : R(\mathcal{U}^b \mathcal{Y}^{\varphi_N}) \in [c_k, c_{k+1})\} \cap \{\omega : R(\mathcal{U}^{t_N} \mathcal{Y}^{\varphi_N}) \in [c_k, c_{k+1})\}.$$

Further, $k(\omega) = k^N(\omega) = \{k : R(\omega \mid \mathcal{U}^{t_N}\mathcal{Y}^{\varphi_N}) \in [c_k, c_{k+1})\}$. From Theorems A.2.8 and A.2.9, it is easy to see that for this solution measure

$$0 \leqslant R^{\delta}(\mathcal{U}^{t_N}\mathcal{Y}^{\varphi_N}) - R(\mathcal{U}^{t_N}\mathcal{Y}^{\varphi_N}) < \varepsilon_0$$

and, thus,

$$0 \leqslant R^{\delta}(\mathcal{U}^{t_N}\mathcal{Y}^{\varphi_{N-1}}) - R(\mathcal{U}^{t_N}\mathcal{Y}^{\varphi_{N-1}}) < \varepsilon_0. \tag{8.18}$$

Let us turn to the next stage of the recursive transformations. Assume

$$\mu_{t_{N-1}}^{t_N}(\Lambda \in \mathcal{U}_{t_{N-1}}^{t_N} \mid \mathcal{U}^{t_{N-1}}\mathcal{Y}^{\varphi_{N-1}}) = \nu(\Lambda \mid \mathcal{U}^{t_{N-1}}\mathcal{Y}^{\varphi_{N-1}},\ A_{k(\omega)}^{N-1}),$$

where, as before,

$$k(\omega) = k^{N-1}(\omega) = \{k : R(\mathcal{U}^{t_{N-1}}\mathcal{Y}^{\varphi_{N-1}}) \in [c_k, c_{k+1})\};$$

$$A_k^{N-1} = \{\omega : R(\mathcal{U}^{t_N}\mathcal{Y}^{\varphi_{N-1}}) \in [c_k, c_{k+1})\} \cap$$
$$\cap \{\omega : R(\mathcal{U}^{t_{N-1}}\mathcal{Y}^{\varphi_{N-1}}) \in [c_k\ c_{k+1})\}.$$

Since

$$0 \leqslant \int R(\mathcal{U}^{t_N}\mathcal{Y}^{\varphi_{N-1}})\, \mu_{t_{N-1}}^{t_N}(d\omega \mid \mathcal{U}^{t_{N-1}}\mathcal{Y}^{\varphi_{N-1}}) - R(\mathcal{U}^{t_{N-1}}\mathcal{Y}^{\varphi_{N-1}}) < \varepsilon_0,$$

from (8.18)

$$0 \leqslant \int R^{\delta}(\mathcal{U}^{t_N}\mathcal{Y}^{\varphi_{N-1}})\, \mu_{t_{N-1}}^{t_N}(d\omega \mid \mathcal{U}^{t_{N-1}}\mathcal{Y}^{\varphi_{N-1}}) -$$
$$- R(\mathcal{U}^{t_{N-1}}\mathcal{Y}^{\varphi_{N-1}}) < 2\varepsilon_0.$$

Continuing this process, we obtain the solution generated by the solution measures

$$\mu_{t_i}^{t_{i+1}}(\Lambda \mid \mathcal{U}^{t_i}\mathcal{Y}^{\varphi_i}) = \nu(\Lambda \mid \mathcal{U}^{t_i}\mathcal{Y}^{\varphi_i},\ A_{k(\omega)}^{i}),$$

$$A_k^i = \{\omega : R(\mathcal{U}^{t_{i+1}}\mathcal{Y}^{\varphi_i}) \in [c_k, c_{k+1})\} \cap \{\omega : R(\mathcal{U}^{t_i}\mathcal{Y}^{\varphi_i}) \in [c_k\ c_{k+1})\},$$
$$i = 0, 1, \ldots, N.$$

It is easy to see that for this solution

$$0 \leqslant R^{\delta} - R < (N+1)\varepsilon_0 = \varepsilon,$$

i.e., it is ε-optimal.

It is also not difficult to construct an ε-optimal solution for a nonstepped index, considering its stepped approximation φ^N. In this, in order to obtain an exact optimal solution, we need to carry out a dual passage to the limit as $N\to\infty$, $\varepsilon\to 0$.

8.4 The Semigroup of Transformations Corresponding to the Solution. Regularity

1. The solution measures $\mu_s^t(\Lambda\,|\,\mathcal{U}^s\mathcal{Y}^{\varphi(s)})$ define a semigroup of transformations T_{st} in the subspaces G_t of the Banach space G_b of $\mathcal{L}^b$-measurable functions ω. The Banach space G_b is defined with the aid of the natural linear operators and the norm

$$\|f\| = \sup_{\omega} f(\omega), \quad f\in G_b \tag{8.19}$$

in variant I and

$$\|f\| = \operatorname{vrai\,sup}_{\omega} f(\omega) \quad \text{(relative to } \nu) \tag{8.20}$$

in variant II. The subspaces $G_t(\subset G_b)$, defined as sets of $\mathcal{L}^t$-measurable functions, themselves form Banach spaces.

For a fixed index φ and a solution δ the transformation T_{st} is defined by the formula

$$T_{st}f = \int f(\omega)\,\mathbf{Q}(d\omega \in \mathcal{U}^t\mathcal{Y}^{\varphi(t)}\,|\,\mathcal{U}^s\mathcal{Y}^{\varphi(s)}) \in G_s,\ f\in G_t. \tag{8.21}$$

This transformation can be considered as a conditional mathematical expectation

$$T_{st}f(\omega) = \mathbf{M}_{\mathrm{Q}}[f(\omega)\,|\,\mathcal{U}^s\mathcal{Y}^{\varphi(s)}], \tag{8.22}$$

corresponding to the single measure $\mathbf{Q}(\Lambda)$, $\Lambda\in\mathcal{B}$ (see paragraph 4 of Sect. 8.1). Using the familiar formula A.1.A (Appendix I) for the repeated mathematical expectation

$$\mathbf{M}_{\mathrm{Q}}[f\,|\,\mathcal{U}^r\mathcal{Y}^{\varphi(r)}] = \mathbf{M}_{\mathrm{Q}}\{\mathbf{M}_{\mathrm{Q}}[f\,|\,\mathcal{U}^s\mathcal{Y}^{\varphi(s)}]\,|\,\mathcal{U}^r\mathcal{Y}^{\varphi(r)}\},$$

where

$$r<s<t,\ f\in G_t,\ \mathbf{M}_{\mathrm{Q}}[f\,|\,\mathcal{U}^s\mathcal{Y}^{\varphi(s)}]\in G_s,$$

from (8.22) we get

$$T_{rt}f = T_{rs}T_{st}f \in G_r \tag{8.23}$$
$$(f\in G_t,\ T_{st}f\in G_s).$$

With the help of transformation (8.21) we can easily write the recursive formulas for the conditional risks:

$$R^{\delta}(\mathcal{U}^s\mathcal{Y}^{\varphi(s)}) = T_{st}R^{\delta}(\mathcal{U}^t\mathcal{Y}^{\varphi(t)});$$
$$R^{\delta} = T_{at}R^{\delta}(\mathcal{U}^t\mathcal{Y}^{\varphi(t)}) = T_{ab}R^{\delta}(\mathcal{U}^b\mathcal{Y}^{\varphi(b)}).$$

2. We will limit ourselves to consideration of optimal and near-optimal solutions. We will assume that the index $\varphi(t)$ has a bounded derivative with respect to t at all points of the interval T except (at most) a finite number of points ("points of nondifferentiability").

Definition 8.4. We will call a controlled process regular if any denumerable set everywhere dense in T, containing the points of nondifferentiability of the index, is an optimal risk-defining set, i.e., if

$$\lim_{N\to\infty} R_{\varphi(\Sigma_N)} = R_{\varphi}. \tag{8.24}$$

The process is called regular on the interval $[s, b]$, if

$$\lim_{N\to\infty} R_{\varphi(\Sigma_N)}(\mathcal{U}^s\mathcal{Y}^{\varphi(s,\Sigma_N)}) = R_{\varphi}(\mathcal{U}^s\mathcal{Y}^{\varphi(s)}).$$

Let us consider those indications of regularity which can be conveniently checked in studying specific problems. Let us assume that:

8.4.A. for any interval $[s, t]$, not containing points of non-differentiability of the index, and for any $\tau\in(s, t)$ the following relation is true:

$$\min_{\omega|\mathcal{U}^s\mathcal{Y}^{\varphi(s)}} \mathbf{M}_{\mathbf{P}}[R(\mathcal{U}^t\mathcal{Y}^{\varphi(t)})\,|\,\mathcal{U}^t\mathcal{Y}^{\varphi(s)}] -$$
$$-\min_{\omega|\mathcal{U}^s\mathcal{Y}^{\varphi(s)}} \mathbf{M}_{\mathbf{P}}\{\min_{\omega|\mathcal{U}^\tau\mathcal{Y}^{\varphi(\tau)}} \mathbf{M}_{\mathbf{P}}[R(\mathcal{U}^t\mathcal{Y}^{\varphi(t)})\,|\,\mathcal{U}^t\mathcal{Y}^{\varphi(\tau)}]\,|\,\mathcal{U}^\tau\mathcal{Y}^{\varphi(s)}\} =$$
$$= (t-s)\,o(1). \tag{8.25}$$

Instead of this condition, it is convenient to check the somewhat stronger condition of the infinitesimal commutativity of the two operations: minimization and averaging;

8.4.B. for any interval $[t-\Delta, t]$ of this type and for every $\varphi'=\varphi(t-\Delta)-c\Delta$ $(0<c<\infty)$ the equation

$$\min_{\omega|\mathcal{U}^{t-\Delta}\mathcal{Y}^{\varphi'}} \mathbf{M}[R(\mathcal{U}^t\mathcal{Y}^{\varphi(t-\Delta)})\,|\,\mathcal{U}^t\mathcal{Y}^{\varphi'}] -$$
$$-\mathbf{M}[\min_{\omega|\mathcal{U}^{t-\Delta}\mathcal{Y}^{\varphi(t-\Delta)}} R(\mathcal{U}^t\mathcal{Y}^{\varphi(t-\Delta)})\,|\,\mathcal{U}^{t-\Delta}\mathcal{Y}^{\varphi'}] = o(1)\,\Delta, \tag{8.26}$$

is valid, where

$$R(\mathcal{U}^t\mathcal{Y}^{\varphi(t-\Delta)}) = \mathbf{M}\,[R(\mathcal{U}^t\mathcal{Y}^{\varphi(t)})\,|\,\mathcal{U}^t\mathcal{Y}^{\varphi(t-\Delta)}],$$

is a $\mathcal{U}^t\mathcal{Y}^{\varphi(t-\Delta)}$-measurable function.

The estimate $o(1)$ [$\to 0$ as $t-s\to 0$, $\Delta\to 0$] in these equations is assumed uniform with respect to all t and ω. By "min" in these (as well as in subsequent formulas) we mean "inf" in the case of variant I and "vrai inf" in the case of variant II.

It is not difficult to check that 8.4.A follows from 8.4.B. To do this, we need to assume

$$\tau = t - \Delta; \quad \varphi' = \varphi(s).$$

In order to obtain (8.25), we must carry out a conditional minimization with respect to $u_s^\tau\,|\,\mathcal{U}^s\mathcal{Y}^{\varphi(s)}$ of the expressions entering into (8.26). Since this minimization is a continuous operation with respect to the metric (8.19) [or according to (8.20)], then the estimate $o(1)\Delta = o(1)(t-s)$ does not change and (8.25) turns out to be satisfied.

The indicated conditions are convenient in that they do not use the idea of optimal solution and hence they can be checked before the solutions are found. The next theorem confirms that they are in fact indications of regularity.

Theorem 8.6. From 8.4.A follows the regularity of the process.

The proof is sufficiently carried out under the assumption that the index has a finite derivative on all intervals T (in the contrary case an analogous examination is carried out in sequence for every interval of differentiability of the index, beginning with the rightmost interval).

Let Σ be an arbitrary sequence of points everywhere dense in T, and S, a sequence of definition of the optimal risk (Theorem 8.3); let Σ_N, S_N be the set of their N first elements.

As a result of its monotonic (nonincreasing) character, the optimal risk $R_{\varphi(\Sigma_N)}$ of a stepped index has a limit as $N\to\infty$, which we will designate $\widetilde{R}_\varphi$. From Definition 8.3 of the optimal risk R_φ we have

$$\widetilde{R}_\varphi \geqslant R_\varphi. \tag{8.27}$$

We need to prove that

$$\widetilde{R}_\varphi = R_\varphi. \tag{8.28}$$

Without loss of generality it is possible to assume that any point is included only once in the sequence S. We will denote by

Δ_N (>0) the length of the smallest elementary interval of the division generated by the set S_N, and we will take $\Delta<\Delta_N$. Select now a finite set of points Σ_Δ from Σ, yielding the Δ-division of the interval T (this can be done since Σ is everywhere dense). The division $\Sigma_\Delta \cup S_N$ obviously will differ from Σ_Δ in that certain elementary intervals of the division Σ_Δ will be divided into two parts by a point (τ) of S_N. According to Theorem 8.2, we have

$$R_{\varphi(S_N)} \geqslant R_{\varphi(\Sigma_\Delta, S_N)} \ (\geqslant R_\varphi). \tag{8.29}$$

At the same time, from (8.25) we can conclude that

$$0 \leqslant R_{\varphi(\Sigma_\Delta)} - R_{\varphi(\Sigma_\Delta, S_N)} \leqslant (b-a)\, o(1). \tag{8.30}$$

In fact, for each elementary interval $[t_k, t_{k+1}) \ni \tau$ of the division Σ_Δ which is divided by a point $\tau \in S_N$, according to (8.25) we have

$$R_{\varphi(\Sigma_\Delta)}(\mathcal{U}^{\tau}\mathcal{Y}^{\varphi(t_k)}) - R_{\varphi(\Sigma_\Delta \cup \tau)}(\mathcal{U}^{\tau}\mathcal{Y}^{\varphi(t_k)}) = (t_{k+1} - t_k)\, o(1).$$

This difference estimate does not change with subsequent averagings and minimizations. Adding the similar differences resulting from the various points of $S_N = \{\tau_1, \ldots, \tau_N\}$, we get

$$R_{\varphi(\Sigma_\Delta)} - R_{\varphi(\Sigma_\Delta, S_N)} = \sum_{i=1}^{N} [R_{\varphi(\Sigma_\Delta \tau_1, \ldots, \tau_{i-1})} - R_{\varphi(\Sigma_\Delta, \tau_1, \ldots, \tau_i)}] \leqslant$$
$$\leqslant (b-a)\, o(1).$$

Comparing (8.29) and (8.30), we find

$$|R_{\varphi(S_N)} - R_{\varphi(\Sigma_\Delta)}| \leqslant R_{\varphi(S_N)} - R_\varphi + (b-a)\, o(1).$$

By decreasing Δ and increasing N the difference $|R_{\varphi(S_N)} - R_{\varphi(\Sigma_\Delta)}|$, according to this formula, can be made arbitrarily small. Consequently,

$$\lim_{\Delta\to 0} R_{\varphi(\Sigma_\Delta)} = \lim_{N\to\infty} R_{\varphi(S_N)} \equiv R_\varphi. \tag{8.31}$$

But

$$\lim_{\Delta\to 0} R_{\varphi(\Sigma_\Delta)} \geqslant \lim_{M\to\infty} R_{\varphi(\Sigma_M)} \ (\equiv \widetilde{R}_\varphi), \tag{8.32}$$

since for every Δ it is possible to select an M such that $\Sigma_M \supset \Sigma_\Delta$ and hence $R_{\varphi(\Sigma_\Delta)} \geqslant R_{\varphi(\Sigma_M)}$ (Theorem 8.2). Comparison of the relations (8.27), (8.31), and (8.32) proves Eq. (8.28). The proof is completed.

In the case of a regular controlled process, the risk R_φ is a uniformly continuous functional of φ on the set $H \ni \varphi$ of stepped indices, for a suitable choice of metric in H. This property can be taken as the primary definition of regularity. Nevertheless, the Definition 8.4 of a regular process given above is more convenient in the sense that it is more easily checked in specific examples.

After the introduction of a metric into H the examination of continuous indices corresponds to the examination of the points of closure $\bar{H}$ of space H. Once the function R_φ is uniformly continuous on H, the closure points $\varphi \in \bar{H}$ naturally are predetermined with respect to continuity.

8.5 Sufficient Coordinates

1. The determination of optimal risks and optimal solutions is facilitated by the introduction of sufficient coordinates.

Definition 8.5. Let there exist:

(1) a family $\{c^t(\omega), t \in T\}$ of $\mathcal{B}^t$-measurable functions $c^t(\omega)$;

(2) a family of $\mathcal{U}^t\mathcal{Y}^{\varphi(t)}$-measurable functions $x_t(\omega)$, $t \in T$ having values in a certain measurable space $(X, \mathcal{X})$, such that the difference

$$R(\omega \mid \mathcal{U}^t\mathcal{Y}^{\varphi(t)}) - \mathbf{M}_Q[c^t(\omega) \mid \mathcal{U}^t\mathcal{Y}^{\varphi(t)}] \equiv S_t(\omega \mid \mathcal{U}^t\mathcal{Y}^{\varphi(t)}) \tag{8.33}$$

is $\mathcal{X}_t$-measurable. Here $\mathcal{X}_t = x_t^{-1}(\mathcal{X}) \subset \mathcal{U}^t\mathcal{Y}^{\varphi(t)}$. This difference we will designate $S_t(\omega|\mathcal{X}_t)$ and call the reduced conditional risk. The space $(X, \mathcal{X})$ we will call the space of sufficient coordinates, and its points, sufficient coordinates for a fixed solution δ.

The reduced conditional risk can be written as

$$S_t(\omega \mid \mathcal{X}_t) = S_t(x_t(\omega)) \quad (t \in T \text{ fixed}),$$

i.e., we can consider an $\mathcal{X}$-measurable function $S_t(x)$ of the sufficient coordinates. Thus the reduced conditional risk depends on ω (on u, y) only through the sufficient coordinates $x = x_t(\omega)$. The convenience of using sufficient coordinates lies in the fact that instead of functions given in a complicated and unclear space of elementary events or in a function space, we consider functions of a considerably simpler argument—sufficient coordinates.

The functions $c^t(\omega)$ can be called the functions of past penalties, and $c(\omega) - c^t(\omega)$, functions of future penalties. In such an interpretation the reduced conditional risk is a conditional mathematical expectation of future penalties.

It is convenient to impose on the sufficient coordinates several requirements stronger than were formulated in the definition.

Definition 8.6. Let there be given a family of past penalties $c^t(\omega)$, $t \in T$ ($c^t(\omega)$ is $\mathscr{B}^t$-measurable). The sufficient coordinates $x_t(\omega)$ form a family of $\mathcal{U}^t\mathcal{Y}^{\varphi(t)}$-measurable functions such that:

8.6.A. they are sufficient for the definition of average penalties:

$$\mathbf{M}_Q [c^t(\omega) - c^s(\omega) \mid \mathcal{U}^s\mathcal{Y}^{\varphi(s)}] = \mathbf{M}_Q [c^t(\omega) - c^s(\omega) \mid \mathcal{X}_s], \quad s < t;$$
$$\mathbf{M}_Q [c(\omega) - c^b(\omega) \mid \mathcal{U}^b\mathcal{Y}^{\varphi(b)}] = \mathbf{M}_Q [c(\omega) - c^b(\omega) \mid \mathcal{X}_b];$$

8.6.B. they are sufficient for the definition of their own future evolution:

$$\mathbf{Q}(\Lambda \in \mathcal{X}_t \mid \mathcal{U}^s\mathcal{Y}^{\varphi(s)}) = \mathbf{Q}(\Lambda \mid \mathcal{X}_s). \tag{8.34}$$

Definitions 8.5 and 8.6 are not equivalent, but there exist simple relations between them, as is partly seen from the following.

Let us show that the sufficient coordinates defined in Definition 8.6 satisfy the conditions of Definition 8.5 (i.e., 8.5 follows from 8.6). Writing (8.33) for t and $s<t$, from the formula

$$R(\mathcal{U}^s\mathcal{Y}^{\varphi(s)}) = \mathbf{M}_Q [R(\mathcal{U}^t\mathcal{Y}^{\varphi(t)}) \mid \mathcal{U}^s\mathcal{Y}^{\varphi(s)}]$$

we have

$$S_s(\omega \mid \mathcal{U}^s\mathcal{Y}^{\varphi(s)}) = \mathbf{M}_Q [c^t(\omega) - c^s(\omega) \mid \mathcal{U}^s\mathcal{Y}^{\varphi(s)}] + \\ + \mathbf{M}_Q [S_t(\omega \mid \mathcal{U}^t\mathcal{Y}^{\varphi(t)}) \mid \mathcal{U}^s\mathcal{Y}^{\varphi(s)}]. \tag{8.35}$$

Assuming here $t = b$, we obtain

$$S_s(\mathcal{U}^s\mathcal{Y}^{\varphi(s)}) = \mathbf{M}_Q [c^b - c^s \mid \mathcal{U}^s\mathcal{Y}^{\varphi(s)}] + \mathbf{M}_Q [S_b(\mathcal{U}^b\mathcal{Y}^{\varphi(b)}) \mid \mathcal{U}^s\mathcal{Y}^{\varphi(s)}].$$

But

$$S_b(\mathcal{U}^b\mathcal{Y}^{\varphi(b)}) = \mathbf{M}[c - c^b \mid \mathcal{U}^b\mathcal{Y}^{\varphi(b)}] = \mathbf{M}[c - c^b \mid \mathcal{X}_b];$$
$$\mathbf{M}_Q [c^b - c^s \mid \mathcal{U}^s\mathcal{Y}^{\varphi(s)}] = \mathbf{M}_Q \mathcal{U}^s [c^b - c^s \mid \mathcal{X}_s]$$

according to 8.6.A; thus

$$S_s(\mathcal{U}^s\mathcal{Y}^{\varphi(s)}) = \mathbf{M}_Q [c^b - c^s \mid \mathcal{X}_s] + \\ + \int \mathbf{M}[c - c^b \mid \mathcal{X}_b] \mathbf{Q}(d\omega \in \mathcal{X}_b \mid \mathcal{U}^s\mathcal{Y}^{\varphi(s)}).$$

According to 8.6.B, instead of $\mathbf{Q}(\Lambda \mid \mathcal{U}^s\mathcal{Y}^{\varphi(s)})$ we can substitute here $\mathbf{Q}(\Lambda \mid \mathcal{X}_s)$, which finally proves the $\mathcal{X}_s$-measurability of the functions $S_s(\mathcal{U}^s\mathcal{Y}^{\varphi(s)})$.

2. The above definition of sufficient coordinates applies to a fixed index and a fixed solution. In examining practical problems, however, the question of selecting sufficient coordinates is solved prior to finding the solution itself. Thus it is more convenient to deal with features of sufficient coordinates that do not demand knowledge of the solution and do not even require the index to be fixed. Let us formulate these:

Definition 8.7. Features of sufficient coordinates:

8.7.A. The coordinates $x_t(\omega)$ are sufficient for the definition of average penalties:

$$\mathbf{M}_{\mathbf{P}}[c^t(\omega) - c^s(\omega) \mid \mathcal{U}^t \mathcal{Y}^{\varphi(s)}] = \mathbf{M}_{\mathbf{P}}[c^t(\omega) - c^s(\omega) \mid \mathcal{U}_s^t \mathcal{X}_s]; \tag{8.36}$$

$$\mathbf{M}_{\mathbf{P}}[c(\omega) - c^b(\omega) \mid \mathcal{U}^b \mathcal{Y}^{\varphi(b)}] = \mathbf{M}_{\mathbf{P}}[c(\omega) - c^b(\omega) \mid \mathcal{X}_b] \tag{8.37}$$

(s, t arbitrary in T, but $s<t$).

This means that for a fixed control u_s^t the conditional average penalties $\mathbf{M}[c^t - c^s \mid \mathcal{U}_s^t \mathcal{Y}^{\varphi(t)}]$ depend on u_a^s, $y_a^{\varphi(s)}$ only through $x_s(\omega)$.

8.7.B. They are sufficient for the probabilistic determination of their own future evolution:

$$\mathbf{P}[x_t(\omega) \in \Gamma \mid \mathcal{U}^t \mathcal{Y}^{\varphi(s)}] = \mathbf{P}(\Gamma \mid \mathcal{U}_s^t \mathcal{X}_s), \quad \Gamma \in \mathcal{X}.$$

This means that for a fixed control u_s^t the indicated conditional probabilities, as well as the conditional mathematical expectations, depend on u_a^s, $y_a^{\varphi(s)}$ only through $x_s(\omega)$.

8.7.C. They are sufficient to indicate the limitations on choice of control for each separate interval. Using the notation introduced in paragraph 1, Sect. 8.1, this condition can be written

$$\mathcal{U}_s''^t(\mathcal{U}^s) = \mathcal{U}_s''^t(\mathcal{X}_s) \quad (U_s^t(u_a^s) = U_s^t(x_s))$$

or

$$\mathcal{U}_s^t(\mathcal{U}^s) = \mathcal{U}_s^t(\mathcal{X}_s), \ (s<t).$$

If we avoid using the concept of a conditional σ-algebra, this condition can be expressed in terms of a conditional minimization

$$\min_{\omega \mid \mathcal{U}^s \mathcal{Y}^{\varphi(s)}} f(\omega) = \min_{\omega \mid \mathcal{X}_s} f(\omega),$$

regardless of what the $\mathcal{U}_s^t \mathcal{X}_s$-measurable function $f(\omega)$ might be.

We will show that from these properties of sufficient coordinates there follows the $\mathcal{X}_t$-measurability of the functions (8.33) for optimal solution, i.e., it follows that they are sufficient coordinates in the sense of Definition 8.5.

Let the division $\{t_1, \ldots, t_N\}$ generate a stepped approximation φ^N to the index φ $(\varphi_k = \varphi(t_k),\ k = 0, 1, \ldots, N)$. For φ^N and the function (8.33) the recursive transformations (8.12) are written in the form

$$S_{t_k}(\omega \mid \mathcal{U}^{t_k}\mathcal{Y}^{\varphi_k}) = \min_{\omega \mid \mathcal{U}^{t_k}\mathcal{Y}^{\varphi_k}} \mathbf{M}_{\mathbf{P}}[c^{t_{k+1}}(\omega) - c^{t_k}(\omega) + S_{t_{k+1}}(\omega \mid \mathcal{U}^{t_{k+1}}\mathcal{Y}^{\varphi_{k+1}}) \mid \mathcal{U}^{t_{k+1}}\mathcal{Y}^{\varphi_k}]. \tag{8.38}$$

If $S_{t_{k+1}}(\omega \mid \mathcal{U}^{t_{k+1}}\mathcal{Y}^{\varphi_{k+1}})$ is an $\mathcal{X}_{k+1}$-measurable function, then it is not difficult to deduce from 8.7.A–C $(t = t_{k+1},\ s = t_k)$, that the function $S_{t_k}(\omega \mid \mathcal{U}^{t_k}\mathcal{Y}^{\varphi_k})$ is also $\mathcal{X}_k$-measurable, where

$$S_{t_k}(x_{t_k}(\omega)) = \min_{\omega \mid \mathcal{X}_{t_k}} \{\mathbf{M}_{\mathbf{P}}[c^{t_{k+1}}(\omega) - c^{t_k}(\omega) + S_{t_{k+1}}(x_{t_{k+1}}(\omega)) \mid \mathcal{U}_{t_k}^{t_{k+1}}\mathcal{X}_{t_k}]\}. \tag{8.39}$$

Thus, the recursive transformations do not destroy the $\mathcal{X}_{t_k}$-measurability of the indicated conditional risks. It remains now only to check the $\mathcal{X}_b$-measurability of the "initial" function

$$S_b(\omega \mid \mathcal{U}^b\mathcal{Y}^{\varphi(b)}) = \mathbf{M}_{\mathbf{P}}[c(\nu) - c^b(\omega) \mid \mathcal{U}^b\mathcal{Y}^{\varphi(b)}].$$

This is true, according to (8.37). Hence the $\mathcal{X}_{t_k}$-measurability of the functions S_{t_k} for any $k = 0, 1, 2, \ldots, N$ is proven for the stepped index φ^N. If we now complete the passage to the limit as $N \to \infty$, $\varphi^N \uparrow \varphi$, the limit function S_t will be $\mathcal{X}_t$-measurable for any t from the risk-defining set.

8.6 Transformation of Functions of Sufficient Coordinates. The Equation of Alternatives

1. Let us examine the Banach space G^x of $\mathcal{X}$-measurable functions in the space of sufficient coordinates $(X, \mathcal{X})$. The natural linear operations and a norm analogous to (8.19) or (8.20) are defined in it (in the latter case, a certain measure $\nu(\Lambda)$, $\Lambda \in \mathcal{X}$, generated, if desired, by the measure $\nu(\Gamma)$, $\Gamma \in \mathcal{U}^b$), is fixed in advance).

The transformation (8.21) introduced earlier defines a transformation T_{st} in the space G^x. In fact, for any $g(x) \in G^x$ the function $g(x_t(\omega)) = f(\omega)$ is $\mathcal{U}^t\mathcal{Y}^{\varphi(t)}$-measurable, i.e., $\in G_t$. Hence we can define a function

$$f'(\omega) = T_{st}f(\omega) = \int f(\omega)\, \mathbf{Q}(d\omega \in \mathcal{X}_t \mid \mathcal{U}^t\mathcal{Y}^{\varphi(t)}) \in G_s, \tag{8.40}$$

which is $\mathcal{X}_s$-measurable in accordance with 8.6.B. Writing this in the form $f'(\omega) = g'(x_s(\omega))$, we can consider the transformation T_{st} of any function $g(x)$ into a function $g'(x) \in G^x$.

Using the conditional measure $\mathbf{Q}_{st}(\Gamma \in \mathcal{X} \mid \mathcal{X})$ in the space of sufficient coordinates, related to the measure (8.34) by

$$\mathbf{Q}(x_t^{-1}(\Gamma) \mid \mathcal{X}_s) = \mathbf{Q}_{st}(\Gamma \mid x_s(\omega)), \quad \Gamma \in \mathcal{X},$$

the transformation $g' = T_{st}g$ can be written

$$(T_{st}g)(x) = \int \mathbf{Q}_{st}(dx' \mid x)\, g(x'). \tag{8.41}$$

As a result of the semigroup property (8.23) of the transformation (8.40), the transformation (8.41) considered here forms a semigroup:

$$T_{rs}T_{st} = T_{rt}, \quad r < s < t.$$

The reduced conditional risk $S_t(x)$ can be considered an element of the space G^x. The transformation formula (8.35) of the reduced risks can be written using T_{st}. Namely, taking into account 8.6.A–B, we get

$$S_s(x) = \mathbf{M}_Q[c^t - c^s \mid x] + T_{st}S_t(x). \tag{8.42}$$

2. The existence of a semigroup of transformations T_{st} recalls the case of a Markov process (Sect. 3.1). The question arises whether this semigroup is connected with a certain Markov process. An examination shows that this is so. The sufficient coordinates turn out to be Markov; this follows from their definition.

Theorem 8.7. The process $\{x_t(\omega),\ t \in T\}$, described by the probabilistic measure $\mathbf{Q}$, is Markov.

Proof. Let us consider times $t_1 < t_2 < t_3$. From the definition of conditional probabilities we have

$$\mathbf{Q}(\Lambda \in \mathcal{X}_{t_3} \mid \mathcal{U}^{t_1}\mathcal{Y}^{\varphi(t_1)}) = \int \mathbf{Q}(\Lambda \mid \mathcal{U}^{t_2}\mathcal{Y}^{\varphi(t_2)})\, \mathbf{Q}(d\omega \in \mathcal{U}^{t_2}\mathcal{Y}^{\varphi(t_2)} \mid \mathcal{U}^{t_1}\mathcal{Y}^{\varphi(t_1)})$$

or, taking into account 8.6.B,

$$\mathbf{Q}(\Lambda \mid \mathcal{X}_{t_1}) = \int \mathbf{Q}(\Lambda \mid \mathcal{X}_{t_2})\, \mathbf{Q}(d\omega \in \mathcal{U}^{t_2}\mathcal{Y}^{\varphi(t_2)} \mid \mathcal{U}^{t_1}\mathcal{Y}^{\varphi(t_1)}).$$

Since $\mathbf{Q}(\Lambda \mid \mathcal{X}_{t_2})$, $\Lambda \in \mathcal{X}_{t_3}$ is a $\mathcal{X}_{t_2}$-measurable function, $\mathbf{Q}(d\omega \in \mathcal{U}^{t_2}\mathcal{Y}^{\varphi(t_2)} \mid \mathcal{U}^{t_1}\mathcal{Y}^{\varphi(t_1)})$ can be replaced here by $\mathbf{Q}(d\omega \in \mathcal{X}_{t_2} \mid \mathcal{U}^{t_1}\mathcal{Y}^{\varphi(t_1)})$, and thus (from 8.6.B) it can also be replaced by $\mathbf{Q}(d\omega \in \mathcal{X}_{t_2} \mid \mathcal{X}_{t_1})$. Thus, the equation takes the form

$$\mathbf{Q}(\Lambda \mid \mathcal{X}_{t_1}) = \int \mathbf{Q}(\Lambda \mid \mathcal{X}_{t_2})\, \mathbf{Q}(d\omega \in \mathcal{X}_{t_2} \mid \mathcal{X}_{t_1}),$$

i.e., it becomes the Chapman-Kolmogorov equation.

From this equation by repeatedly using the Radon-Nikodim theorem, it is possible to obtain in sequence the equations

$$\mathbf{Q}(\Lambda \in \mathcal{X}_{t_3} \mid \mathcal{X}_{t_1}\mathcal{X}_{t_2}) = \mathbf{Q}(\Lambda \mid \mathcal{X}_{t_2}),\ \mathbf{Q}(\Lambda \in \mathcal{X}_{t_4} \mid \mathcal{X}_{t_1}\mathcal{X}_{t_2}\mathcal{X}_{t_3}) = \mathbf{Q}(\Lambda \mid \mathcal{X}_{t_1})$$
$$(t_1 < t_2 < \ldots), \text{ etc.,}$$

thus proving the Markov character of the process.

According to this theorem, the sufficient coordinates form a Markov process after the choice of the solution δ, defining, as was shown in paragraph 4, Sect. 8.1, the combined measure $\mathbf{Q}$. It is possible to assert more. The sufficient coordinates also form a Markov process relative to the probabilistic measures $\mathbf{P}(\cdot \mid \mathcal{U}^t)$, assigned in the condition of the problem (paragraph 2, Sect. 8.1). Here, of course, we should fix the control u_a^t on a sufficiently large interval $[a, t]$. In order to avoid discussion of this each time, we will fix the control $u \in U$ on the entire interval.

Theorem 8.8. The process $\{x_t(\omega),\ t \in T\}$, described for a fixed control $u \in U$ by the probabilistic measure $\mathbf{P}(\cdot \mid \mathcal{U}^b)$, is Markov.

The proof is analogous to the preceding one with the difference that in place of condition 8.6.B, we need to use condition 8.7.B.

The Markov process considered in Theorem 8.8 defines its semigroup of transformations in G^x. Since these transformations correspond to a fixed control u, we will designate them as $T_{st}(u)$:

$$(T_{st}(u)\, g)(x_s) = \int \mathbf{P}(dx_t(\omega) \in \mathcal{X} \mid u, x_s)\, g(x_t(\omega)).$$

3. Once we introduce the semigroups of transformations T_{st}, $T_{st}(u)$, we can examine their infinitesimal operators. Let A_t be the infinitesimal operator defined by

$$A_t g = \lim_{\Delta \downarrow 0} \frac{T_{t-\Delta,t}\, g - g}{\Delta} \tag{8.43}$$

on the set $D \subset G^x$ of those functions g for which the limit exists. In the same way, for each $u \in U$ we define the infinitesimal operator $A_t(u)$ of transformations $T_{st}(u)$ and the region of its definition $D(u) \subset G^x$.

Using Eq. (8.42), we form the difference

$$\frac{S_{t-\Delta}(x) - S_t(x)}{\Delta} = \mathbf{M}_Q \left[\frac{c^t - c^{t-\Delta}}{\Delta} \middle| x \right] + \frac{T_{t-\Delta,t} S_t - S_t}{\Delta}$$

and pass to the limit as $\Delta \downarrow 0$. If the function c^t is differentiable with respect to t:

$$\lim_{\Delta \downarrow 0} \frac{c^t - c^{t-\Delta}}{\Delta} = C_t;$$

$$\lim_{\Delta \downarrow 0} \mathbf{M}_Q \left[\frac{c^t - c^{t-\Delta}}{\Delta} \middle| x \right] = \mathbf{M}_Q [C_t | x] \tag{8.44}$$

(and if $S_t \in D$), ultimately we will get the equation

$$-\frac{\partial S_t(x)}{\partial t} = \mathbf{M}_Q [C_t | x] + (A_t S_t)(x). \tag{8.45}$$

In the contrary case the corresponding differential equation would have the form

$$-dS_t(x) = \mathbf{M}_Q [dc^t | x] + d^* L^*(t) S_t(x), \tag{8.46}$$

where dL^* is the differential infinitesimal operator defined in paragraph 1, Sect. 3.1.

We will now write the differential equation for the reduced risk using the infinitesimal operator of the second semigroup. To do this we turn to Eq. (8.39), corresponding to the prelimit index. The function in braces on its right side is $\mathcal{U}_{t_k}^{t_{k+1}} \mathcal{X}_{t_k}$-measurable, hence the minimization with respect to $\omega | \mathcal{X}_{t_k}$ reduces to a minimization with respect to $u_{t_k}^{t_{k+1}} | \mathcal{X}_{t_k}$. In Eq. (8.39) it is possible to write any of these variants, and also the variant $u | \mathcal{X}_{t_k}$. Thus, we have

$$\frac{S_{t_k}(x) - S_{t_{k+1}}(x)}{\Delta} = \min_{u|x} \left\{ \mathbf{M}_P \left[\frac{c^{t_{k+1}} - c^{t_k}}{\Delta} \middle| u, x \right] + \right.$$
$$\left. + \frac{T_{t_k t_{k+1}}(u) S_{t_{k+1}} - S_{t_{k+1}}}{\Delta} \right\} \tag{8.47}$$

$(x = x_{t_k},\ \Delta = t_{k+1} - t_k)$.

Passing to the limit as $\varphi^N \uparrow \varphi$, $t_k \to t$, $t_{k+1} \to t$, we get from this

$$-\frac{\partial S_t(x)}{\partial t} = \min_{u|x} \left\{ \mathbf{M}_{\mathrm{P}} [C_t | u, x] + A_t(u) S_t(x) \right\}, \tag{8.48}$$

if

$$\frac{c^{t_{k+1}} - c^{t_k}}{\Delta} \to C_t; \tag{8.49}$$

and

$$\frac{T_{t_k t_{k+1}}(u) S_{t_{k+1}} - S_{t_{k+1}}}{\Delta} \to A_t(u) S_t \quad \text{as} \quad t_k \to t, \; t_{k+1} \to t. \tag{8.50}$$

The convergence (8.49), as can easily be seen, follows from the condition of differentiability (8.44). Condition (8.50) is possibly somewhat stronger than the natural condition

$$\frac{T_{t-\Delta,t}(u) S_t - S_t}{\Delta} \to A_t(u) S_t, \; u \in U$$

(i.e., the condition $S_t \in \bigcap_u D(u)$).

The natural generalization of Eqs. (8.48) to the case of a nondifferentiable penalty and a nondifferentiable semigroup, in analogy with (8.46), has the form

$$-dS_t(x) = \min_{u|x} \{ \mathbf{M}_{\mathrm{P}} [dc^t | u, x] + d^* L^*(t, u) S_t(x) \}. \tag{8.51}$$

Here and in (8.48) $x \in X$ is a point in the space of the sufficient coordinates and $u = u_a^b$ is the control function. The expression subject to minimization, however, actually depends only on its values in the vicinity of the point t.

The minimization in Eq. (8.48) or (8.51) corresponds to the selection of an optimal alternative (selection of an optimal "infinitesimal control" u_t^{t+dt} from a series of possible ones); thus we will call it the equation of alternatives. As was noted, it corresponds to the "initial" condition

$$S_b(x) = \mathbf{M}_{\mathrm{P}} [c(\omega) - c^b(\omega) | x_b(\omega) = x].$$

The solution of this equation for reversed time permits the subsequent determination of $S_t(x)$ and the optimal (or near optimal) solution measures. The value $S_a(x)$ found at the last step gives the complete risk $R = c^a + S_a$.

4. The conditions under which the differentiations (8.34), (8.44), and (8.50) are valid and under which the form of Eqs. (8.45) and

(8.48) does not depend on the particular method of passing to the limit are connected with the condition of regularity of the controlled process (Sect. 8.4). Let us examine here several auxiliary concepts and sufficient conditions for regularity which can be conveniently checked in the solution of specific problems.

For simplicity, in this section we assume that the index $\varphi(t)$ everywhere has a bounded first derivative with respect to t.

Definition 8.8. We will call regular spaces $\mathring{D}_t \subset G^x$, $t \in T$, those sets of functions such that for each $g \in \mathring{D}_t$ and any $\Delta > 0$:

8.8.A. there exists a measurable function $g' \in D^0_{t-\Delta}$ differing from the function

$$\min_{\omega | \mathcal{U}^{t-\Delta} \mathcal{Y}^{\varphi(t-\Delta)}} \mathbf{M}_\mathbf{P} [c^t - c^{t-\Delta} + g(x_t(\omega)) \mid \mathcal{U}^t \mathcal{Y}^{\varphi(t-\Delta)})] \tag{8.52}$$

by $o(1)\Delta$. According to 8.7.A–C, this condition can be written

$$g'(x) = \min_{u|x} \{\mathbf{M}_\mathbf{P} [c^t - c^{t-\Delta} \mid u, x_{t-\Delta} = x] + (T_{t-\Delta, t}(u)\, g)(x)\} + o(1)\Delta. \tag{8.53}$$

8.8.B. There further exists a function $\psi_t(x, g)$, independent of Δ and continuously dependent on t and $g (\in \mathring{D}_t)$, which satisfies the equation

$$g'(x) - g(x) = \psi_t(x, g)\,\Delta + o(1)\,\Delta. \tag{8.54}$$

From comparison of (8.53) and (8.54), there obviously follows

$$\min_{u|x} \left\{ \mathbf{M}_\mathbf{P} \left[\frac{c^t - c^{t-\Delta}}{\Delta} \middle| u, x \right] + \frac{T_{t-\Delta, t}\, g - g}{\Delta} \right\} = \psi_t(x, g) + o(1). \tag{8.55}$$

The estimate $o(1)$ here is taken in the sense of the norm (8.19) or (8.20), i.e., it is assumed uniform with respect to x.

The value of these concepts is apparent from the following theorem:

Theorem 8.9. If $S(b)$ belongs to the regular space $\mathring{D}_b$, then
(1) the process is regular in the sense of Definition 8.4;
(2) the reduced conditional risk satisfies the equation

$$-\frac{\partial S_t(x)}{\partial t} = \psi(x, S_t). \tag{8.56}$$

Proof. Let Σ be a denumerable sequence everywhere dense in T. We will examine the Δ-division $\Sigma_N \subset \Sigma$ of the interval $[a, b]$ by the points $t_1 < t_2 < \dots < t_N$, and use condition 8.8.A on each elementary interval $[t_k, t_{k+1}]$. This condition allows us to find in sequence the functions (we will designate them $\widetilde{S}_{t_k}$) belonging to the regular space $\widetilde{S}_{t_k} \in D^\circ_{t_k}$. Taking into account 8.8.A, we can compare them with the optimal risks $S^N_{t_k}$ for the given division. Adding the deviations of $o(1)\Delta$, we have $|\widetilde{S}_{t_k} - S^N_{t_k}| = o(1)\ (b - t_k)$ and in particular $|\widetilde{R}_{\varphi^N} - R_{\varphi^N}| = o(1)\,(b-a)$ [here we use the continuity of the transformation (8.52) relative to the metric introduced into the space G^x]. From this result follows the convergence of the sequences $\widetilde{S}_{t_k}\,(\rightarrow \widetilde{S}^\Sigma_t)$ and $\widetilde{R}_{\varphi N}\,(\rightarrow \widetilde{R}^\Sigma_\varphi)$ as $\Delta \rightarrow 0$, i.e., $N \rightarrow \infty$ and $\Sigma_N \rightarrow \Sigma$ (since $S^N_{t_k}$, $R_{\varphi N}$ converge), and also the equality of the limits

$$\lim \widetilde{S}_{t_k} = \lim S^N_{t_k} \equiv S^\Sigma_t \quad (t = \lim t_k);$$

$$\lim \widetilde{R}_{\varphi N} = \lim R_{\varphi N} \equiv R^\Sigma_\varphi.$$

We will now use 8.8.B. Assuming $g = \widetilde{S}_{t_{k+1}}$, $g' = \widetilde{S}_{t_k}$ in (8.54) and summing over k, we have

$$\widetilde{S}_{t_l} - \widetilde{S}_{t_N} = \sum_{k=l}^{N} \psi_{t_{k+1}}(x, \widetilde{S}_{t_{k+1}})\,(t_{k+1} - t_k) + o(1)\,(b - t_l).$$

Passing to the limit as $\Delta \rightarrow 0$, $t_l \rightarrow t$, we get

$$S^\Sigma_t - S^\Sigma_b = \int_t^b \psi_\tau(x, S^\Sigma_\tau)\,d\tau \tag{8.57}$$

and

$$-\frac{\partial S^\Sigma_t(x)}{\partial t} = \psi_t(x, S^\Sigma_t) \tag{8.58}$$

because of the continuity of the function $\psi_t(x, S_t)$. Assertion (2) of the theorem is proven.

Further, the result (8.57) does not depend on the particular method of division (on Σ); it remains the same for any sequence Σ everywhere dense. The same thus applies to the solution $S^\Sigma_t(x)$ of Eq. (8.58). Among such sequences there is necessarily a defining sequence for the optimal risk. In fact, if S is a risk-defining sequence and Σ is an everywhere dense sequence, then, as we can see from the discussion in paragraphs 2 and 3, Sect. 8.2, the union of sequences $\Sigma' = S \cup \Sigma$, in which elements from S and from Σ follow alternately, is also a risk-defining sequence. Thus, Eq. (8.58) is valid for the sequence Σ', i.e., it is satisfied by the optimal risks $S^\Sigma_t = S^{\Sigma'}_t = S_t$. The proof is completed.

If the conditions of Theorem 8.9, and the condition $S_t \in D$ in (8.44), for which Eq. (8.45) is valid, are fulfilled, then Eqs. (8.45) and (8.56) obviously coincide and

$$\psi_t(x, S_t) = \mathbf{M}_Q [C_t \mid x] + A_t S_t. \tag{8.59}$$

8.7 The Case of a Markov Basic Process

In the work above, we did not make any assumptions about Markov characteristics of the processes under consideration. As a result of the definition of sufficient coordinates, Markov characteristics, nevertheless, did appear. This is indirect evidence of the fact that the concept of sufficient coordinates will be productive precisely in the examination of Markov and related processes. In the present paragraph we will assume that the basic process is Markov and will show that in this case the most essential part of the sufficient coordinates constitutes *a posteriori* probabilities, i.e., a "secondary *a posteriori* process" (Sect. 5.6). Since the study of Markov *a posteriori* probabilities is included in the theory of conditional Markov processes, from this follows the effectiveness of the application of the latter to the theory of optimal control.

1. The concepts and notation related to the basic process were compiled in paragraph 2, Sect. 8.1. Let the fixed control u_a^t define the probabilities $\mathbf{P}(\cdot \mid u_a^t)$ of a process $z_a^t = \{z_\tau, a \leqslant \tau \leqslant t\}$. If by $\mathscr{Z}^t(u_a^t)$ we designate the σ-algebra defined by the conditions imposed on z_a^t, then in accordance with the earlier notation, we have

$$\mathscr{Z}^t(\mathscr{U}^t) \subset \mathscr{A}^t(\mathscr{U}^t); \quad \mathscr{U}^t\mathscr{Z}^t(\mathscr{U}^t) \subset \mathscr{B}^t.$$

Let $\mathscr{Z}_s^t(u_a^t, z_a^s)$ and $\mathscr{Z}_t(u_a^t, z_a^t)$ be the σ-algebras defined by the conditions imposed on z_s^t and z_t, respectively. Then the Markov properties of the basic process $\{z_t\}$ can be formulated as properties of the measure $\mathbf{P}(\cdot \mid u)$, namely,

$$\mathbf{P}(\Lambda \mid u, \mathscr{Z}^t(u)) = \mathbf{P}(\Lambda \mid u, \mathscr{Z}_t(u, z_a^t)), \quad \Lambda \in \mathscr{Z}_t^b(u, z_a^t) \tag{8.60}$$

(a.e.P.)

Let us assume now that the choice of the control u affects the probabilities $\mathbf{P}$ but not the state space of the process $\{z_t\}$, i.e., that this space is the same for all possible controls. Let us assume further that the state space corresponding to the instant t does not depend on z_a^t, i.e., it is the same for various z_a^t. These conditions can be written

8.9.A. $\mathscr{Z}_t(u_a^t, z_a^t) = \mathscr{Z}_t$

(independent of u_a^t, z_a^t).

The control $u \in U$ we will assume to be uncoupled:

8.9.B. $$\mathcal{U}_s^t(u_a^s) = \mathcal{U}_s^t, \quad s < t$$

(independent of u_a^s).

In conformity with 8.9.A, the Markov conditions (8.60) will be taken in the form

8.9.C. $$\mathbf{P}(\Lambda \mid u_a^t, z_a^s) = \mathbf{P}(\Lambda \mid u_s^t, z_s), \quad \Lambda \in \mathcal{Z}_s^b \cap \mathcal{B}^t, \quad s < t.$$

The remaining assumptions are relative to the observable process and the penalty functions. We will confine ourselves to the cases of most practical interest, in which $\varphi(t) = t$ [the case of a second continuous index $\varphi'(t)$ can be reduced to this by the substitution $t' = \varphi'(t)$]. The observed process y_t we will define (aside from u_a^t) by the process z_a^t:

8.9.D. $$\mathcal{Y}^t(u_a^t) \subset \mathcal{Z}^t.$$

Finally, the future penalties are determined by the future values z_s^b of the process z:

8.9.E. $c^t - c^s$ is not only a $\mathcal{B}^t$-measurable, but also a $\mathcal{U}_s^t\mathcal{Z}_s^b$-measurable function; $c - c^b$ is $\mathcal{Z}_b$-measurable.

Theorem 8.10. By satisfying assumptions 8.9.A–E, the conditional probabilities $W_t(\Lambda \in \mathcal{Z}_t) = \mathbf{P}(\Lambda \mid \mathcal{U}^t\mathcal{Y}^t)$ form sufficient coordinates (for optimal solution).

Proof. In order to prove the theorem we will verify that the properties 8.7.A–C of sufficient coordinates are satisfied. The fulfillment of 8.7.C necessarily follows from 8.9.A–B. Let us prove 8.7.A. We will designate by $\mathcal{W}_t$ the σ-algebra derived through the conditions imposed on W_t. Using 8.9.E, we have

$$\int [c^t(\omega') - c^s(\omega')]\, \mathbf{P}(d\omega' \mid \mathcal{U}^t\mathcal{Y}^s) =$$
$$= \iint [c^t(\omega') - c^s(\omega')]\, \mathbf{P}(d\omega' \in \mathcal{U}_s^t\mathcal{Z}_s^b \mid \mathcal{U}^t\mathcal{Y}^s\mathcal{Z}_s)\mathbf{P}(d\omega \mid \mathcal{U}^t\mathcal{Y}^s). \tag{8.61}$$

On the strength of the Markov condition 8.9.C (and also 8.9.D)

$$\mathbf{P}(d\omega \in \mathcal{Z}_s^b \mid \mathcal{U}^t\mathcal{Y}^s\mathcal{Z}_s) = \mathbf{P}(d\omega \mid \mathcal{U}_s^t\mathcal{Z}_s);$$

thus

$$\mathbf{M}[c^t - c^s \mid \mathcal{U}^t\mathcal{Y}^s] = \iint [c^t(\omega') - c^s(\omega')]\, \mathbf{P}(d\omega' \mid \mathcal{U}_s^t\mathcal{Z}_s)\, W_s(d\omega \in \mathcal{Z}_s). \quad (8.62)$$

This function is therefore $\mathcal{U}_s^t\mathcal{W}_s$-measurable:

$$\mathbf{M}[c^t - c^s \mid \mathcal{U}^t\mathcal{Y}^s] = \mathbf{M}[c^t - c^s \mid \mathcal{U}_s^t\mathcal{W}_s].$$

That (8.36) is satisfied is verified. In addition to this, from the $\mathcal{Z}_b$-measurability of the functions $c - c^b$ (see 8.9.E), we can easily find the equation

$$\mathbf{M}[c - c^b \mid \mathcal{U}^b\mathcal{Y}^b] = \int (c - c^b)\, W_b(d\omega \in \mathcal{Z}_b) = \mathbf{M}[c - c^b \mid \mathcal{W}_b],$$

supporting (8.37).

The verification of the last property 8.7.B can be carried out by methods similar to those used in the proof of Theorems 5.6 and 5.9. As follows from the theory developed in paragraph 2, Sect. 5.6, the *a posteriori* probability $W_t(\Gamma \in \mathcal{Z}_t) = \mathbf{P}(\Gamma \mid \mathcal{U}^t\mathcal{Y}^t)$ for a Markov process (condition 8.9.C) is measurable relative to the σ-algebra $\mathcal{W}_s\mathcal{U}_s^t\mathcal{Y}_s^t$, $s<t$. This can be shown using formula (5.83) [in the present case with the existence of control, the *a posteriori* measure V_s^t is $\mathcal{U}_s^t\mathcal{Y}_s^t$-measurable]. This measurability is equivalent to the relation $\mathcal{W}_t \subset \mathcal{W}_s\mathcal{U}_s^t\mathcal{Y}_s^t$, or to the $\mathcal{W}_s\mathcal{U}_s^t\mathcal{Y}_s^t$-measurability of the indicator

$$I_B(\omega) = I(B \mid \mathcal{U}^t\mathcal{Y}^t) = I(B \mid \mathcal{W}_s\mathcal{U}_s^t\mathcal{Y}_s^t)$$

of the set $B \in \mathcal{W}_t$. Broadening the σ-algebras in the condition, we obviously can write

$$I(B \mid \mathcal{U}^t\mathcal{Y}^t) = I(B \mid \mathcal{U}^t\mathcal{Y}^t\mathcal{W}_s\mathcal{Z}_s) = I(B \mid \mathcal{U}_s^t\mathcal{Y}_s^t\mathcal{W}_s\mathcal{Z}_s). \quad (8.63)$$

Let us express the probability $\mathbf{P}(B \mid \mathcal{U}^t\mathcal{Y}^s)$ in the form of a conditional mathematical expectation:

$$\mathbf{P}(B \mid \mathcal{U}^t\mathcal{Y}^s) = \mathbf{M}\{\mathbf{M}[I(B \mid \mathcal{U}^t\mathcal{Y}^t\mathcal{W}_s\mathcal{Z}_s) \mid \mathcal{U}^t\mathcal{Y}^s\mathcal{W}_s\mathcal{Z}_s] \mid \mathcal{U}^t\mathcal{Y}^s\}.$$

Substituting into this (8.63) and taking into account that

$$\mathbf{M}[I(B \mid \mathcal{U}_s^t\mathcal{Y}_s^t\mathcal{W}_s\mathcal{Z}_s) \mid \mathcal{U}^t\mathcal{Y}^s\mathcal{W}_s\mathcal{Z}_s] = \mathbf{M}[I(B \mid \mathcal{U}_s^t\mathcal{Y}_s^t\mathcal{W}_s\mathcal{Z}_s) \mid \mathcal{W}_s\mathcal{U}_s^t\mathcal{Z}_s] = \\ = \mathbf{P}[B \mid \mathcal{W}_s\mathcal{U}_s^t\mathcal{Z}_s] \quad (8.63a)$$

as a result of the Markov condition 8.9.C [see (5.80)],* we obtain

---

*In comparison with (5.80) we need to keep in mind that

$$\mathcal{W}_s = \mathcal{F}_{pr}; \quad \mathcal{U}^s\mathcal{Y}^s\mathcal{W}_s = \mathcal{F}'_{pr} \supset \mathcal{F}_{pr}; \quad \mathcal{Y}_s^t = \mathcal{F}_b.$$

Then the application of (5.80) yields

$$\mathbf{M}[\mathbf{P}(B \mid \mathcal{F}_{pr}\mathcal{Z}_s\mathcal{F}_b\mathcal{U}_s^t) \mid \mathcal{F}'_{pr}\mathcal{Z}_s\mathcal{U}_s^t] = \mathbf{P}(B \mid \mathcal{F}_{pr}\mathcal{Z}_s\mathcal{U}_s^t),$$

which coincides with (8.63a).

$$\mathbf{P}(B \mid \mathcal{U}^t\mathcal{Y}^s) = \int \mathbf{M}[I_B(\omega) \mid \mathcal{W}_s\mathcal{U}_s^t\mathcal{Z}_s]\, \mathbf{P}(d\omega \in \mathcal{Z}_s \mid \mathcal{U}^t\mathcal{Y}^s) =$$

$$= \int \mathbf{M}[I_B(\omega) \mid \mathcal{W}_s\mathcal{U}_s^t\mathcal{Z}_s]\, W_s(d\omega).$$

As can be seen from this, the probability $\mathbf{P}(B \mid \mathcal{U}^t\mathcal{Y}^s)$, $B \in \mathcal{W}_t$ is $\mathcal{W}_s\mathcal{U}_s^t$-measurable because of the $\mathcal{W}_s\mathcal{U}_s^t\mathcal{Z}_s$-measurability of the function $\mathbf{M}[I_B(\omega) \mid \mathcal{W}_s\mathcal{U}_s^t\mathcal{Z}_s]$. This proves 8.7.B and completes the proof of the theorem.

2. The results obtained above for uncoupled control may be generalized to the case of coupled control. Let us assume that the set U of controls u is Markov coupled as in Definition 8.1. This means that there exists a function $\tilde{u}_t(u_a^t)$ and corresponding σ-algebras $\tilde{\mathcal{U}}_t$, such that $\mathcal{U}_s^t(\mathcal{U}^s) = \mathcal{U}_s^t(\tilde{\mathcal{U}}_s)$, $s<t$. Conditions 8.9.A–E in this case should be modified, changing them to more general ones. In place of 8.9.A–B we will have

8.10.A-B.

$$\mathcal{U}_s^t(u_a^s) = \mathcal{U}_s^t(\tilde{u}_s); \tag{8.64}$$

$$\mathcal{Z}_t(u_a^t, z_a^t) = \mathcal{Z}_t(\tilde{u}_t); \qquad \mathcal{Z}_s^t(u_a^t, z_a^s) = \mathcal{Z}_s^t(\tilde{u}_s, u_s^t). \tag{8.65}$$

It is now assumed that the state space of the basic process can depend on the preceding control u_a^s, but this dependence is reduced to dependence on a Markov process $\tilde{u}_s$. The dependence on the Markov coordinate can now be included in the Markov condition:

8.10.C. $\mathbf{P}(\Lambda \mid u_a^t, z_a^s) = \mathbf{P}(\Lambda \mid \tilde{u}_s, u_s^t, z_s)$, $\Lambda \in \mathcal{Z}_s^b \cap \mathcal{B}^t$ $(s<t)$.

We can also generalize the other conditions analogously:

8.10.D. $\mathcal{Y}_s^t(u_a^t, z_a^s) = \mathcal{Y}_s^t(\tilde{u}_s, u_s^t) \subset \mathcal{Z}_s^t(\tilde{u}_s, u_s^t)$;

8.10.E. $c^t - c^s$ is not only a $\mathcal{B}^t$-measurable function, but also a $\tilde{\mathcal{U}}_s\mathcal{U}_s^t\mathcal{Z}_s^b$-measurable function; $c - c^b$ is $\tilde{\mathcal{U}}_b\mathcal{Z}_b$-measurable.

Theorem 8.11. Under conditions 8.10.A–E the combination $x_t = (\tilde{u}_t, W_t)$ of the Markov coordinate and *a posteriori* probabilities $W_t(\Lambda \in \mathcal{Z}_t(u_t)) = \mathbf{P}(\Delta \mid \mathcal{U}^t\mathcal{Y}^t)$ serves as the sufficient coordinates.

The proof is analogous to the proof of the preceding theorem. Satisfaction of 8.7.C follows from 8.10.A–B. In order to prove 8.7.A, we need to write an equation of the type (8.61) and (8.62). Instead of (8.61), according to 8.10.E, we now have

$$\mathbf{M}[c^t - c^s \mid \mathcal{U}^t\mathcal{Y}^s] = \int [c^t(\omega') - c^s(\omega')]\, \mathbf{P}(d\omega' \in \tilde{\mathcal{U}}_s\mathcal{U}_s^t\mathcal{Z}_s^b \mid \mathcal{U}^t\mathcal{Y}^s\mathcal{Z}_s) \times$$

$$\times \mathbf{P}(d\omega \mid \mathcal{U}^t\mathcal{Y}^s).$$

According to 8.10.C,

$$\mathbf{P}(\Lambda \mid \mathcal{U}^t \mathcal{Y}^s \mathcal{Z}_s) = \mathbf{P}(\Lambda \mid \widetilde{\mathcal{U}}_s \mathcal{U}_s^t \mathcal{Z}_s), \quad \Lambda \in \mathcal{Z}_s^b \cap \mathcal{B}^t;$$

thus,

$$\mathbf{M}[c^t - c^s \mid \mathcal{U}^t \mathcal{Y}^s] = \int \mathbf{M}[c^t - c^s \mid \widetilde{\mathcal{U}}_s \mathcal{U}_s^t \mathcal{Z}_s] \, \mathbf{P}(d\omega \mid \mathcal{U}^t \mathcal{Y}^s).$$

But the measure $\mathbf{P}(d\omega \in \widetilde{\mathcal{U}}_s \mathcal{U}_s^t \mathcal{Z}_s \mid \mathcal{U}^t \mathcal{Y}^s)$ is entirely determined by the measure $W_s(A \in \mathcal{Z}_s \mid \mathcal{U}^t \mathcal{Y}^s)$ and the values $\widetilde{u}_s$, u_s^t (the values $\widetilde{u}_s$, u_s^t are uniquely assigned as soon as u_a^t is fixed). From this we have

$$\mathbf{M}[c^t - c^s \mid \mathcal{U}^t \mathcal{Y}^s] = \mathbf{M}[c^t - c^s \mid \widetilde{\mathcal{U}}_s \mathcal{U}_s^t \mathcal{W}_s].$$

We see that the difference, as compared with the corresponding formulas of the preceding theorem, lies only in the fact that in the condition of the mathematical expectations and probabilities there is, in addition to $\mathcal{U}_s^t \mathcal{W}_s$, also the σ-algebra $\widetilde{\mathcal{U}}_s$. With the same changes we can carry out the proof that (8.37) and condition 8.7.B are satisfied. Here again we use the circumstance that for a fixed control u_a^t the value of the coordinate $\widetilde{u}_t = \widetilde{u}_t(u_a^t) = \widetilde{u}_t(\widetilde{u}_s, u_s^t)$ as a function of $\widetilde{u}_s$ and u_s^t is uniquely assigned. Thus the measure $\mathbf{P}(\Gamma \in \widetilde{\mathcal{U}}_t \mid \mathcal{U}^t \mathcal{Y}^s)$ is concentrated on the set $\{\widetilde{u}_t = \widetilde{u}_t(\widetilde{u}_s, u_s^t)\}$. In other words, the first variable of the pair $(\widetilde{u}_t, W_t)$ is deterministically defined for fixed $\widetilde{u}_s$, u_s^t $(s<t)$. The probabilistic measure $\mathbf{P}(B \in \mathcal{W}_t \mid \mathcal{U}^t \mathcal{Y}^s)$ corresponds to the second variable W_t. The same method as was used earlier (with the indicated modification) is used to find the equation

$$\mathbf{P}(B \mid \mathcal{U}^t \mathcal{Y}^s) = \mathbf{P}(B \mid \widetilde{\mathcal{U}}_s \mathcal{U}_s^t \mathcal{W}_s), \quad B \in \mathcal{W}_t.$$

Finally, condition 8.7.B turns out to be verified for both variables u_t and W_t.

3. These theorems show the importance of the role played in control theory by the *a posteriori* probabilities W_t, or variables equivalent to them (the "secondary *a posteriori* process" in the terminology of paragraph 2, Sect. 5.6). As shown in Sect. 5.6, these probabilities represent a Markov process (Theorem 5.9) and thus a secondary *a posteriori* operator $\mathcal{L}(t)$ can be introduced for them. We will assume the existence of the derivative $d\mathcal{L}(t)/dt$, having the meaning of the usual (defined following Dynkin [3]) infinitesimal operator for the Markov process $\{W_t\}$.

In the case considered here, the transition probabilities of the controlled process, and thus the infinitesimal operator also, depend on the control $u \in U$. To indicate this, we will write $d\mathcal{L}(t, u)/dt$. Using this operator we can write the equation of alternatives (8.48).

In order to show this, let us for definiteness assume the case 8.9.A–E. Here for sufficient coordinates x in the formulas (8.43), (8.47)–(8.50) we will take W_t. From the definition of the operator $d\mathcal{L}/dt$ we have

$$\frac{T_{t-\Delta,t}(u)\,g-g}{\Delta}\to\frac{d\mathcal{L}(t,u)}{dt}g \text{ as } \Delta\to 0,\ g\in D(u)$$

(here $T_{st}(u)$ is a "secondary" operator). Thus, if the convergence (8.50) is valid,

$$\frac{T_{t_k t_{k+1}}(u)\cdot S_{t_{k+1}}-S_{t_{k+1}}}{t_{k+1}-t_k}\to\frac{d\mathcal{L}(t,u)}{dt}S_t \text{ as } t_{k+1}\to t,\ t_k\to t,$$

$$S_{t_k}\to S_t\in D(u).$$

Assuming that condition (8.49) is satisfied and that $S_t\in\bigcap_u D(u)$, we obtain from (8.47) by passing to the limit,

$$-\frac{\partial S_t(W)}{\partial t}=\min_{u|W}\left\{\mathbf{M}\,[C_t\,|\,u,W]+\frac{d\mathcal{L}(t,u)}{dt}S_t(W)\right\}, \qquad (8.66)$$

i.e.,

$$A_t(u)=\frac{d\mathcal{L}(t,u)}{dt}.$$

4. As an illustration of the above assertions, let us examine a specific case. Suppose we have the combined Markov process $\{z_t\}=\{x_t,\ y_t(x_t)\}$ considered in Sects. 6.2–6.4, representing the choice of a set of diffusion processes $\{y_t(\alpha),\ \alpha=1,\dots,m\}$ and the Markov transitions $x_t=\alpha$ between them. We are observing realizations of diffusion processes. In order to satisfy the requirements 8.9.A–D, we will assume that the parameters $a_\rho(\alpha,y,t,u)$, $b_{\rho\sigma}(\alpha,y,t,u)$, $p_{\alpha\beta}(t,u)$ of the combined process at each instant of time depend only on the instantaneous value u_t (at the same time instant) of the control process $\{u_t,\ t\in T\}$ (i.e., they are $\mathcal{U}_t$-measurable functions). Let us say further

$$c^t-c^s=\int_s^t C_\tau(u_\tau,z_\tau)\,d\tau,$$

where $C_\tau(u_\tau,z_\tau)$ is a $\mathcal{U}_\tau\mathcal{Z}_\tau$-measurable function.

Then 8.9.E will also be satisfied, since c^t-c^s will be $\mathcal{U}_s^t\mathcal{Z}_s^t$-measurable (here $\mathcal{B}^t=\mathcal{U}^t\mathcal{Z}^t$). According to Theorem 8.10, as sufficient coordinates in this case we will have the components of the secondary *a posteriori* process examined in Sect. 6.4, i.e., the variables (w_α, y_ρ). The reduced conditional risk will be a function of these variables: $S_t(w_\alpha, y_\rho)$. In order to derive the equation of alternatives in this case, we need only substitute (6.41) into (8.66). As a result we will have

$$-\frac{\partial S_t}{\partial t} = \min_{u_t}\left\{\mathbf{M}_{ps} C_t + w_\beta p_{\beta\alpha} \frac{\partial S_t}{\partial w_\alpha} + \mathbf{M}_{ps} a_\rho \frac{\partial S_t}{\partial y_\rho} + \right.$$

$$+ \frac{1}{2} w_\alpha [a_{\rho'}(\alpha) - \mathbf{M}_{ps} a_{\rho'}] b^{-1}_{\rho'\sigma'} [a_{\sigma'}(\beta) - \mathbf{M}_{ps} a_{\sigma'}] w_\beta \frac{\partial^2 S_t}{\partial w_\alpha \partial w_\beta} +$$

$$+ w_\alpha [a_\rho(\alpha) - \mathbf{M}_{ps} a_\rho] \frac{\partial^2 S_t}{\partial w_\alpha \partial y_\rho} + \frac{1}{2} \mathbf{M}_{ps} b_{\rho\sigma} \frac{\partial^2 S_t}{\partial y_\rho \partial y_\sigma}.$$

Here the minimization with respect to u has turned into a minimization with respect to u_t, since the expression in the brackets depends only on this value.

From this example we can see that the results of the theory of conditional Markov processes in Part II are immediately applicable to the theory of optimal control presented here.

8.8 Generalization to Game Theory

In concluding this chapter we will touch upon the question of extending the general theory presented here to the theory of games. As in the nongame presentation, the main assumption necessary for the theory is the requirement that the information available to the players must not decrease with the passage of time.

1. The generalization to the case of antagonistic games (with corresponding information) is direct and natural to such a degree that it is not necessary to repeat the previous formulation. Thus, we will concentrate our attention on the differences from the nongame case.

Instead of a single control $u = \underline{u}$ we need now to take the pair $u = (\underline{u}, \bar{u})$. The controls $\underline{u}$ and $\bar{u}$ are at the disposal of the first and second players, respectively. The measurability conditions which earlier applied to one control now apply to the pair.

For a stepped index $\varphi^N(t)$ with jumps at the points $\{t_1, \dots, t_N\}$ the solution measure separates into the product

$$\mu_s^t(d\underline{u}_s^t\, d\bar{u}_s^t \mid u_a^s, y_a^{\varphi(s)}) = \underline{\mu}_k(d\underline{u}_s^t \mid u_a^s, y_a^{\varphi(s)})\, \bar{\mu}_k(d\bar{u}_s^t \mid u_a^s, y_a^{\varphi(s)})$$

$$(s = t_k,\ t = t_{k+1}),$$

i.e.,

$$\mu_s^t(AB\,|\,\mathcal{U}^s\mathcal{Y}^{\varphi(s)}) = \underline{\mu}_k(A\,|\,\mathcal{U}^s\mathcal{Y}^{\varphi(s)})\,\overline{\mu}_k(B\,|\,\mathcal{U}^s\mathcal{Y}^{\varphi(s)}),$$
$$A \in \underline{\mathcal{U}}_s^t,\quad B \in \overline{\mathcal{U}}_s^t.$$

In formula (8.12), rather than a conditional minimization, we now need to use a conditional (with condition $|\mathcal{U}^{t_k}\mathcal{Y}^{\varphi_k}$) minimax

$$R_{\varphi^N}(\mathcal{U}^{t_k}\mathcal{Y}^{\varphi_k}) = \min_{\underline{\mu}_k}\max_{\overline{\mu}_k}\int R_{\varphi^N}(\mathcal{U}^{t_{k+1}}\mathcal{Y}^{\varphi_k})\,\mu_{t_k}^{t_{k+1}}(d\omega\,|\,\mathcal{U}^{t_k}\mathcal{Y}^{\varphi_k}). \tag{8.68}$$

The monotonic relations indicated in paragraph 2, Sect. 8.2, and Definition 8.3 lose their meaning and Theorems 8.1–8.5 turn out to be false. Similarly, Sect. 8.3 is subject to a certain amount of change; nevertheless, the subsequent sections do not need essential changes. The concept of regularity can be formulated without reference to the defining set of the optimal risk, as the requirement that all sets everywhere dense in T should lead to the same must be optimal risk. The indications of regularity 8.4.A, 8.4.B, and 8.8.A–B remain unchanged.

The concept of sufficient coordinates also retains it meaning. For the reduced conditional risk, Eq. (8.68) takes the form

$$S_{t_k}(x) = \min_{\underline{\mu}_k}\max_{\overline{\mu}_k}\int \mathbf{M}\,[c^{t_{k+1}} - c^{t_k} + S_{t_{k+1}}(x_{t_{k+1}})\,|\,u_{t_k}^{t_{k+1}},\ x_{t_k} = x]\ \times$$
$$\times\ \underline{\mu}_k(d\underline{u}_{t_k}^{t_{k+1}}\,|\,x)\,\overline{\mu}_k(d\overline{u}_{t_k}^{t_{k+1}}\,|\,x).$$

It serves not only as a recursive definition of the reduced risk, but also for finding the optimal solution measures $\underline{\mu}_k$, $\overline{\mu}_k$. The solution for a continuous index is obtained by passage to the limit from the stepped indices to the continuous. The other material from Sects. 8.6 and 8.7 also retains its meaning.

As we know, in the theory of antagonistic games randomization is essential, i.e., it brings a definite advantage. Nevertheless, in the time-sequential form of the theory described in the preceding paragraphs, there appear certain additional justifications for the disappearance of the essential randomization. In some problems the randomization is essential for the prelimit stepped indices, but loses significance with passage to the continuous limit. In other words, if we exchange the minimax in (8.68) for the sequential maximization and minimization

$$R'_{\varphi^N}(\mathcal{U}^{t_k}\mathcal{Y}^{\varphi_k}) = \min_{\omega|\mathcal{U}^{t_k}\mathcal{Y}^{\varphi_k}}\ \max_{\omega|\mathcal{U}^{t_k}\underline{\mathcal{U}}_{t_k}^{t_{k+1}}\mathcal{Y}^{\varphi_k}} \mathbf{M}\,[R'_{\varphi^N}(\mathcal{U}^{t_{k+1}}\mathcal{Y}^{\varphi_{k+1}})|\,\mathcal{U}^{t_{k+1}}\mathcal{Y}^{\varphi_k}]$$

or

$$R''_{\varphi^N}(\mathcal{U}^{t_k}\mathcal{Y}^{\varphi_k}) = \max_{\omega|\mathcal{U}^{t_k}\mathcal{Y}^{\varphi_k}}\ \min_{\omega|\mathcal{U}^{t_k}\overline{\mathcal{U}}_{t_k}^{t_{k+1}}\mathcal{Y}^{\varphi_k}} \mathbf{M}\,[R''_{\varphi^N}(\mathcal{U}^{t_{k+1}}\mathcal{Y}^{\varphi_{k+1}})\,|\,\mathcal{U}^{t_{k+1}}\mathcal{Y}^{\varphi_k}]$$

(where $R'_{\varphi^N} \geqslant R_{\varphi^N} \geqslant R''_{\varphi^N}$), then in the limit as $\varphi^N \to \varphi$ we may find coinciding results: $R'_\varphi = R_\varphi = R''_\varphi$. Of course, not all cases are of this type, apparently, and at times even after transition to the continuous index the randomization can retain its significance. Risks defined by recursion relations with the operations

$$\min_{\omega | \mathcal{U}^{t_k} \mathcal{Y}^{\varphi_k}} \mathbf{M} \Big[\max_{\omega | \mathcal{U}^{t_k} \underline{\mathcal{U}}_{t_k}^{t_{k+1}} \mathcal{Y}^{\varphi_{k+1}}} R_{\varphi^N} (\mathcal{U}^{t_{k+1}} \mathcal{Y}^{\varphi_{k+1}}) \,|\, \mathcal{U}^{t_k} \underline{\mathcal{U}}_{t_k}^{t_{k+1}} \mathcal{Y}^{\varphi_k} \Big],$$

are majorizing for risks with continuous index. Analogously, the operations

$$\max_{\omega | \mathcal{U}^{t_k} \mathcal{Y}^{\varphi_k}} \mathbf{M} \Big[\min_{\omega | \mathcal{U}^{t_k} \overline{\mathcal{U}}_{t_k}^{t_{k+1}} \mathcal{Y}^{\varphi_{k+1}}} R_{\varphi^N} (\mathcal{U}^{t_{k+1}} \mathcal{Y}^{\varphi_{k+1}}) \,|\, \mathcal{U}^{t_k} \overline{\mathcal{U}}_{t_k}^{t_{k+1}} \mathcal{Y}^{\varphi_k} \Big]$$

give lower-bound risks. These risks can be used to construct a generalization of the theory of Sects. 8.2 and 8.3 to the game case.

2. Less important for applications is the generalization of the theory to the case of nonantagonistic games of several players. In such a generalized theory, of course, all the difficulties which are characteristic of the elementary theory of nonantagonistic games remain. Let us formulate the general statement of the problem: there are n players and n penalty functions: $c^{(i)}$, $i = 1, \ldots, n$. Any ith player is interested in minimizing his risk

$$R^{(i)} = \mathbf{M}_Q c^{(i)},$$

having at his disposal for the choice of control $u^{(i)}$ his informational data $l^t_{(i)}$ at each instant of time t. The requirement that these data should not decrease with time now is apparently not sufficient for the construction of a productive theory. Thus we assume that the informational data are the same for all players:

$$l^t_{(1)} = \ldots = l^t_{(n)} \equiv l^t = (u^t_a,\ y^{\varphi(t)}_{\varphi(a)}),$$
$$u_t = (u^{(1)}_t,\ \ldots,\ u^{(n)}_t).$$

For a stepped index $\varphi(t)$ the solution is determined by the choice of solution measures

$$\mu_{t_k}^{t_{k+1}} (du_{t_k}^{t_{k+1}} \,\Big|\, \mathcal{U}^{t_k} \mathcal{Y}^{\varphi_k}).$$

At each kth stage there is an optimal solution measure as a function of the n conditional risks:

$$R^{(i)} (\mathcal{U}^{t_{k+1}} \mathcal{Y}^{\varphi_k}),\ i = 1, \ldots n,$$

namely,

$$\mu_{t_k}^{t_{k+1}}(\cdot\,|\,\mathcal{U}^{t_k}\mathcal{Y}^{\varphi_k}) = \Phi\,\{R^{(1)}(\mathcal{U}^{t_{k+1}}\mathcal{Y}^{\varphi_k}),\ \ldots,\ R^{(n)}(\mathcal{U}^{t_{k+1}}\mathcal{Y}^{\varphi_k})\}. \qquad (8.69)$$

An appropriate algorithm is chosen from some consideration on the level of the elementary (single-stage) theory of games. The chosen solution measure determines the conditional mathematical expectation

$$\mathbf{M}_{\mathbf{P}}\,\{\mathbf{M}_\mu\,[R^{(i)}(\mathcal{U}^{t_{k+1}}\mathcal{Y}^{\varphi_k})\,|\,\mathcal{U}^{t_k}\mathcal{Y}^{\varphi_k}]\,|\,\mathcal{U}^{t_k}\mathcal{Y}^{\varphi_{k-1}}\}.$$

If there is a redistribution of resources (losses) among the players, this can be taken into account by defining, for example, the conditional risks at the instant t_k by the formula

$$R^{(i)}(\mathcal{U}^{t_k}\mathcal{Y}^{\varphi_k}) = \sum_j \gamma_{ij}\,\mathbf{M}_\mu\ [R^{(j)}(\mathcal{U}^{t_{k+1}}\mathcal{Y}^{\varphi_k})\,|\,\mathcal{U}^{t_k}\mathcal{Y}^{\varphi_k}]. \qquad (8.70)$$

Thus we will have the recursive transformation

$$R^{(1)}(\mathcal{U}^{t_{k+1}}\mathcal{Y}^{\varphi_k}),\ \ldots,\ R^{(n)}(\mathcal{U}^{t_{k+1}}\mathcal{Y}^{\varphi_k}) \to$$
$$\to R^{(1)}(\mathcal{U}^{t_k}\mathcal{Y}^{\varphi_{k-1}}),\ \ldots,\ R^{(n)}(\mathcal{U}^{t_k}\mathcal{Y}^{\varphi_{k-1}})$$

(we recall that $\mathcal{U}^{t_k}\mathcal{Y}^{\varphi_{k-1}} \subset \mathcal{U}^{t_{k+1}}\mathcal{Y}^{\varphi_k}$). The explicit form of this transformation and the very concept of optimality, of course, depend on the assumption of the principle of agreement of interests. Difficulties encountered in this area are related to the single-stage theory of games. If, however, this principle is fixed, then the algorithms (8.69) and (8.70) are defined by it. Thus it is possible to calculate the final risks $R^{(i)}(\mathcal{U}^a\mathcal{Y}^{\varphi(a)}) \equiv R^{(i)}$, and also to carry out the passage to the limit from the stepped index to the continuous.

The combination of the solution measures (8.69) and the probabilities $\mathbf{P}(\cdot\,|\,\mathcal{U}^t)$ assigned in the condition of the problem defines, as earlier, the complete measure Q of the process optimally controlled.

CHAPTER 9

Optimal Nonlinear Filtering

The synthesis methods for optimal filters presented here are based on the theory of conditional Markov processes. They were developed by the author as they applied to various practical problems [6, 7, 10–12]. Aside from this work we would like to mention the work by Bolshakov and Repin [1] related to this area. Their basic method is linearization of the expressions for the logarithm of the *a posteriori* probability or the likelihood ratio. The resulting linear integral equations are solved by the same methods as in the theory of linear filtering. Thus the methods of Bolshakov and Repin stand, so to speak, half way between the methods of linear and nonlinear filtering. In our problem the solution of integral equations for the synthesis of the linear part of the filtering system does not arise.

If we have in mind the practical application of the theory, it is necessary to take note of one condition not mentioned in the monograph. It is related to a supplementary approximation. The problem lies in the fact that the number of variables replacing the distribution density is often, strictly speaking, infinite, but not all of them are of equal importance. In a practical application of the equations it is important that the number of variables not be large. Thus there arises the problem of selecting from the variables the most important and rejecting the remainder, accepting a deterioration in the quality of filtering. This deterioration, if not great, is justified by the simplification of the construction. As can be seen from this, the question of the amount of this deterioration, and the question of which variables should be selected in order that the deterioration be a minimum, are of interest. These questions at present are little studied.

We will devote considerable attention to examination of the relations between the theories of nonlinear and linear optimal filtering.

The problem of nonlinear optimal filtering is naturally a logical continuation and development of the problem of linear filtering (in the broad sense). As we know, this historically earlier classical problem is solved by the formulation and solution of regression equations. These equations, the solution of which is trivial for a small number of random variables, change into an infinite system of equations or into an integral equation (specifically into the Wiener-Hopf equation) with an infinite number of random variables, for example, in the case of a stationary process. The classical solution of these problems in the stationary case (on the half-line) is given by Kolmogorov [2] and Wiener [1]. These results found their way into numerous texts and served as the point of departure for the construction of nonstationary generalizations.

A series of results in this direction is summarized in the books of Laning and Battin [1] and Pugachev [1].

It should be noted that an effective explicit solution of the regression equations for a semi-infinite or finite interval in the stationary case is possible only for processes having a rational spectral density, although the Kolmogorov-Wiener theory allows the solution to be written in integral form for a somewhat more general case. A Gaussian process with a rational spectral density, as we know, is a component of a multidimensional Markov process. Thus the effective solution of the linear filtering problem turns out to be closely related to the Markov property of the process. From this it follows that an effective solution of the linear filtering problem is possible if and only if the process falls in the domain of the theory of conditional Markov processes. This conclusion, not obvious on the surface, shows the close interconnection of the two theories, which are entirely different in content and original premises: in one, linear transformation, the mean-square criterion, and any processes are examined; and in the other, any transformations, any criterion, and Markov processes.

In addition to methods based on the theory of conditional Markov processes, other ways of solving problems of optimal filtering are also possible. Among the first references on nonlinear filtering belongs the work of Zadeh [1], in which the optimal transformation from a definite class of nonlinear transformations is found. Another form of nonlinear transformation is examined in the work of Kuznetsov, Stratonovich, and Tikhonov [2]. In such an approach the expansion coefficients of the transformation in question with respect to selected functions are the unknowns. A system of equations is written for these coefficients, but their solution is exceedingly difficult.

In certain special problems particular approaches to the problem of nonlinear filtering turn out to be expedient. Thus, for the filtering of pulsed signals the author [9] worked out a method based on the theory of correlated random points (Stratonovich [8], Sect. 6).

The solution of the nonlinear filtering problem using the theory of conditional Markov processes has a number of special advantages over other methods. The recursive transformations of the *a posteriori* measures are characteristic of this theory. The basic unit of a nonlinear filter can be synthesized as a device realizing these recursive transformations. The algorithm of these transformations can be defined without particular difficulty and can be realized as a block with a feedback connection. In this manner the filter synthesis does not involve laborious calculation. The resulting complicated nonlinear transformation is the result of simpler cascaded transformations. Of course, other variants of the application of the theory are also possible. In the case of continuous time and diffusion processes the apparatus of differential equations is adequate for the theory. This situation leads to a series of favorable consequences. Because of this we can solve not only filtering problems considering *a posteriori* probabilities, but also more complex "secondary" problems, considering functions of *a posteriori* probabilities. For these functions we are able to obtain differential equations to which correspond secondary *a posteriori* infinitesimal operators (Sects. 5.6 and 6.4). Secondary problems arise in considering the performance quality of the nonlinear filter. The theory of conditional Markov processes allows the equation for the average loss function to be written.

A similar equation is used in Sect. 9.6, where for one specific problem a comparison of the effectiveness of a linear and a nonlinear filter is made. The problem is selected to be such that it fits into the sphere of applicability of both theories. Since the theory of linear filtering finds the optimal transformation in the class of linear transformations, and the theory of nonlinear filtering, in the class of all transformations, then the nonlinear filter certainly gives better results. There exists the question of the amount of the difference. For both optimal transformations it is possible to find the exact expression for the average risk. Comparison indicates that the ratio of the average risk of a linear transformation to the risk of a nonlinear one tends to infinity as the intensity of the noise tends to zero (i.e., as each risk tends to zero). Comparison of the quality of linear and nonlinear filtering for this problem (using a somewhat different criterion) was made by Kul'man and Stratonovich in [1], where related results are given.

In Sect. 9.5 linear filtering is considered as a special case of nonlinear filtering. The method used here allows solution of the Wiener-Hopf equation to be avoided, i.e., it seems more convenient than the method of the Wiener theory. The equations of the theory of optimal linear filtering cited in Sect. 9.5 were obtained by the author in [7]. They are totally insensitive to change of the length of the interval of observation, being equally applicable to a finite and a semiinfinite interval, and to a stationary and a nonstationary process. Equivalent equations were later derived by Kalman and Bucy [1] (Eq. IV).

9.1 Presentation of the Problem

The problem of optimal nonlinear filtering can be posed as a degenerate special case of the general problem of optimal control formulated in the preceding chapter.

Let the control u_t (in this respect the term "estimator" appears to be more suitable) corresponding to the instant t be a function $\{u_{t\tau}, \tau \in T_t\}$ on a certain subset $T_t \subset T$. The penalty functions, let us say, have the form

$$c(\omega) = \int_T dt \int_{T_t} C_{t\tau}(u_{t\tau}, z_\tau) F_t(d\tau);$$
$$c^t(\omega) = \int_{s \leqslant t} ds \int_{T_s} C_{s\tau}(u_{s\tau}, z_\tau) F_s(d\tau). \tag{9.1}$$

Here $F_t(\Lambda)$ [where t is fixed] is a measure on Borel subsets of $T_t \ni \tau$, and $C_{t\tau}(u_{t\tau}, z_\tau)$, a function of $u_{t\tau}$ and z_τ, i.e., a $\mathcal{U}_t\mathcal{Z}_\tau$-measurable function of ω. We assume that the conditions of measurability and integrability with respect to t and τ are satisfied. Finally, $c^t(\omega) - c^s(\omega)$ is a $\mathcal{U}_s^t\mathcal{Z}^b$-measurable function.

We assume that the probabilities $\mathbf{P}(\cdot \mid u) = \mathbf{P}(\cdot)$ of the basic process $\{z_t(\omega)\}$ do not depend on the control (estimator) $u(\mathcal{A}^t \supset \mathcal{Z}^b, t \in T)$. The observed process $\{y_t(\omega)\} = \{y_t(z_t(\omega))\}$ is also independent of the estimator but depends on the value of z_t at the same instant of time. Finally, it is assumed that the estimators $u_{t\tau}$ corresponding to various t and τ can be selected independently of one another (uncoupled control $\{u_{t\tau}\}$ as a function of two variables).

With these assumptions the minimization of the conditional average risk can be carried out independently for nonoverlapping rectangles in the t, τ plane and even for each point (t, τ). Here the solution measures $\mu_{t_k}^{t_{k+1}}(d\omega \in \mathcal{U}_{t_k}^{t_{k+1}} \mid \mathcal{U}^{t_k}\mathcal{Y}^{\varphi_k})$ for the stepped index φ^N lose their dependence on $u_a^{t_k}$:

$$\mu_{t_k}^{t_{k+1}}(du_{t_k}^{t_{k+1}} \mid \mathcal{U}^{t_k}\mathcal{Y}^{\varphi_k}) = \mu_{t_k}^{t_{k+1}}(du_{t_k}^{t_{k+1}} \mid \mathcal{Y}^{\varphi_k}). \tag{9.2}$$

In fact, writing the recursive relation (8.38) for $k = N$, we have

$$S_{t_N}(\mathcal{U}^{t_N}\mathcal{Y}^{\varphi_N}) = \min_{u_{t_N}^b \mid \mathcal{U}^{t_N}\mathcal{Y}^{\varphi_N}} \int (c - c^{t_N}) \mathbf{P}(d\omega \mid \mathcal{U}^b\mathcal{Y}^{\varphi_N}). \tag{9.3}$$

In view of the fact that

$$\mathbf{P}(d\omega \in \mathscr{Z}^b \mid \mathscr{U}^b \mathscr{Y}^{\varphi_N}) \ (= \mathbf{P}(d\omega \mid \mathscr{Y}^{\varphi_N}))$$

does not depend on u, the expression in (9.3) subject to minimization does not depend on $u_a^{t_N}$. Thus $\mu_{t_N}^b$ and $S_{t_N} (= S_{t_N}(\mathscr{Y}^{\varphi_N}))$ do not depend on $u_a^{t_N}$. Taking this into account, the second relation (8.38) for $k = N-1$ can be written in the form

$$S_{t_{N-1}} = \min_{u_{t_{N-1}}^{t_N} \mid \mathscr{U}^{t_{N-1}} \mathscr{Y}^{t_{N-1}}} \left[\int (c^{t_N} - c^{t_{N-1}}) \mathbf{P}(d\omega \in \mathscr{Z}^b \mid \mathscr{Y}^{\varphi_{N-1}}) \right] + \\ + \int S_{t_N}(\mathscr{Y}^{\varphi_N}) \mathbf{P}(d\omega \mid \overline{\mathscr{Y}}^{\varphi_{N-1}}) \Big],$$

since

$$\mathbf{P}(d\omega \in \mathscr{Z}^b \mid \mathscr{U}^{t_N} \mathscr{Y}^{\varphi_{N-1}}) = \mathbf{P}(d\omega \mid \mathscr{Y}^{\varphi_{N-1}}).$$

From this it is apparent that $\mu_{t_{N-1}}^{t_N}$ and $S_{t_{N-1}}$ do not depend on $u_a^{t_{N-1}}$. Continuing the examination, in an analogous manner we can see that all solution measures (9.2) and reduced risks S_{t_k} are independent of $u_a^{t_k}$.

From the above follows the fact that the optimal solution measure (9.2) is found, on the strength of (9.1), by the minimization of the expression

$$\mathbf{M}\left[\int_{t_k}^{t_{k+1}} dt \int_{T_t} C_{t\tau}(u_{t\tau}, z_\tau) F_t(d\tau) \mid \mathscr{Y}^{\varphi_k} \right] \equiv r_{t_k}^{t_{k+1}}(u_{t_k}^{t_{k+1}}, y_a^{\varphi_k}),$$

i.e.,

$$\int r_{t_k}^{t_{k+1}}(u_{t_k}^{t_{k+1}}, y^{\varphi_k}) \mu_{t_k}^{t_{k+1}}(du_{t_k}^{t_{k+1}} \mid y_a^{\varphi_k}) = \\ = \min_{u_{t_k}^{t_{k+1}} \mid y_a^{\varphi_k}} r_{t_k}^{t_{k+1}}(u_{t_k}^{t_{k+1}}, y_a^{\varphi_k}) \equiv \rho_{t_k}^{t_{k+1}}(y_a^{\varphi_k}).$$

The total average risk for the selected stepped index can be written

$$R_{\varphi N} = S_a = \sum_k \mathbf{M} \rho_{t_k}^{t_{k+1}}(y_a^{\varphi_k}).$$

Let us turn to consideration of the continuous index $\varphi(t) = t$. The independence of the result from the particular method of passing to the limit as $N \to \infty$, $\varphi^N \to \varphi$ is assured by checking that the regularity condition (8.26) is satisfied. In this respect it has the form

$$\rho^{t}_{\varphi'}(y_a^{\varphi'}) - \rho^{t-\Delta}_{\varphi'}(y_a^{\varphi'}) - \mathbf{M}\,[\rho^{t}_{t-\Delta}(y_a^{t-\Delta}) \mid y_a^{\varphi'}] = o(1)\,\Delta$$
$$(\varphi' = t - \Delta - c\Delta,\ 0 < c < \infty).$$

Taking into account the definition of $\rho_{t_k}^{t_{k+1}}$, we see that this condition is satisfied if

$$\min_{u_{t\tau}} \mathbf{M}\,[C_{t\tau}(u_{t\tau}, z_\tau) \mid y_a^{\varphi'}] - \mathbf{M}\,\{\min_{u_{t\tau}} \mathbf{M}\,[C_{t\tau}(u_{t\tau}, z_\tau) \mid y_a^{t-\Delta}] \mid y_a^{\varphi'}\} \to 0$$

as $t - \Delta - \varphi' \to 0$ $(\tau \in [t - \Delta, t])$. This last relation is true since

$$\mathbf{M}\,[C_{t\tau}(u_{t\tau}, z_\tau) \mid y_a^{\varphi'}] - \mathbf{M}\,[C_{t\tau}(u_{t\tau}, z_\tau) \mid y_a^{t-\Delta}] \to 0 \text{ (a.c.)}$$

as $t - \Delta - \varphi' \to 0$. Thus regularity is verified. In addition,

$$\mathbf{M}\,[C_{t\tau}(u_{t\tau}, z_\tau) \mid y_a^{t-\Delta}] - \mathbf{M}\,[C_{t\tau}(u_{t\tau}, z_\tau) \mid y_a^{t}] \to 0 \text{ (a.c.)}$$

as $\Delta \to 0$; thus in the process of passing to the limit the extremal function $\{u_{t\tau}^N\}$, corresponding to φ^N and determined from the conditions $r_{t_k}^{t_{k+1}}(u_{t_k}^{t_{k+1}}, y_a^{\varphi_k}) = \rho_{t_k}^{t_{k+1}}(y_a^{\varphi_k})$, yields a risk tending to the risk of the optimal control, defined by the minimization

$$\min_{u_{t\tau}} \mathbf{M}\,[C_{t\tau}(u_{t\tau}, z_\tau) \mid y_a^t].$$

If for this optimal control the conditions of measurability and integrability with respect to t and τ [see (9.1)] are satisfied, then it actually corresponds to the minimum total risk.

Thus the optimal estimator $u_{t\tau}$ is found as the result of the minimization of the expression

$$s_{t\tau}(u_{t\tau} \mid y_a^t) = \mathbf{M}\,[C_{t\tau}(u_{t\tau}, z_\tau) \mid y_a^t] = \int C_{t\tau}(u_{t\tau}, z_\tau)\,\mathbf{P}(dz_\tau \mid y_a^t). \qquad (9.4)$$

Since the function $C_{t\tau}(u_{t\tau}, z_\tau)$ is assigned by the conditions of the problem, to find the algorithm $d_{t\tau}(y_a^t) = u_{t\tau}$ of the optimal filter we need to know how the *a posteriori* probabilities $\mathbf{P}(dz_\tau \mid y_a^t)$ are expressed through the observed process. This question has already been examined in Chapters 5–7 for a Markov process z_t. Here we will apply the results obtained in those chapters.

In certain important special cases for $F_t(\Lambda)$ we can take the measure

$$F_t(\Lambda) = \begin{cases} 1, & \text{if } \Lambda \ni t; \\ 0, & \text{if } \Lambda \not\ni t \end{cases} \quad (\text{i.e., } F_t = \delta(\tau - t)). \qquad (9.5)$$

Then we need only consider the function

$$u_{tt},\ s_{tt}(u_{tt} \mid y_a^t) = \int C_{tt}(u_{tt}, z_t)\, \mathbf{P}(dz_t \mid y_a^t) \qquad (9.5a)$$

and the *a posteriori* probabilities $\mathbf{P}(dz_t \mid y_a^t) = W_t(dz_t)$. This results in a simplification of the filtering problem.

9.2 Equations and Block Diagram of the Optimal Nonlinear Filter

In this section we will consider nonlinear filtering without the above simplification. The basic process $\{z_t, t \in T\}$ is assumed to be Markov. We will use the notation of Chapters 5-7.

The *a posteriori* probability $\mathbf{P}(dz_\tau \mid y_a^t)$ is expressed differently by the *a posteriori* process $\{W_s\}$ for $\tau > t$ and for $\tau < t$. If $\tau > t$, the probability $\mathbf{P}(dz_\tau \mid y_a^t)$ can be obtained from $W_t(dz_t)$ using the *a priori* transition probability:

$$\mathbf{P}(dz_\tau \mid y_a^t) = \int_{z_t} W_t(dz_t)\, \mathbf{P}(dz_\tau \mid z_t) \qquad (\tau > t).$$

This expression can be considered a solution of the differential equation

$$d_u \mathbf{P}(dz_u \mid y_a^t) = [\mathbf{P}(\cdot \mid y_a^t)\, dL_{pr}](dz_u), \qquad (9.6)$$
$$t \leqslant u \leqslant \tau$$

with "initial" condition

$$\mathbf{P}(dz_u \mid y_a^t) = W_t(dz_u) \text{ for } u = t.$$

Thus it is possible to determine $\mathbf{P}(dz_\tau \mid y_a^t)$ for any $\tau > t$, if we first determine the measure $W_t(dz_t)$.

Analogously, we will examine how it is possible to find $\mathbf{P}(dz_\sigma \mid y_a^t)$, $\sigma < t$. To do this we will use formula (5.50):

$$\mathbf{P}(dz_\sigma \mid y_a^t) = W_\sigma(dz_\sigma)\, \widetilde{V}_\sigma^t(z_\sigma, \Omega). \qquad (9.7)$$

Here the likelihood function $\widetilde{V}_\sigma{}^t(z, \Omega)$ is the solution of Eq. (5.59) or (5.67) (where it is necessary to replace t, u by s, t and to assume $s \in [\sigma, t]$) with the "initial" condition

$$\widetilde{V}_s^t(z, \Omega) = 1, \text{ if } s = t.$$

The infinitesimal operator $d\widetilde{L}(s)$ of these equations is in turn expressed in terms of W_s.

Alternatively, $\mathbf{P}(dz_\sigma | y_a^t) = P_\sigma$ can be obtained by solving Eq. (5.68a) on the interval $\sigma \leqslant s \leqslant t$ under the condition

$$P_s = W_t \text{ for } s = t,$$

which is the "initial" condition in reverse time.

Thus the *a posteriori* probabilities $\mathbf{P}(dz_\tau | y_a^t)$, $\mathbf{P}(dz_\sigma | y_a^t)$, $\tau > t$, $\sigma < t$ can be found if we previously determine the *a posteriori* process $\{W_s, s \leqslant t\}$. The latter is found as the solution of Eq. (5.57), (5.61), or (5.66).

After obtaining the *a posteriori* probabilities it is not difficult to find expressions of the type (9.4) and, using these, the optimal estimator functions.

This method of finding optimal estimators can be realized using automatically acting equipment for the filter. Its block diagram is given in the illustration, where $\sigma < t < \tau$.

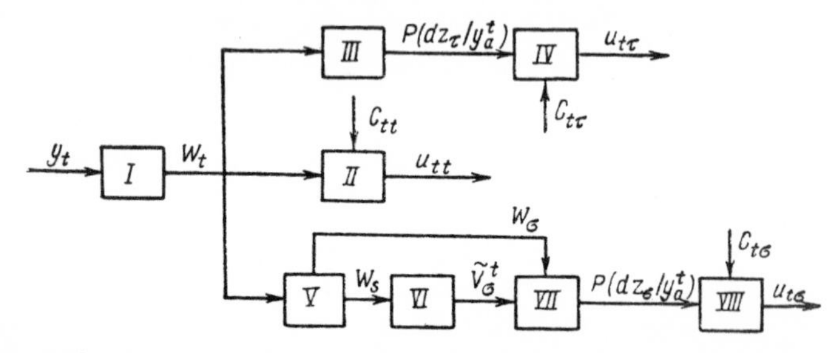

For definiteness we will discuss the specific case considered in Chapter 6 of a process having several states. Using the *a posteriori* infinitesimal operator found there, we find that the basic equation of nonlinear filtering, determining the *a posteriori* process $\{w_\alpha(t)\}$, has the form (6.31)

$$\begin{aligned} dw_\alpha = w_\gamma p_{\gamma\alpha} dt + w_\alpha [a_{\rho'}(\alpha) - \mathbf{M}_{ps} a_{\rho'}] b^{-1}_{\rho'\sigma'} dy_{\sigma'} - \\ - \frac{1}{2} w_\alpha \Big\{ [a_{\rho'}(\alpha) a_{\sigma'}(\alpha) - \mathbf{M}_{ps} a_{\rho'} a_{\sigma'}] b^{-1}_{\rho'\sigma'} + \\ + \left[\frac{\partial a_{\rho'}}{\partial y_\pi}(\alpha) - \mathbf{M}_{ps} \frac{\partial a_{\rho'}}{\partial y_\pi} \right] b^{-1}_{\rho'\sigma'} b_{\sigma'\pi} + \\ + [a_{\rho'}(\alpha) - \mathbf{M}_{ps} a_{\rho'}] \frac{\partial b^{-1}_{\rho'\sigma'}}{\partial y_\pi} b_{\sigma'\pi} \Big\} dt. \end{aligned} \tag{9.8}$$

Block I in the illustration represents this equation and thus realizes the transformation of the observed process $\{y_t\}$ into the *a posteriori* process $\{w_\alpha(t)\}$.

If the measure $F_t(\Lambda)$ has the form (9.5) [the case of filtering without lag or prediction], then in order to obtain the estimator u_{tt}

we need only to construct block II, which finds and supplies that value of u_{tt} for which the expression

$$\sum_{\alpha} C_{tt}(u_{tt}, \alpha)\, w_{\alpha}(t)$$

is a minimum.

If the estimators $u_{t\tau}$, $\tau > t$, are of interest, then we should insert block III, which represents Eq. (9.6), i.e., the equation

$$dp_{\alpha}(u) = \sum_{\gamma} p_{\gamma}(u)\, p_{\gamma\alpha} dt, \quad t \leqslant u \leqslant \tau$$

$$(p_{\alpha}(u) = \mathbf{P}\{x_u = \alpha \mid y_a^t\})$$

with the "initial" condition

$$p_{\alpha}(t) = w_{\alpha}(t)$$

(it is of course required that physically this process occur on a different, considerably faster, time scale). After the definition of $p_{\alpha}(\tau)$, block IV yields the estimator $u_{t\tau}$ corresponding to the minimum of the expression

$$\sum_{\alpha} C_{t\tau}(u_{t\tau}, \alpha)\, p_{\alpha}(\tau).$$

Finally, we will consider the apparatus serving to determine the estimators $u_{t\sigma}$, $\sigma < t$. Block V remembers the past process $\{W_s, s \leqslant t\}$ and sends to block VI at various instants of time the necessary values of this process. Block VI represents Eq. (5.67), which has in this case the form

$$\begin{aligned} -d_s\tilde{V}_s^t(\alpha, \Omega) &= p_{\alpha\beta}\tilde{V}_s^t(\beta, \Omega)\, dt + \\ &+ \tilde{V}_s^t(\alpha, \Omega)\{[a_{\rho'}(\alpha) - \mathbf{M}_{ps} a_{\rho'}]\, b_{\rho'\sigma'}^{-1} dy_{\sigma'} - \\ &- \frac{dt}{2}[a_{\rho'}(\alpha)\, a_{\sigma'}(\alpha) - \mathbf{M}_{ps} a_{\rho'} a_{\sigma'}]\, b_{\rho'\sigma'}^{-1} - \\ &- \frac{dt}{2}\left[\frac{\partial a_{\rho'}(\alpha)}{\partial y_{\pi}} - \mathbf{M}_{ps}\frac{\partial a_{\rho'}}{\partial y_{\pi}}\right] b_{\rho'\sigma'}^{-1} b_{\sigma'\pi} - \\ &- \frac{dt}{2}[a_{\rho'}(\alpha) - \mathbf{M}_{ps} a_{\rho'}]\frac{\partial b_{\rho'\sigma'}^{-1}}{\partial y_{\pi}}\, b_{\sigma'\pi}\Big\} \end{aligned} \tag{9.9}$$

with the "initial" condition

$$\tilde{V}_t^t(\alpha, \Omega) = 1$$

and with a reverse flow of time (similar to that of block III on a different time scale). At its output we get the process $\tilde{V}_s^t(\alpha, \Omega)$. Block VII forms the combination (9.7), i.e., the *a posteriori* probabilities

$$\mathbf{P}(x_\sigma = \alpha \mid y_a^t) = w_\alpha(\sigma)\,\tilde{V}_\sigma^t(\alpha, \Omega).$$

Blocks VI and VII can be replaced by blocks representing the equation

$$dp_\beta = \left[\sum_\alpha w_\alpha\, p_{\alpha\beta}\, \frac{p_\beta}{w_\beta} - w_\beta \sum_\gamma p_{\beta\gamma}\, \frac{p_\gamma}{w_\gamma}\right] dt$$

with the "initial" conditions $p_\beta = w_\beta$ for $s = t$. In fact, it was already noted that Eq. (5.68a) in the case in question takes the form (6.39a). The final block, VIII, finding the minimum of the expression

$$\sum_\alpha C_{t\sigma}(u_{t\sigma}, \alpha)\,\mathbf{P}(x_\sigma = \alpha \mid y_a^t),$$

yields the optimal estimator $u_{t\sigma}$.

In the specific case examined in Sect. 6.5 of a process having two states, the above equations and expressions are simplified. Thus, Eq. (9.8) takes the form (6.43), and Eq. (9.9) becomes (6.44).

9.3 Example of an *A Posteriori* Process Having an Infinite Number of States

The filter is constructed analogously in the case when the *a posteriori* process has an infinite number of states. For simplicity, in the future we will limit ourselves to the case (9.5).

At the conclusion of Chapter 6 it was noted that the results obtained in that chapter can be extended to the case when the Markov process $\{\alpha(t)\}$ can take a value from an infinite set.

Let α have the meaning of the phase of a narrow-band process taking values in the set $[0, 2\pi]$. *A priori* let us assume that the phase is a pure diffusion process, i.e., that it is described by the infinitesimal operator

$$dL_{pr}(t) = \frac{1}{2}\, dt\, D\, \frac{\partial^2}{\partial\alpha^2}, \tag{9.10}$$

where the diffusion coefficient D is a constant.

We observe a mixture of the narrow-band process $B_0 \cos(\omega_0 t + \alpha(t))$ and white noise having a spectral intensity $2N$. This case, as we know, can be formulated thus: we observe two diffusion processes $\{y_1(t)\}$, $\{y_2(t)\}$, which for fixed α are described by the drift parameters

$$a_1(t) = B_0 \cos\alpha; \quad a_2(t) = B_0 \sin\alpha$$

and the local variance matrix

$$\begin{pmatrix} b_{11} & b_{12} \\ b_{21} & b_{22} \end{pmatrix} = \begin{pmatrix} N & 0 \\ 0 & N \end{pmatrix}.$$

Applying formulas (6.47) and (6.48) to this example, we obtain the *a posteriori* infinitesimal operator

$$dL^*(t) = \frac{1}{2}\, dt\, D\, \frac{\partial^2}{\partial \alpha^2} + \frac{B_0}{N} (\cos\alpha\, d^* y_1 + \sin\alpha\, d^* y_2).$$

If we write this in the form

$$dL^*(t) = A^* dt + A_\rho^*\, d^* y_\rho,$$

then obviously

$$A^* = \frac{1}{2} D\, \frac{\partial^2}{\partial \alpha^2}; \quad A_1^* = \frac{B_0}{N} \cos\alpha; \quad A_2^* = \frac{B_0}{N} \sin\alpha.$$

We use formula (3.71) to find the infinitesimal operator

$$dL(t) = A dt + A_\rho dy_\rho.$$

This yields

$$A = A^* - \frac{1}{2} A_\rho^* A_\sigma^* b_{\rho\sigma} = \frac{1}{2} D\, \frac{\partial^2}{\partial \alpha^2} - \frac{1}{2} \frac{B_0^2}{N} \cos^2\alpha - \frac{1}{2} \frac{B_0^2}{N} \sin^2\alpha$$

$$(A_\rho = A_\rho^*).$$

Hence

$$dL(t) = \frac{1}{2}\, dt D\, \frac{\partial^2}{\partial \alpha^2} + \frac{B_0}{N} (\cos\alpha\, dy_1 + \sin\alpha\, dy_2) - \frac{B_0^2}{2N} dt. \quad (9.10a)$$

Now we can write the basic equations of the optimal filter (5.57), (5.61), and (5.66), determining the *a posteriori* probabilities W_t, which correspond to block I in the illustration above. If

$$w_t(\alpha) = \frac{W_t(d\alpha)}{d\alpha}$$

is the *a posteriori* probability density, then according to (9.10) and (5.66) we have

$$dw_t(\alpha) = \frac{1}{2}\, dt D\, \frac{\partial^2 w_t(\alpha)}{\partial \alpha^2} + \frac{B_0}{N} [(\cos\alpha - c_1)\, dy_1 + $$
$$+ (\sin\alpha - s_1)\, dy_2]\, w_t(\alpha), \quad (9.11)$$

where

$$c_1 = \mathbf{M}_{ps} \cos\alpha = \int \cos\alpha\, w_t(\alpha)\, d\alpha; \ s_1 = \mathbf{M}_{ps} \sin\alpha = \int \sin\alpha\, w_t(\alpha)\, d\alpha.$$

With specification of the initial density, let us say, $w_{t_0}(\alpha) = p_0(\alpha)$, this equation uniquely defines the ***a posteriori*** measure.

If we assign a quality criterion using the penalty function $C(u, \alpha)$, then we can find the value $u(t) \equiv \alpha_0(t) = d_t(y_a^t)$ of the optimal estimator of the unknown phase (here d_t is the solution algorithm). It corresponds to the minimum of the expression

$$\min_u \int C(u, \alpha)\, w_t(\alpha)\, d\alpha = \int C(\alpha_0(t), \alpha)\, w_t(\alpha)\, d\alpha. \tag{9.12}$$

Let us select for definiteness the quadratic quality criterion with respect to the narrow-band signal $B_0 \cos(\omega_0 t + \alpha)$. Namely, let us assume,

$$C(u, \alpha) = \frac{\omega_0}{2\pi} \int_t^{t+\frac{2\pi}{\omega_0}} [B_0 \cos(\omega_0 t' + u) - B_0 \cos(\omega_0 t' + \alpha)]^2\, dt' =$$

$$= B_0^2 [1 - \cos(u - \alpha)].$$

Then the expression subject to minimization in (9.12) will be

$$\int C(u, \alpha)\, w_t(\alpha)\, d\alpha = B_0^2 [1 - c_1 \cos u - s_1 \sin u]. \tag{9.13}$$

The minimum of this expression is easily found. The value of the estimator of the phase is determined by the relations

$$\tan\alpha_0 = \frac{s_1}{c_1}; \quad \sin\alpha_0 = \frac{s_1}{\sqrt{s_1^2 + c_1^2}}$$

Thus, the estimator, i.e., the filtered narrow-band signal, can be written

$$s_0(t) = B_0 \cos(\omega_0 t + \alpha_0) = B_0 \frac{c_1}{\sqrt{s_1^2 + c_1^2}} \cos\omega_0 t -$$

$$- B_0 \frac{s_1}{\sqrt{s_1^2 + c_1^2}} \sin\omega_0 t. \tag{9.14}$$

The final block II in the illustration gives the value of the estimator of the phase $\alpha_0(t) = \operatorname{arc\,tan} \frac{s_1}{c_1}$ or the filtered signal (9.14).

In order to facilitate the construction of block I (see the illustration), Eq. (9.11) for the distribution density $w_t(\alpha)$ can be replaced by equivalent equations written for completely different parameters replacing $w_t(\alpha)$. Thus, for example, it is possible to introduce the parameters $s_n(t)$, $c_n(t)$, $n=1, 2, \ldots$, defined by the formula

$$w_t(\alpha) = \frac{1}{2\pi} + \frac{1}{\pi} \sum_{n=1}^{\infty} (s_n(t) \sin n\alpha + c_n(t) \cos n\alpha), \tag{9.15}$$

i.e.,

$$s_n(t) = \mathbf{M}_{ps} \sin n\alpha = \int_0^{2\pi} \sin n\alpha \, w_t(\alpha)\, d\alpha;$$

$$c_n(t) = \int_0^{2\pi} \cos n\alpha \, w_t(\alpha) d\alpha. \tag{9.16}$$

Substituting (9.15) into (9.11) and comparing separately the terms corresponding to the various functions $\sin n\alpha$, $\cos n\alpha$, we get for the parameters (9.16) the system of equations

$$\begin{aligned}
ds_1 &= -\frac{1}{2} Ds_1 dt + \frac{B_0}{2D} dy_1 (s_2 - 2s_1c_1) + \frac{B_0}{2D} dy_2 (1 - c_2 - 2s_1^2);\\
dc_1 &= -\frac{1}{2} Dc_1 dt + \frac{B_0}{2D} dy_1 (1 + c_1 - 2c_1^2) +\\
&\quad + \frac{B_0}{2D} dy_2 (s_2 - 2s_1c_1);\\
ds_n &= -\frac{1}{2} Dn^2 s_n dt + \frac{B_0}{2D} dy_1 (s_{n-1} + s_{n+1} - 2s_n c_1) +\\
&\quad + \frac{B_0}{2D} dy_2 (c_{n-1} - c_{n+1} - 2s_1 s_n);\\
dc_n &= -\frac{1}{2} Dn^2 c_n dt + \frac{B_0}{2D} dy_1 (c_{n+1} + c_{n-1} - 2c_1 c_n) +\\
&\quad + \frac{B_0}{2D} dy_2 (s_{n+1} - s_{n-1} - 2s_1 c_n),\\
&\qquad n = 2, 3, \ldots .
\end{aligned} \tag{9.17}$$

This is equivalent to Eq. (9.11), and block I can be synthesized in accordance with these equations.

The initial distribution is naturally taken to be uniform. This corresponds to zero initial conditions

$$s_n(t_0) = 0; \quad c_n(t_0) = 0, \quad n = 1, 2, \ldots .$$

The processes $s_1(t)$ and $c_1(t)$ generated in block I can immediately be used to form the filtered signal in accordance with formula

(9.14), and similarly for the evaluation of the quality of filtering. From (9.13) we have

$$\mathbf{M}\,[C(\alpha_0, \alpha) \mid y_a^t] = B_0^2 [1 - \sqrt{s_1^2(t) + c_1^2(t)}];$$

$$\mathbf{M} C(\alpha_0, \alpha) = B_0^2 \mathbf{M} [1 - \sqrt{s_1^2(t) + c_1^2(t)}].$$

Thus knowing $s_1(t)$ and $c_1(t)$, we can judge the size of the average penalties.

9.4 Other Examples of Processes Having an Infinite Number of States

1. Let us assume now that the *a priori* process $\{x_t\}$ is a one-dimensional Markov process on a line and is described by the infinitesimal operator

$$dL_{pr}(t) = \left(\frac{b}{2} \frac{\partial^2}{\partial x^2} + a(x) \frac{\partial}{\partial x} \right) dt$$

(b a constant). We observe the sum of this and white noise, or, what is essentially the same, the observed process

$$y_1(t) = \int_{t_0}^{t} x(\tau)\, d\tau + \zeta(t), \tag{9.18}$$

where $\zeta(t)$ is a Wiener process: $\mathbf{M}\zeta = 0$; $\mathbf{M}\Delta\zeta^2 = N\Delta t$. Obviously the process (9.18) has a drift parameter $a_1 = x$ and local variance $b_{11} = N$.

Utilizing formulas (6.47) and (6.48) as we did in Sect. 9.3, as well as (3.71), we can find the *a posteriori* infinitesimal operators

$$dL^*(t) = dL_{pr}(t) + \frac{1}{N} x\, d^* y_1;$$

$$dL(t) = dL_{pr}(t) + \frac{1}{N} x\, dy_1 - \frac{1}{2N} x^2 dt.$$

Thus the basic equation (5.66) of optimal filtering, determining the *a posteriori* distribution density, has the form

$$dw_t(x) = \frac{1}{2} b\, dt \frac{\partial^2 w_t}{\partial x^2} - dt \frac{\partial}{\partial x} [a(x) w_t] + \frac{dy_1}{N} [x - \mathbf{M}_{ps} x] w_t -$$

$$- \frac{dt}{2N} [x^2 - \mathbf{M}_{ps} x^2] w_t, \tag{9.19}$$

or, more briefly,

$$\dot{w} = \frac{b}{2}\frac{\partial^2 w_t}{\partial x^2} - \frac{\partial}{\partial x}[a(x)w] + \frac{w}{N}\Big\{\dot{y}_1[x - \mathbf{M}_{ps}x] - $$
$$- \frac{1}{2}[x^2 - \mathbf{M}_{ps}x^2]\Big\}$$
$$\left(\mathbf{M}_{ps} \ldots = \int \ldots w(x)\,dx\right).$$

2. Let us examine a somewhat more complex case. Let the process $\{x(t)\}$ be the same as in the preceding section, but rather than observing the sum of the process and white noise, we will observe the sum

$$y(t) = x(t) + \xi(t)$$

of the process and an exponentially correlated Gaussian process $\xi(t)$ $(\mathbf{M}\xi(t) = 0;\ \mathbf{M}\xi(t)\xi(t+\tau) = \sigma^2 e^{-\beta|\tau|})$. The latter is Markov and is determined by the infinitesimal operator

$$(dL_{pr})_\xi = \beta\left(\sigma^2\frac{\partial^2}{\partial\xi^2} - \xi\frac{\partial}{\partial\xi}\right)dt$$

or by the equation

$$\beta^{-1}d\xi + \xi dt = d\zeta \tag{9.20}$$
$$\left(\mathbf{M}\zeta = 0;\ \mathbf{M}\Delta\zeta^2 = N\Delta t = 2\frac{\sigma^2}{\beta}\Delta t\right).$$

The two-dimensional process $(x(t), y(t))$ is naturally also Markov; it has parameters

$$a_x = a(x);\ a_y = a(x) - \beta\xi = a(x) - \beta(y - x);$$
$$\begin{pmatrix} b_{xx} & b_{xy} \\ b_{yx} & b_{yy} \end{pmatrix} = \begin{pmatrix} b & b \\ b & b + 2\beta\sigma^2 \end{pmatrix}.$$

We see that we are observing one component of a two-dimensional Markov process; thus this example relates to the conditional Markov process studied in Chapter 7. Further, it is a special case (where $a'(\xi) = -\beta\xi$ and b, b' are constant) of the first example in Sect. 7.3. Applying the formulas from there, we have

$$(b + 2\beta\sigma^2)\,dL(t) = b\beta\sigma^2 dt\frac{\partial^2}{\partial x^2} + [bdy + (2\beta\sigma^2 a(x) -$$
$$- b\beta x + b\beta y)\,dt]\frac{\partial}{\partial x} + (a(x) + \beta x - \beta y)\left[dy - \frac{1}{2}(a(x) + \right.$$
$$\left. + \beta x - \beta y)\,dt\right] - \frac{dt}{2}\left[b\frac{\partial a(x)}{\partial x} - 2\beta^2\sigma^2\right]$$

and

$$\dot{w} = \frac{b\beta\sigma^2}{b+2\beta\sigma^2}\frac{\partial^2 w}{\partial x^2} - \frac{\partial}{\partial x}\left[\left(\frac{b\dot{y}}{b+2\beta\sigma^2} + \right.\right.$$

$$\left.\left. + \beta\,\frac{2\sigma^2 a(x) - bx + by}{b+2\beta\sigma^2}\right) w\right] + [F - \mathbf{M}_{ps}F]\,w;$$

$$(b+2\beta\sigma^2)\,F = [a(x) + \beta x](\dot{y} + \beta y) - \frac{1}{2}[a(x)+\beta x]^2 -$$

$$-\frac{1}{2}\,b\,\frac{\partial a(x)}{\partial x}. \qquad (9.21)$$

It can be shown that Eq. (9.21) with probability 1 goes over to Eq. (9.19) if we pass to the limit as $\beta \to \infty$ in such a way that $2\sigma^2/\beta = N$ remains constant. In the process it is necessary to take into account that

$$\beta^{-1}dy + y\,dt = \beta^{-1}dx + x\,dt + \beta^{-1}d\xi + \xi\,dt$$

becomes the differential dy_1 of the process (9.18), since $\beta^{-1}dx + x\,dt$ becomes $x\,dt$, and the expression (9.20) is a differential of a Wiener process.

3. Either of Eqs. (9.19) or (9.21) can be written in the form

$$\dot{w}(x) = B\frac{\partial^2 w}{\partial x^2} - \frac{\partial}{\partial x}[G(x)\,w] + [F(x) - \mathbf{M}_{ps}F]\,w. \qquad (9.22)$$

We will choose the estimator $x_0(t) = d_t(y_a^t)$ of the signal ($d_t(\cdot)$ being the solution function) using the maximum-likelihood criterion, i.e., we will choose the "most probable" value. In this case it is convenient to assume

$$w_t(x) = \exp\left\{c(t) - \sum_{n=2}^{\infty}\frac{1}{n!}h_n(t)\,[x - x_0(t)]^n\right\} \qquad (9.23)$$

and to replace Eq. (9.22) by a system of equations for the parameters $x_0(t)$, $h_2(t)$, $h_3(t)$, ... Replacing (9.22) by the equation for $\ln w_t(x)$, inserting (9.23), and comparing terms of the expansion for various powers $(x - x_0)^n$, we get the system of equations

$$-h_2\dot{x}_0 = Bh_3 - G(x_0)\,h_2 + \frac{\partial^2 G}{\partial x^2}(x_0) - \frac{\partial F}{\partial x}(x_0);$$

$$\dot{h}_n - h_{n+1}\dot{x}_0 = Bh_{n+2} - B\sum_{k=1}^{n-1}\frac{n!}{k!\,(n-k)!}\,h_{k+1}h_{n-k+1} -$$

$$-\sum_{k=0}^{n-1}\frac{n!}{k!\,(n-k)!}\,\frac{\partial^k G}{\partial x^k}(x_0)\,h_{n-k+1} + \frac{\partial^{n+1}G}{\partial x^{n+1}}(x_0) - \frac{\partial^n F}{\partial x^n}(x_0), \qquad (9.24)$$

$$n \geqslant 2.$$

In the absence of initial information the initial values of the parameters h_n can be assumed to be zero: $h_2(t_0) = h_3(t_0) = \ldots = 0$.

The optimal filter operates in accordance with these equations and produces at the output an estimate, i.e., the filtered signal $x_0(t)$. As we can see from (9.22), this (for $h_2 > 0$) actually corresponds to the maximum of the function $w_t(x)$. The size of the second parameter $h_2(t)$ yields a measure of the quality of filtering indicating the degree of *a posteriori* precision.

9.5 Transition to Linear Filtering

1. As can be seen from the examples in Sects. 9.3 and 9.4, the basic equation of optimal filtering is often written for an infinite number of variables: a probability distribution density or a denumerable set of parameters replacing it. From the point of view of the practical realization of the filter, of course, it is desirable to have to deal with only a finite number of variables. This can be attained by "quantizing" the state space of the conditional process (replacing it by a space with a finite number of states) or by terminating the chain of equations of the type (9.17) or (9.24).

Of course, in general, these methods involve a deterioration of the quality of filtering. In certain specific cases, however, the equation for the distribution density can, without error, be replaced by an equation in a finite number of variables equivalent to it in precision. This is valid when the *a posteriori* density distribution is exactly Gaussian.

Let us examine the multidimensional analog of Eq. (9.22), having the form

$$\dot{w}(x) = \frac{\partial^2}{\partial x_\alpha \partial x_\beta}[B_{\alpha\beta}(x)w] - \frac{\partial}{\partial x_\alpha}[G_\alpha(x)w] + [F(x) - \mathbf{M}_{ps}F]w, \quad (9.25)$$

where $B_{\alpha\beta}(x)$, $G_\alpha(x)$, $F(x)$ are certain functions of t and a point $x = (x_1, \ldots, x_r)$ of an r-dimensional space R_r, defined by the theory of conditional Markov processes. Equations of a similar type are obtained, in particular, in those cases examined in Chapter 7 and at the end of Chapter 6 (if $\alpha(t)$ is a diffusion process).

Let us formulate the conditions under which the *a posteriori* density $w_t(x)$ will be Gaussian if the initial density $w_{t_0}(x)$ is Gaussian.

9.1.A. The elements of matrix $B_{\alpha\beta}$ are constant (independent of x).
9.1.B. The functions $G_\alpha(x) = g_\alpha + G_{\alpha\beta}x_\beta$ depend linearly on x.
9.1.C. The function $F(x) = f + F_\alpha x_\alpha + \frac{1}{2}F_{\alpha\beta}x_\alpha x_\beta$ depends on x linearly and quadratically.

Then, substituting

$$w_t(x) = \exp\left\{c(t) - \frac{1}{2}\sum_{\alpha,\beta} h_{\alpha\beta}(x_\alpha - m_\alpha)(x_\beta - m_\beta)\right\} \tag{9.26}$$

into (9.25), in analogy with (9.24), we obtain the equation

$$h_{\alpha\beta}[\dot{m}_\beta - G_\beta(m)] = \frac{\partial F}{\partial x_\alpha}(m);$$

$$\dot{h}_{\alpha\beta} = -2h_{\alpha\gamma}B_{\gamma\delta}h_{\delta\beta} - h_{\alpha\gamma}G_{\gamma\beta} - h_{\beta\gamma}G_{\gamma\alpha} - F_{\alpha\beta}. \tag{9.27}$$

To these equations correspond the initial conditions

$$m_\alpha(t_0) = \overset{\circ}{m}_\alpha; \; h_{\alpha\beta}(t_0) = \overset{\circ}{h}_{\alpha\beta},$$

where $\overset{\circ}{m}_\alpha$, $\overset{\circ}{h}_{\alpha\beta}$ are the parameters of an initial Gaussian distribution;

$$w_{t_0}(x) = \text{const} \exp\left\{-\frac{1}{2}\overset{\circ}{h}_{\alpha\beta}(x_\alpha - \overset{\circ}{m}_\alpha)(x_\beta - \overset{\circ}{m}_\beta)\right\}.$$

Introducing the inverse matrix

$$\| k_{\alpha\beta} \| = \| h_{\alpha\beta} \|^{-1},$$

Eqs. (9.27) can be transformed to the form

$$\dot{m}_\alpha = G_\alpha(m) + k_{\alpha\beta}\frac{\partial F}{\partial x_\beta}(m) = g_\alpha + k_{\alpha\beta}F_\beta + (G_{\alpha\gamma} + k_{\alpha\beta}F_{\beta\gamma})\, m_\gamma;$$

$$\dot{k}_{\alpha\beta} = 2B_{\alpha\beta} + G_{\alpha\gamma}k_{\gamma\beta} + G_{\beta\gamma}k_{\gamma\alpha} + k_{\alpha\gamma}F_{\gamma\delta}k_{\delta\beta}. \tag{9.28}$$

Usually, in the realization of requirements 9.1.A–C only the functions g_α, F_α turn out to be dependent on the observed process $\{y(t)\}$ (and linearly at that). Correspondingly, the filter equations (9.28) define a linear transformation of the observed signal $\{y(t)\}$ into the estimator $\{m(t)\}$. Thus in this case the equations define a linear optimal filter but, generally speaking, a nonstationary one.

2. Let us turn now to the examples of Sect. 9.4. Conditions 9.1.A–C will be satisfied for Eqs. (9.19) and (9.21) if $a(x)$ is a linear function, say, $a(x) = \nu - \gamma x$. Then in (9.22) we have for the case (9.19)

$$B = \frac{1}{2}b; \; G(x) = \nu - \gamma x; \; F = \frac{1}{N}\left(x\dot{y} - \frac{1}{2}x^2\right)$$

and Eqs. (9.28) take the form

$$\dot{m} = \nu - \gamma m + \frac{k}{N}(\dot{y}_1 - m);$$
$$\dot{k} + 2\gamma k = b - \frac{k^2}{N} \quad (m \equiv x_\circ). \tag{9.29}$$

Let us turn to the other example, i.e., to Eq. (9.21). For it

$$B = \frac{b\beta\sigma^2}{b + 2\beta\sigma^2}; \; G(x) = \frac{2\beta\sigma^2\nu + b(\dot{y} + \beta y) - \beta(b + 2\gamma\sigma^2)x}{b + 2\beta\sigma^2};$$

$$F = f + \frac{(\beta - \gamma)(\dot{y} + \beta y - \nu)x - \frac{1}{2}(\beta - \gamma)^2 x^2}{b + 2\beta\sigma^2}.$$

Thus the filter equations (9.28) yield

$$\dot{m} = -\frac{\beta + 2\gamma\sigma^2}{\beta + 2\beta\sigma^2} m + \frac{2\beta\sigma^2\nu + b(\dot{y} + \beta y)}{\beta + 2\beta\sigma^2} +$$
$$+ k\frac{\beta - \gamma}{\beta + 2\beta\sigma^2}[\dot{y} + \beta y - \nu - (\beta - \gamma)m]; \tag{9.30}$$
$$\dot{k} = \frac{2b\beta\sigma^2}{b + 2\beta\sigma^2} - 2\frac{b + 2\gamma\sigma^2}{b + 2\beta\sigma^2}\beta k - \frac{(\beta - \gamma)^2}{b + 2\beta\sigma^2}k^2.$$

Of special interest is the case of stationary filtering, in which the process parameters do not depend on time and the time at which filtering begins is the distant past: $t - t_0 \to \infty$. Then the *a posteriori* variance k is constant and can be found from the filter equations by setting the derivative $\dot{k}$ equal to zero. Solving the resulting quadratic equation, we find that for cases (9.29) and (9.30) the stationary variances are, respectively,

$$k = \sqrt{\gamma^2 N^2 + Nb} - \gamma N;$$
$$k = (\beta - \gamma)^{-2}[\sqrt{(b + 2\gamma\sigma^2)^2\beta^2 + 2b\beta\sigma^2(\beta - \gamma)^2} - (b + 2\gamma\sigma^2)\beta]. \tag{9.31}$$

The solution to the filtering problem resulting from this stationary approximation can also be obtained using the Wiener theory of linear filtering. However, the manner of solution presented here, explicitly using the Markov properties of the processes, requires fewer calculations. Even more important are the advantages of this method in the treatment of the case of nonstationary filtering. Formulas (9.28) also give the solution of the problem for a finite operation time $t - t_0$ and for process parameters changing in time.

3. Let us examine an important case of a multidimensional conditional Markov process for which requirements 9.1.A–C are satisfied. Namely, let us assume that we have an $(m + l)$-dimensional diffusion process $\{z_j\}$ and that we are observing l of its components, as in Chapter 7. But, in addition to this, let us assume that the

local variances b_{jk} are independent of z, that the drifts are linearly dependent

$$a_j(z, t) = \nu_j + d_{jk} z_k, \quad j = 1, \ldots, m + l$$

and that $c = 0$ (we can assume, of course, $c = c_0 + c_j z_j + \frac{1}{2} c_{jk} z_j z_k$, but from a practical point of view this is of little interest).

In order to write the *a posteriori* infinitesimal operator and Eq. (9.25) for this case, we need only make use of formulas (7.16) and (7.19). With the above assumptions a number of terms in these formulas disappear and we have

$$\begin{aligned}
2B_{\alpha\beta} &= b_{\alpha\beta} - b_{\alpha\sigma'} b^{-1}_{\sigma'\rho'} b_{\rho'\beta}; \\
G_\alpha(x) &= a_\alpha(x, y, t) + b_{\alpha\rho'} b^{-1}_{\rho'\sigma'} [\dot{y}_{\sigma'} - a_{\sigma'}(x, y, t)] = \\
&= \nu_\alpha + d_{\alpha\pi} y_\pi + b_{\alpha\rho'} b^{-1}_{\rho'\sigma'} (\dot{y}_{\sigma'} - \nu_{\sigma'} - d_{\sigma'\pi} y_\pi) + \\
&\quad + (d_{\alpha\beta} - b_{\alpha\rho'} b^{-1}_{\rho'\sigma'} d_{\sigma'\beta}) x_\beta, \qquad (9.32) \\
F(x) &= -\frac{1}{2} b_{j\rho'} b^{-1}_{\rho'\sigma'} d_{\sigma' j} + (\nu_{\rho'} + d_{\rho'\pi} y_\pi + d_{\rho'\alpha} x_\alpha) b^{-1}_{\rho'\sigma'} (\dot{y}_{\sigma'} - \\
&\quad - \frac{1}{2} \nu_{\sigma'} - \frac{1}{2} d_{\sigma'\rho} y_\rho - \frac{1}{2} d_{\sigma'\beta} x_\beta).
\end{aligned}$$

Conditions 9.1.A–C are satisfied, the *a posteriori* distribution density is Gaussian, and we can write without difficulty Eqs. (9.28) for its parameters:

$$\begin{aligned}
\dot{m}_\alpha &= G_\alpha(m) + [\dot{y}_{\sigma'} - a_{\sigma'}(m, y, t)] b^{-1}_{\sigma'\rho'} d_{\rho'\beta} k_{\beta\alpha} = \\
&= a_\alpha(m, y, t) + [\dot{y}_{\sigma'} - a_{\sigma'}(m, y, t)] b^{-1}_{\sigma'\rho'} [b_{\rho'\alpha} + d_{\rho'\beta} k_{\beta\alpha}]; \\
\dot{k}_{\alpha\beta} &= 2B_{\alpha\beta} + (d_{\alpha\gamma} - b_{\alpha\rho'} b^{-1}_{\rho'\sigma'} d_{\sigma'\gamma}) k_{\gamma\beta} + \\
&\quad + (d_{\beta\gamma} - b_{\beta\rho'} b^{-1}_{\rho'\sigma'} d_{\sigma'\gamma}) k_{\gamma\alpha} - k_{\alpha\gamma} d_{\rho'\gamma} b^{-1}_{\rho'\sigma'} d_{\sigma'\delta} k_{\delta\beta}. \qquad (9.33)
\end{aligned}$$

The earlier equations (9.30) are special cases of these formulas.

The observed coordinates $\{y_\rho\}$ and the *a posteriori* probability distribution $w_t(x)$ of the remaining coordinates form in combination, according to Theorem 5.9, a secondary Markov process. Since the *a posteriori* distribution $w_t(x)$ is defined by the parameters $\{m_\alpha\}$, $\{k_{\alpha\beta}\}$, where the variation of the parameter $k_{\alpha\beta}(t)$ is nonrandom and can be calculated in advance, it is convenient to substitute for $w_t(x)$ the *a posteriori* means $\{m_\alpha\}$. Then there will remain only the variables $\{m_\alpha, y_\rho\}$, which in combination will compose the secondary *a posteriori* Markov process. To these variables correspond, as can be seen from (9.33), the secondary *a posteriori* infinitesimal operator

$$\frac{d\mathscr{L}}{dt} = a_\alpha(m, y, t)\frac{\partial}{\partial m_\alpha} + a_\rho(m, y, t)\frac{\partial}{\partial y_\rho} +$$
$$+\frac{1}{2}(b_{\rho'\alpha} + d_{\rho'\gamma}k_{\gamma\alpha})\, b^{-1}_{\rho'\sigma'}(b_{\sigma'\beta} + d_{\sigma'\delta}k_{\delta\beta})\frac{\partial^2}{\partial x_\alpha \partial x_\beta} +$$
$$+ b_{\pi\sigma'}b^{-1}_{\sigma'\rho'}(b_{\rho'\alpha} + d_{\rho'\beta}k_{\beta\alpha})\frac{\partial^2}{\partial x_\alpha \partial y_\pi} + \frac{1}{2} b_{\pi\rho}\frac{\partial^2}{\partial y_\pi \partial y_\rho} \tag{9.34}$$

(the functions $k_{\alpha\beta}(t)$ are assumed known).

The secondary Markov process $\{m_\alpha, y_\rho\}$ occurs in the same $(m+l)$-dimensional space as the *a priori* process $z = \{x_\alpha, y_\rho\}$.

9.6 Comparison of the Effectiveness of Linear and Nonlinear Filtering for One Example

In this section we will examine the nonlinear and linear filtering of a Markov pulsed signal having two states $\eta(t) = \pm 1$, combined with white noise, and using the mean-square criterion. The *a priori* probabilities $\mathrm{P}\{\eta(t) = \pm 1\} = p_{1,2}$, let us say, satisfy the equation

$$\dot{p}_1 = -\dot{p}_2 = -\mu p_1 + \nu p_2, \tag{9.35}$$

where μ and ν are constant. We observe the process

$$y(t) = \int_a^t \eta(\tau)\, d\tau + \zeta(t) \tag{9.36}$$

($\zeta(t)$ being a Wiener process; $\mathbf{M}\zeta = 0$; $\mathbf{M}\Delta\zeta^2 = N\Delta t$).

1. Nonlinear filtering. This example is a particular case of the process with a finite number of states examined in Chapter 6 and Sect. 9.2. The basic equation of the nonlinear filter has the form (6.43), where now $y_\rho = y$, $a_\rho(1) = 1$; $a_\rho(2) = -1$, $b_{\rho\sigma} = N$. If we introduce the notation $w_1 - w_2 = z$, this equation will take the form

$$\dot{z} = \nu - \mu - (\mu + \nu) z + N^{-1}(1 - z^2)\dot{y}. \tag{9.37}$$

This shows the transformations which must be carried out on $\{y(t)\}$ to obtain $\{z(t)\}$, and thus the *a posteriori* probabilities $w_{1,2} = \frac{1 \pm z}{2}$.

Let $u(t) = \eta_0(t)$ be the estimator of the signal $\eta(t)$ corresponding to the mean-square quality criterion. Then obviously

$$\eta_0(t) = \mathbf{M}[\eta(t) \mid y_a^t] = z(t) \tag{9.38}$$

and the average penalty per unit time is

$$r_{\text{nonlin.}} = \mathbf{M}\{[\eta(t) - \eta_0(t)]^2\} = \mathbf{MM}\{[\eta(t) - \eta_0(t)]^2 \mid y_a^t\} =$$
$$= \mathbf{M}[1 - z^2(t)]. \tag{9.39}$$

Formulas (9.37) and (9.38) give in this case the solution of the nonlinear filtering problem without prediction or lag [case (9.5)]. For completeness we will also give the solution of the problem with prediction or lag, i.e., we will show a method of finding the estimators $\mathrm{M}[\eta(\tau) \mid y_a^t]$, $\tau > t$ and $\mathrm{M}[\eta(\sigma) \mid y_a^t]$, $\sigma < t$.

The solution of Eqs. (9.6) and (9.35) with the initial condition $p_{1,2}(t) = w_{1,2}(t)$ in this case is found without difficulty. It has the form

$$\mathbf{M}[\eta(\tau) \mid y_a^t] = \frac{\nu - \mu}{\mu + \nu} + \left[z(t) - \frac{\nu - \mu}{\mu + \nu}\right] e^{-(\mu+\nu)(\tau - t)}, \quad \tau > t.$$

Further, in the other case $\sigma < t$, applying formula (9.7), we have

$$\mathbf{P}\{\eta(\sigma) = 1 \mid y_a^t\} = \frac{1 + z(\sigma)}{2} \widetilde{V}_\sigma^t(1, \Omega); \tag{9.40}$$

$$\mathbf{P}\{\eta(\sigma) = -1 \mid y_a^t\} = \frac{1 - z(\sigma)}{2} \widetilde{V}_\sigma^t(-1, \Omega). \tag{9.41}$$

If we designate

$$\widetilde{V}_s^t(1, \Omega) - \widetilde{V}_s^t(-1, \Omega) = v(s)$$

and use the fact that the sum of the expressions (9.40) and (9.41) is equal to unity:

$$\frac{1}{2}\left[\widetilde{V}_s^t(1, \Omega) + \widetilde{V}_s^t(-1, \Omega)\right] + \frac{1}{2} z(s) v(s) = 1,$$

we will have

$$\widetilde{V}_s^t(\pm 1, \Omega) = 1 - \frac{1}{2} z(s) v(s) \pm \frac{1}{2} v(s)$$

and thus

$$\mathbf{M}[\eta(\sigma) \mid y_a^t] = \frac{1 + z(\sigma)}{2} \widetilde{V}_\sigma^t(1, \Omega) - \frac{1 - z(\sigma)}{2} \widetilde{V}_\sigma^t(-1, \Omega) =$$
$$= z(\sigma) + \frac{1}{2} v(\sigma)[1 - z^2(\sigma)]. \tag{9.42}$$

The function $z(\sigma)$ entering into this is defined by Eq. (9.37), and for the function $v(s)$, from (6.44) we obtain the equation

$$-\dot{v}(s) = -(\mu + \nu)\, v(s) + \frac{2}{N}\,[1 - z(s)\, v(s)]\, \dot{y}(s) \quad (s \leqslant t)$$

having a reverse flow of time and an "initial" condition

$$v(t) = 0.$$

It is also possible to use the equation written immediately in terms of the variable $x(\sigma) = p_1(\sigma) - p_2(\sigma)$, which results from the above equations, or more simply, from Eq. (6.45a). It has the form

$$\dot{x}(s) = -\mu\, \frac{(1-x)(1+z)}{1-z} + \nu\, \frac{(1+x)(1-z)}{1+z}$$

and is completed by the "initial" condition $x(t) = z(t)$.

The quality of the estimator $\mathbf{M}[\eta(\sigma) \mid y_a^t] = x(\sigma)$ (9.42) under the least squares criterion is given by the formula

$$\mathbf{M}\{[\eta(\sigma) - \eta_0(\sigma)]^2 \mid y_a^t\} = 1 - \left\{z(\sigma) + \frac{1}{2}\, v(\sigma)\,[1 - z^2(\sigma)]\right\}^2 = 1 - x^2(\sigma).$$

We return now to filtering (9.38) without prediction or lag. We will calculate the average penalty (9.39) per unit time for the steady-state stationary mode of filtering.

Equation (9.37) defines the process $\{z(t)\}$ as a certain "secondary" *a posteriori* Markov process. In the stationary mode of filtering it is stationary. If by $p_{st}(z)$ we designate the stationary one-dimensional probability distribution density of this process, then the average penalty (9.39), obviously, can be written

$$r_{\text{nonlin.}} = \int_{-1}^{1} (1 - z^2)\, p_{st}(z)\, dz. \tag{9.43}$$

Let us find the stationary density $p_{st}(z)$. As noted in Chapter 6, the "secondary" *a posteriori* process $\{w_1, y\}$ corresponds to the infinitesimal operator (6.46), having in this case the form

$$\frac{d\mathcal{L}}{dt} = (\nu w_2 - \mu w_1)\, \frac{\partial}{\partial w_1} + (w_1 - w_2)\, \frac{\partial}{\partial y} + \frac{2}{N}\, w_1^2 w_2^2\, \frac{\partial^2}{\partial w_1^2} +$$
$$+ 2 w_1 w_2\, \frac{\partial^2}{\partial w_1\, \partial y} + \frac{N}{2}\, \frac{\partial^2}{\partial y^2} \quad (w_2 = 1 - w_1).$$

In view of the fact that the coefficients $\nu w_2 - \mu w_1$, $\frac{2}{N}\, w_1^2 w_2^2$ do not depend on y, the one-dimensional process $\{w_1\}$ is itself Markov and has, evidently, the infinitesimal operator

$$\frac{d\mathscr{L}'}{dt} = (\nu w_2 - \mu w_1)\frac{\partial}{\partial w_1} + \frac{2}{N} w_1^2 w_2^2 \frac{\partial^2}{\partial w_1^2}. \tag{9.44}$$

Carrying out the change of variable $z = w_1 - w_2 = 2w_1 - 1$, it is not difficult to find that in this case to Eq. (9.37) corresponds the infinitesimal operator

$$\frac{d\mathscr{L}_z}{dt} = \frac{1}{2N}(1 - z^2)^2 \frac{\partial^2}{\partial z^2} + [\nu - \mu - (\mu + \nu) z] \frac{\partial}{\partial z}$$

of the process $\{z(t)\}$. Writing the Fokker-Planck equation

$$\dot{p}(z) = \frac{1}{2N} \frac{\partial^2}{\partial z^2} [(1 - z^2)^2 p(z)] - \frac{\partial}{\partial z} \{[\nu - \mu - (\mu + \nu) z] p(z)\}$$

and setting to zero the derivative $\dot{p}_{st} = 0$, in the usual way we obtain the stationary distribution density

$$p_{st}(z)\, dz = \frac{\text{const}}{(1 - z^2)^2} \exp\left\{2N \int^z [\nu - \mu - (\mu + \nu) x] \frac{dx}{(1 - x^2)^2}\right\} dz. \tag{9.45}$$

It is convenient to introduce a new variable φ using the formula

$$\frac{1}{1 - z^2} = \cosh^2 \frac{\varphi}{2} = \frac{1}{2}(1 + \cosh \varphi).$$

Then the stationary distribution (9.45) will have the form

$$p_{st}(\varphi)\, d\varphi = \text{const}(\cosh \varphi + 1) \exp\left\{\frac{N}{2}(\nu - \mu)(\sinh \varphi + \varphi) - \frac{N}{2}(\mu + \nu)\cosh \varphi\right\} d\varphi.$$

Using (9.43) and evaluating the resulting integrals using the familar formula 6.444.1 of the handbook by I. S. Gradshteyn and I. M. Ryzhik [1], we find

$$r_{\text{nonlin.}} = \mathbf{M}(1 - z^2) = \frac{4K_q(N\sqrt{\mu\nu})}{2K_q(N\sqrt{\mu\nu}) + \sqrt{\frac{\nu}{\mu}} K_{q+1}(N\sqrt{\mu\nu}) + \sqrt{\frac{\mu}{\nu}} K_{1-q}(N\sqrt{\mu\nu})} \tag{9.46}$$

$$\left(q = \frac{1}{2} N(\nu - \mu)\right).$$

In the symmetric case $\mu = \nu$ we have

$$r_{\text{nonlin.}} = \frac{2K_0(\mu N)}{K_0(\mu N) + K_1(\mu N)}. \tag{9.47}$$

For small arguments $\mu N \ll 1$ this function is determined by the approximate formula

$$r_{\text{nonlin.}} = 2\mu N \ln \frac{2}{\gamma \mu N} + O\left[\left(\mu N \ln \frac{1}{\mu N}\right)^2\right], \quad \gamma = 1.781\ldots. \tag{9.48}$$

With further increase in the argument μN it increases to unity.

2. **Linear filtering.** For linear filtering the optimal transformation $\eta_0(t) = d_t(y_a^t)$ is sought in the class of linear transformations. As before, we take the mean-square criterion of optimality. The optimal transformation can be found by solving the corresponding regression equation. Only the correlation functions of the signals $\eta(t)$, $y(t)$ enter into this equation. In the present case, as we can easily see, the correlation functions have the form

$$\begin{gathered} k_{\eta\eta}(\tau) = \frac{4\mu\nu}{(\mu+\nu)^2} e^{-(\mu+\nu)|\tau|}; \quad k_{\eta\dot{y}}(\tau) = k_{\eta\eta}(\tau); \\ k_{\dot{y}\dot{y}}(\tau) = k_{\eta\eta}(\tau) + N\delta(\tau). \end{gathered} \tag{9.49}$$

The regression equation in this non-Gaussian case coincides with the equation for Gaussian processes $\eta(t)$, $y(t)$ having the same correlation functions. Thus the optimal linear transformation is the same as the optimal linear transformation for Gaussian processes. Hence in order to find the optimal linear transformation, we can assume that the processes $\eta(t)$, $y(t)$ are Gaussian and have correlation function (9.49). Since such processes are Markov, we can again apply the theory of conditional Markov processes, but this time in the form presented in Sect. 9.5.

Thus we will consider that $\{\eta(t)\}$ is a Gauss-Markov process with correlation functions (9.49), i.e., a process corresponding to the infinitesimal operator

$$dL_{pr} = \left[\frac{4\mu\nu}{\mu+\nu} \frac{\partial^2}{\partial\eta^2} - (\mu+\nu)\eta \frac{\partial}{\partial\eta}\right] dt.$$

We observe the combination (9.36) of the process with white noise. This case was already studied in paragraph 1, Sect. 9.4 and in paragraph 2, Sect. 9.5. According to (9.29), the optimal linear transformation has the form

$$\dot{\eta}_0 + (\mu+\nu)\eta_0 + \frac{k}{N}\eta_0 = \frac{k}{N} y, \tag{9.50}$$

where

$$\dot{k} + 2(\mu+\nu)k = \frac{8\mu\nu}{\mu+\nu} - \frac{k^2}{N}.$$

In the stationary case the *a posteriori* variance $k(t)$ takes on its stationary value

$$k = k_{st} = \sqrt{(\mu+\nu)^2 N^2 + \frac{8\mu\nu N}{\mu+\nu}} - (\mu+\nu) N \qquad (9.51)$$

[see (9.31)].

It can easily be seen that the average penalty $M\{[\eta(t) - \eta_0(t)]^2 \, y_a^t\}$ per unit time is the same as for Gaussian processes having the *a posteriori* variance $k(t)$. Since this is not random, the second averaging does not introduce any changes and

$$r_{\text{lin.}} = \mathbf{M}[\eta(t) - \eta_0(t)]^2 = \sqrt{(\mu+\nu)^2 N^2 + \frac{8\mu\nu N}{\mu+\nu}} - (\mu+\nu) N. \qquad (9.52)$$

A similar average penalty is also valid for a reference non-Gaussian process, for it has the same second moments.

It is understood that the results (9.50) and (9.51) can also be obtained from the Wiener theory.

3. Let us compare the errors (9.46) and (9.52) of linear and nonlinear filtering. Since in nonlinear filtering the class of transformations from which the optimal is chosen is not restricted by anything, while in linear filtering it is restricted to linear transformations, nonlinear filtering necessarily is not worse than linear, and thus $r_{\text{nonlin.}} \leqslant r_{\text{lin.}}$. Of interest, nevertheless, is the question of how much smaller $r_{\text{nonlin.}}$ is than $r_{\text{lin.}}$.

Confining ourselves to the symmetric case $\mu = \nu$, for linear filtering [in contrast to formula (9.47)] from (9.52) we have

$$r_{\text{lin.}} = 2\sqrt{\mu^2 N^2 + \mu N} - 2\mu N;$$

in particular,

$$r_{\text{lin.}} = 2\sqrt{\mu N} + O(\mu N)$$

for $\mu N \ll 1$. Comparison of this expression with (9.48) yields

$$\frac{r_{\text{nonlin.}}}{r_{\text{lin.}}} = \sqrt{\mu N} \ln \frac{2}{\gamma \mu N} \left[1 + O\left((\mu N)^{1/2}\right)\right].$$

Thus

$$\frac{r_{\text{nonlin.}}}{r_{\text{lin.}}} \to 0 \quad \text{as} \quad \mu N \to 0,$$

i.e., for small errors the effectiveness of nonlinear filtering is considerably higher than that of linear.

CHAPTER 10

Problems of Optimal Process Termination

We will examine a somewhat more general controlled process, namely, the case of a terminating process. Let us now assume that in addition to finding estimator solutions (filtering), we must find the optimal instant of process termination. In this formulation, the theory presented in the present chapter is, on the one hand, a generalization of the theory of optimal filtering presented in Chapter 9, and, on the other, a generalization of the sequential analysis of Wald [1]. The generalization proceeds from two viewpoints. In the first, we consider the case of continuous time and calculate the corresponding differential equations for the risks. In the second, we carry out a synthesis of sequential analysis and optimal filtering (finding estimator solutions in the course of the process and at the instant of its termination). These generalizations are carried out by the author in [15].

Differential equations for risks in continuous time applicable to the problem of Wald are considered by Mikhalevich [1, 2]. From the point of view of the present theory, the problem studied by Wald and Mikhalevich is degenerate, since *a priori* transitions are absent (see Supplement, p. 320). If such transitions are permitted, the solution of these problems will become more difficult, and it will not be easy to do without the theory of conditional Markov processes.

In Sect. 10.6, as an example we will study the problem of finding the optimal termination of a process with two states. We permit transitions between them. The solution is carried out using the theory of conditional Markov processes and as a result we find the risk function and the boundary of the region of termination for various values of the parameters of the problem. Since this problem is a generalization of the problem of Wald, the results obtained, if we exclude *a priori* changes of the state, go over to the corresponding results of Wald and Mikhalevich and the results of the Supplement.

In addition, the problem considered in Sect. 10.6 in a second case (when we have one-way changes of state) becomes a Bayesian variant of the problem of Kolmogorov and Shiryayev, presented by them at the Sixth All-Union Conference on the Theory of Probability and Mathematical Statistics (Vilnius, 1960). The non-Bayesian solution of this problem, obtained without the use of recursive differential equations for the risks, is published in the papers of Shiryayev [1–3]. The Bayesian solution (expected risk and boundaries of regions of termination, as functions of the parameters of the problem) was found by Stratonovich [15]. It is presented in paragraph 4 of the Supplement. These results, of course, are obtained as special cases of the results of Sect. 10.6.

10.1 Presentation of the Problem. Penalty Function

Let us designate by $\vartheta \in [a, b]$ the instant of termination of the process. Let the penalty function have the form

$$c(\omega) = \int_a^\vartheta dt \int_{\tau<t} C_{t\tau}(u_{t\tau}, z_\tau) F_\tau(d\tau) + \int_{\tau<\vartheta} C'_{\vartheta\tau}(u'_{\vartheta\tau}, z_\tau) F'_\vartheta(d\tau). \qquad (10.1)$$

Here $C_{t\tau}(u_{t\tau}, z_\tau)$, $F_t(d\tau)$ have the same meaning as in formula (9.1). The function $C'_{t\tau}(u'_{t\tau}, z_\tau)$ and the measure $F'_t(d\tau)$ have an analogous meaning: $C'_{t\tau}(u'_{t\tau}, z_\tau)$ is a function of $u'_{t\tau}$ and z_τ, and $F'_\vartheta(d\tau)$ is a measure of the Borel sets of a certain (in general depending on ϑ) subset of the interval $[a, \vartheta]$. The conditions of measurability and integrability are assumed to be satisfied.

The estimators $u_{t\tau}$, $u'_{\vartheta\tau}$ of the control are assumed to be uncoupled (Sect. 8.1), i.e., assumed to be independent choices of the estimators. In order to bring this problem into the form considered in Sect. 8.1, in place of the time instant Θ we will consider the step function

$$\bar{u}_t = \begin{cases} 1 & \text{for } t \leqslant \vartheta; \\ 0 & \text{for } t > \vartheta \end{cases} \qquad (10.2)$$

as a component of the control u_t. The penalty function (10.1) obviously can be written in this case as

$$c(\omega) = \int_T dt\, \bar{u}_t \int C_{t\tau}(u_{t\tau}, z_\tau) F_t(d\tau) - \int_T d\bar{u}_t \int C'_{t\tau}(u'_{t\tau}, z_\tau) F'_t(d\tau). \quad (10.3)$$

Let us set up a control in this problem corresponding to the concept of control in Sect. 8.1. If the control is considered to be continued in the interval $[\vartheta, b]$, then clearly we can assume

$$u_t = \begin{cases} \bar{u}_t, u_{t\cdot} & \text{for } \bar{u}_t = 1, \ \bar{u}_{t+0} = 1; \\ \bar{u}_t, u'_{t\cdot} & \text{for } \bar{u}_t = 1, \ \bar{u}_{t+0} = 0; \\ \bar{u}_t & \text{for } \bar{u}_t = 0. \end{cases} \tag{10.4}$$

Here and subsequently a point is written in place of the second index τ, and indicates that it runs through all possible values. Such a control is coupled. If $\bar{u}_r = 1$, then the control u_r^s $(r<s)$ can be either a function

$$\{u_{t\cdot}, t \in [r, s]\}$$

(if the process does not terminate on $[r, s]$), or a triplet

$$\vartheta, \ \{u_{t\cdot}, t \in [r, \vartheta)\}, \ u'_\vartheta$$

(if the process terminates at an instant $\vartheta \in [r, s]$). If, however, $\bar{u}_r = 0$, no freedom remains in the choice of control. Turning to Definition 8.1, we see that the present control process is a Markov coupled process, and further is a simple degenerate case of such a process. The role of the Markov coordinate is played by the function (10.2): $\tilde{u}_t = \bar{u}_t$.

The basic process $\{z_t\}$ enters into expressions (10.1) and (10.3). The conditions imposed on z_s^t determine the σ-algebra $\mathcal{Z}_s^t$, which we assume does not depend on u and z_a^s. Fixing the control u_a^s assigns the probabilities $\mathbf{P}(\Lambda \mid u_a^s)$ of the events $\Lambda \in \mathcal{A}^s(u_a^s)$ coupled by this process. Here we can proceed in two ways. We can assume that the process $\{z_t\}$ actually terminates and consider that $\mathcal{A}^s = \mathcal{Z}_a^{\min(s, \vartheta)}$. Or we can consider that the process $\{z_t\}$ does not terminate, but stop all contact with it. Then we can assume $\mathcal{A}^s \supset \mathcal{Z}^b$, as was done in Chapter 9, and remove the limits $\tau < t$ and $\tau < \vartheta$ in formula (10.1). Let us stop with this variant, in which the events $\Lambda \in \mathcal{Z}^t$ $(t > \vartheta)$ have a hypothetical character. The measure will be assumed to be independent of the control: $\mathbf{P}(\Lambda \mid u_a^s) = \mathbf{P}(\Lambda)$, $\Lambda \in \mathcal{Z}^b$. From this it follows that in this chapter we are not considering problems related to dynamic programming, in which the choice of control intrinsically influences the flow of the basic process.

The observed process $\{y_t\}$ is assumed to depend on the value of the basic process at the same instant of time: $y_t = y_t(z_t)$, so that $\mathcal{Y}^t \subset \mathcal{Z}^t$. We take the solution index of most interest in practice, $\varphi(t) = t$.

10.2 Sufficient Coordinates and Conditional Risks

In accordance with Definition 8.5, in addition to the penalty function (10.3), we will consider functions of "past penalties"

$$c^t(\omega) = \int_a^t d\bar{u}_t \int C_{t\tau}(u_{t\tau}, z_\tau) F_t(d\tau) - \int_a^t d\bar{u}_t \int C'_{t\tau}(u'_{t\tau}, z_t) F'_t(d\tau)$$

$$(c^b(\omega) = c(\omega)). \tag{10.5}$$

We will introduce the sufficient coordinates for this problem.

The basic process $\{z_t\}$ will be assumed Markov. Thus the theory developed in paragraph 2, Sect. 8.7 can be applied to the problem under examination, taking into account that the control (10.4) is Markov coupled. We will check that conditions 8.10.A–E are satisfied. That (8.64) is satisfied was noted earlier. In addition to this, it was pointed out that $\mathcal{Z}_s^t(u, z_a^s)$ does not depend on u, z_a^s. This is a stronger condition than (8.65). Since the measure $\mathbf{P}$ on $\mathcal{Z}^b$ does not depend on the control, the Markov condition

$$\mathbf{P}(\Lambda \mid \mathcal{Z}_a^s) = \mathbf{P}(\Lambda \mid \mathcal{Z}_s), \quad \Lambda \in \mathcal{Z}_s^b$$

similarly is stronger than 8.10.C. Condition 8.10.D is satisfied since the observed process $y_t = y_t(z_t)$ does not depend on u. It remains to check 8.10.E. In order for the difference

$$c^s - c^r = \int_r^s d\bar{u}_t \int C_{t\tau}(u_{t\tau}, z_\tau) F_t(d\tau) - \int_r^s d\bar{u}_t \int C'_{t\tau}(u'_{t\tau}, z_\tau) F'_t(d\tau)$$

to be $\mathcal{U}_r^s \mathcal{Z}_r^b$-measurable, it is clearly sufficient for each measure $F_t(\Gamma)$ and $F'_t(\Gamma)$ to vanish on sets $\Gamma \subset [a, t)$. We assume that this condition holds true. In particular, it is valid in the important case when the measure F_t and the measure F'_t have the form (9.5).

As a result of these conditions we can apply Theorem 8.11, which states that we can use the *a posteriori* probabilities W_t (or parameters replacing them) and the coordinate $\bar{u}_t$ as sufficient coordinates. The latter takes one of the two values 1 or 0; thus the reduced conditional risk $S_t(\omega \mid \mathcal{X}_t) = S_t(\bar{u}_t, W_t)$ is in this case a pair of functions

$$S_t(1, W_t), \; S_t(0, W_t).$$

It is not difficult to write the recursive relations (8.38) for the reduced conditional risks. Substituting the index $\varphi(t) = t$ in place of the stepwise approximation

$$\varphi^N(t) = t_k \quad \text{for} \quad t \in [t_k, t_{k+1})$$
$$(t_{k+1} - t_k < \Delta)$$

from (8.39) we have

$$S_{t_k}(\bar{u}_{t_k}, W_{t_k}) = \min_{u_t^{t_{k+1}} | \bar{u}_{t_k}, W_{t_k}} \mathbf{M}[c^{t_{k+1}} - c^{t_k} +$$

$$+ S_{t_{k+1}}(\bar{u}_{t_{k+1}}, W_{t_{k+1}}) | \bar{u}_{t_k} u_{t_k}^{t_{k+1}}, W_{t_k}]. \qquad (10.6)$$

For $\bar{u}_{t_k} = 0$ there is no choice and

$$S_{t_k}(0, W_{t_k}) = \mathbf{M}[c - c^t | \tilde{u}_{t_k} = 0, W_{t_k}] = 0,$$

since from (10.5) $c - c^t = 0$ for $t > \vartheta$.

For $\bar{u}_{t_k} = 1$, minimization with respect to $u_{t_k}^{t_{k+1}}$ will be carried out in two steps: first we will minimize over $\{u_{t\cdot}, t \in [t_k, t_{k+1}]\} \cap [t_k, \vartheta)\}$ and u'_ϑ where the function $\bar{u}_{t_k}^{t_{k+1}}$ is fixed, and then over $\bar{u}_{t_k}^{t_{k+1}}$, i.e., over $\vartheta\ (\geqslant t_k)$. In the first stage of the minimization, it is clear that we have

$$\min_{u_{t_k}^{t_{k+1}} | \bar{u}_{t_k}^{t_{k+1}}} \mathbf{M}(c^{t_{k+1}} - c^{t_k} | 1, u_{t_k}^{t_{k+1}}, W_{t_k}] =$$

$$= \int_{t_k}^{t_{k+1}} s_t^\Delta \bar{u}_t \, dt - \int_{t_k}^{t_{k+1}} s_t'^\Delta \, d\bar{u}_t, \qquad (10.7)$$

where

$$s_t^\Delta = \int \min_{u_{t\tau}} \mathbf{M}[C_{t\tau}(u_{t\tau}, z_\tau) | W_{t_k}] F_t(d\tau);$$

$$s_t'^\Delta = \int \min_{u'_{t\tau}} \mathbf{M}[C'_{t\tau}(u'_{t\tau}, z_\tau) | W_{t_k}] F'_t(d\tau). \qquad (10.8)$$

Substituting (10.7) into (10.6), for $u_{t_k} = 1$ we obtain

$$S_{t_k}(1, W_{t_k}) = \min\Big\{\min_{t_k \leqslant \vartheta < t_{k+1}} \Big[\int_{t_k}^{\vartheta} s_t^\Delta \, dt + s_\vartheta'^\Delta,$$

$$\int_{t_k}^{t_{k+1}} s_t^\Delta \, dt + \mathbf{M}[S_{t_{k+1}}(1, W_{t_{k+1}}) | W_{t_k}\Big]\Big\}. \qquad (10.9)$$

For brevity in the formulas it is convenient to assume $s_t^\Delta dt + ds_t'^\Delta \geqslant 0$ for all t, whence (10.9) takes the form

$$S_{t_k}(1, W_{t_k}) = \min\Big\{s'_{t_k}(W_{t_k}), \int_{t_k}^{t_{k+1}} s_t^\Delta \, dt + \mathbf{M}[S_{t_{k+1}}(1, W_{t_{k+1}}) | W_{t_k}]\Big\}. \qquad (10.10)$$

Here $s_{t_k}^{'\Delta}$ is written $s'_{t_k}(W_{t_k})$ in accordance with the notation

$$s_t(W_t) = \int \min_{u_{t\tau}} \mathbf{M}[C_{t\tau}(u_{t\tau}, z_\tau) \mid W_t] F_t(d\tau);$$

$$s'_t(W_t) = \int \min_{u'_{t\tau}} \mathbf{M}[C'_{t\tau}(u'_{t\tau}, z_\tau) \mid W_t] F'_t(d\tau). \tag{10.11}$$

It is assumed that as a result of the minimization with respect to the estimator controls u_t and u'_t in (10.8) and (10.11), we obtain measurable and integrable functions, which can easily be checked in specific problems. Since

$$\mathbf{M}[C_{t\tau}(u_{t\tau}, z_\tau) \mid W_{t_k}] = \mathbf{M}[C_{t\tau}(u_{t\tau}, z_\tau) \mid W_t] + o(1)$$

and

$$s_t^\Delta = \mathbf{M}[s_t(W_t) \mid W_{t_k}] + o(1); \; o(1) \to 0 \text{ as } t - t_k \to 0 \text{ (a.c.)},$$

in (10.10) we can replace s_t^Δ by s_t. This yields

$$S_{t_k}(1, W_{t_k}) = \min\left\{s'_{t_k}(W_{t_k}), \mathbf{M}\left[\int_{t_k}^{t_{k+1}} s_t(W_t)\,dt + \right.\right.$$
$$\left.\left. + S_{t_{k+1}}(1, W_{t_{k+1}}) \mid W_{t_k}\right]\right\} + o(t_{k+1} - t_k). \tag{10.12}$$

In accordance with (10.1) and (10.5), to these recursion relations we need to add the "initial" condition: $S_b(1, W) = s'_b(W)$.

10.3 Passage to a Continuous Index. Differential Equation for the Risks

In order to carry out the passage to the limit of a continuous index $\varphi^N(t) \to t$, $\Delta \to 0$, and to prove that the results do not depend on a particular choice of Δ-division $\{t_1, \ldots, t_N\}$, it is convenient to use the concept of regular spaces D_t^0, $t \in T$, introduced in paragraph 4 of Sect. 8.6. If $S_b(1, W_b) \in D_b^0$, then instead of the sequence of conditional risks

$$S_b(1, W), \; S_{t_N}(1, W), \; S_{t_{N-1}}(1, W), \ldots,$$

determined by formula (10.12), we can consider the sequence of functions

$$S_b(1, W), \; \widetilde{S}_{t_N}(1, W), \; \widetilde{S}_{t_{N-1}}(1, W), \ldots,$$

belonging to regions of regularity: $\widetilde{S}_{t_k}(1, W) \in \overset{\circ}{D}_{t_k}$. These functions, from Definition 8.8, are coupled corresponding to (8.53) as

$$\widetilde{S}_{t_k}(1, W) = \min \left\{ s'_{t_k}(W), \mathbf{M}\left[\int_{t_k}^{t_{k+1}} s_t(W_t)\, dt \mid W_{t_k} = W \right] + \right.$$
$$\left. + T_{t_k t_{k+1}} \widetilde{S}_{t_{k+1}}(1, W) \right\} + o(\Delta), \tag{10.13}$$

by analogy to (10.12), which can also be written in the form (8.54):

$$\widetilde{S}_{t_k}(1, W) - \widetilde{S}_{t_{k+1}}(1, W) = \psi_{t_{k+1}}(W, \widetilde{S}_{t_{k+1}})(t_{k+1} - t_k) + o(\Delta).$$

Here $\psi_{t_{k+1}}$ is a function not depending on Δ, equal on the strength of (8.55) and (10.13) in the limit to

$$\psi_t(W, \widetilde{S}_t) = \lim_{\Delta \to 0} \Delta^{-1} \left\{ \min \left[s'_{t-\Delta}, \mathbf{M}\left[\int_{t-\Delta}^{t} s_\tau\, d\tau \mid W_{t-\Delta} = W \right] + \right. \right.$$
$$\left. \left. + T_{t-\Delta, t} \widetilde{S}_t \right] - \widetilde{S}_t \right\} = \lim_{\Delta \to 0} \min \left\{ \frac{s'_{t-\Delta} - \widetilde{S}_t}{\Delta}, \mathbf{M}\left[\frac{1}{\Delta} \int_{t-\Delta}^{t} s_\tau\, d\tau \mid W \right] + \right.$$
$$\left. + \frac{T_{t-\Delta, t} - 1}{\Delta} \widetilde{S}_t \right\}. \tag{10.14}$$

Application of Theorem 8.9 provides a complete basis for the passage to the limit $\varphi^N(t) \to t$, $\Delta \to 0$. According to this the resulting reduced risk, as a function of continuous time, satisfies the equation

$$-\frac{\partial S_t(W)}{\partial t} = \psi_t(W, S_t(W)) \quad (S_t(W) \equiv S_t(1, W)). \tag{10.15}$$

The existence of the limit (10.14) results from the existence of regular spaces. Let us assume that the function s_t is continuous, so that

$$\mathbf{M}\left[\frac{1}{\Delta} \int_{t-\Delta}^{t} s_\tau\, d\tau \mid W_{t-\Delta} = W \right] = s_t(W) + o(1). \tag{10.16}$$

In the minimization in (10.14), two values, which we will call for brevity A and B, are compared. We will consider the region Ξ_1 (in the space of *a posteriori* probabilities W) where

$$\lim_{\Delta \to 0} \min [A, B] = \lim_{\Delta \to 0} B. \tag{10.17}$$

Analogously we define a second region

$$\Xi_2 = \{W : \lim_{\Delta\to 0} \min [A, B] = \lim_{\Delta\to 0} A\}. \tag{10.18}$$

From the existence of the limit (10.14) there follows the existence of the limit

$$\lim_{\Delta\to 0}\left\{\mathbf{M}\left[\frac{1}{\Delta}\int_{t-\Delta}^{t} s_\tau\, d\tau \mid W\right] + \frac{T_{t-\Delta,t}\widetilde{S}_t - \widetilde{S}_t}{\Delta}\right\}$$

in the region Ξ_1. Since from (10.16) we have

$$\lim_{\Delta\to 0}\mathbf{M}\left[\frac{1}{\Delta}\int_{t-\Delta}^{t} s_\tau\, d\tau \mid W\right] = s_t(W),$$

the limit

$$\lim_{\Delta\to 0}\Delta^{-1}[T_{t-\Delta,t}\widetilde{S}_t - \widetilde{S}_t] = A_t\widetilde{S}_t, \tag{10.19}$$

exists in Ξ_1, and thus

$$\varphi_t(W, \widetilde{S}_t) = s_t(W) + (A_t\widetilde{S}_t)(W) \quad \text{in} \quad \Xi_1.$$

Analogously we can prove the existence of the limit

$$\lim_{\Delta\to 0}\frac{s'_{t-\Delta} - S_t}{\Delta} \equiv -\ddot{s}'_t(W) \quad \text{in} \quad \Xi_2. \tag{10.20}$$

It can be called $\dot{s}'_t(W)$. Equation (10.15) takes the form

$$-\frac{\partial S_t(W)}{\partial t} = \begin{cases} s_t(W) + (A_t S_t)(W) & \text{in} \quad \Xi_1; \\ -\ddot{s}'_t(W) & \text{in} \quad \Xi_2. \end{cases} \tag{10.21}$$

The operator A_t entering into (10.19) and (10.21) is nothing other than the secondary *a posteriori* operator

$$A_t = \frac{d\,\mathscr{L}(t)}{dt}, \tag{10.22}$$

i.e., the infinitesimal operator of the secondary Markov process $\{w_t\}$ (see paragraph 2, Sect. 5.6).

As can be seen from (10.13), the reduced risk $S_t(W)$ cannot exceed $s'_t(W)$. Thus, the space of conditional probabilities W can be partitioned into two regions:

$$\Xi = \{W : S_t(W) < s_t'(W)\}$$

and

$$\Xi^c = \{W : S_t(W) = s_t'(W)\}.$$

Turning to the definition (10.17) of region Ξ_1, we can easily see that the region Ξ belongs to Ξ_1 if s_t' is a continuous function of t. In the following we will make the stronger assumption that s_t' is a differentiable function of t.

From the definition (10.18) of region Ξ_2, taking into account (10.14) and (10.20), we can show that $\Xi_2 \subset \Xi^c$. But once $\widetilde{S}_t = s_t'$ in Ξ_2, the limit in (10.20) is nothing other than a partial derivative with respect to time:

$$\ddot{s}_t(W) = \frac{\partial s_t'(W)}{\partial t}.$$

We will give an additional form of Eq. (10.15). We will denote by H the region in which the limit (10.19) exists (obviously $\Xi_1 \subset H$). In the region Ξ^c the expression (10.14) can be written

$$\psi_t(W, S_t) = \lim_{\Delta \to 0} \min \left\{ -\frac{\partial s_t'}{\partial t} + o(1),\ s_t + o(1) + \frac{T_{t-\Delta,t} - 1}{\Delta} S_t \right\}.$$

Thus in the region $\Xi^c H$, after passing to the limit as $\Delta \to 0$, we will have

$$-\frac{\partial S_t}{\partial t} = \min \left\{ -\frac{ds_t'}{\partial t},\ s_t + A_t S_t \right\} \quad (W \in \Xi^c H).$$

If

$$\ddot{s}_t + s_t + A_t S_t < 0, \tag{10.23}$$

then a point of the region $\Xi^c H$ belongs to Ξ_1, and if

$$\ddot{s}_t + s_t + A_t S_t > 0, \tag{10.24}$$

then it belongs to Ξ_2.

Now we can describe the functions making up the regular space. They have the following properties.

10.1.A. If $g \in D_t^0$, then $g \leqslant s_t'$, where $g(W) = s_t'(W)$ in its region Ξ_2.

10.1.B. For $g \in D_t^0$ there exists a limit of the type (10.19) in the region Ξ_1.

In addition, the conditions of continuity of the functions belonging to the region of regularity are usually satisfied.

10.1.C. If

$$s_t'(W) \text{ u } T_{t-\Delta,t}g \equiv g_\Delta \quad (\Delta > 0, \quad g \in D_t^0) \tag{10.25}$$

are continuous functions of W, then the functions $g(W)$ and $\psi(W, g)$ are continuous.

Proof. of 10.1.C. We will write (10.13) in the form

$$D_{t-\Delta}^0 \ni g_\Delta' = \min\{s_{t-\Delta}', \ s_{t-\Delta}\Delta + g_\Delta\} + o(\Delta).$$

From this we have

$$g_\Delta' = \widetilde{g}_\Delta + O(\Delta), \tag{10.26}$$

where by $\widetilde{g}_\Delta$ we mean the function

$$\widetilde{g}_\Delta = \min[s_{t-\Delta}', g_\Delta],$$

which is continuous as a result of the continuity of the functions (10.25). Comparison of (10.26) with the equation $g_\Delta' - g = O(\Delta)$, which follows from (8.54), yields

$$\widetilde{g}_\Delta - g = O(\Delta). \tag{10.27}$$

Since the estimate $O(\Delta)$ is uniform here, from the continuity of $\widetilde{g}_\Delta$ there follows the continuity of the function g.

Thus g is continuous when $g \in D_t^0$. Consequently, g_Δ' is continuous for any given $\Delta > 0$, since $g_\Delta' \in D_{t-\Delta}^0$. From this follows the continuity of the function $(g_\Delta' - g)/\Delta$ for any $\Delta > 0$. But as we can see from (8.54),

$$\frac{g_\Delta' - g}{\Delta} - \psi_t(W, g) = o(1).$$

This relation proves the continuity of the function $\psi_t(W, g)$, by analogy to the manner in which (10.27) proved the continuity of g.

Corollary to 10.1.C. Using the continuity with respect to W of the function $\psi(W, S)$, we can obtain a certain relation valid at all points W^Γ which belong to both the closure of region Ξ_1 and the closure of region Ξ_2. Choosing a sequence of points from Ξ_1 converging to W^Γ, and a sequence of points from Ξ_2 converging to the same limit, and taking into account that for both sequences the same limit

$$\lim_{W \to W^\Gamma} \psi(W, S) = \psi(W^\Gamma, S),$$

is valid, we obtain

$$\lim_{\Xi_1 \ni W \to W^\Gamma} [s_t(W) + A_t S_t] = \lim_{\Xi_2 \ni W \to W^\Gamma} \left[-\frac{\partial s_t'}{\partial t}(W) \right].$$

If the functions $s_t(W)$, $\frac{\partial s_t'}{\partial t}(W)$ are continuous with respect to W, then as a result

$$\frac{\partial s_t'}{\partial t}(W^\Gamma) + s_t(W^\Gamma) + \lim_{\Xi_1 \in W \to W^\Gamma} A_t S_t = 0.$$

10.4 One-Dimensional Case

Let us dwell in somewhat more detail on the simple special case when the space of *a posteriori* probabilities W is reduced to the one-dimensional space R_1. By x we will denote the coordinate of the latter. We will assume that the secondary Markov process $\{x_t\}$ is diffusional and that to it there corresponds an infinitesimal operator (10.22) of the following simple form:

$$A_t = \frac{1}{2} \frac{\partial^2}{\partial x^2}$$

(the diffusion coefficient is constant).

Certain more complex one-dimensional cases can be reduced to this using a change of the variable x. Let us assume that $s_t'(x)$, $s_t(x)$ are continuously differentiable functions of both variables, and in addition that $s_t'(x)$ is twice differentiable with respect to x. For later convenience we will assume that the condition

$$\frac{\partial s_t'(x)}{\partial t} + s_t(x) + \frac{1}{2} \frac{\partial^2 s_t'(x)}{\partial x^2} > 0 \tag{10.29}$$

is satisfied.

If $S_\sigma(x) \in D_\sigma^0$, for some $\sigma \in [a, b]$, then $S_t(x) \in D_t^0$ for earlier instants of time $t < \sigma$. We will examine what form the regions Ξ_1, Ξ_2 [generally speaking, depending on time: $\Xi_1 = \Xi_1(t)$, $\Xi_2 = \Xi_2(t)$] take in this case.

Since in $\Xi^c \supset \Xi_2$ the function $S_t(x)$ coincides with s_t', on the strength of the double differentiability of the latter the limit

$$\lim_{\Delta\to 0}\frac{T_{t-\Delta,t}-I}{\Delta}S_t(x)=\lim_{\Delta\to 0}\frac{T_{t-\Delta,t}-I}{\Delta}s_t'(x)=\frac{1}{2}\frac{\partial^2 s_t'(x)}{\partial x^2}$$

exists, at least at all interior points of the region Ξ^c (i.e., for $W \in \mathrm{Int}\,\Xi^c$). The condition (10.24) at these points takes the form

$$\frac{\partial s_t'}{\partial t}+s_t+\frac{1}{2}\frac{\partial^2 s_t'}{\partial x^2}>0.$$

From (10.29) it follows that this is satisfied at all points $\mathrm{Int}\,\Xi^c$, so that

$$\mathrm{Int}\,\Xi^c \subset \Xi_2.$$

In Sect. 10.3 it was remarked that

$$\Xi \subset \Xi_1, \tag{10.30}$$

thus we need to examine the points of the "boundary"

$$\Gamma = R_1 - \Xi - \mathrm{Int}\,\Xi^c.$$

We will use the continuity of $\psi_t(x, S_t)$ which was discussed in 10.1.C (the continuity of the function (10.25) in this case is obviously valid).

At a point x^Γ belonging to the closure of the region Ξ and to the closure of region $\mathrm{Int}\,\Xi^c$, we can carry out a passage to the limit in two ways: remaining within the boundaries of the one, or of the other, region. Since

$$\psi_t(x,S_t)=\begin{cases} s_t+\dfrac{1}{2}\dfrac{\partial^2 S_t}{\partial x^2} & \text{in } \mathrm{Int}\,\Xi, \\ -\dfrac{\partial s_t'}{\partial t} & \text{in } \Xi^c; \end{cases}$$

comparing the limits we obtain

$$\frac{\partial s_t'}{\partial t}(x^\Gamma)+s_t(x^\Gamma)+\frac{1}{2}\lim_{\Xi\ni x\to x^\Gamma}\frac{\partial^2 S_t}{\partial x^2}=0. \tag{10.31}$$

Let us assume, for example, that region Ξ lies to the right of the boundary point x^Γ, and Ξ^c to the left. Assuming that the function $S_t(x)$ can be expanded into a Taylor series in the indicated regions, we have

$$S_t(x)=s_t'(x^\Gamma)+S_1\cdot(x-x^\Gamma)+\frac{1}{2}S_2(x-x^\Gamma)^2+$$
$$+\frac{1}{6}S_3\,(x-x^\Gamma)^3+\ldots \text{ for } x>x^\Gamma;$$

$$S_t(x)=s_t'(x)=s_t'(x^\Gamma)+s_1'\cdot(x-x^\Gamma)+\frac{1}{2}s_2'(x-x^\Gamma)^2+$$
$$+\frac{1}{6}s_3'\,(x-x^\Gamma)^3+\ldots \text{ for } x<x^\Gamma.$$

Carrying out a term by term average, we find

$$(T_\Delta S_t)(x) = \frac{1}{\sqrt{2\pi\Delta}} \int e^{\frac{-(x-y)^2}{2\Delta}} S_t(y)\,dy = s_t'(x^\Gamma) +$$
$$+ \sqrt{\Delta}\, S_1 G_1\left(\frac{x-x^\Gamma}{\sqrt{\Delta}}\right) - \sqrt{\Delta}\, s_1' G_1\left(-\frac{x-x^\Gamma}{\sqrt{\Delta}}\right) +$$
$$+ \frac{\Delta}{2} S_2 G_2\left(\frac{x-x^\Gamma}{\sqrt{\Delta}}\right) + \frac{\Delta}{2} s_2' G_2\left(-\frac{x-x^\Gamma}{\sqrt{\Delta}}\right) + \ldots. \quad (10.32)$$

Here

$$G_n(\xi) = \frac{1}{\sqrt{2\pi}} \int_0^\infty e^{-\frac{(\xi-\eta)^2}{2}} \eta^n\,d\eta.$$

Expression (10.32) should be substituted into the recursion relation (10.13), which in this case has the form

$$\widetilde{S}_{t-\Delta}(x) = \min\left[s_t'(x) - \frac{\partial s_t'(x)}{\partial t}\Delta,\ s_t(x)\Delta + T_\Delta S_t\right] + o(\Delta). \quad (10.33)$$

Let us examine the boundary point x^Γ in order to determine whether it belongs to region Ξ_1 or to Ξ_2. Setting $x = x^\Gamma$ in (10.32), we get from (10.33)

$$\widetilde{S}_{t-\Delta}(x^\Gamma) = s_t'(x^\Gamma) + \min\left[-\frac{\partial s_t'}{\partial t}(x^\Gamma)\Delta,\ s_t(x^\Gamma)\Delta +\right.$$
$$\left. + \sqrt{\Delta}\, G_1(0)(S_1 - s_1') + \frac{\Delta}{2} G_2(0)(S_2 + s_2')\right] + o(\Delta). \quad (10.34)$$

The relation $\widetilde{S}_{t-\Delta} - S_t = O(\Delta)$ resulting from (8.54), written for the point x^Γ, thus leads to the condition

$$\min[0, S_1 - s_1'] = 0 \quad \left(S_1 = \frac{\partial S_t}{\partial x}(x^\Gamma + 0),\ s_1' = \frac{\partial s_t'}{\partial x}(x^\Gamma)\right). \quad (10.35)$$

But $s_1' \geqslant S_1$, since $s_t'(x) > S_t(x)$ for $x > x^\Gamma$ (i.e., in Ξ). Hence (10.35) yields the condition for continuity of the first derivative at the boundary point:

$$\lim_{\Xi \ni x \to x^\Gamma} \frac{\partial S_t(x)}{\partial x} = \frac{\partial s_t'}{\partial x}(x^\Gamma). \quad (10.36)$$

A similar condition for the problem of Wald for continuous time was apparently first obtained by Mikhalevich [2].

From (10.34) and (10.36) we have

$$\widetilde{S}_{t-\Delta}(x^{\Gamma}) = S_t(x^{\Gamma}) + \Delta \min\left[-\frac{\partial s_t'}{\partial t}(x^{\Gamma}),\ s_t(x^{\Gamma}) + \right.$$

$$\left. + \frac{1}{4}(S_2 + s_2')\right] + o(\Delta).$$

In order to determine which of the values in question here is larger, we will use relations (10.29) and (10.31). Having calculated half the sum of the expressions on the left sides of these, we get

$$\frac{\partial s_t'}{\partial t}(x^{\Gamma}) + s_t(x^{\Gamma}) + \frac{1}{4}(S_2 + s_2') > 0.$$

Thus

$$\widetilde{S}_{t-\Delta}(x^{\Gamma}) = S_t(x^{\Gamma}) - \Delta \frac{\partial s_t'}{\partial t}(x^{\Gamma}) + o(\Delta),$$

so that the point x^{Γ} belongs to the region Ξ_2 ($\Xi_1 = \Xi$, $\Xi_2 = \Xi^c$).

Using condition (10.36), we find the derivative

$$\frac{dx_t^{\Gamma}}{dt} = -\lim_{\Delta \to 0} \frac{x_{t-\Delta}^{\Gamma} - x_t^{\Gamma}}{\Delta} \tag{10.37}$$

of the quantity $x^{\Gamma} = x_t^{\Gamma}$ considered as a function of time. The indicated condition should be satisfied at the point (x_t^{Γ}, t) and at the point $(x_{t-\Delta}^{\Gamma},\ t-\Delta)$:

$$\frac{\partial s_t'}{\partial x}(x_t^{\Gamma}) = \frac{\partial S_t}{\partial x}(x_t^{\Gamma}+); \qquad \frac{\partial s_{t-\Delta}'}{\partial x}(x_{t-\Delta}^{\Gamma}) = \frac{\partial S_{t-\Delta}}{\partial x}(x_{t-\Delta}^{\Gamma}+). \tag{10.38}$$

Here $x_{\tau}^{\Gamma}+$ indicates the limit corresponding to region Ξ. Using the fact that for points of this region

$$S_{t-\Delta}(x) = S_t(x) + s_t(x)\Delta + \frac{\Delta}{2}\frac{\partial^2 S_t}{\partial x^2} + o(\Delta),$$

we have

$$\frac{\partial S_{t-\Delta}}{\partial x}(x_{t-\Delta}^{\Gamma}+) = \frac{\partial S_t}{\partial x}(x_{t-\Delta}^{\Gamma}+) + \Delta\frac{\partial s_t}{\partial x}(x_t^{\Gamma}+) +$$

$$+ \frac{\Delta}{2}\frac{\partial^3 S_t}{\partial x^3}(x_t^{\Gamma}+) + o(\Delta) = \frac{\partial S_t}{\partial x}(x_t^{\Gamma}+) +$$

$$+ \frac{\partial^2 S_t}{\partial x^2}(x_t^{\Gamma}+)(x_{t-\Delta}^{\Gamma} - x_t^{\Gamma}) + \Delta\frac{\partial s_t}{\partial x}(x_t^{\Gamma}+) +$$

$$+ \frac{\Delta}{2}\frac{\partial^3 S_t}{\partial x^3}(x_t^{\Gamma}+) + o(\Delta).$$

Assuming that the corresponding derivatives exist, in addition to this we have

$$\frac{\partial s'_{t-\Delta}}{\partial x}(x^{\Gamma}_{t-\Delta}) = \frac{\partial s'_t}{\partial x}(x^{\Gamma}_t) - \frac{\partial^2 s'_t}{\partial x\,\partial t}(x^{\Gamma}_t)\,\Delta + \frac{\partial^2 s'_t}{\partial x^2}(x^{\Gamma}_t)\,(x^{\Gamma}_{t-\Delta} - x^{\Gamma}_t) + o(\Delta).$$

Substituting these expressions into (10.38), we get

$$\left[\frac{\partial^2 s'_t}{\partial x^2}(x^{\Gamma}_t) - \frac{\partial^2 S_t}{\partial x^2}(x^{\Gamma}_t +)\right](x^{\Gamma}_{t-\Delta} - x^{\Gamma}_t) = \left[\frac{\partial^2 s'_t}{\partial x\,\partial t}(x^{\Gamma}_t) + \frac{\partial s_t}{\partial x}(x^{\Gamma}_t) + \frac{1}{2}\,\frac{\partial^3 S_t}{\partial x^3}(x^{\Gamma}_t +)\right]\Delta + o(\Delta).$$

Carrying out the passage to the limit (10.37), we finally get

$$\frac{dx^{\Gamma}_t}{\partial t} = -\left.\frac{\dfrac{\partial}{\partial x}\left(\dfrac{\partial s'_t}{\partial t} + s_t + \dfrac{1}{2}\,\dfrac{\partial^2 S_t}{\partial x^2}\right)}{\dfrac{\partial^2 s'_t}{\partial x^2} - \dfrac{\partial^2 S_t}{\partial x^2}}\right|_{x=x^{\Gamma}_t+}.$$

In concluding this section we will give a description of the regular spaces D^0_t, $t \in T$. In the case in question, the space D^0_t consists of functions $g(x)$:

(1) continuous and having a continuous first derivative [see 10.1.C and (10.36)],

(2) not exceeding $s'_t(x)$ [see 10.1.A],

(3) twice differentiable in the region

$$\Xi = \{x:\ g(x) < s'_t(x)\}$$

[see 10.1.B and (10.30)],

(4) satisfying on the boundary of the region Ξ the condition

$$\frac{\partial s'_t(x)}{\partial t} + s_t(x) + \frac{1}{2}\,\frac{\partial^2 S_t}{\partial x^2}(x+) = 0$$

[see (10.31)].

The necessity of these properties was argued previously, and the sufficiency can easily and immediately be checked.

The results obtained in this section can also be generalized to the case of a more complex operator (10.22)

10.5 Optimal Solutions

The general theory in Chapter 8 guarantees the existence of ε-optimal solutions. In the problems examined here we can show the existence of exact optimal solutions, i.e., solutions corresponding exactly to the optimal risk.

We will briefly describe these solutions. We will begin with the estimators

$$u_{t\tau} = d_{t\tau}(y_a^t) = d_{t\tau}(W_t); \quad u'_{t\tau} = d'_{t\tau}(y_\alpha^t) = d'_{t\tau}(W_t).$$

From formulas (10.11), we see that the optimal estimators are determined by the conditions

$$\min_{u_{t\tau}} \mathbf{M}[C_{t\tau}(u_{t\tau}, z_\tau) \mid W_t] = \mathbf{M}[C_{t\tau}(d_{t\tau}(W_t), z_\tau) \mid W_t];$$

$$\min_{u'_{t\tau}} \mathbf{M}[C'_{t\tau}(u'_{t\tau}, z_\tau) \mid W_t] = \mathbf{M}[C'_{t\tau}(d'_{t\tau}(W_t), z_\tau) \mid W_t].$$

These functions exist if the minimum (lower bound) is attained on the admissible set $U_{t\tau}$ (or $U'_{t\tau}$) of controls $u_{t\tau}$ (or $u'_{t\tau}$). The functions $d_{t\tau}$, $d'_{t\tau}$ here turn out to be $\mathcal{W}_t$-measurable (they depend on y_a^t only through W_t). The functions (10.11), important for the determination of the optimal instant of termination, obviously are equal to

$$s_t(W_t) = \int \mathbf{M}[C_{t\tau}(d_{t\tau}(W_t), z_\tau) \mid W_t] F_t(d\tau);$$

$$s'_t(W_t) = \int \mathbf{M}[C'_{t\tau}(d'_{t\tau}(W_t), z_\tau) \mid W_t] F'_t(d\tau).$$

Let us turn now to consideration of the solution $D(y) = \vartheta$, determining the instant ϑ of the termination of the process. For a fixed Δ-division $\{t_1, \ldots, t_N\}$ we clearly have the following rule for the optimal solution: the function $D^\Delta(y) = D^\Delta(W_a^b)$ is equal to that instant of time when the trajectory $W_a^b = \{W_t,\ t \in [a, b]\}$ first enters the set

$$\Phi^\Delta = \bigcup_k \{t, W : t = t_k, \quad W \in \Xi^c(t_k)\}.$$

In other words,

$$D^\Delta(W_a^b) = \min\{t : (t, W_t) \in \Phi^\Delta\}.$$

We will consider in addition

$$\Phi = \{t, W : t \in T,\ W \in \Xi^c(t)\}.$$

Of course, the set Φ is not the limit $\lim_{\Delta \to 0} \Phi^\Delta$, but if $\{W_t\}$ is a continuous function of time (for a fixed point ω), then, as can easily be seen,

$$\inf\{t:(t,W_t)\in\Phi\}=\lim_{\Delta\to 0}\min\{t:(t,W_t)\in\Phi^\Delta\}.$$

As the solution rule $D(W_a^b)$ we will choose the first instant of attaining the region of termination Φ:

$$D(W_a^b)=\inf\{t:(t,W_t)\in\Phi\}, \tag{10.39}$$

so that

$$D(W_a^b)=\lim_{\Delta\to 0}D^\Delta(W_a^b) \tag{10.40}$$

for a continuous trajectory W_a^b. But in the diffusional case the trajectory W_a^b is continuous with probability 1; hence relation (10.40) is true almost certainly.

The solutions $D^\Delta(W_a^b)$, $D(W_a^b)$ define risks

$$R^\Delta=\mathbf{M}\left[\int_0^{D^\Delta(W_a^b)}s_t(W_t)\,dt+s'_{D^\Delta(W_a^b)}\left(W_{D^\Delta(W_a^b)}\right)\right];$$

$$R^0=\mathbf{M}\left[\int_0^{D(W_a^b)}s_t(W_t)\,dt+s'_{D(W_a^b)}\left(W_{D(W_a^b)}\right)\right].$$

The convergence of (10.40), being valid with probability 1, allows the proof (assuming the functions $s'_t(w)$ are continuous with respect to t) of the relation

$$\lim_{\Delta\to 0}R^\Delta=R^0. \tag{10.41}$$

But from the recursion relations (10.12) and the general theory (Chapter 8) it follows that the limit

$$\lim_{\Delta\to 0}R^\Delta=R \tag{10.42}$$

is the optimal risk. Comparison of (10.41) and (10.42) brings us to the conclusion that the solution (10.40) is exactly optimal.

From the described method of constructing the solution rules $D(W_a^b), D^\Delta(W_a^b)$ there results the following property: if the trajectories W_a^b and $\widetilde{W}_a^b$ coincide on the interval $a\leqslant t\leqslant D(W_a^b)$, then

$$D(\widetilde{W}_a^b)=D(W_a^b)$$

(and analogously for D^Δ). Somewhat symbolically this property can be written

$$D(W_a^b)=D(W_a^D)=D(y_a^D).$$

10.6 Example. The Termination of a Markov Process with Two States

Let us consider as an example the problem of detecting and terminating a Markov process η_t having two states, described in Sects. 9.6 and 6.5. We observe the sum of this process and white noise or, equivalently, the process (9.36). In this case the basic Markov process is a combination of two processes: $z_t = (\eta_t, y_t)$.

Let us suppose that at the instant of termination we must estimate which state $\eta_t = \pm 1$ is realized. For a continuing process the estimation is not carried out. Then the estimating control $u_{t\tau}$ is absent and the function $u'_{t\tau}$ takes on one of two values, say, 1 or 2. The measures $F(d\tau), F'(d\tau)$, let us say, have the simple form (9.5), and the corresponding penalties

$$C_{tt}(u_{tt}, z_t) = \begin{cases} A_1 & \text{for} \quad \eta_t = 1; \\ A_2 & \text{for} \quad \eta_t = -1 \end{cases} \tag{10.43}$$

(depending in general on the state η_t) and the penalties for termination

$$C'_{tt}(u'_{tt} = i, z_t) = \begin{cases} B_{i1} & \text{for} \quad \eta_t = 1 \\ B_{i2} & \text{for} \quad \eta_t = -1 \end{cases} \quad (i = 1, 2) \tag{10.43a}$$

are constant.

A sufficient coordinate in this problem is the *a posteriori* probability w_1. Let us form the corresponding functions (10.11), which do not depend on time:

$$s_t(w_1) \equiv s(w_1) = A_1 w_1 + A_2 w_2 = A_2 + (A_1 - A_2) w_1;$$
$$s'_t(w_1) \equiv s'(w_1) = \min[B_{11} w_1 + B_{12} w_2, B_{21} w_1 + B_{22} w_2].$$

It is clear that the optimal estimator has the form

$$d'_{tt}(y_a^t) = d'_{tt}(w_1(t)) = \begin{cases} 1 & \text{for} \quad B_{1j} w_j(t) \leqslant B_{2j} w_j(t); \\ 2 & \text{for} \quad B_{1j} w_j(t) > B_{2j} w_j(t) \end{cases}$$

(we imply summation over j).

The optimal termination is accomplished at that instant in time when the trajectory $w_1(t)$ enters the "region of termination"

$$S_t(w_1) = s'(w_1).$$

The position of the region of termination in the (t, w_1) plane is determined at the same time as the reduced conditional risk $S_t(w_1)$

is found. It satisfies Eq. (10.21). The infinitesimal operator (10.22) corresponding to this case was found earlier [formula (9.44)].

Applying the theory of Sects. 8.6, 10.3, and 10.4, we find that if the function $S_t(w_1)$ belongs to the regular space D_t^0 for some $t=\tau$, the $S_t(w_1)$ belongs to the regular space D_t^0 for smaller times $t<\tau$. In the "region of continuation," where $S_t(w_1) < s'(w_1)$, it satisfies the equation

$$-\frac{\partial S_t}{\partial t} = \frac{2}{N} w_1^2 w_2^2 \frac{\partial^2 S_t}{\partial w_1^2} + (\nu w_2 - \mu w_1)\frac{\partial S_t}{\partial w_1} + A_1 w_1 + A_2 w_2. \quad (10.44)$$

On the boundary Γ of the region of termination the function and its first derivative are continuous:

$$S_t(w_1) = B_{11}w_1 + B_{12}w_2; \quad \frac{\partial S_t(w_1)}{\partial w_1} = B_{11} - B_{12} \quad (10.45)$$

for $w_1 \in \Gamma$ and $B_{1j}w_j < B_{2j}w_j$;

$$S_t(w_1) = B_{21}w_1 + B_{22}w_2; \quad \frac{\partial S_t(w_1)}{\partial w_1} = B_{21} - B_{22} \quad (10.46)$$

for $w_1 \in \Gamma$ and $B_{1j}w_j > B_{2j}w_j$.

In addition, on the boundary $\Gamma \ni w_1^\Gamma$ the condition

$$\frac{2}{N} w_1^{\Gamma^2} w_2^{\Gamma^2} \frac{\partial^2 S_t}{\partial w_1^2}(w_1^\Gamma +) + (\nu w_2^\Gamma - \mu w_1^\Gamma)\frac{\partial S_t}{\partial w_1}(w_1^\Gamma) + A_1 w_1^\Gamma + B_1 w_2^\Gamma = 0$$

$$(w_2^\Gamma = 1 - w_1^\Gamma)$$

is satisfied [see (10.31)].

The solution of Eq. (10.44) with the described boundary conditions and the defined "initial" condition

$$S_b(w_1) = f_0(w_1) \quad (10.47)$$

determines the function $S_t(w_1)$ and the boundaries of the region of termination.

Of great practical interest is the case in which the end point b is remote and the particular choice of terminal penalties (10.47) has only a slight effect. For this the length of time $b-t$ should considerably exceed the other time constants of the problem:

$$b - t \gg \frac{1}{\mu} + \frac{1}{\nu}, \quad b - t \gg N.$$

In fulfilling these conditions it is possible to consider the stationary solutions $S^0(w_1)$ of Eq. (10.44), for which $\frac{\partial S_t}{\partial t} = 0$.

Reasoning formally, in the selection of a certain terminal function $f_0(w_1)$ $(\in D^0)$ we assume that there exists a unique solution $S_t(w_1)$ of Eq. (10.44) having the described conditions and, in addition, that the limit

$$\lim_{b\to\infty} S_t(w_1) = S^0(w_1) \tag{10.48}$$

exists.

Then this limit must satisfy the equation

$$\frac{2}{N} w_1^2 w_2^2 \frac{d^2 S^0}{\partial w_1^2} + (\nu w_2 - \mu w_1) \frac{dS^0}{dw_1} + A_1 w_1 + A_2 w_2 = 0 \tag{10.49}$$

in the region of continuation where $S^0(w_1) < s'(w_1)$. On the boundary Γ it satisfies the conditions

$$S^0(w_1) = s'(w_1); \quad \frac{dS^0}{dw_1}(w_1) = \frac{ds'(w_1)}{dw_1}, \tag{10.50}$$

analogous to (10.45) and (10.46).

In Eq. (10.49) we will write $A_1 w_1 + A_2 w_2$ in the form

$$D + D'(\nu w_2 - \mu w_1),$$
$$D = \frac{A_2 - A_1}{\mu + \nu}; \quad D = \frac{\nu A_1 + \mu A_2}{\mu + \nu} \tag{10.51}$$

and introduce a function

$$e^{\varphi(w_1)} = \left(\frac{w_1}{w_2}\right)^{\frac{N}{2}(\nu-\mu)} \exp\left\{-\frac{N}{2}\left(\frac{\nu}{w_1} + \frac{\mu}{w_2}\right)\right\}, \tag{10.52}$$

such that

$$\frac{d\varphi(w_1)}{dw_1} = \frac{N}{2} \frac{\nu w_2 - \mu w_1}{w_1^2 w_2^2}.$$

Then (10.49) will take the form

$$\frac{d^2 S^0}{dw_1^2} + \frac{d\varphi}{dw_1}\frac{dS^0}{dw_1} + D'\frac{d\varphi}{dw_1} + \frac{1}{2}\frac{ND}{w_1^2 w_2^2} = 0.$$

Integrating this equation, we have

$$\frac{dS^0(w_1)}{dw_1} = -D' - \frac{1}{2} N D e^{-\varphi(w_1)} \int_{\frac{\nu}{\mu+\nu}}^{w_1} e^{\varphi(\xi)} \frac{d\xi}{\xi^2(1-\xi)^2} + C_1 e^{-\varphi(w_1)}. \tag{10.53}$$

A second integration yields

$$S^0(w_1) = -D'w_1 - \frac{1}{2} NDf_1(w_1) + C_1 f_2(w_1) + C_2.$$

Here

$$f_1(w_1) = \int_{\frac{\nu}{\mu+\nu}}^{w_1} dw e^{-\varphi(w)} \int_{\frac{\nu}{\mu+\nu}}^{w} e^{\varphi(\xi)} \frac{d\xi}{\xi^2(1-\xi)^2};$$

$$f_2(w_1) = \int_{\frac{\nu}{\mu+\nu}}^{w_1} e^{-\varphi(w)} dw; \tag{10.55}$$

C_1 and C_2 are constants of integration.

At points of the boundary Γ, according to (10.50), the graph of the function (10.54) touches the curve $S = s'(w_1)$, in other words, the curve

$$S = s'(w_1) + D'w_1 + \frac{1}{2} NDf_1(w_1) \equiv F(w_1) \tag{10.56}$$

touches the curve $S = C_1 f_2(w_1) + C_2$:

$$F(w_1) = C_1 f_2(w_1) + C_2; \quad \frac{dF}{dw_1}(w_1) = C_1 \frac{df_2}{dw_1}(w_1) \text{ for } w_1 \in \Gamma.$$

It is convenient to introduce a new variable $v = f_2(w_1)$ [we will denote the inverse function by ψ: $w_1 = \psi(v)$]. Then the curve $C_1 f_2(w_1) + C_2 = C_1 v + C_2$ becomes a straight line. According to the above, it should touch the curve $F(\psi(v))$ at points $w_1 \in \Gamma$. From this there results an effective method of finding points of the boundary Γ: it is necessary to construct the function $F(\psi(v))$ graphically, and, using the arbitrary constants C_1 and C_2, to draw a straight line touching the constructed curve at two points. If v' and v'' are two such points of contact and if on the entire interval $v' < v < v''$ the inequality

$$F(\psi(v)) > C_1 v + C_2, \text{ i.e., } s'(w_1) > S^0(w_1), \text{ for } w_1' = \psi(v') < w_1 < w_1'' = \psi(v''),$$

is true, then this interval will be the region of continuation and the points v', v'' (or w_1', w_1'') will form the boundary of the region of termination.

Let us assume that $D > 0$. This corresponds to the case of greatest practical interest in which the continuation of the observations requires certain expenditures. Qualitative analysis of the curve $F(\psi(v))$ shows that in this case there is always an interval of continuation of observations if the point of discontinuity of the function $s'(w_1)$ falls on the interval (0,1).

In certain cases the interval of continuation of observations is not bounded on both sides by points of termination.

It can adjoin the point $w_1=0$ (i.e., coincide with the interval $[0, w_1''))$, or the point $w_1=1$ (coincide with the interval $(w_1', 1])$.

Then instead of conditions (10.50), at the boundary point $w_1=0$ (or $w_1=1$), we need to use the trivial condition

$$\left|\frac{dS^0(w_1)}{dw_1}\right| < \infty \quad \text{for } w_1 = 0 \quad \text{(or 1).} \tag{10.57}$$

This determines the constant C_1 in expressions (10.53) and (10.54):

$$C_1 = -\frac{1}{2} ND \int_0^{\frac{\nu}{\mu+\nu}} e^{\varphi(\xi)} \frac{d\xi}{\xi^2(1-\xi)^2} \tag{10.58}$$

(for definiteness, in (10.57) we choose the point $w_1=0$), so that

$$\frac{dS^0(w_1)}{dw_1} = -D' - \frac{1}{2} NDe^{-\varphi(w_1)} \int_0^{w_1} e^{\varphi(\xi)} \frac{d\xi}{\xi^2(1-\xi)^2}.$$

The slope to be used in drawing the previously described straight line touching the curve $F(\psi(v))$ is now fixed. According to (10.56), (10.55), and (10.58), it coincides with the asymptotic slope of the curve $F(\psi(v))$:

$$\frac{dF}{dv} = e^{\varphi} \frac{dF}{dw_1} = \frac{1}{2} ND \int_{\frac{\nu}{\mu+\nu}}^{w_1} e^{\varphi(\xi)} \frac{d\xi}{\xi^2(1-\xi)^2} + o(1) \rightarrow C_1$$

as $v \rightarrow -\infty$ (i.e., as $w_1 \rightarrow 0$), since $e^{\varphi}\left(\frac{ds'}{dw_1} + D'\right) = o(1)$.

By a parallel shift of the straight line we find the tangent to the curve $F(\psi(v))$. This determines the point of tangency v''. If $F(\psi(v)) > C_1 v + C_2$ with $v < v''$ [i.e., with $w_1 < w_1'' = \psi(v'')$], then the interval $[0, w_1'')$ is an interval of continuation of observations. Analogously we construct the interval $(w_1', 0]$, if it exists.

With fixed values of the constants we can find only certain regions of continuation of the described types. In some specific cases it may happen that the regions of continuation do not exist. This means that for the given values of the constants the problem is posed incorrectly and the limit (10.48) does not exist.

Above it was assumed that $\mu > 0$, $\nu > 0$; however, the formulas obtained above are also applicable in the case when one or both of these values equals zero. In these cases the problem under consideration reduces to simpler problems, some of which are examined in the Supplement.

CHAPTER 11

Selection of Optimal Observation and Optimal Control of the Process

In this chapter we will examine more general problems than in the two preceding chapters: we will assume that the observed or controlled process intrinsically depends on the control selected. In Sect. 11.1 we will solve the problem of selecting an optimal observation. It is assumed that observation of the process is associated with definite losses so that it is profitable only in a threatening situation. The theory permits an answer to the question of when to make an observation and when not to.

The problems of Sects. 11.2 and 11.3 involve the choice of the optimal control. They pertain to dynamic programming in the case of continuous time. Similar problems often arise in the theory of automatic control in the presence of noise. A series of related problems was examined in the work of Stratonovich [18, 19], Stratonovich and Shmal'gauzen [1], and Shmal'gauzen [1].

The problems illustrate the application of the general methods of the theory of optimal control based on the theory of conditional Markov processes. The field of application of these methods is very broad. A condition necessary to ensure that the basic process is Markov is not very limiting. In fact, by increasing the number of components of the Markov process it is possible to find one such process which will approximate any process to within any previously assigned precision. This in effect removes some of the principal limits to the area of application of the methods.

It is true that the actual solution of the problems for a large number of sufficient coordinates becomes very time-consuming, and this creates practical limits to the field of applications. In the light of the above it is clear that the main difficulty with which we must deal in the examination of more and more complex problems is the increase of the number of sufficient coordinates. Such an increase is examined in a series of examples in Sect. 11.4.

11.1 Problems of Optimal Observation

In Chapter 9, which was devoted to the choice of optimal estimates, the behavior of the basic process z_t and of the observed process $y_t = y_t\ (z_t)$ is assumed to be independent of the obtained solutions. In terms of the σ-algebras introduced in Sect. 8.1, this is expressed by the fact that $\mathcal{A}^t(u)$ does not depend on u and for all $t \in T$ contains $\mathcal{Z}^b$; the σ-algebra of the observations $\mathcal{Y}^t(u)$ also does not depend on u and is contained in $\mathcal{Z}^t$.

The passage to a more general case will be accomplished if we assume that the observed process depends on the control: $y_t = y_t\ (z_t,\ u)$ or that the probabilities of the basic process depend on the control. The first case, in which $y_t\ (z_t, u)$ explicitly depends on u, but $\mathcal{A}^t \supset \mathcal{Z}^b$, $t \in T$, can be considered a case of controlled observation. The observer-operator here can select the optimal method of observation, but cannot influence the flow of the basic process: $\mathbf{P}\ (\Lambda \mid u) = \mathbf{P}\ (\Lambda),\ \Lambda \in \mathcal{Z}^b$.

The second case, in which the observer-operator can essentially influence the probabilities (and perhaps even the state space) of the basic process, i.e., in which $\mathcal{A}^t(u_a^t)$ includes $\mathcal{Z}^t(u)$, but is essentially less than $\mathcal{Z}^{t'}\ (u),\ t' > t$, relates to dynamic programming.

The general theory developed in Chapter 8 includes any of these cases. In this chapter we will examine both problems of choice of optimal observations and problems of dynamic programming.

The problems of optimal process termination discussed in Chapter 10 take an intermediate place between problems of selection of optimal estimates and problems of selection of optimal observation or control. The theory of Chapter 10 goes beyond the framework of optimal filtering since the observer-operator is in a position to influence the flow of the process. But this influence is of a very primitive sort: the intervention of the observer-operator can only halt the basic process or the process of observation. In the problems which will be examined subsequently, the inclusion of the observer-operator will have more significance.

1. Let $\{\eta_t\}$ be the Markov process with two states of which we spoke in Sects. 9.6 and 10.6. The value $\eta_t = 1$ can be interpreted as the presence of disorder in some industrial process at time t, and the value $\eta_t = -1$ as its absence. The disorder can come and go, as described by the coefficients ν, μ in Eq. (9.35) for the *a priori* probabilities. As earlier, let the observed process have the form (9.36), but now the observer-operator will determine whether it is necessary to make an observation or not. We will introduce a control function $\overline{\overline{u}}_t$ related to this determination: $\overline{\overline{u}}_t = 1$ if the observer makes an observation at time t, and $\overline{\overline{u}}_t = 0$ if not.

The advisability of ceasing the observation (under specific conditions) we explain by the fact that the observation is expensive, i.e., is associated with certain losses. In order to include this, we will supplement the penalties (10.43) by a term depending on $\bar{\bar{u}}_t$:

$$C_{tt} = G\bar{\bar{u}}_t + \begin{cases} A_1 & \text{for } \eta_t = 1; \\ A_2 & \text{for } \eta_t = -1. \end{cases} \tag{11.1}$$

In the presence of a disorder it is not economically advantageous to continue the production process. Thus the problem of the observer-operator is the termination of the process under appropriate conditions. In this respect this problem is analogous to the problems examined in Chapter 10, and we will continue to use the concepts and notations introduced there.

Let us assume that at the instant of termination $t = \vartheta$ we penalize only unjustified (erroneous) termination. This corresponds to penalties for termination more specific than (10.43a):

$$C'_{tt} = \begin{cases} 0 & \text{for } \eta_t = 1; \\ B & \text{for } \eta_t = -1. \end{cases} \tag{11.2}$$

Adding to $\bar{\bar{u}}_t$ the step function (10.2), we see that in this problem the role of the control process u_t is played by the pair $(\bar{\bar{u}}_t, \bar{u}_t)$, or what is the same, the pair $(\bar{\bar{u}}_t \bar{u}_t, \bar{u}_t)$. Taking into account the above penalties (11.1) and (11.2), we write the penalty function (10.5) as

$$c^t(\omega) = \int_a^t \left[A_1 \frac{1+\eta_s}{2} + A_2 \frac{1-\eta_s}{2} + G\bar{\bar{u}}_s \right] \bar{u}_s \, ds - \int_a^t B \frac{1-\eta_s}{2} \, d\bar{u}_s. \tag{11.3}$$

Let us introduce the sufficient coordinates for this problem and examine the corresponding recursion relation (8.39) [for $\varphi_k = t_k$]. As in Chapter 10, sufficient coordinates are (according to Theorem 8.11) the quantity $\bar{u}_t$ and the *a posteriori* probability

$$w_1(t) = \mathbf{P}[\eta_t = 1 \mid y_\tau, \ \tau \in J_t], \tag{11.4}$$

where

$$J_t = [a, t] \cap \{s : \bar{\bar{u}}_s = 1\}.$$

It is desirable to restrict ourselves to functions $\{\bar{\bar{u}}_t, t \in T\}$ which are Borel measurable. Then the integral $G\int \bar{\bar{u}}_s \bar{u}_s ds$ in (11.3) will exist. In addition, the set J_t will be taken as the union of at most a denumerable number of disjoint intervals:

$$J_t = \bigcup_j [\tau'_j, \tau''_j].$$

On each interval (τ'_j, τ''_j) the *a posteriori* probability $w_1(\tau)$ as a function of τ satisfies Eq. (6.43), which takes the form

$$\frac{dw_1(\tau)}{d\tau} = \nu w_2 - \mu w_1 + \frac{2}{N} w_1 w_2 \frac{dy}{d\tau}, \tag{11.5}$$

while on each interval (τ''_j, τ'_{j+1}) it satisfies an equation of the form (9.35),

$$\frac{dw_1(\tau)}{d\tau} = \nu w_2 - \mu w_1. \tag{11.6}$$

Thus the probability $w_1(t)$ can be obtained as the solution of alternating Eqs. (11.5) and (11.6), using a continuity condition at the boundary points $\ldots, \tau'_j, \tau''_j, \tau'_{j+1}, \ldots$. If a value $w_1(t_k)$ is assigned and the control $\bar{u}_{t_k}^{t_{k+1}}$ is known, then using the above method we can find $w_1(t_{k+1}) = w_1(w_1(t_k), \bar{\bar{u}}_{t_k}^{t_{k+1}}, y_{t_k}^{t_{k+1}})$ and the corresponding probability distribution $\mathbf{P}(dw_1(t_{k+1}) \mid \bar{\bar{u}}_{t_k}^{t_{k+1}}, w_1(t_k))$. Let us consider the transformation

$$(T_{t_k t_{k+1}}(\bar{\bar{u}}_{t_k}^{t_{k+1}}) g)(w_1) = \int g(w'_1) \mathbf{P}(dw'_1 \mid \bar{\bar{u}}_{t_k}^{t_{k+1}}, w_1). \tag{11.7}$$

It is convenient to introduce the notation

$$\Delta\bar{\bar{u}} = \int_{t_k}^{t_{k+1}} \bar{\bar{u}}_t \, dt.$$

As can easily be seen, if $\Delta\bar{\bar{u}} = t_{k+1} - t_k \equiv \Delta$, then on almost the entire interval (t_k, t_{k+1}) Eq. (11.5) is valid, and if $\Delta\bar{\bar{u}} = 0$, then on this interval Eq. (11.6) is valid almost everywhere. To the first equation there corresponds the infinitesimal operator (9.44)

$$\frac{dL'}{dr} = \frac{2}{N} w_1^2 w_2^2 \frac{\partial^2}{\partial w_1^2} + (\nu w_2 - \mu w_1) \frac{\partial}{\partial w_1},$$

and to the second the operator

$$\frac{dL''}{dt} = (\nu w_2 - \mu w_1) \frac{\partial}{\partial w_1}.$$

Consequently, on the assumption that $g(w_1)$ is twice differentiable, we have

$$T_{t_k t_{k+1}}(\bar{\bar{u}}_{t_k}^{t_{k+1}})\, g = g + \left[\frac{2}{N}\, w_1^2 w_2^2 \frac{\partial^2 g}{\partial w_1^2} + (\nu w_2 - \mu w_1)\frac{\partial g}{\partial w_1}\right]\Delta + o(\Delta)$$

$$\text{for } \Delta\bar{\bar{u}} = \Delta;$$

$$T_{t_k t_{k+1}}(\bar{\bar{u}}_{t_k}^{t_{k+1}})\, g = g + (\nu w_2 - \mu w_1)\frac{\partial g}{\partial w_1}\,\Delta + o(\Delta) \text{ for } \Delta\bar{\bar{u}} = 0.$$

It is not difficult to see that in the intermediate case, when $0 < \Delta\bar{\bar{u}} < \Delta$, the following interpolation formula is valid:

$$T_{t_k t_{k+1}}(\bar{\bar{u}}_{t_k}^{t_{k+1}})\, g = g + \frac{2}{N}\, w_1^2 w_2^2 \frac{\partial^2 g}{\partial w_1^2}\,\Delta\bar{\bar{u}} + (\nu w_2 - \mu w_1)\frac{\partial g}{\partial w_1}\,\Delta + o(\Delta). \quad (11.8)$$

Thus the operator (11.7), if we disregard the quantity $o(\Delta)$, depends on $\bar{\bar{u}}_{t_k}^{t_{k+1}}$ only through $\Delta\bar{\bar{u}}$.

Let us use the above results in the recursion relation (8.39). Taking into consideration (11.3), as in the derivation of (10.9), we will minimize the first with respect to $\bar{\bar{u}}_{t_k}^{t_{k+1}}$ (with fixed functions $\{\bar{u}_t\}$), and then with respect to $\bar{u}_{t_k}^{t_{k+1}}$, i.e., with respect to $\vartheta \in [t_k, t_{k+1})$. Then (8.39) will have the form

$$S_{t_k}(1, w_1) = \min\Big\{\min_{\bar{\bar{u}}_{t_k}^{t_{k+1}}}[(A_1 w_1 + A_2 w_2)\,\Delta + o(\Delta) + G\Delta\bar{\bar{u}} +$$

$$+ T_{t_k t_{k+1}}(\bar{\bar{u}}_{t_k}^{t_{k+1}})\, S_{t_{k+1}}(1, w_1)],\ \min_{\vartheta\in[t_k, t_{k+1})}[(A_1 w_1 + A_2 w_2)(\vartheta - t_k) +$$

$$+ o(\Delta) + \mathbf{M}(B\, w_2(\vartheta)\,|\, w_1)]\Big\}. \quad (11.9)$$

Here we used the equations

$$\mathbf{M}[C_{tt}\,|\, w_1(t)] = A_1 w_1(t) + A_2 w_2(t) + G\bar{\bar{u}}_t;$$

$$\mathbf{M}[C'_{tt}\,|\, w_1(t)] = B w_2(t)$$

resulting from (11.1) and (11.2). At points where $S_{t_{k+1}}(1, w_1)$ is twice differentiable with respect to w_1, according to (11.8) we have

$$S_{t_k}(1, w_1) = \min\Big\{\min_{0\leqslant\Delta\bar{\bar{u}}\leqslant\Delta}\Big[(A_1 w_1 + A_2 w_2)\,\Delta + G\Delta\bar{\bar{u}} +$$

$$+ S_{t_{k+1}}(1, w_1) + \frac{2}{N}\, w_1^2 w_2^2 \frac{\partial^2 S_{t_{k+1}}}{\partial w_1^2}\,\Delta\bar{\bar{u}} + (\nu w_2 - \mu w_1)\frac{\partial S_{t_{k+1}}}{\partial w_1}\,\Delta\Big],$$

$$\min_{t_k\leqslant\vartheta< t_{k+1}}[B w_2 - B(\nu w_2 - \mu w_1)(\vartheta - t_k) +$$

$$+ (A_1 w_1 + A_2 w_2)(\vartheta - t_k)]\Big\} + o(\Delta). \quad (11.10)$$

Because of the linearity in Δu and Θ of the expressions entering into this, the minima are attained at the end points, so that

$$S_{t_k}(1, w_1) = \min\Big\{S_{t_{k+1}}(1, w_1) + \Big[(\nu w_2 - \mu w_1)\frac{\partial S_{t_{k+1}}}{\partial w_1} + A_1 w_1 + A_2 w_2\Big]\Delta,$$

$$S_{t_{k+1}}(1, w_1) + \Big[\frac{2}{N} w_1^2 w_2^2 \frac{\partial^2 S_{t_{k+1}}}{\partial w_1^2} + (\nu w_2 - \mu w_1)\frac{\partial S_{t_{k+1}}}{\partial w_1} + A_1 w_1 + A_2 w_2 + G\Big]\Delta, \tag{11.11}$$

$$B w_2,\ B w_2 + [A_1 w_1 + A_2 w_2 - B(\nu w_2 - \mu w_1)]\Delta\Big\} + o(\Delta).$$

We will denote the expressions in the brackets in order as H_1, H_2, H_3, H_4. Let Ξ_i be that region of the interval $[0,1] \ni w_1$ where

$$\lim_{\Delta\to 0}\frac{1}{\Delta}[\min_j(H_j, j = 1, \ldots, 4) - S_{t_k}] = \lim_{\Delta\to 0}\frac{1}{\Delta}[H_i - S_{t_k}].$$

As in Chapter 10, we assume that the function $S_{t_{k+1}}$ belongs to the region of regularity $D^0_{t_{k+1}}$ (Sect. 8.6). Such functions, as can be seen from (11.11), do not exceed Bw_2. In the region $\Xi^c = \Xi_3 \cup \Xi_4$ they are equal to Bw_2, and in the regions Ξ_1, Ξ_2 ($\subset \Xi$) they are less than Bw_2.

Functions S belonging to the region of regularity are, in addition, continuous with respect to w_1, and the function $\psi_t(w_1, S)$ corresponding to them is continuous. This can be proven in the same way as in Sect. 10.3 (proof of 10.1.C).

After passage to the limit $\Delta \to 0$ the recursion relation (11.11) becomes a differential equation

$$-\frac{\partial S_t(1, w_1)}{\partial t} = \psi_t(w_1, S_t(1, w_1)),$$

where

$$\psi_t(w_1, S_t) = (\nu w_2 - \mu w_1)\frac{\partial S_t}{\partial w_1} + A_1 w_1 + A_2 w_2 \quad \text{in } \Xi_1;$$

$$\psi_t(w_1, S_t) = \frac{2}{N} w_1^2 w_2^2 \frac{\partial^2 S_t}{\partial w_1^2} + (\nu\mu_2 - \mu w_1)\frac{\partial S_t}{\partial w_1} + A_1 w_1 + A_2 w_2 + G \text{ in } \Xi_2.$$

To this we adjoin the boundary condition

$$S_t(w_1) = B(1 - w_1) \text{ (on the boundary of the region } \Xi^c). \qquad (11.12)$$

Region $\Xi_4(t)$ is "unstable"; it becomes $\Xi_2(t')$ for smaller times $t' < t$ and thus does not require special examination.

From the continuity of $\psi(w_1, S_t)$ there follows also the boundary condition

$$\lim_{\Xi_2 \ni w_1 \to w_1'} \left[\frac{2}{N} w_1^2 w_2^2 \frac{\partial^2 S_t}{\partial w_1^2} + (\nu w_2 - \mu w_1) \frac{\partial S_t}{\partial w_1} \right] + G =$$
$$= \lim_{\Xi_1 \ni w_1 \to w_1'} \left[(\nu w_2 - \mu w_1) \frac{\partial S_t}{\partial w_1} \right] \qquad (11.13)$$

on the boundary w_1' between regions Ξ_1 and Ξ_2.

In this problem we are especially interested in the steady-state regime, i.e., in the limit function (10.48) and the limit of the stable regions Ξ_1, Ξ_2, $\Xi_3 = \Xi^c$ (because of the "instability" of $\Xi_4(t)$ no stable region Ξ_4 is present).

Assuming that the limit (10.48) exists, we obtain for it the equation

$$\psi_t(w_1, S^0(w_1)) = 0,$$

i.e.,

$$(\nu w_2 - \mu w_1) \frac{dS^0}{dw_1} + A_1 w_1 + A_2 w_2 = 0 \quad \text{in } \Xi_1 \qquad (11.14)$$

and

$$\frac{2}{N} w_1^2 w_2^2 \frac{d^2 S^0}{\partial w_1^2} + (\nu w_2 - \mu w_1) \frac{dS^0}{dw_1} + A_1 w_1 + A_2 w_1 + G = 0 \quad \text{in } \Xi_2. \qquad (11.15)$$

2. The boundary conditions (11.12) and (11.13) turn out to be insufficient for the solution of the problem. To them it is necessary to add the condition of continuity of the derivative

$$\frac{dS^0}{dw_1}(w_1'') = -B \qquad (11.16)$$

on the boundary w_1'' between the regions Ξ_2 and Ξ^c. This condition is analogous to the condition (10.36) and is justified in the same way.

Let us also find supplementary conditions of continuity of the derivative on the boundary $\Gamma \ni w_1'$ between regions Ξ_1 and Ξ_2, using Eqs. (11.10) and (11.11), which for $S^\circ(w_1)$ can be written

$$S^0(w_1) = \min\{ \min_{0 \leqslant \Delta\bar{\bar{u}} \leqslant \Delta} [T_\Delta(\Delta\bar{\bar{u}}) S^0 + (A_1 w_1 + A_2 w_2)\Delta + G\Delta\bar{\bar{u}}], Bw_2\} + o(\Delta).$$

For points not too distant from this boundary (not included in Ξ^c) we have

$$S^0(w_1) = \min_{0 \leqslant \Delta\bar{\bar{u}} \leqslant \Delta} [T_\Delta(\Delta\bar{\bar{u}}) S^0 + G\Delta\bar{\bar{u}}] + (A_1 w_1 + A_2 w_2)\Delta + o(\Delta). \quad (11.17)$$

We will assume first that the function has a jump in its derivative:

$$S^0(w_1) = \begin{cases} S^0(w_1') + S_1^-(w_1 - w_1') + \dots & \text{for } w_1 < w_1'; \\ S^0(w_1') + S_1^+ \cdot (w_1 - w_1') + \dots & \text{for } w_1 > w_1', \end{cases}$$

and consider in (11.17) the point $w_1 = w^* \equiv w_1' - \frac{1}{2} a'\Delta$ ($a' = \nu - (\mu + \nu) w_1'$). For it

$$S^0(w^*) = \min_{0 \leqslant \Delta\bar{\bar{u}} < \Delta} \left[(2\pi b' \Delta\bar{\bar{u}})^{-\frac{1}{2}} \int e^{-\frac{(w^* - w + a'\Delta)^2}{2b'\Delta\bar{\bar{u}}}} S^0(w)\, dw + G\Delta\bar{\bar{u}} \right] + (A_1 w_1' + A w_2')\Delta + o(\Delta) \quad (11.18)$$

$$\left(b' = \frac{4}{N} w_1'^2 w_2'^2 \right).$$

If $S_1^+ < S_1^-$ (deflection is upward), then from (11.18) it is easy to find that the minimum is attained for $\Delta\bar{\bar{u}} = \Delta$. In this case the right side of (11.18) is equal to $S^0(w^*) + \sqrt{\Delta} G_1(0) \cdot (S_1^+ - S_1^-) + O(\Delta)$ as in formula (10.34). It cannot coincide with $S^0(w^*)$, and we come to a contradiction.

If $S_1^+ > S_1^-$ (deflection is downward), then the minimum on the right side of (11.18) is attained for $\Delta\bar{\bar{u}} = 0$ and the right side is equal to

$$S^0(w^* + a'\Delta) + (A_1 w_1' + A_2 w_2')\Delta + o(\Delta) = S^0\left(w' + \frac{1}{2} a'\Delta\right) + (A_1 w_1' + A_2 w_2')\Delta + o(\Delta).$$

In this case it differs from $S^0(w^*)$ by an amount

$$S^0\left(w_1' + \frac{1}{2} a'\Delta\right) - S^0\left(w_1' - \frac{1}{2} a'\Delta\right) + (A_1 w_1' + A_2 w_2')\Delta + o(\Delta) = \frac{1}{2}(S_1^+ + S_1^-) a'\Delta + (A_1 w_1' + A_2 w_2')\Delta + o(\Delta) = \frac{1}{2}(S_1^+ - S_1^-) a'\Delta + o(\Delta)$$

[the latter on the strength of (11.14)], if Ξ_1 lies to the left of w_1', and by an amount

$$\frac{1}{2}(S_1^- - S_1^+)\,a'\,\Delta + o(\Delta),$$

if to the right. This again, however, contradicts Eq. (11.18). There remains only the possibility of coincidence of the derivatives S_1^+, S_1^- from the right and from the left:

$$\frac{dS^0}{dw_1}(w_1' + 0) = \frac{dS^0}{dw_1}(w_1' - 0). \qquad (11.19)$$

3. Let us turn to the solution of Eqs. (11.14) and (11.15) with the boundary conditions (11.16), (11.19), and (11.12).

Integrating (11.15) using (11.19), we have in Ξ_2

$$\frac{dS^0(w_1)}{dw_1} = -\frac{N}{2}e^{-\varphi(w_1)}\int_{w'_1}^{w_1} e^{\varphi(\xi_1)}\,\frac{A_1\xi_1 + A_2\xi_2 + G}{\xi_1^2\,\xi_2^2}\,d\,\xi_1 +$$

$$+ e^{-\varphi(w_1)+\varphi(w'_1)}\,\frac{dS^0}{dw_1}(w_1')_{\Xi_1} \quad (\xi_2 = 1 - \xi_1), \qquad (11.20)$$

where

$$\frac{dS^0}{dw_1}(w_1)_{\Xi_1} = -\frac{A_1 w_1 + A_2 w_2}{\nu w_2 - \mu w_1} = -D' - \frac{D}{\nu w_2 - \mu w_1} \qquad (11.21)$$

on the strength of (11.14). The function φ, as well as D and D', is defined by formulas (10.52) and (10.51).

If we assume $w_1 = w_1''$, then according to (11.16) from this we obtain an equation

$$Be^{\varphi(w''_1)} = \frac{N}{2}\int_{w'_1}^{w''_1} e^{\varphi(\xi_1)}\,\frac{A_1\xi_1 + A_2\xi_2 + G}{\xi_1^2\,\xi_2^2}\,d\xi_1 - e^{\varphi(w'_1)}\,\frac{dS^0}{dw_1}(w_1')_{\Xi_1}, \qquad (11.22)$$

connecting the boundary points w_1', w_1''. It is assumed here that the region Ξ_2 borders on one side region Ξ_1 and on the other, region Ξ^c; to study other cases is not difficult.

The boundary points w_1', w_1'' are not completely determined by Eq. (11.22). Nevertheless, the available freedom in their selection is substantially limited: the position of one point is determined by the position of the other. By differentiating this equation we can find a relation between perturbations of the points:

$$(w_1'' w_2'')^{-2} e^{\varphi(w''_1)} [-(\nu w_2'' - \mu w_1'') B + A_1 w_1'' + A_2 w_2'' + G] \delta w_1'' =$$
$$= (w_1' w_2')^{-2} e^{\varphi(w'_1)} \left[\frac{2}{N} w_1'^2 w_2'^2 \frac{d^2 S^0}{dw_1^2} (w_1')_{\Xi_1} + \right.$$
$$\left. + (\nu w_2' - \mu w_1') \frac{dS^0}{dw_1} (w_1')_{\Xi_1} + A_1 w_1' + A_2 w_2' + G \right] \delta w_1'. \qquad (11.23)$$

Taking into account condition (11.12) and integrating the expressions (11.20) and (11.21) for the derivative $\frac{dS^0}{dw_1}$, we can find the function S°, and, in particular, its value in the region Ξ_1:

$$S^0(w_1) = \int_{w'_1}^{w_1} \frac{dS^0}{dw_1} (\xi_1)_{\Xi_1} d\xi_1 + \int_{w''_1}^{w'_1} \frac{dS_0}{dw_1} (\xi_1)_{\Xi_2} d\xi_1 + B(1 - w_1''). \qquad (11.24)$$

Since the quantities w_1', w_1'' are connected by only one equation (11.22), the remaining freedom in their selection should also be removed. To do this we will require that to the desired values w_1', w_1'' there correspond an extremum (a minimum) of the function (11.24). Taking the variation of (11.24) and using (11.16) and (11.21), we have

$$\delta S^0(w_1) = \int_{w''_1}^{w'_1} \frac{\partial}{\partial w_1'} \left[\frac{dS^0}{dw_1} (\xi_1)_{\Xi_2} \right] d\xi_1 \cdot \delta w_1'.$$

Differentiating expression (11.20), we find

$$\delta S^0(w_1) = J \frac{N}{2} (w_1' w_2')^{-2} e^{\varphi(w'_1)} \left[\frac{2}{N} w_1'^2 w_2'^2 \frac{d^2 S^0}{dw_1^2} (w_1')_{\Xi_1} + \right.$$
$$\left. + (\nu w_2' - \mu w_1') \frac{dS^0}{dw_1} (w_1')_{\Xi_1} + A_1 w_1' + A_2 w_2' + G \right] \delta w_1' =$$
$$= J \frac{N}{2} (w_1'' w_2'')^{-2} e^{\varphi(w''_1)} [-(\nu w_2'' - \mu w_1'') B +$$
$$+ A_1 w_1'' + A_2 w_2'' + G] \delta w_1''$$

where $J = \int_{w''_1}^{w'_1} e^{-\varphi(\xi_1)} d\xi_1$; the second equality follows from (11.23).

Thus the variation $\delta S^0(w_1)$ vanishes if the equation

$$\frac{2}{N} w_1'^2 w_2'^2 \frac{d^2 S^0}{dw_1^2} (w_1')_{\Xi_1} + (\nu w_2' - \mu w_1') \frac{dS^0}{dw_1} (w_1')_{\Xi_1} +$$
$$+ A_1 w_1' + A_2 w_2' + G = 0$$

or the equation

$$-(\nu w_2'' - \mu w_1'') B + A_1 w_1'' + A_2 w_2'' + G = 0 \qquad (11.26)$$

is satisfied.

We will choose one of these two equations. It was pointed out above (p. 279) that there are no points of the region Ξ_4 in the region $\Xi^c = \Xi_3$, i.e., in that region

$$-(\nu w_2 - \mu w_1) B + A_1 w_1 + A_2 w_2 \geqslant 0.$$

Hence in the region Ξ^c and on its boundary w_1'',

$$-(\nu w_2 - \mu w_1) B + A_1 w_1 + A_2 w_2 + G > 0,$$

since $G > 0$, so that Eq. (11.26) cannot be satisfied. Thus as the condition definitely determining w_1', w_1'', we will use the remaining Eq. (11.25).

Comparing (11.25) and (11.15) and taking into account the continuity of the first derivative (11.19), it can easily be seen that this condition can be formulated as the condition of continuity of the second derivative at the boundary points:

$$\frac{d^2 S^0}{dw_1^2}(w_1' + 0) = \frac{d^2 S^0}{dw_1^2}(w_1' - 0).$$

In addition, if we take into account (11.14) and (11.20), this condition can take the form

$$\frac{d^2 S^0}{dw_1^2}(w_1')_{\Xi_1} = -\frac{1}{2} \frac{GN}{w_1'^2 (1 - w_1')^2}.$$

Differentiating (11.21), we thus obtain

$$\frac{\nu A_1 + \mu A_2}{[\nu - (\mu + \nu) w_1']^2} = \frac{1}{2} \frac{GN}{w_1'^2 (1 - w_1')^2}$$

or, assuming that $\nu A_1 + \mu A_2 > 0$,

$$w_1'(1 - w_1') = \left(\frac{1}{2} \frac{GN}{\nu A_1 + \mu A_2}\right)^{\frac{1}{2}} [\nu - (\mu + \nu) w_1'] \qquad (11.27)$$

(we choose the root w_1' lying between zero and $\frac{\nu}{\mu + \nu}$).

The second boundary w_1'' of the region Ξ_2 is found from Eq. (11.22).

The distribution of the regions Ξ_1, Ξ_2, Ξ^c usually is as follows: the region without observations Ξ_1 takes the rightmost position, coinciding with the segment $(0, w_1')$, the region of observation Ξ_2 is the segment (w_1', w_1''), and the region of stopping is the segment $(w_1'', 1)$. As long as the *a posteriori* probability $w_1(t)$ belongs to Ξ_1, the situation is not threatening and carrying out observations is not profitable. The region of observation (w_1', w_1'') is a threatening zone and in it observation of the process is justified. The value of $w_1(t)$ at each instant of time is a measure of the threat of the situation; when it reaches the critical value w_1'', an alarm should be given, i.e., the process should be stopped.

The described regime of operation and the distribution of the regions are not valid for all, but only for normal, values of the parameters of the problem. In some cases a different situation is possible. Since region Ξ_2 can be absent, regions $\Xi_1 = (0, w_1^\Gamma)$ and $\Xi^c = (w_1^\Gamma, 1)$ can immediately adjoin each other. From (11.14) and (11.16) it is not difficult to obtain the condition

$$B = \frac{A_1 w_1^\Gamma + A_2 w_2^\Gamma}{\nu w_2^\Gamma - \mu w_1^\Gamma} \quad \left(= D' + \frac{D}{\nu - (\mu + \nu)\, w_1^\Gamma}\right), \tag{11.28}$$

determining the boundary w_1^Γ in this case.

As is indicated by an analysis of the functions (11.20) and (11.21), such a distribution of regions is valid when the root of Eq. (11.27) is greater than the root of Eq. (11.28). In the contrary case, when $w_1^\Gamma > w_1'$, i.e.,

$$D' + \frac{D}{\nu - (\mu + \nu)\, w_1'} < B \qquad (D > 0),$$

the regions have the usual distribution described above.

11.2 Problems of Optimal Control of a Markov Process Having Two States

Let us turn to problems in which the probabilistic characteristics of the basic process depend on the control selected, so that the observer-operator, accepting a solution, influences the flow of the process.

We will begin with a specific problem, to some extent similar to the problems concerned with the appearance of disorder examined in Sects. 10.6 and 11.1. Let us assume that the process with two states $\eta_t = \pm 1$ and the observed processes are the same. The observation of particular losses is not required and is not penalized. As opposed to the preceding problems, in a threatening situation (probable disorder $\eta_t = 1$) let us now assume it is not necessary to stop the entire process, but only to change to certain overload operating conditions with a high probability of causing the disorder to disappear. In such an overload condition the equation for the *a priori* probabilities (9.35) is replaced by the equation

$$\dot{p}_1 = -\dot{p}_2 = -\mu' p_1 + \nu' p_2,$$

where $\mu' - \mu = \lambda > 0$. The second parameter, for simplicity, we will assume to be the same as earlier: $\nu' = \nu$.

The observer-operator at each instant of time t has one of two alternatives: to operate under normal conditions ($u_t = 0$) or to change to the overload conditions ($u_t = 1$).

It is naturally valid to consider the overload condition to be expensive and to include its cost in the penalty function, assuming

$$C_{tt} = Gu_t + \begin{cases} A_1 & \text{for} \quad \eta_t = 1; \\ A_2 & \text{for} \quad \eta_t = -1. \end{cases}$$

The recursion relation (8.39) rather than (11.9) will now have the form

$$S_{t-\Delta}(w_1) = \min_{u_{t-\Delta}^t} \{(A_1 w_1 + A_2 w_2)\Delta + o(\Delta) + G\Delta u + T_{t-\Delta, t}(u_{t-\Delta}^t) S_t\}, \tag{11.29}$$

where

$$\Delta u = \int_{t-\Delta}^{t} u_\tau \, d\tau.$$

From (9.44) the infinitesimal operator of the process w_1 equals

$$\frac{d\mathscr{L}'}{dt} = (\nu w_2 - \mu w_1)\frac{\partial}{\partial w_1} + \frac{2}{N} w_1^2 w_2^2 \frac{\partial^2}{\partial w_1^2},$$

if u_t is equal to zero in the vicinity of the point t, and equals

$$\frac{d\mathscr{L}''}{dt} = [\nu w_2 - (\mu + \lambda) w_1] \frac{\partial}{\partial w_1} + \frac{2}{N} w_1^2 w_2^2 \frac{\partial^2}{\partial w_1^2},$$

if u_t is equal to unity. Assuming that the function $g(w_1) = S_t(w_1)$ is twice differentiable, we have

$$T_{t-\Delta, t}(u_{t-\Delta}^t) g = g + \left[\frac{2}{N} w_1^2 w_2^2 \frac{\partial^2 g}{\partial w_1^2} + (\nu w_2 - \mu w_1)\frac{\partial g}{\partial w_1}\right]\Delta - \lambda w_1 \frac{\partial g}{\partial w_1} \Delta u + o(\Delta),$$

so that the relation (11.29) takes the form

$$S_{t-\Delta}(w_1) = S_t(w_1) + \left[\frac{2}{N} w_1^2 w_2^2 \frac{\partial^2 S_t}{\partial w_1^2} + (\nu w_2 - \mu w_1)\frac{\partial S_t}{\partial w_1} + \right.$$

$$\left. + A_1 w_1 + A_2 w_2\right]\Delta + \min_{0 \leqslant \Delta u \leqslant \Delta}\left\{G\,\Delta u - \lambda w_1 \frac{\partial S_t}{\partial w_1}\Delta u\right\} + o(\Delta). \quad (11.30)$$

Thus the function $S_t(w_1)$, belonging to the space of regularity, satisfies the equation

$$-\frac{\partial S_t}{\partial t} = \frac{2}{N} w_1^2 w_2^2 \frac{\partial^2 S_t}{\partial w_1^2} + (\nu w_2 - \mu w_1)\frac{\partial S_t}{\partial w_1} + A_1 w_1 + A_2 w_2 \quad (11.31)$$

in region Ξ_1 where

$$G > \lambda w_1 \frac{\partial S_t}{\partial w_1}(w_1), \quad (11.32)$$

and the equation

$$-\frac{\partial S_t}{\partial t} = \frac{2}{N} w_1^2 w_2^2 \frac{\partial^2 S_t}{\partial w_1^2} +$$

$$+ [\nu w_2 - (\mu + \lambda) w_1]\frac{\partial S_t}{\partial w_1^2} + A_1 w_1 + A_2 w_2 + G \quad (11.33)$$

in region Ξ_2 where

$$G < \lambda w_1 \frac{\partial S_t}{\partial w_1}(w_1). \quad (11.34)$$

If we do not assume in the beginning that the function $S_t(w_1)$ is twice differentiable with respect to w_1, Eqs. (11.31) and (11.33) for $S_t \in D^\circ$ will result from the Definition 8.8 of the space of regularity D°. In analogy with Sect. 10.4 it is possible to prove that the first derivative $\frac{\partial S_t}{\partial w_1}$ is continuous on the common boundary $\Gamma \ni w_1^\Gamma$ of regions Ξ_1 and Ξ_2. For from (11.32) and (11.34) as a result of passages to the limit $\Xi_1 \ni w_1 \to w_1^\Gamma$ and $\Xi_2 \ni w_1' \to w_1^\Gamma$ we will have

$$\frac{\partial S_t}{\partial w_1}(w_1^\Gamma) = \frac{G}{\lambda w_1^\Gamma}. \quad (11.35)$$

In addition, comparing (11.31) and (11.33), as a result of the continuity (with respect to w_1) of the function $\frac{\partial S_t}{\partial t}$ we obtain the continuity of the second derivative

$$\frac{\partial^2 S_t}{\partial w_1^2}(w_1^\Gamma + 0) = \frac{\partial^2 S_t}{\partial w_1^2}(w_1^\Gamma - 0)$$

on the boundary Γ.

To these equations we need to add the "initial" condition

$$S_b(w_1) = f_0(w_1), \tag{11.36}$$

corresponding to the end point in time. At the first time instant the function $S_a(w_1(a))$ coincides with the full risk R.

Considering the parameters of the problem to be constant, we will examine the steady-state conditions of operation. For this we will let $b-t$ approach infinity. The steady state is characterized by average losses per unit time

$$\gamma = \lim_{b-t\to\infty} \frac{S_t(w_1)}{b-t}, \tag{11.37}$$

which do not depend on w_1.

We assume that the limit (11.37) and the limit

$$f(w_1) = \lim_{b-t\to\infty} [S_t(w_1) - \gamma(b-\gamma)] \tag{11.38}$$

exist, which to a degree do not depend on the choice of the terminal function (11.36). Since $S_t(w_1)$ depends only on the difference of time $b-t$ (and not on t and b separately), the limit function (11.38) [as well as γ] turns out to be independent of time: $\frac{\partial f}{\partial t} = 0$. Taking this into consideration in substituting the expression

$$S_t(w_1) = \gamma(b-t) + f(w_1) + o(1)$$

into Eq. (11.31), we obtain

$$\gamma - \frac{\partial}{\partial t} o(1) = \frac{2}{N} w_1^2 w_2^2 \frac{\partial^2 f}{\partial w_1^2} + (\nu w_2 - \mu w_1) \frac{\partial f}{\partial w_1} + A_1 w_1 + A_2 w_2 + \frac{\partial^2}{\partial w_1^2} o(1) + \frac{\partial}{\partial w_1} o(1) \tag{11.39a}$$

and, passing to the limit as $b-t\to\infty$,

$$\frac{2}{N} w_1^2 w_2^2 \frac{d^2 f}{dw_1^2} + (\nu w_2 - \mu w_1) \frac{df}{dw_1} + A_1 w_1 + A_2 w_2 - \gamma = 0, \tag{11.39}$$

provided that

$$\frac{\partial}{\partial t} o(1) = o(1); \quad \frac{\partial}{\partial w_1} o(1) = o(1); \quad \frac{\partial^2}{\partial w_1^2} o(1) = o(1).$$

Condition (11.32), defining the region Ξ_1 which is now independent of time and in which (11.39) is valid, takes the form

$$\frac{df}{dw_1}(w_1) < \frac{G}{\lambda w_1}. \tag{11.40}$$

Analogously, from (11.33) we obtain the equation

$$\frac{2}{N} w_1^2 w_2^2 \frac{d^2 f}{dw_1^2} + [\nu w_2 - (\mu + \lambda) w_1] \frac{df}{dw_1} + A_1 w_1 + A_2 w_2 + G - \gamma = 0, \tag{11.41}$$

which is satisfied in region Ξ_2 where

$$\frac{df}{dw_1}(w_1) > \frac{G}{\lambda w_1}. \tag{11.42}$$

On the common boundary w_1^Γ of regions Ξ_1 and Ξ_2 continuity conditions on the two derivatives (the first and the second), and the relation

$$\frac{df}{dw_1}(w_1^\Gamma) = \frac{G}{\lambda w_1^\Gamma}, \tag{11.43}$$

which follows from (11.35), are satisfied.

For a complete definition of the function $f(w_1)$ we need to add also boundary conditions on the sufficient coordinates, i.e., conditions at the points $w_1 = 0$ and $w_1 = 1$. In this problem they have the trivial form

$$\left|\frac{df}{dw_1}(0)\right| < \infty; \quad \left|\frac{df}{dw_1}(1)\right| < \infty. \tag{11.44}$$

As can be supported by analysis of the results, regions Ξ_1 and Ξ_2 have this natural distribution: the region of normal operation Ξ_1 is situated on the left and is the interval $[0, w_1^\Gamma)$, and the region of overload operation coincides with the interval $(w_1^\Gamma, 1]$. Integrating Eq. (11.39) taking the first condition of (11.44) into account, we get

$$\frac{df}{dw_1}(w_1) = \frac{N}{2} e^{-\varphi(w_1)} \int_0^{w_1} e^{\varphi(\xi)} \frac{\gamma - A_1 \xi - A_2 (1-\xi)}{\xi^2 (1-\xi)^2} d\xi, \; w_1 < w_1^\Gamma, \tag{11.45}$$

where $\varphi(w_1)$ is defined by formula (10.52). Analogously, (11.41) and the second condition of (11.44) yield

$$\frac{df}{dw_1}(w_1) = -\frac{N}{2} e^{-\varphi_\lambda(w_1)} \int_{w_1}^{1} e^{\varphi_\lambda(\xi)} \frac{\gamma - A_1 \xi - A_2 (1-\xi) - G}{\xi^2 (1-\xi)^2} d\xi,$$

$$w_1 > w_1^\Gamma \tag{11.46}$$

$$\left(\varphi_\lambda(w_1) = \frac{1}{2} N \left[(\nu - \mu - \lambda) \ln \frac{w_1}{w_2} - \frac{\nu}{w_1} - \frac{\mu + \lambda}{w_2}\right]\right).$$

Condition (11.43) and the continuity condition on the first derivative, if we use (11.45) and (11.46), yield a system of two equations

$$w_1^\Gamma e^{-\varphi(w_1^\Gamma)} \int_0^{w_1^\Gamma} e^{\varphi(\xi)} \frac{\gamma - A_1\xi - A_2(1-\xi)}{\xi^2(1-\xi)^2} d\xi = \frac{2G}{N\lambda};$$

$$w_1^\Gamma e^{-\varphi_\lambda(w_1^\Gamma)} \int_{w_1^\Gamma}^1 e^{\varphi_\lambda(\xi)} \frac{A_1\xi + A_2(1-\xi) + G - \gamma}{\xi^2(1-\xi)^2} d\xi = \frac{2G}{N\lambda},$$

which allows the two unknowns w_1^Γ and γ to be determined.

By integrating expressions (11.45) and (11.46) we find the function $f(w_1)$ to within an additive constant. In the stationary theory this constant remains undefined since its value is determined by a particular choice of the function $f_0(w_1)$ in condition (11.36). For its determination we would need a solution of the nonstationary equations (11.31) and (11.33).

An analysis of expression (11.45) for values of w_1 near 1 shows that

$$\frac{df}{dw_1}(w_1) = \frac{A_1 + G - \gamma}{\mu + \lambda} + o_{1-w_1}(1)$$

$$(o_{1-w_1}(1) \to 0 \quad \text{as} \quad w_1 \to 1).$$

Using this to test the inequalities (11.40) and (11.42), we get the relation

$$\frac{A_1 + G - \gamma}{\mu + \lambda} > \frac{G}{\lambda},$$

i.e.,

$$\frac{\lambda}{\mu}(A_1 - \gamma) > G,$$

as a necessary condition for the above normal distribution of the regions Ξ_1, Ξ_2. This is nothing other than a condition of the economic justifiability of the overload operation. If it is not satisfied, the region Ξ_2 of overload operation is entirely absent.

11.3 Another Problem of Optimal Control. Tracking a Random Point

While in the preceding problems the reference process η_t was a process with two states, here we will examine the case when it is a diffusion process. The problem described below is typical for automatic control.

Let us assume the process $\xi(t)$ has a constant diffusion coefficient D and a constant drift a. We observe its sum with white noise, or, what is essentially the same, the process

$$y_1(t) = \int_{\tau \leqslant t} \xi(\tau)\, d\tau + \zeta_1(t), \tag{11.47}$$

where $\zeta_1(t)$ is a Wiener process: $\mathbf{M}\zeta_1 = 0$; $\mathbf{M}\Delta\zeta_1^2 = N\Delta t$. In addition, we have the process $y_2(t)$ [coordinate of the regulated plant] which is also assumed to be known to the observer-operator. Let this be described by the equation

$$dy_2(t) = du_t + d\zeta_2. \tag{11.48}$$

Here $\zeta_2(t)$ is a Wiener process with a variance parameter $\varkappa$:

$$\mathbf{M}\,\zeta_2 = 0; \quad \mathbf{M}\,\Delta\zeta_2^2 = \varkappa \Delta t,$$

and du_t is a perturbation caused by the servomotor which is controlled by the observer-operator. The process $\{u_t\}$ is in this problem the control process. We will assume that the speed of the servomotor is limited in absolute value by the quantity u_0, i.e., that

$$|u(t_2) - u(t_1)| \leqslant u_0 |t_2 - t_1|. \tag{11.49}$$

Disregarding the inertia of the servomotor, we will not introduce other limitations on the control process.

Let us assume that the purpose of the tracking system is to cause the process $y_2(t)$ to follow more closely the coordinate $\xi(t)$ of the random point. If $C(\xi - y_2)$ is a function expressing the optimality criterion, then the penalty function will have the form

$$c^t = \int_{\tau \leqslant t} C(\xi(\tau) - y_2(\tau))\, d\tau. \tag{11.50}$$

In this problem the basic Markov process z_t is diffusional and consists of three components $\xi(t)$, $y_1(t)$, $y_2(t)$, the latter two components being observed. Similar cases were examined in Chapter 7. The *a priori* infinitesimal operator of the basic process has the form

$$dL_{pr} = dt\left(a\frac{\partial}{\partial \xi} + \xi \frac{\partial}{\partial y_1}\right) + du_t \frac{\partial}{\partial y_2} + \frac{dt}{2}\left(D\frac{\partial^2}{\partial \xi^2} + N\frac{\partial^2}{\partial y_1^2} + \varkappa \frac{\partial^2}{\partial y_2^2}\right). \tag{11.51}$$

Checking the criteria 8.7.A–C indicates that (for an appropriate choice of terminal penalties c—c^b) the observed processes $y_1(t)$ and $y_2(t)$ and the *a posteriori* probability distribution density $w_t(\xi)$ together form sufficient coordinates. If the initial distribution $w_a(\xi)$ is Gaussian, then at any other instant of time the *a posteriori* distribution will be Gaussian:

$$w_t(\xi)=\frac{1}{\sqrt{2\pi k_t}}\, e^{-\frac{(\xi-m_t)^2}{2k_t}}. \qquad (11.52)$$

Thus, instead of examining the *a posteriori* density (11.52), we can examine its parameters m_t, k_t. A similar simplification was studied in Sect. 9.5. The process with operator (11.51) is related to the processes dealt with in paragraphs 1 and 3 of Sect. 9.5 (independent of the coordinates of the local variances and the linearity of the drifts). Thus the results compiled there are applicable to this problem.

After replacing the distribution density (11.52) by the parameters m_t, k_t, the variables m_t, k_t, $y_1(t)$, $y_2(t)$ will be the sufficient coordinates. We will obtain equations for m_t, k_t by specializing the formulas (9.33). Taking into account the simple form of the local parameter in (11.55), we find

$$m_t=a+\frac{k_t}{N}(\dot{y}_1-m_t);$$
$$\dot{k}_t=D-\frac{k_t^2}{N}. \qquad (11.53)$$

If k_0 is the initial value of the *a posteriori* variance, then the solution of the second equation of (11.33) has the form

$$k_t=\sqrt{DN}\,\frac{(k_0+\sqrt{DN})\,e^{2t\sqrt{\frac{D}{N}}}+k_0-\sqrt{DN}}{(k_0+\sqrt{DN})\,e^{2t\sqrt{\frac{D}{N}}}-k_0+\sqrt{DN}}=$$
$$=\sqrt{DN}\,\frac{k_0\cosh t\sqrt{\frac{D}{N}}+\sqrt{DN}\sinh t\sqrt{\frac{D}{N}}}{k_0\sinh t\sqrt{\frac{D}{N}}+\sqrt{DN}\cosh t\sqrt{\frac{D}{N}}} \qquad (11.54)$$

This parameter, since it is thus determined, can be removed from the number of sufficient coordinates if we consider the function $S_t(k_t, m_t, y_1(t), y_2(t))$ as a function of time and the remaining sufficient coordinates. Then we will have three sufficient coordinates m_t, $y_1(t)$, $y_2(t)$. In accordance with formula (9.34) they have a secondary *a posteriori* infinitesimal operator

$$d\mathscr{L}_3(t)=dt\left(a\frac{\partial}{\partial m}+m\frac{\partial}{\partial y_1}\right)+du_t\frac{\partial}{\partial y_2}+$$
$$+\frac{dt}{2}\left(\frac{k_t^2}{N}\frac{\partial^2}{\partial m^2}+2k_t\frac{\partial^2}{\partial m\,\partial y_1}+N\frac{\partial^2}{\partial y_1^2}+\varkappa\frac{\partial^2}{\partial y_2^2}\right). \quad (11.54)$$

In view of the fact that the function $C(\xi-y_2)$ in (11.50) depends not on the three coordinates ξ, y_1, y_2 separately, but only on the difference $\xi-y_2$, it is possible in this problem to abbreviate further the number of sufficient coordinates. The function

$$s_t(m_t, y_1, y_2)=\int C(\xi-y_2)\,w_t(\xi)\,d\xi=$$
$$=\frac{1}{\sqrt{2\pi k_t}}\int C(m_t-y_2+\eta)\,e^{-\frac{\eta^2}{2k_t}}\,d\eta \quad (11.55)$$

depends only on the difference $m_t-y_2(t)\equiv x(t)$. If, in particular, $C(\xi-y_2)=(\xi-y_2)^2$, then

$$s_t(m_t, y_1, y_2)=[m_t-y_2(t)]^2+k_t=x^2(t)+k_t. \quad (11.56)$$

As follows from the form of the operator (11.54), the two-dimensional process (m_t, y_2) is itself Markov and has an operator

$$d\mathscr{L}_2=dt\,a\frac{\partial}{\partial m}+du_t\frac{\partial}{\partial y_2}+\frac{dt}{2}\left(\frac{k_t^2}{N}\frac{\partial^2}{\partial m^2}+\varkappa\frac{\partial^2}{\partial y_2^2}\right) \quad (11.57)$$

Moreover, the difference $x(t)=m_t-y_2(t)$ is a one-dimensional Markov process with operator

$$d\mathscr{L}=(a\,dt-du_t)\frac{\partial}{\partial x}+\frac{dt}{2}\left(\frac{k_t^2}{N}+\varkappa\right)\frac{\partial^2}{\partial x^2}. \quad (11.58)$$

Thus condition 8.7.B does not require the addition to x_t of any other coordinates. As follows from (11.55), (11.56), and the simple character of the limitations (11.49), this is also not required by the other conditions 8.7.A, C, so that $x(t)$ is the unique sufficient coordinate.

The subsequent examination is analogous to the examination in the preceding paragraph. The analog of Eq. (11.30) resulting from (11.58) has the form

$$S_{t-\Delta}(x)=S_t(x)+\frac{\Delta}{2}\left(\frac{k_t^2}{N}+\varkappa\right)\frac{\partial^2 S_t(x)}{\partial x^2}+$$
$$+\min_{-u_0\Delta\leqslant\Delta u\leqslant u_0\Delta}(a\Delta-\Delta u)\frac{\partial S_t(x)}{\partial x}+(x^2+k_t)\Delta+o(\Delta), \quad (11.59)$$
$$(\Delta u=u_t-u_{t-\Delta}).$$

Here we choose the mean-square quality criterion, leading to the function (11.56). For functions $S_t(x)$ belonging to the space of regularity, the equation

$$-\frac{\partial S_t}{\partial t}=\frac{1}{2}\left(\frac{k_t^2}{N}+\varkappa\right)\frac{\partial^2 S_t}{\partial x^2}+(a-u_0)\frac{\partial S_t}{\partial x}+x^2+k_t \quad (11.60)$$

is valid in region Ξ_1 where

$$\frac{\partial S_t}{\partial x}>0, \quad (11.61)$$

and the equation

$$-\frac{\partial S_t}{\partial t}=\frac{1}{2}\left(\frac{k_t^2}{N}+\varkappa\right)\frac{\partial^2 S_t}{\partial x^2}+(a+u_0)\frac{\partial S_t}{\partial x}+x^2+k_t \quad (11.62)$$

in region Ξ_2 where

$$\frac{\partial S_t}{\partial x}<0. \quad (11.63)$$

As in Sect. 11.2 on the common boundary $\Gamma \ni x_\Gamma$ of regions Ξ_1 and Ξ_2 continuity conditions for the first and second derivatives are satisfied:

$$\frac{\partial S_t}{\partial x}(x_\Gamma+0)=\frac{\partial S_t}{\partial x}(x_\Gamma-0);\quad \frac{\partial^2 S_t}{\partial x^2}(x_\Gamma+0)=\frac{\partial^2 S_t}{\partial x^2}(x_\Gamma-0).$$

The second of these conditions is less universal, being valid only because on both sides of the boundary there are identical penalties and diffusion coefficients. From (11.61) and (11.63) and from the continuity of the first derivative, there follows the additional boundary condition

$$\frac{\partial S_t}{\partial x}(x_\Gamma)=0. \quad (11.64)$$

As in the preceding problem we can examine the steady-state operation. For this we need to assume the existence of limits (11.37) and (11.38), and that the first of these does not depend on x. For the limit function $f(x)$ we now have the equation

$$\frac{1}{2}\left(\frac{k^2}{N}+\varkappa\right)\frac{d^2 f}{dx^2}+(a-u_0)\frac{df}{dx}+x^2+k-\gamma=0 \quad (11.65)$$

in Ξ_1, where $\frac{df}{dx}>0$, and the equation

$$\frac{1}{2}\left(\frac{k^2}{N}+\varkappa\right)\frac{d^2f}{dx^2}+(a+u_0)\frac{df}{dx}+x^2+k-\gamma=0 \qquad (11.66)$$

in Ξ_2, where $\frac{df}{dx}<0$. In deriving these equations we used the fact that, in the equation analogous to (11.39a), in passing to the limit as $b-t\to\infty$ the variance k_t, according to (11.54), tends to the limit $k\equiv k_\infty=\sqrt{DN}$.

On the boundary x_Γ the condition

$$\frac{df}{dx}(x_\Gamma)=0 \qquad (11.67)$$

is valid [see (11.64)].

In contrast to the previous problem, the region of the sufficient coordinates is now not an interval but the unbounded line. To supplement the definition of the function $\frac{df}{dx}(x)$, instead of (11.44) we now need to add certain conditions at infinity. We will require that the function $\frac{df}{dx}(x)$ have a limited increase at infinity, namely,

$$\left|\frac{df}{dx}(x)\right|=O\left(s_\infty(x)\right).$$

Here $s_\infty(x)$ is the limit as $t\to\infty$ of the function (11.55), i.e., the result of inserting $k_t=k$. Applied to the function (11.56) this condition leads to the requirement that the function $\frac{df}{dt}$ increase no more rapidly than quadratically. Taking into account the general solution

$$\frac{df(x)}{dx}=-\beta\int_{x_0}^{x}e^{-\beta(a\mp u_0)(x-y)}(y^2+k-\gamma)\,dy+C_1e^{-\beta(a\mp u_0)x}$$

$$\left(\beta^{-1}=\frac{1}{2}\left(\frac{k^2}{N}+\varkappa\right)\right)$$

of Eqs. (11.65) and (11.66), we find that this is possible only if $u_0>|a|$. The region of large positive values of x belongs to the region Ξ_1, and there

$$\frac{df(x)}{dx}=\beta\int_{x}^{\infty}e^{-\beta(u_0-a)(y-x)}(y^2+k-\gamma)\,dy=$$

$$=\frac{1}{u_0-a}\left[x^2+\frac{2x}{\beta(u_0-a)}+\frac{2}{\beta^2(u_0-a)^2}+k-\gamma\right]. \qquad (11.67)$$

The region of large negative values of x belongs to Ξ_2, and there

$$\frac{df(x)}{dx} = -\beta \int_{-\infty}^{x} e^{-\beta(u_0+a)(x-y)} (y^2 + k - \gamma)\, dy =$$

$$= -\frac{1}{u_0+a}\left[x^2 - \frac{2x}{\beta(u_0+a)} + \frac{2}{\beta^2 (u_0+a)^2} + k - \gamma\right]. \qquad (11.68)$$

Equating expressions (11.67) and (11.68) to zero, by (11.64) we obtain two equations defining x_Γ and γ. The solution of these equations leads to the result

$$x_\Gamma = -\frac{a}{u_0^2 - a^2}\left(\frac{k^2}{N} + \varkappa\right); \ \gamma = k + \frac{1}{2}\left(\frac{k^2}{N} + \varkappa\right)\frac{u_0^2 + a^2}{(u_0^2 - a^2)^2}. \qquad (11.69)$$

It can be verified that for $x > x_\Gamma$, the inequality $\frac{df}{dx} > 0$ is satisfied, while for $\frac{df}{dx} < 0$, $x < x_\Gamma$.

In fact, as we can see from (11.65) and (11.66), the two parabolas (11.67) and (11.68) have at the point x_Γ the same derivative

$$\frac{d^2 f}{dx^2}(x_\Gamma) = \beta(\gamma - k - x_\Gamma^2).$$

i.e., they are touching. According to (11.69) this is positive:

$$\frac{d^2 f}{dx^2}(x_\Gamma) = \frac{\frac{k^2}{N} + \varkappa}{u_0^2 - a^2} > 0,$$

so that the above inequalities are in fact satisfied.

By integrating (11.67) and (11.68) it is not difficult to find the function $f(x)$ to within an additive constant.

This solution of the problem is found in the work of Stratonovich and Shmal'gauzen.

11.4 Increase of the Number of Sufficient Coordinates

The methods presented in this chapter in principle are applicable to a large number of problems. In passing from simpler problems to more complex ones the applicability of the methods as a rule is not disturbed; however, there occurs an increase in the number of sufficient coordinates, so that actual solution of the problem is in fact more complicated.

To illustrate this we will consider a more complex case of the example treated in Sect. 11.3.

1. Let us assume that the penalty function C entering into (11.50) depends not only on the difference $\xi - y_2$, but also on each argument separately, for example,

$$C(\xi - y_2, y_2) = C_0(y_2)(\xi - y_2)^2. \tag{11.70}$$

This means that for various positions of the object there are needed, broadly speaking, various precisions of tracking. Then the difference $x = m - y_2$ will not be a sufficient coordinate. Namely, requirement 8.7.A will not be met, since the coordinate y_2 or m will also be needed to express the average penalties. The coordinate pair x, m (or x, y_2) will be sufficient. Taking into account the form of the infinitesimal operator (11.57) and averaging (11.70) in analogy with (11.55), we obtain the equation

$$-\frac{\partial S_t(x, m)}{\partial t} = \frac{1}{2}\left(\frac{k_t^2}{N} + \varkappa\right)\frac{\partial^2 S_t}{\partial x^2} + \frac{k_t^2}{N}\frac{\partial^2 S_t}{\partial x\, \partial m} + \frac{k_t^2}{2N}\frac{\partial^2 S_t}{\partial m^2} + \tag{11.71}$$

$$+ (a \mp u_0)\frac{\partial S_t}{\partial x} + a\frac{\partial S_t}{\partial m} + C_0(m - x)(x_t^2 + k_t)$$

in $\Xi_{1,2}$, generalizing (11.60) and (11.62).

2. Let us assume now that the complication involves not the penalty function, but the diffusion process $\xi(t)$ which is to be tracked. Let us assume that its drift coefficient is not constant, but has the form

$$a(\xi) = a^0 + a^1\xi.$$

Applying formula (9.34) to this case, instead of (11.57) we obtain the secondary *a posteriori* operator

$$d\mathscr{L}_2 = dt\,(a^0 + a^1 m)\frac{\partial}{\partial m} + du_t\frac{\partial}{\partial y_2} +$$

$$+ \frac{dt}{2}\left(\frac{k_t^2}{N}\frac{\partial^2}{\partial m^2} + \varkappa\frac{\partial^2}{\partial y_2^2}\right). \tag{11.72}$$

The one-dimensional process $x = m - y_2$ is now not Markov, but is a component of the two-dimensional Markov process (x, m). Condition 8.7.B is not satisfied for x, although the other requirements 8.7.A, C can be satisfied. The second coordinate m must be added to x, upon which all requirements are met.

From (11.72), the basic equation in this case will have the form

$$-\frac{\partial S_t(x, m)}{\partial t} = \frac{1}{2}\left(\frac{k_t^2}{N} + \varkappa\right)\frac{\partial^2 S_t}{\partial x^2} + \frac{k_t^2}{N}\frac{\partial^2 S_t}{\partial x\, \partial m} + \frac{k_t^2}{2N}\frac{\partial^2 S_t}{\partial m^2} +$$

$$+ (a^0 + a^1 m \mp u_0)\frac{\partial S_t}{\partial x} + (a^0 + a^1 m)\frac{\partial S_t}{\partial m} + x^2 + k_t \tag{11.73}$$

in $\Xi_{1,2}$.

3. Let us assume now that the increase in complexity involves only the operation of the servomotor. We will assume that for various situations of the regulated plant (for various y_2), the operating conditions of the servomotor are different and its maximum speed depends on y_2:

$$|u_t - u_{t-\Delta}| \leqslant \int_{t-\Delta}^{t} u_0(y_2(\tau))\,d\tau = u_0(y_2(t))\,\Delta + o(\Delta). \tag{11.74}$$

In this case the coordinate x suffices for the fulfillment of requirements 8.7.A, B, but is not sufficient to express the constraint (11.74) on the control (8.7.C is not satisfied). Inclusion of the coordinate y_2 (or m) corrects the situation. As can easily be seen, here the basic equation has the form

$$-\frac{\partial S_t(x, m)}{\partial t} = \frac{1}{2}\left(\frac{k_t^2}{N} + \varkappa\right)\frac{\partial^2 S_t}{\partial x^2} + \frac{k_t^2}{N}\frac{\partial^2 S_t}{\partial x\,\partial m} + \frac{k_t^2}{2N}\frac{\partial^2 S_t}{\partial m^2} +$$
$$+ [a \mp u_0(m - x)]\frac{\partial S_t}{\partial x} + a\frac{\partial S_t}{\partial m} + x^2 + k_t \tag{11.75}$$

in $\Xi_{1,2}$.

To each of the equations (11.71), (11.73), and (11.75) there correspond the same conditions (11.61), (11.63), and the same condition (11.64) on the common boundary of regions Ξ_1 and Ξ_2.

We can also easily write the combined equation corresponding to the simultaneous effect of the complicating factors above.

4. Let us consider separately one important cause for increase of the number of sufficient coordinates. In the application of these methods, based on conditional Markov processes, the Markov characteristics of the processes are of primary importance. From a practical point of view, this condition is not very restrictive, since a process which is in reality non-Markov can be represented as a component of a multidimensional Markov process with any required precision.

In this sense, if we ignore the errors connected with such a substitution, the non-Markov character of the processes is not a barrier to application of the theory. To increase the accuracy of the approximation, broadly speaking, we need to increase the number of components of the multidimensional Markov process. Thus more precise inclusion of the non-Markov character of the process involves increasing the number of sufficient coordinates.

The possibility of replacing (with arbitrary accuracy) a non-Markov process by a Markov process enlarges the area of applicability of the theory. Of course, the increase in the number of sufficient coordinates makes it more difficult to carry out the calculations and to obtain specific results. Since an increase in the accuracy of the approximation is related to increased complexity of the calculations, in solving specific practical problems we should strive for a reasonable compromise in choosing an accuracy of the approximation.

We will demonstrate the increase in the number of sufficient coordinates resulting from inclusion of the non-Markov character of the process with an example of the problem solved in Sect. 11.3. Let us assume that the process $\xi(t)$ which is being tracked is not Markov: the probabilities of its future values depend not only on $\xi(t)$, but, let us say, also on the derivative $\eta(t)=\frac{d\xi(t)}{dt}$. If dependence on higher derivatives can be excluded, then the two-dimensional process (ξ, η) will be Markov. Let us assume that the corresponding infinitesimal operator is

$$\frac{dL}{dt}=\frac{1}{2}\lambda^2 D\frac{\partial^2}{\partial\eta^2}-\lambda\eta\frac{\partial}{\partial\eta}+(a+\eta)\frac{\partial}{\partial\xi}.$$

The latter was chosen such that as $\lambda\to\infty$ the process $\xi(t)$ examined previously in Sect. 11.3 would be obtained.

As previously, we suppose that we are observing the process (11.47) and y_2. The joint process ξ, η, y_1, y_2 has an operator

$$dL_{pr}=dt\left[-\lambda\eta\frac{\partial}{\partial\eta}+(a+\eta)\frac{\partial}{\partial\xi}+\xi\frac{\partial}{\partial y_1}+\frac{1}{2}\lambda^2 D\frac{\partial^2}{\partial\eta^2}+\right.$$
$$\left.+\frac{1}{2}N\frac{\partial^2}{\partial y_1^2}\right]+du_t\frac{\partial}{\partial y_2}+\frac{\varkappa}{2}dt\frac{\partial^2}{\partial y_2^2}.$$

Using formulas (9.33) and (9.34), we can write the equations

$$\dot{m}=a+m_\eta+\frac{1}{N}k_{\xi\xi}(\dot{y}_1-m);$$

$$\dot{m}_\eta=-\lambda m_\eta+\frac{1}{N}k_{\xi\eta}(\dot{y}_1-m)$$

for the *a posteriori* mathematical expectations $m=\mathbf{M}_{ps}\xi$, $m_\eta=\mathbf{M}_{ps}\eta$, the equations for the *a posteriori* variances

$$\dot{k}_{\xi\xi}=2k_{\xi\eta}-\frac{1}{N}k_{\xi\xi}^2;$$

$$\dot{k}_{\xi\eta}=k_{\eta\eta}-\lambda k_{\xi\eta}-\frac{1}{N}k_{\xi\xi}k_{\xi\eta}; \qquad (11.76)$$

$$\dot{k}_{\eta\eta}=\lambda^2 D-2\lambda k_{\eta\eta}-\frac{1}{N}k_{\xi\eta}^2,$$

and the expression for the secondary *a posteriori* infinitesimal operator:

$$d\mathscr{L} = dt\left[-\lambda m_\eta \frac{\partial}{\partial m_\eta} + (a+m_\eta)\frac{\partial}{\partial m} + m\frac{\partial}{\partial y_1} + \right.$$
$$+\frac{1}{2N}k_{\xi\xi}^2\frac{\partial^2}{\partial m^2} + \frac{1}{2N}k_{\xi\eta}^2\frac{\partial^2}{\partial m_\eta^2} + \frac{N}{2}\frac{\partial^2}{\partial y_1^2} + \frac{1}{N}k_{\xi\xi}k_{\xi\eta}\frac{\partial^2}{\partial m\,\partial m_\eta} + \qquad (11.77)$$
$$\left.+k_{\xi\xi}\frac{\partial^2}{\partial m\,\partial y_1} + k_{\xi\eta}\frac{\partial^2}{\partial m_\eta\,\partial y_1}\right] + du_t\frac{\partial}{\partial y_2} + \frac{\varkappa}{2}dt\frac{\partial^2}{\partial y_2^2}.$$

As can be verified, the variables $x = m - y_2$, m_η now serve as sufficient coordinates. Taking into account (11.77), we obtain the basic equation

$$-\frac{\partial S_t(x, m_\eta)}{\partial t} = -\lambda m_\eta \frac{\partial S_t}{\partial m_\eta} + (a + m_\eta \mp u_0)\frac{\partial S_t}{\partial x} +$$
$$+\frac{1}{2}\left(\frac{k_{\xi\xi}^2}{N} + \varkappa\right)\frac{\partial^2 S_t}{\partial x^2} + \frac{1}{2N}k_{\xi\eta}^2\frac{\partial^2 S_t}{\partial m_\eta^2} + \frac{1}{N}k_{\xi\xi}k_{\xi\eta}\frac{\partial^2 S_t}{\partial x\,\partial m_\eta} + x^2 + k_{\xi\xi} \qquad (11.78)$$

in $\Xi_{1,2}$. Thus the inclusion of a non-Markov character of the process $\xi(t)$ carried out here caused an additional coordinate m_η to appear.

5. In an analogous manner we can include a non-Markov motion of the regulated plant. Let us assume $y_2(t)$ is a component of a two-dimensional Markov process $(y_2(t),\ v(t) = \dot{y}_2(t))$, whence Eq. (11.48) is replaced by the equation

$$\lambda^{-1}dv(t) + v(t)\,dt = du_t + d\zeta_2(t), \qquad (11.79)$$

where $\zeta_2(t)$ is the same Wiener process. To the latter equation there corresponds the infinitesimal operator

$$dL_{pr} = dt\,v\frac{\partial}{\partial y_2} + \lambda(du_t - v\,dt)\frac{\partial}{\partial v} + \frac{\varkappa}{2}\lambda^2 dt\frac{\partial^2}{\partial v^2}. \qquad (11.80)$$

The transition from (11.48) to (11.79) can be supported by considering the inertia of the regulated plant. If we carry out the passage to the limit as $\lambda\to\infty$ (the inertia tends to zero), then (11.79) obviously will become (11.48).

Condition 8.7.B now requires the addition of the variable $v(t)$ to the sufficient coordinates. Replacing the operator

$$du_t\frac{\partial}{\partial y_2} + \frac{\varkappa}{2}\frac{\partial^2}{\partial y_2^2}$$

by the operator (11.80) we obtain in this case the basic equation in the form

$$-\frac{\partial S_t(x, v)}{\partial t} = (a - v)\frac{\partial S_t}{\partial x} - \lambda(v \pm u_0)\frac{\partial S_t}{\partial v} +$$
$$+\frac{1}{2}\frac{k_t^2}{N}\frac{\partial^2 S_t}{\partial x^2} + \frac{\varkappa}{2}\lambda^2\frac{\partial^2 S_t}{\partial v^2} + x^2 + k_t \qquad (11.81)$$

in regions $\Xi_{1,2}$, where

$$\operatorname{sign} \frac{\partial S_t}{\partial v} = \pm 1.$$

In analogy with the preceding, on the common boundary Γ of the indicated regions the conditions of continuity and vanishing of the first derivative $\frac{\partial S_t}{\partial v}$ are satisfied.

6. As a result of the increase of the number of variables, the solution of Eqs. (11.71), (11.73), (11.75), (11.78), and (11.81) is noticeably more difficult than that of Eqs. (11.60) and (11.62); thus for the former we cannot obtain general and exact results. Nevertheless, in various special cases, if we use special relations among the parameters of the problem, we can apply this or that asymptotic method (method of a small parameter), and obtain approximate results with its aid.

Thus, in the work of Stratonovich [18] there was developed and applied to solution of the stationary variant of Eq. (11.73) an asymptotic method involving small coefficients for the diffusion terms (terms with second derivatives). There the solution is found by successive approximations, results of the first approximation being found without particular difficulty.

In other special cases other approximate methods can be developed. Suppose, for example, it is of interest to study the case when the causes considered in the present section, which result in increased complexity of the equations, do not have a large effect on the final results, and do not strongly influence the problem examined in Sect. 11.3. Then it is possible to calculate the effect to the first approximation, to the second, etc., using the usual methods of successive approximations which, as a rule, can be applied in such a situation.

Without considering the usual methods of successive approximations for the solution of Eqs. (11.71), (11.73), and (11.75), we will give a simple approximate solution for them in the special case in question. We will consider for definiteness Eq. (11.73). For each particular value of the coordinate m there is established a quasi-stationary probability distribution for the second coordinate x. The coordinate m in this process cannot change appreciably. To the quasi-stationary fluctuations in x, as we can see from (11.73), there corresponds the equation

$$\frac{1}{2}\left(\frac{k_t^2}{N} + \varkappa\right) \frac{\partial^2 \widetilde{S}}{\partial x^2} + (a^0 + a^1 m \mp u_0) \frac{\partial \widetilde{S}}{\partial x} + x^2 + k = \widetilde{\gamma}(m).$$

Solving this, in analogy with Sect. 11.3 (11.69), we find the quasi-stationary average penalties and the quasi-stationary boundary, both depending on m:

$$\widetilde{\gamma}(m) = k_t + \frac{1}{2}\left(\frac{k_t^2}{N} + \varkappa\right)^2 \frac{u_0^2 + (a^0 + a^1 m)^2}{[u_0^2 - (a^0 + a^1 m)^2]^2},$$

$$x_\Gamma(m) = -\frac{(a^0 + a^1 m)(k_t^2 N^{-1} + \varkappa)}{u_0^2 - (a^0 + a^1 m)^2}.$$

After this we can turn to examination of diffusion of the second coordinate m. If $S_t(m)$ is a function depending only on the variable m (averaged with respect to fluctuations of the second variable x), then, as is not difficult to see using (11.72), it is described by the approximate equation

$$-\frac{\partial S_t(m)}{\partial t} = \frac{1}{2}\frac{k_t^2}{N}\frac{\partial^2 S_t}{\partial m^2} + (a^0 + a^1 m)\frac{\partial S_t}{\partial m} + \widetilde{\gamma}(m).$$

The exploitation of standard methods gives a basis for the cited results and permits us to obtain more precise results corresponding to higher approximations. The condition for the applicability of these results and approximations is that the value of the coefficient a^1 must be small.

7. Finally, let us examine in more detail one method of successive approximations, useful for finding the solution of Eq. (11.78), which is similar to the method presented in the book by Stratonovich ([8], pp. 106-110, 115-117). As in the above case, the condition for its applicability is proximity to the undisturbed conditions, i.e., a large value of the parameter λ.

We will examine the stationary solution, as at the end of Sect. 11.3. The equation for the stationary *a posteriori* variance is obtained by setting the time derivatives in (11.76) to zero. This yields

$$k_{\xi\eta} = \frac{k_{\xi\xi}^2}{2N};\quad k_{\eta\eta} = \frac{\lambda}{2N}k_{\xi\xi}^2 + \frac{1}{2N^2}k_{\xi\xi}^3;$$

$$k_{\xi\xi}^2 + \frac{1}{\lambda N}k_{\xi\xi}^3 + \frac{1}{4\lambda^2 N^2}k_{\xi\xi}^4 = DN.$$

It is not difficult to obtain the asymptotic solutions of these equations:

$$k_{\xi\xi} = \sqrt{DN} - \frac{D}{2\lambda} + O(\lambda^{-2});$$

$$k_{\xi\eta} = \frac{D}{2} - \frac{D}{2\lambda}\sqrt{\frac{D}{N}} + O(\lambda^{-2}).$$

Introducing a variable $y = \sqrt{2\lambda N}\eta_0/k_{\xi\xi}$, we write the stationary variant of Eq. (11.78):

$$\lambda\left(\frac{\partial^2 f}{\partial y^2} - y\frac{\partial f}{\partial y}\right) + \sqrt{\lambda}\varkappa_1 \frac{\partial^2 f}{\partial y\,\partial x} + \left(a + \frac{\alpha}{\sqrt{\lambda}}y \mp u^0\right)\frac{\partial f}{\partial x} +$$

$$+ \frac{\varkappa_2}{2}\frac{\partial^2 f}{\partial x^2} + x^2 + k_{\xi\xi} - \gamma = 0 \qquad (11.82)$$

$$\left(\varkappa_1 = k_{\xi\eta}\sqrt{\frac{2}{N}};\ \varkappa_2 = \frac{k_{\xi\xi}^2}{N} + \varkappa;\ \alpha = \frac{k_{\xi\xi}}{\sqrt{2N}}\right).$$

In place of one function of two variables, we will examine the sequence of functions of one variable

$$f_n(x) = \int_{-\infty}^{\infty} f(x, y)\,F^{(n+1)}(y)\,dy = (-1)^n \int_{-\infty}^{\infty} \frac{\partial^n f(x, y)}{\partial y^n} F^{(1)}(y)\,dy \qquad (11.83)$$

$$\left(n = 0, 1, 2, \ldots;\ F^{(n+1)}(y) = \frac{1}{\sqrt{2\pi}}\frac{d^n}{dy^n}e^{-\frac{y^2}{2}}\right).$$

In order to obtain equations for these, we will multiply (11.82) by $F^{(n+1)}(y)$ and integrate over y. In considering terms containing derivatives with respect to y, it is convenient to carry out an integration by parts. In addition, we need to use the relations

$$\frac{d^2F^{(n+1)}(y)}{dy^2} + \frac{d}{\partial y}[yF^{(n+1)}(y)] + nF^{(n+1)}(y) = 0;$$

$$yF^{(n+1)}(y) = -F^{(n+2)}(y) - nF^{(n)}(y).$$

Then from (11.82) we will have for $n = 0$

$$a\frac{df_0}{dx} + \frac{\varkappa_2}{2}\frac{d^2f_0}{dx^2} - u_0\int F^{(1)}\left|\frac{\partial f}{\partial x}\right|dy + x^2 + k_{\xi\xi} - \gamma -$$

$$-\sqrt{\lambda}\varkappa_1'\frac{df_1}{dx} = 0 \quad \left(\varkappa_1' = \varkappa_1 + \frac{\alpha}{\lambda}\right) \qquad (11.84)$$

and

$$f_n = -\frac{\alpha}{\lambda\sqrt{\lambda}}\frac{df_{n-1}}{dx} + \frac{a}{n\lambda}\frac{df_n}{dx} + \frac{\varkappa_2}{2n\lambda}\frac{d^2f_n}{dx^2} -$$

$$-\frac{u_0}{n\lambda}\int F^{(n+1)}\left|\frac{\partial f}{\partial x}\right|dy - \frac{\varkappa_1'}{n\sqrt{\lambda}}\frac{df_{n+1}}{dx} \qquad (11.85)$$

for $n \geqslant 1$. Let us first substitute

$$f_1 = -\frac{\alpha}{\lambda\sqrt{\lambda}}\frac{df_0}{dx} + \frac{\alpha}{\lambda}\frac{df_1}{dx} + \frac{\varkappa_2}{2\lambda}\frac{d^2f_1}{dx^2} -$$

$$-\frac{u_0}{\lambda}\int F^{(2)}\left|\frac{\partial f}{\partial x}\right|dy - \frac{\varkappa_1'}{\sqrt{\lambda}}\frac{df_2}{dx} \qquad (11.86)$$

into Eq. (11.84). Then we will substitute into the resulting equation the analogous expressions from (11.85) for f_2 and f_1, then into the result the expressions for f_3, f_2, f_1, etc. These substitutions will add to the equation all new terms for the progressing order with regard to $\lambda^{-\frac{1}{2}}$. The leading terms (terms of the lowest degree of the parameter $\lambda^{-\frac{1}{2}}$) nevertheless are already formed as a result of the first substitutions and further substitutions do not influence them. Retaining only such leading terms, we write the resulting equation in the form

$$a\frac{df_0}{dx}+\frac{\varkappa_2}{2}\frac{d^2f_0}{dx}-u_0\int F^{(1)}\left|\frac{\partial f}{dx}\right|dy+x^2+k_{\xi\xi}-\gamma+$$

$$+\frac{\varkappa_1'a}{\lambda}\frac{d^2f_0}{dx^2}+\frac{\varkappa_1'a}{\lambda^2}\left(a\frac{d}{dx}+\frac{\varkappa_2}{2}\frac{d^2}{dx^2}\right)\frac{d^2f_0}{dx^2}+$$

$$+\frac{\varkappa_1'u_0}{\sqrt{\lambda}}\frac{d}{dx}\int F^{(2)}\left|\frac{\partial f}{\partial x}\right|dy+O(\lambda^{-3}). \tag{11.87}$$

If these multiple substitutions are carried out in Eq. (11.86) or in the analogous equation for f_2 (or $f_3,\ldots$), we will find that f_1 is of the order of $\lambda^{-\frac{3}{2}}$, f_2 of the order of λ^{-3}, etc.

The integral terms, containing $\int F^{(n+1)}\left|\frac{\partial f}{\partial x}\right|dy$, should in the resulting expressions, for example, in Eq. (11.87), be expressed in terms of $f_0, f_1,\ldots$ and in the final calculation in terms of the function f_0 and its derivatives. We will show how this can be done. Writing the function $f(x, y)$ in terms of derivatives

$$f(x, y)=\sum_{k=0}^{\infty}\frac{1}{k!}f^{(k)}(x, 0)\,y^k \tag{11.88}$$

and substituting into (11.83), we have

$$f_n(x)=(-1)^n\sum_{l=0}^{\infty}\frac{1}{l!}f^{(n+l)}(x, 0)\,\overline{y^l}, \tag{11.89}$$

where

$$\overline{y^l}=\int F^{(1)}(y)\,y^l\,dy=\begin{cases}1\cdot3\cdot5\ldots(l-1) & \text{for even } l;\\ 0 & \text{for odd } l.\end{cases}$$

The equations can be regarded as equations involving $\{f^{(k)}, k=0, 1,\ldots\}$. Taking into account that the functions f_n (and hence also $f^{(n)}$) decrease with increasing n as powers of the small parameter $\lambda^{-\frac{3}{2}}$, it is not difficult to solve the system of equations (11.89) and to find $\{f^{(k)}\}$ to within a specified degree of precision, for example,

$$f(x, 0)=f_0(x)-\frac{1}{2}f_2(x)+\ldots;$$

$$f^{(1)}(x, 0)=-f_1(x)+\frac{1}{2}f_3(x)+\ldots; \tag{11.90}$$

$$f^{(2)}(x, 0)=f_2(x)+\ldots.$$

Thus $\{f^{(k)}\}$ are expressed in terms of $\{f_n\}$. Thus the integral

$$\int F^{(n+1)}\left|\frac{\partial f}{\partial x}\right|dy=\int F^{(n+1)}(y)\left|\frac{\partial}{\partial x}\sum_{k=0}^{\infty}\frac{1}{k!}f^{(k)}(x,0)\,y^k\right|dy$$

is also expressed in terms of $\{f_n\}$. The multiple substitutions (11.85) result in the fact that this integral in the final calculation is expressed in terms of f_0. As a result, Eq. (11.87) becomes a closed equation in the function $f_0(x)$ and can be used for its determination. The equation for the switching time

$$\frac{\partial}{\partial x}\sum_{k=0}^{\infty}\frac{1}{k!}f^{(k)}(x,0)\,y_\Gamma^k(x)=0 \qquad (11.91)$$

for the same reason is expressed only in terms of the function $f_0(x)$. Actual calculations are facilitated by the presence of the small parameter and by the fact that the calculations can be carried out only to within a precision of a selected power of this parameter.

In order to illustrate this method, we will find the first correction to the undisturbed regime. Retaining only the first (largest) correction in terms [in (11.87)], we have

$$a\frac{df_0}{dx}+\frac{\varkappa_2}{2}\frac{d^2f_0}{dx^2}-u_0\int F^{(1)}\left|\frac{\partial f}{\partial x}\right|dy+x^2+k_\xi-\gamma+$$

$$+\frac{\varkappa_1'\alpha}{\lambda}\frac{d^2f_0}{dx^2}=0. \qquad (11.92)$$

In accordance with the selected precision, here we can assume

$$\int F^{(1)}\left|\frac{\partial f}{\partial x}\right|dy=\int F^{(1)}(y)\left|\frac{df_0}{dx}-\frac{df_1}{dx}y+O(\lambda^{-3})\right|dy=$$

$$=\int F^{(1)}(y)\left|\frac{df_0}{dx}+\frac{\alpha y}{\lambda\sqrt{\lambda}}\frac{d^2f_0}{\partial x^2}+O(\lambda^{-\frac{5}{2}})\right|dy.$$

This integral thus equals $\left|\frac{df_0}{dx}\right|$ in those places where $\left|\frac{df_0}{dx}\right|\gg \alpha\lambda^{-\frac{3}{2}}\left|\frac{d^2f_0}{dx^2}\right|$, i.e., in the overwhelming majority of places. A more complex expression for it is valid in region B, where $\left|\frac{\partial f_0}{dx}\right|\sim \alpha\lambda^{-\frac{3}{2}}\left|\frac{d^2f_0}{dx^2}\right|$. Let x_Γ be a point defined by the condition $\frac{df_0}{dx}(x_\Gamma)=0$. The region in question contains this point, and in it $\frac{df_0}{dx}=\frac{d^2f_0}{dx^2}(x_\Gamma)(x-x_\Gamma)+O(\lambda^{-3})$. Thus in region B

$$\int F^{(1)}\left|\frac{\partial f}{dx}\right|dy=\left|\frac{d^2f_0}{dx^2}(x_\Gamma)\right|\cdot\int F^{(1)}(y)\left|x-x_\Gamma+\alpha\lambda^{-\frac{3}{2}}y\right|dy.$$

The difference between this function and $\left|\frac{df_0}{dx}\right|$ is equal to

$$\int F^{(1)}\left|\frac{\partial f}{\partial x}\right|dy-\left|\frac{df_0}{dx}\right|=\left|\frac{d^2f_0}{dx^2}(x_\Gamma)\right|\left[\int F^{(1)}(y)\left|x-x_\Gamma+\right.\right.$$

$$\left.\left.+\alpha\lambda^{-\frac{3}{2}}y\right|dy-|x-x_\Gamma|\right]=\alpha\lambda^{-\frac{3}{2}}\left|\frac{d^2f_0}{dx^2}(x_\Gamma)\right|\varphi(x), \qquad (11.93)$$

$$\left(\varphi(x)=\int F^{(1)}(y)\left[\left|\alpha^{-1}\lambda^{3/2}(x-x_\Gamma)+y\right|-\alpha^{-1}\lambda^{3/2}|x-x_\Gamma|\right]dy\right).$$

The line of switching defined by (11.91) in this approximation is a straight line: $y_\Gamma(x)=\alpha^{-1}\lambda^{3/2}(x-x_\Gamma)$. In fact, from (11.88), (11.90), and (11.86) we have

$$f(x,y)=f_0(x)-f_1(x)y+\ldots=f_0(x)-\frac{\alpha}{\lambda\sqrt{\lambda}}\frac{df_0}{dx}(x)y+\ldots$$

and thus

$$\frac{\partial f}{\partial x}(x,y)=\frac{df_0}{dx}(x)-\frac{\alpha}{\lambda\sqrt{\lambda}}\frac{d^2f_0}{dx^2}(x)y+\ldots=$$

$$=\frac{d^2f_0}{dx^2}(x_\Gamma)(x-x_\Gamma)-\frac{\alpha}{\lambda\sqrt{\lambda}}\frac{df_0}{dx^2}(x_\Gamma)y+\ldots.$$

From this, setting the modulus to zero, we obtain the indicated result. Equation (11.92) as a result of (11.93) takes the form

$$\left(\frac{\varkappa_2}{2}+\frac{\varkappa_1'\alpha}{\lambda}\right)\frac{d^2f_0}{dx^2}+a\frac{df_0}{dx}-u_0\left|\frac{df_0}{dx}\right|-$$

$$-\frac{\alpha u_0}{\lambda\sqrt{\lambda}}\left|\frac{d^2f_0}{dx^2}(x_\Gamma)\right|\varphi(x)+x^2+k_{\xi\xi}-\gamma=0,$$

analogous to (11.65) and (11.66). The function $\varphi(x)$ appears in region B, which has a small width $\sim\alpha\lambda^{-\frac{3}{2}}$ along the x axis and in this approximation has little effect on the result. The main difference from the results of Sect. 11.3 is thus reduced to the fact that the diffusion coefficient $\varkappa_2=\frac{k^2}{N}+\varkappa$ is replaced by $\frac{k_{\xi\xi}^2}{N}+\varkappa+\frac{k_{\xi\xi}k_{\xi\eta}}{\lambda N}+O(\lambda^{-2})$.

The increase in the number of sufficient coordinates when supplementary factors complicating the problem are present, illustrated in this section, can be considered typical. The corresponding increase in difficulties of calculation requires development of new, occasionally unique, approximate methods of calculation.

APPENDIX I

Conditional Measures and Mathematical Expectations Using Nonnormalized Measures

The formulas and concepts of conditional measures and conditional mathematical expectations used here are direct generalizations of the usual formulas and concepts. The generalization relates to the case when the measure is not probabilistic, i.e., when the measure of the entire space is not equal to 1.

Let us assume we are given a space with measure $(\Omega, \mathcal{F}, \mu)$, where $\mu(\Omega) < \infty$. Mathematical expectation will be defined by the formula

$$\mathbf{M}_{\mu}\xi = \frac{1}{\mu(\Omega)} \int_{\Omega} \xi(\omega)\, \mu(d\omega), \tag{A.1.1}$$

if $\xi(\omega)$ is an $\mathcal{F}$-measurable summable function on Ω. With this definition, clearly

$$\mathbf{M}_{\mu} 1 = 1.$$

Suppose we have a σ-algebra $\mathcal{F}_1 \subset \mathcal{F}$. The conditional measure $\mu(\Gamma \in \mathcal{F} \mid \mathcal{F}_1)$ will be defined as the Radon-Nikodim derivative (on $\mathcal{F}_1$) of the measure $\mu(\cdot\Gamma)$ relative to the measure $\mu(\cdot)$:

$$\mu(\Gamma \in \mathcal{F} \mid \mathcal{F}_1) = \frac{\mu(d\omega\Gamma)}{\mu(d\omega \in \mathcal{F}_1)}. \tag{A.1.2}$$

Such a definition is possible, for $\mu(\Lambda\Gamma) = 0$ whenever $\mu(\Lambda) = 0$.

According to this definition,

$$\mu(\Lambda\Gamma) = \int_{\Lambda} \mu(\Gamma \mid \mathcal{F}_1)\, \mu(d\omega \in \mathcal{F}_1), \quad \Gamma \in \mathcal{F}, \ \Lambda \in \mathcal{F}_1$$

or, using a clearer notation,

$$\mu(dx\,dy) = \mu(dx \mid y)\,\mu(dy).$$

If there exist monotonic σ-algebras, $\mathcal{F}_1 \subset \mathcal{F}_2 \subset \ldots \subset \mathcal{F}_N = \mathcal{F}$, then in analogy with the preceding, we can define the conditional measures

$$\mu(A \in \mathcal{F}_k \mid \mathcal{F}_{k-1}) = \frac{\mu(d\omega A)}{\mu(d\omega \in \mathcal{F}_{k-1})}, \quad k = 2, \ldots, N.$$

From this we have

$$\mu(A \in \mathcal{F}_k) = \int \mu(A \mid \mathcal{F}_{k-1})\,\mu(d\omega' \in \mathcal{F}_{k-1}).$$

Writing $\mu(d\omega' \in \mathcal{F}_{k-1})$ here using a similar formula

$$\mu(B \in \mathcal{F}_{k-1}) = \int \mu(B \mid \mathcal{F}_{k-2})\,\mu(d\omega'' \in \mathcal{F}_{k-2}),$$

and similarly expressing the other probabilities

$$\mu(d\omega \in \mathcal{F}_{k-2}),\ \mu(d\omega \in \mathcal{F}_{k-3}), \ldots,$$

we obtain

$$\mu(A \in \mathcal{F}_k) = \int \ldots \int \mu(A \mid \mathcal{F}_{k-1})\,\mu(d\omega' \in \mathcal{F}_{k-1} \mid \mathcal{F}_{k-2})\,\mu(d\omega'' \in \mathcal{F}_{k-2} \mid \mathcal{F}_{k-3}) \ldots \mu(d\omega \in \mathcal{F}_1). \quad (A.1.3)$$

This formula agrees with the usual such formulas for conditional probabilities. It can be written in the more obvious form

$$\mu(dx\,dy\,dz \ldots du) = \mu(dx \mid y, z, \ldots, u)\,\mu(dy \mid z, \ldots, u) \ldots \mu(du).$$

With the conditional measure (A.1.2) we will associate the conditional mathematical expectation

$$\mathbf{M}_\mu[\xi \mid \mathcal{F}_1] = \frac{1}{\mu(\Omega \mid \mathcal{F}_1)} \int_\Omega \xi(\omega)\,\mu(d\omega \mid \mathcal{F}_1)$$

in accordance with formula (A.1.1). But, as can be seen from (A.1.2), $\mu(\Omega \mid \mathcal{F}_1) = 1$; hence the conditional mathematical expectation can be written more simply:

$$\mathbf{M}_\mu[\xi \mid \mathcal{F}_1] = \int \xi(\omega)\,\mu(d\omega \mid \mathcal{F}_1). \quad (A.1.4)$$

Of course, instead of $\mathcal{F}_1$ we can also use here any other σ-algebra, for example, $\mathcal{F}_k$.

The natural relation $\mathbf{M}_\mu[1|\mathcal{F}_1]=1$ for a conditional mathematical expectation also is retained. Thus also in this case the conditional mathematical expectation has the sense of a certain average value of the function, regardless of the fact that the reference measure μ is not normalized to unity.

Assume $\mathcal{F}_1 \subset \mathcal{F}_2 \subset \mathcal{F}$. As in the probabilistic case (when $\mu(\Omega)=1$), the conditional mathematical expectation has the following properties:

A.1.A.

$$\mathbf{M}_\mu\{\mathbf{M}_\mu[\xi|\mathcal{F}_2]|\mathcal{F}_1\} = \mathbf{M}_\mu[\xi|\mathcal{F}_1] \quad \text{(almost everywhere);}$$

A.1.B. if $\xi(\omega)$ is $\mathcal{F}_1$-measurable, then

$$\mathbf{M}_\mu[\xi|\mathcal{F}_2] = \xi(\omega) \text{ (a.e.).}$$

Property A.1.A follows from the relation

$$\int \mu(A|\mathcal{F}_2)\,\mu(d\omega \in \mathcal{F}_2|\mathcal{F}_1) = \mu(A|\mathcal{F}_1), \; A \in \mathcal{F},$$

which results if we assume in (A.1.3) first $(\mathcal{F}_1,\ldots,\mathcal{F}_k) = (\mathcal{F}_1, \mathcal{F}_2, \mathcal{F})$ $(k=3)$, and then $(\mathcal{F}_1,\ldots,\mathcal{F}_k) = (\mathcal{F}_1, \mathcal{F})$ $(k=2)$, and equate the results.

Let us check property A.1.B. As a result of the $\mathcal{F}_1$-measurability (and hence the $\mathcal{F}_2$-measurability) of the function $\xi(\omega)$ the relation

$$\mathbf{M}_\mu[\xi|\mathcal{F}_2] = \int \xi(\omega)\,\mu(d\omega|\mathcal{F}_2)$$

can be written

$$\mathbf{M}_\mu[\xi|\mathcal{F}_2] = \int \xi(\omega)\,\mu(d\omega \in \mathcal{F}_2|\mathcal{F}_2).$$

But according to (A.1.2), the measure $\mu(\Lambda \in \mathcal{F}_2|\mathcal{F}_2)$ is trivial:

$$\mu(\Lambda \in \mathcal{F}_2|\mathcal{F}_2) = I_\Lambda(\omega) \quad \text{(a.e.)}$$

where $I_\Lambda(\omega)$ is the indicator of the set Λ. Thus

$$\int \xi(\omega')\,\mu(d\omega' \in \mathcal{F}_2|\mathcal{F}_2) = \int \xi(\omega')\,I_{d\omega}'(\omega) = \xi(\omega),$$

of which we can be convinced after replacing the integral by the prelimit sum and passing to the limit.

Thus we see that for nonprobabilistic measures it is also possible to introduce conditional measures and conditional mathematical expectations with characteristics analogous to the usual characteristics valid for probabilistic measures.

APPENDIX II

Conditional Minimization

Variant I.

Let us assume we are given a space Ω and both σ-algebras of its subsets $\mathcal{F}_1 \subset \mathcal{F}_2$. Further, on Ω we are given an $\mathcal{F}_2$-measurable function $f(\omega)$.

Definition A.2.1. The conditional lower bound

$$\inf_{\omega | \mathcal{F}_1} f(\omega) = \tilde{f}(\omega)$$

is a function with the properties:

A.2.1.A. it is defined on Ω and is $\mathcal{F}_1$-measurable;
A.2.1.B. if $\Gamma \in \mathcal{F}_1$ is not empty, then

$$\inf_{\omega \in \Gamma} \tilde{f}(\omega) = \inf_{\omega \in \Gamma} f(\omega).$$

Theorem A.2.1. This definition assigns a unique conditional lower bound.

Proof. Let $\tilde{f}_1(\omega)$, $\tilde{f}_2(\omega)$ be two such functions which are not the same. Then there exists $\varepsilon > 0$ and a nonempty set Γ_ε on which one function exceeds the other by more than ε, that is,

$$\Gamma_\varepsilon = \{\omega : \tilde{f}_1(\omega) - \tilde{f}_2(\omega) > \varepsilon\}. \tag{A.2.1}$$

From A.2.1.A we have $\Gamma_\varepsilon \in \mathcal{F}_1$. Taking into account A.2.1.B, we obtain

$$\inf_{\Gamma_\varepsilon} \tilde{f}_1(\omega) = \inf_{\Gamma_\varepsilon} \tilde{f}_2(\omega), \tag{A.2.2}$$

since each side equals $\inf [f(\omega), \omega \in \Gamma_\varepsilon]$. But according to (A.2.1)

$$\inf_{\Gamma_\varepsilon} \tilde{f}_1(\omega) - \inf_{\Gamma_\varepsilon} \tilde{f}_2(\omega) > \varepsilon. \tag{A.2.3}$$

This contradiction proves the equality of the functions $\tilde{f}_1(\omega) = \tilde{f}_2(\omega)$.

Theorem A.2.2. The conditional lower bound satisfies the relation

$$\tilde{f}(\omega) \leqslant f(\omega). \tag{A.2.4}$$

Proof. Let us choose any point $\omega_0 \in \Omega$ and consider the interval $I_\varepsilon = \{\tilde{f}(\omega_0), \tilde{f}(\omega_0) + \varepsilon\}$. From A.2.1.A, the set $\{\omega : \tilde{f}(\omega) \in I_\varepsilon\} = \Gamma$ belongs to $\mathcal{F}_1$. Obviously, it is not empty. Applying A.2.1.B to this set, we obtain

$$\tilde{f}(\omega_0) = \inf_{\omega \in \Gamma} f(\omega).$$

From this (A.2.4) follows at the point ω_0, since $\omega_0 \in \Gamma$.

Theorem A.2.3. Let $\mu(\Lambda | \mathcal{F}_1)$ be a certain conditional probabilistic measure on $(\Omega, \mathcal{F}_2)$, i.e., a function of the pair $(\Lambda, \omega) \in \mathcal{F}_2 \times \Omega$, which is $\mathcal{F}_1$-measurable with respect to the second argument and where $\Lambda \in \mathcal{F}_1$ results in the trivial measure

$$\mu(\Lambda \in \mathcal{F}_1 | \mathcal{F}_1) = I_\Lambda(\omega) \tag{A.2.5}$$

($I_\Lambda(\omega)$ is the indicator of the set Λ). Then

$$\tilde{f}(\omega) \leqslant \int f(\omega') \mu(d\omega' | \mathcal{F}_1), \tag{A.2.6}$$

if the integral on the right side exists for all ω.

Proof. Using (A.2.4), we have

$$\int f(\omega') \mu(d\omega' | \mathcal{F}_1) \geqslant \int \tilde{f}(\omega') \mu(d\omega' \in \mathcal{F}_2 | \mathcal{F}_1).$$

The integral on the right side of this equation from A.2.1.A can be written

$$\int \tilde{f}(\omega') \mu(d\omega' \in \mathcal{F}_1 | \mathcal{F}_1).$$

Using the trivial form (A.2.5) of the measure in the integral, we have

$$\int \tilde{f}(\omega') \mu(d\omega' | \mathcal{F}_1) = \int \tilde{f}(\omega') I_{d\omega'}(\omega) = \tilde{f}(\omega).$$

We can be convinced of the correctness of this in more detail, if we consider the integral to be the limit of the corresponding sum. Comparison of the above relations proves (A.2.6).

Theorem A.2.4. For any $\varepsilon > 0$ there exists an $\mathcal{F}_1$-measurable function $\omega^*(\omega)$ [with values in Ω] such that

$$f(\omega^*(\omega)) < \tilde{f}(\omega) + \varepsilon. \tag{A.2.7}$$

Proof. We will carry out an ε-division of the real line by means of the points ..., c_1, c_2, ... $(0 < c_{k+1} - c_k < \varepsilon)$. With each elementary interval we associate the set

$$\Gamma_k = \{\omega : \tilde{f}(\omega) \in [c_k, c_{k+1})\}.$$

From A.2.1.A this is $\in \mathcal{F}_1$. If it is not empty, then according to A.2.1.B we have

$$\inf_{\omega \in \Gamma_k} f(\omega) \in [c_k, c_{k+1}), \quad \inf_{\omega \in \Gamma_k} f(\omega) < c_{k+1}.$$

Hence it is possible to find a point $\omega_k^* \in \Gamma_k$ such that

$$f(\omega_k^*) < c_{k+1}. \tag{A.2.8}$$

The union of all nonempty sets $\ldots, \Gamma_1, \Gamma_2, \ldots$ coincides with Ω.

Fixing the set of selected points $\ldots, \omega_1^*, \omega_2^*, \ldots$, we define the function on Ω:

$$\omega^*(\omega) = \omega_k^* \quad \text{for} \quad \omega \in \Gamma_k.$$

Obviously, the inequality (A.2.7) will be satisfied, since the points ω and $\omega^*(\omega)$ belong to the same Γ_k and thus $\tilde{f}(\omega)$, $f(\omega^*(\omega))$ belong to the same interval (c_k, c_{k+1}) [the inequality $c_k \leqslant f(\omega_k^*) < c_{k+1}$ follows from (A.2.8) and (A.2.4)].

It remains to check the $\mathcal{F}_1$-measurability of this function $\omega^*(\omega)$. According to its definition, it is measurable relative to the σ-algebra constructed on the sets ..., Γ_1, Γ_2,.... But $\sigma(\ldots, \Gamma_1, \Gamma_2, \ldots) \subset \mathcal{F}_1$, since every $\Gamma_k \in \mathcal{F}_1$. The theorem is proven.

Theorem A.2.5. For any $\varepsilon > 0$ there exists a conditional probabilistic measure $\mu(\Lambda \subset \mathcal{F}_2 | \mathcal{F}_1)$ such that

$$\int f(\omega') \mu(d\omega' | \mathcal{F}_1) < \tilde{f}(\omega) + \varepsilon. \tag{A.2.9}$$

Proof. The construction of a measure possessing this property can be carried out in analogy with the construction of the function $\omega^*(\omega)$. For $\omega \in \Gamma_k$ (see the preceding proof) we will define the measure $\mu(\Lambda | \omega \in \Gamma_k)$ to be concentrated on the nonempty set

$$A_k = \Gamma_k \cap \{\omega : f(\omega) \in [c_k, c_{k+1})\} \in \mathcal{F}_2,$$

assuming

$$\mu(A_k \mid \omega \in \Gamma_k) = 1; \ \mu(\Omega - A_k \mid \omega \in \Gamma_k) = 0$$

(on the subsets $\Lambda \subset A_k$ the measure can be defined arbitrarily). Then, as can easily be seen,

$$\mu(\Gamma_k \mid \omega \in \Gamma_k) = 1; \ \int f(\omega')\,\mu(d\omega' \mid \omega \in \Gamma_k) \in [c_k, c_{k+1}].$$

The measure $\mu(\Lambda \mid \omega \in \Gamma_k)$ thus satisfies the condition (A.2.5) and inequality (A.2.9). As a function of ω it is measurable relative to $\sigma(\ldots, \Gamma_1, \Gamma_2, \ldots) \subset \mathcal{F}_1$, which completes the proof.

The above examination still does not guarantee that the conditional lower bound assigned by the Definition A.2.1 always exists. Thus it is advisable to construct a function with the required properties.

Let us examine the function

$$\varphi_\Gamma = \inf [f(\omega), \ \omega \in \Gamma]$$

on the sets of the σ-algebra $\mathcal{F}_1$. We will denote by K_ω the class of sets from $\mathcal{F}_1$ which contain a point $\omega \in \Omega$. We will define a function $\tilde{\tilde{f}}(\omega)$ by the formula

$$\tilde{\tilde{f}}(\omega) = \sup_{\Gamma \in K_\omega} \varphi_\Gamma. \tag{A.2.10}$$

We calculate a series of relations for this function. Since $\omega \in A$ for every $A \in K_\omega$, then

$$f(\omega) \geqslant \inf [f(\omega), \ \omega \in A] \equiv \varphi_A.$$

Taking into account (A.2.10), from this we obtain

$$f(\omega) \geqslant \tilde{\tilde{f}}(\omega). \tag{A.2.11}$$

Let us further take a certain Γ and a point $\omega \in \Gamma$. Obviously, $\Gamma \in K_\omega$, so that from (A.2.10)

$$\tilde{\tilde{f}}(\omega) \geqslant \varphi_\Gamma, \ \inf_{\omega \in \Gamma} \tilde{\tilde{f}}(\omega) \geqslant \varphi_\Gamma. \tag{A.2.12}$$

But according to (A.2.11),

$$\inf_{\omega \in \Gamma} \tilde{\tilde{f}}(\omega) \leqslant \inf_{\omega \in \Gamma} f(\omega) \ (\equiv \varphi_\Gamma).$$

Comparing (A.2.12) and (A.2.13) we obtain

$$\inf_{\omega\in\Gamma} \tilde{\tilde{f}}(\omega) = \varphi_\Gamma,$$

i.e., we prove property A.2.1.B.

In order to prove that $\tilde{\tilde{f}}(\omega)$ coincides with the conditional lower bound given in Definition A.2.1, it remains to prove its $\mathcal{F}_1$-measurability. Without additional assumptions we can prove the somewhat weaker (than $\tilde{\tilde{f}}^{-1}(\mathcal{B}) \subset \mathcal{F}_1$) assertion: if the points ω_1, ω_2 cannot be separated by any of the sets from $\mathcal{F}_1$, then the points $\tilde{\tilde{f}}(\omega_1)$, $\tilde{\tilde{f}}(\omega_2)$ cannot be separated by any set from $\mathcal{B}$ (Borel set).

Of course, in the majority of specific cases the function (A.2.10) is $\mathcal{F}_1$-measurable. Measurable spaces $(\Omega, \mathcal{F}_2)$ having this property for any $\mathcal{F}_1 \subset \mathcal{F}_2$ and f can be called normal.

Variant II.

This theory can be generalized to the case of a space having a measure $(\Omega, \mathcal{F}_2, \nu)$ such that in it ω-functions belonging to the same equivalence class would not be distinguished. Many results and observations carry over to this case with the one change that assertions true everywhere are replaced by assertions true ν-almost everywhere, i.e., to within subsets of a set of measure zero.

Definition A.2.2. The absolute conditional minimum

$$\operatorname*{vrai\,inf}_{\omega|\mathcal{F}_1} f(\omega) = \tilde{f}(\omega), \quad \mathcal{F}_1 \subset \mathcal{F}_2$$

is a function having these properties:

2.2.A. it is defined almost everywhere in Ω and almost everywhere coincides with an $\mathcal{F}_1$-measurable function;

2.2.B. if $\Gamma \in \mathcal{F}_1$ is a set of nonzero measures, then

$$\operatorname*{vrai\,inf}_{\omega\in\Gamma} \tilde{f}(\omega) = \operatorname*{vrai\,inf}_{\omega\in\Gamma} f(\omega) \quad \text{(a.e.}\nu).$$

Theorem A.2.6. The above-defined function exists and is unique to within an equivalence.

Proof. The uniqueness is proven in analogy with Theorem A.2.1 with the difference that the nonempty set Γ_ε is replaced by a set of nonzero measure. And, in addition, relations (A.2.2) and (A.2.3) are taken as satisfied almost everywhere.

The proof of existence is essentially new. The formula

$$\nu(\Gamma)\varphi_\Gamma = \nu(\Gamma) \operatorname*{vrai\,inf}_{\omega\in\Gamma} f(\omega) \tag{A.2.14}$$

defines on $\mathcal{F}_1 \ni \Gamma$ a semiadditive set function, for, as we can easily see,

$$\nu(\Gamma_1+\Gamma_2)\varphi_{\Gamma_1+\Gamma_2} \leqslant \nu(\Gamma_1)\varphi_{\Gamma_1}+\nu(\Gamma_2)\varphi_{\Gamma_2} \text{ for } \nu(\Gamma_1\Gamma_2)\ 0 \qquad (A.2.15)$$

(since from the definition of φ_Γ follows the relation $\varphi_{\Gamma_1+\Gamma_2} \leqslant \varphi_{\Gamma_i}$, $i=1, 2$, if $\nu(\Gamma_i)\neq 0$).

On $\mathcal{F}_1 \ni A$ it is possible to define a measure

$$\rho(A)=\sup_{A=A_1+\ldots+A_n}[\nu(A_1)\varphi_{A_1}+\ldots+\nu(A_n)\varphi_{A_n}]. \qquad (A.2.16)$$

Here the upper bound is taken over all possible divisions $A_1+\ldots+A_n$, $A_i\in\mathcal{F}_1(\nu(A_iA_j)=0$ where $i\neq j)$ of the set A.

As can be seen from the definition, the absolute continuity of $\rho\ll\nu$ is valid. Applying the Radon-Nikodim theorem to the measure $\rho(A)$, $\nu(A)$, $A\in\mathcal{F}_1$, we prove the existence of a function $\widetilde{f}(\omega)$ having property A.2.2.A.

The semiadditive property (A.2.15) and formula (A.2.16) lead to the relation

$$\nu(\Gamma)\varphi_\Gamma \leqslant \rho(\Gamma), \qquad (A.2.17)$$

i.e., to the inequality

$$\varphi_\Gamma \leqslant \frac{1}{\nu(\Gamma)}\int_\Gamma \widetilde{f}(\omega')\,\nu(d\omega') \equiv \mathbf{M}_\nu[\widetilde{f}(\omega)\mid\omega\in\Gamma]$$

for any nonzero $\Gamma\in\mathcal{F}_1$.

From (A.2.16) we deduce that it is possible to find a sequence of divisions

$$A_1^l+\ldots+A_{n_l}^l=A \quad (A_i^l\in\mathcal{F}_1)$$

such that

$$\rho(A)=\lim_{l\to\infty}\sum_{i=1}^{n_l}\nu(A_i^l)\,\varphi_{A_i^l}. \qquad (A.2.18)$$

Let us introduce a function

$$\chi^l(\omega)=\widetilde{f}(\omega)-\varphi^l(\omega)=\widetilde{f}(\omega)-\varphi_{A_i^l} \text{ for } \omega\in A_i^l,\ \nu(A_i^l)>0,$$

which is nonnegative almost everywhere because of inequality (A.2.17) [which would be violated for the set $\Gamma=\{\omega:\chi^l(\omega)<0\}$]. Taking into account (A.2.18) and the equation $\rho(A)=\int_A\widetilde{f}(\omega)\ \nu\ (d\omega)$, we find that this tends in the mean to zero:

$$\lim_{l\to\infty}\int_A\chi^l(\omega)\,\nu(d\omega)=0.$$

From this it follows that $\chi^l(\omega)$ has measure zero, and from this fact we easily find

$$\text{vrai sup}\, \chi^l(\omega) = \text{vrai sup}\, |\chi^l(\omega)| \to 0$$

and

$$\text{vrai}\inf_A \tilde{f}(\omega) \leftarrow \text{vrai}\inf_A \varphi^l(\omega) \; (= \min[\varphi_{A_i^l} : \nu(A_i^l) > 0, \; i = 1, \ldots, n_l]). \tag{A.2.19}$$

In view of the fact that from the definition (A.2.14) of the function φ_Γ for any division $A = A_1^l + \ldots + A_{n_l}^l$ we have

$$\varphi_A = \min[\varphi_{A_i^l} : \nu(A_i^l) > 0; \; i = 1, \ldots, n_l],$$

(A.2.19) brings us as a consequence to the equation

$$\text{vrai}\inf_{\omega \in A} \tilde{f}(\omega) = \varphi_A.$$

Requirement A.2.2.B, and thus the entire theorem, is proven.

We see that variant II has the advantage over variant I that the existence theorem is proven without supplementary assumptions.

A modification of Theorem A.2.2 in this variant is:

Theorem A.2.7. The absolute conditional minimum almost everywhere satisfies the inequality

$$\tilde{f}(\omega) \equiv \text{vrai}\inf_{\omega' | \mathcal{F}_1} f(\omega') \leqslant f(\omega). \tag{A.2.20}$$

For proof it is sufficient to show that

$$\text{vrai}\inf_E \tilde{f}(\omega) \leqslant \text{vrai}\inf_E f(\omega), \tag{A.2.21}$$

for any set $E \in \mathcal{F}_2$ of nonzero measure.

Having fixed $E \in \mathcal{F}_2$, $\nu(E) > 0$, we will examine the interval

$$J = [\text{vrai}\inf_E \tilde{f}, \; \text{vrai}\sup_E \tilde{f}]$$

and the set

$$\Gamma = \{\omega : \tilde{f}(\omega) \in J\} \in \mathcal{F}_1.$$

It is obvious that (to within the null set) this contains the original set: $\Gamma \supset E$ and $\nu(\Gamma) > 0$. Applying A.2.2.B, we have thus

$$\operatorname*{vrai\,inf}_{E} \tilde{f}(\omega) = \operatorname*{vrai\,inf}_{\Gamma} \tilde{f}(\omega) = \operatorname*{vrai\,inf}_{\Gamma} f(\omega) \leqslant \operatorname*{vrai\,inf}_{E} f(\omega),$$

which proves (A.2.21) and hence also (A.2.20).

Let us formulate a modification of Theorems A.2.3 and A.2.5.

Theorem A.2.8. For any conditional measure $\mu\,(\Lambda \in \mathcal{F}_2 | \mathcal{F}_1)$, the inequality

$$\operatorname*{vrai\,inf}_{\omega|\mathcal{F}_1} f(\omega) \leqslant \int f(\omega)\,\mu\,(d\omega\,|\,\mathcal{F}_1)$$

is true.

Theorem A.2.9. For any $\varepsilon > 0$ there exists a conditional probabilistic measure $\mu\,(\Lambda \in \mathcal{F}_2\,|\,\mathcal{F}_1)$ such that

$$\int f(\omega)\,\mu\,(d\omega\,|\,\mathcal{F}_1) < \operatorname*{vrai\,inf}_{\omega|\mathcal{F}_1} f(\omega) + \varepsilon.$$

In these theorems the conditional probabilistic measure can be defined (differently from the variant I) not for all points, $\omega \in \Omega$, but rather for almost all points, i.e., it is a usual conditional probabilitstic measure. The proof of the theorem is entirely analogous to the proof in variant I.

In conclusion we would like to show that the conditional infinum examined in Supplement 2 exists for some σ-algebras of practical interest. In using the results of the theorems on optimal control given in Chapter 8 in practice, it is convenient to consider the σ-algebras examined in the following theorem.

Theorem A.2.10. Assume that we are given a space Ω of certain functions $g_1(\omega)$, $g_2(\omega)$. We define a σ-algebra $\mathcal{F}_1$ as the minimal σ-algebra containing all possible sets $\{\omega:\ G_1\,(g_1(\omega)) \leqslant C_1\}$, where C_1 is an arbitrary number and G_1 an arbitrary function. (With no loss of generality it can be assumed that $C_1 = 0$.) Analogously,

$$\mathcal{F}_2 = \sigma(\{\omega:\ G_1\,(g_1\,(\omega)) \leqslant 0\ ;\ G_2\,(g_2\,(\omega)) \leqslant 0\})$$

Then

$$\tilde{f}(\omega) = \inf_{\omega' \in B_\omega} f(\omega'),$$

where

$$B_\omega = \{\omega':\ g_1\,(\omega') = g_1\,(\omega)\},$$

is a conditional lower bound in the sense of Definition A.2.1.

Proof. It is easy to see that the set B_ω, and thus also the function $\tilde{f}(\omega)$, depends on ω only through the function $g_1(\omega)$. Thus, $\tilde{f}(\omega)$ is some function of $g_1(\omega)$: $\tilde{f}(\omega) = \tilde{G}(g_1(\omega))$. From this follows the $\mathcal{F}_1$-measurability of $\tilde{f}(\omega)$, i.e., property of A.2.1.A.

In order to prove A.2.1.B, it is sufficient to prove it for one typical set

$$\Gamma = \{\omega : G(g_1(\omega)) \in [a, b]\}$$

(where G, a, b are fixed). Taking into account (A.2.22), we have

$$\inf_{\omega \in \Gamma} \tilde{f}(\omega) = \inf_{\omega' \in B_\Gamma} f(\omega'),$$

where

$$B_\Gamma = \bigcup_{\omega \in \Gamma} B_\omega .$$

But the condition $\omega \in \Gamma$ is equivalent to the condition $G(g_1(\omega)) \in [a, b]$. Taking into account the special form of the sets B, we find that the set B_Γ coincides with Γ.

SUPPLEMENT

Solution of Certain Problems of Mathematical Statistics and Sequential Analysis

In order to master the methods related to differential equations and formulated with the aid of the theory of conditional Markov processes, it is useful to become acquainted with the problems examined below. They are to a certain extent singular, and hence simpler. Thus in problems 2 and 3 *a priori* transitions are absent, and in problem 4 transitions are possible only in one direction. Thus it is not necessary to use the theory of conditional Markov processes in these problems, but it is very helpful. It facilitates the construction of the differential equation, and, most importantly, prepares the reader for the application of the theory in more complex problems when there are, for example, two-directional *a priori* transitions between the states. Solution of this or other more complex problems without systematic application of the theory of conditional Markov processes would be difficult.

In this supplement we will not use the main material of the book (which was written later) to a great extent. Thus the supplement can be read to some degree independently.

We will begin with a somewhat unusual example of optimal filtering solved without construction of an equation for the conditional risks. In the following problems such an equation can play a large role.

1. **Filtering with a disorder signal.** Assume x_t is the only variable parameter, and can take on all possible real values. The interval $-a<x<a$ we will call the "working interval." When x_t belongs to this interval, a possibly more precise estimate of its value from the filter is required. The corresponding solution $u_{tt}=d_{tt}\ (y)$ (where $y=y_0^t$ are the observed values) is the result of the filtering. Let us estimate the quality of filtering by the penalty function

$$C_{tt}(x, u) = \begin{cases} 0 & \text{for } |u-x| < \mu; \\ C & \text{for } |u-x| \geqslant \mu; \end{cases} \quad (1)$$

$$(|x| < a, \ |u| < a).$$

Passage of the value of x_t beyond the limits of the working interval signifies "disorder" and the filter should signal this until x_t returns to the working interval. If the system does not signal disorder at hand, than a penalty A is assessed per unit time. For incorrect signaling a penalty B is levied per unit time. Suppose that the disorder signal results from the solution $d_{tt}(y) = u'$ (u' does not belong to the working interval); then the penalty matrix, in addition to (1), will be defined by the equations

$$\begin{aligned} C_{tt}(x, u) &= A \quad \text{for} \quad |x| \geqslant a, \ |u| < a; \\ C_{tt}(x, u') &= B \quad \text{for} \quad |x| < a. \end{aligned}$$

Let us assume for definiteness that the *a posteriori* distributions are Gaussian:

$$\mathbf{P}(dx_t \mid y_0^t) = \frac{1}{\sqrt{2\pi}\,\sigma} e^{-\frac{(x-m)^2}{2\sigma^2}} dx, \tag{2}$$

where $m = m_t(y)$, $\sigma = \sigma_t(y)$ are functions determined using the equations of the theory of conditional Markov processes. This problem is solved by the methods presented in Sects. 9.1 and 9.2 [case (9.5)]. Here m and σ serve as sufficient coordinates. Substituting (1) and (2) into (9.5a), we find the function

$$s_{tt} = s(u \mid y) = A\left[F\left(\frac{m-a}{\sigma}\right) + 1 - F\left(\frac{m+a}{\sigma}\right)\right] +$$

$$+ C\begin{cases} F\left(\frac{m+a}{\sigma}\right) - F\left(\frac{m-u+\mu}{\sigma}\right), & a-\mu < u < a; \\ F\left(\frac{m+a}{\sigma}\right) - F\left(\frac{m-u+\mu}{\sigma}\right) + F\left(\frac{m-u-\mu}{\sigma}\right) - F\left(\frac{m-a}{\sigma}\right), & |u| < a-\mu; \\ F\left(\frac{m-u-\mu}{\sigma}\right) - F\left(\frac{m-a}{\sigma}\right), & -a < u < -a+\mu; \end{cases}$$

and

$$s(u' \mid y) = B\left[F\left(\frac{m+a}{\sigma}\right) - F\left(\frac{m-a}{\sigma}\right)\right], \tag{3}$$

where

$$F(v) = \frac{1}{\sqrt{2\pi}} \int_0^v e^{-\frac{\varepsilon^2}{2}} d\varepsilon. \tag{3a}$$

Having fixed the values m and σ, we will seek the minima of this function. Comparing the values of the function on the interval

$a-\mu<u<a$, we see that the minimum is attained at the point $u=a-\mu$ and is equal to

$$s(a-\mu\,|\,y)=A\left[F\left(\frac{m-a}{\sigma}\right)+1-F\left(\frac{m+a}{\sigma}\right)\right]+$$
$$+C\left[F\left(\frac{m+a}{\sigma}\right)-F\left(\frac{m-a+2\mu}{\sigma}\right)\right]. \qquad (4)$$

Analogously, the minimum on the interval $-a<u<-a+\mu$ is

$$s(-a+\mu\,|\,x)=A\left[F\left(\frac{m-a}{\sigma}\right)+1-F\left(\frac{m+a}{\sigma}\right)\right]+$$
$$+C\left[F\left(\frac{m+a-2\mu}{\sigma}\right)-F\left(\frac{m-a}{\sigma}\right)\right]. \qquad (5)$$

On the segment $-a+\mu<u<a-\mu$ the minimum is attained at the point $u=m$ and equals

$$s(m\,|\,y)=A\left[F\left(\frac{m-a}{\sigma}\right)+1-F\left(\frac{m+a}{\sigma}\right)\right]+$$
$$+C\left[F\left(\frac{m+a}{\sigma}\right)-F\left(\frac{m-a}{\sigma}\right)-2F\left(\frac{\mu}{\sigma}\right)\right]. \qquad (6)$$

Selecting from (4)–(6) the smallest value, we obtain the filtering rule

$$d_t(y)=\begin{cases} a-\mu & \text{for } m>a-\mu; \\ m, & -a+\mu<m<a-\mu; \\ -a+\mu, & m<-a+\mu \end{cases}$$

(when $|m|$ is less than the critical value m^* introduced below).

The rule for signaling disorder is obtained by comparing (3) with the smallest value from (4)–(6):

$$d_t(y)=u' \quad \text{for} \quad |m|\geqslant m^*.$$

Here the critical value m^* is found from the equation

$$\left(1+\frac{B}{A}\right)\left[F\left(\frac{m^*-a}{\sigma}\right)-F\left(\frac{m^*+a}{\sigma}\right)\right]+$$
$$+\frac{C}{A}\left[F\left(\frac{m^*+a}{\sigma}\right)-F\left(\frac{m^*-a+2\mu}{\sigma}\right)\right]+1=0.$$

2. **The simple Wald problem.** Let us carry out independent sequential trials in which the constant unknown parameter being

estimated can take on only one of two possible values, $x = x_1$ or x_2. If $f(\dot{y} \mid x)$ is the distribution density of the reference at each trial, then the *a posteriori* probability after the nth trial will be

$$W(x) \equiv \mathbf{P}(x \mid \dot{y}_1^n) = \frac{1}{N} \mathbf{P}(x) f(\dot{y}_1 \mid x) \ldots f(\dot{y}_n \mid x), \tag{7}$$

where

$$N = \sum_{i=1}^{2} \mathbf{P}(x_i) f(\dot{y}_1 \mid x_i) \ldots f(\dot{y}_n \mid x_i)$$

is a normalizing factor and $\dot{y}_1, \ldots, \dot{y}_n$ are the observed values.

In the case of continuous observation, after observation of the continuous set of values $\dot{y}_0^t = \{\dot{y}_\tau : 0 \leqslant \tau \leqslant t\}$ formula (7) is replaced by the continuous analog

$$W(x) = \frac{1}{N} \mathbf{P}(x) \exp\left\{\int_0^t \psi_\tau(\dot{y}_\tau, x)\, d\tau\right\}, \tag{8}$$

where the form of the function $\psi_\tau(\dot{y}_\tau, x)$ is determined by the conditions of the problem.* Thus if we observe the signal $\dot{y}_t = s_t(x) + \xi_t$, equal to the sum of the useful signal $s_t(x)$ and white noise $\xi_t = d\zeta_t/dt$ ($\mathbf{M}\xi_t = 0$; $\mathbf{M}\xi_t\xi_{t+\tau} = \varkappa\delta(\tau)$; ζ_t is a Wiener process), then as we know, formula (8) takes the form

$$W(x) = \frac{1}{N} \mathbf{P}(x) \exp\left\{\frac{1}{\varkappa} \int_0^t \left[\dot{y}_\tau - \frac{s_\tau(x)}{2}\right] s_\tau(x)\, d\tau\right\}. \tag{9}$$

This stochastic integral is equivalent to the stochastic differential equation

$$\frac{dw_1}{dt} = -\frac{dw_2}{dt} = \frac{s_1 - s_2}{\varkappa}\left[\dot{y}_t - \frac{s_1 + s_2}{2}\right] w_1(1 - w_1) \tag{10}$$

$$(w_i = W(x_i);\ s_i = s_t(x_i))$$

or

$$dw_1 = \frac{s_1 - s_2}{\varkappa}\left[dy - \frac{s_1 + s_2}{2}\, dt\right] w_1(1 - w_1) \left(y = \int_0^t \dot{y}_\tau\, d\tau\right).$$

This equation is a singular special case of the simplest equation (6.43) of the theory of conditional Markov processes (for a process having two states).

---

*In passing we will note that in the case of observation of a Poisson process $\dot{y}_t = \sum_\zeta \delta(t - t_\zeta)$ with density $\beta_t(x)$ the function $\psi_t(\dot{y}_t, x)$ has the form $\dot{y}_t \ln \beta_t(x) - \beta_t(x)$.

We wish to find the estimate $u = x_1$ or x_2 corresponding to the minimum average risk with the following penalties: (1) penalty A for an incorrect final estimate $u=x_2$; (2) penalty B for an incorrect estimate $u=x_1$; (3) penalty C for observation per unit time. To these conditions corresponds the penalty matrix

$$\| C'_{tt}(x, u) \| = \left\| \begin{matrix} C'_{tt}(x_1, x_1) & C'_{tt}(x_1, x_2) \\ C'_{tt}(x_2, x_1) & C'_{tt}(x_2, x_2) \end{matrix} \right\| = \left\| \begin{matrix} 0 & A \\ B & 0 \end{matrix} \right\|; \tag{11}$$

$$C_{tt}(x, u) = C.$$

The reduced conditional risk $S(w_1, t) = \mathbf{M}[c(\omega) - c^t(\omega) \mid y_0^t]$ [see (10.3) and (10.5) where F_t, F'_t have the form (9.5)] depends only on time and the *a posteriori* probability w_1. It is determined by the basic equation (10.12), which in this case can be written

$$S(w_1, t) = \min[Aw_1, B(1 - w_1), C\Delta + \mathbf{M}_{ps}S(w_1 + \Delta w, t + \Delta) + o(\Delta)], \tag{12}$$

where the averaging symbol $\mathbf{M}_{ps} = \mathbf{M}[\cdot \mid y_0^t] = \mathbf{M}[\cdot \mid w_1]$ applies only to $\Delta w = w_1(t+\Delta) - w_1(t)$.

We will assume $A, B, C, \varkappa, s_{1,2}$ to be constant and examine "truncated" observation processes not exceeding an assigned value T in duration. This means that the observation process is terminated at the instant $t=T$ and we accept the decision $u = x_1$ or x_2 corresponding to the minimal risk

$$S(w_1, T) = \min[Aw_1, B(1 - w_1)], \tag{13}$$

if this process did not terminate earlier. Equation (13) serves as the "initial condition" (for reverse time flow) for the determination of $S(w_1, t)$ using (12).

At interior points of the region of continuing observations, the function $S(w_1, T)$ satisfies the equation

$$S(w_1, t) = C\Delta + \mathbf{M}_{ps}S(w_1 + \Delta w, t + \Delta) + o(\Delta)$$

and hence has derivatives $\frac{\partial S}{\partial w_1}$, $\frac{\partial^2 S}{\partial w_1^2}$. This follows from the diffusional nature of the changes (10) of the process $w_1(t)$ and can be proven in the same way as the existence of these derivatives is proven in the derivation of the usual Kolmogorov equation. If this proof is not carried out, the existence of the derivatives should be postulated in addition.

Let us examine the *a posteriori* average entering into (12). Expanding $S(w_1 + \Delta w, t + \Delta)$ into a Taylor series, we find

$$\mathbf{M}_{ps} S(w_1 + \Delta w, t + \Delta) = S(w_1, t + \Delta) + \frac{\partial S(w_1, t + \Delta)}{\partial w_1} \mathbf{M}_{ps} \Delta w +$$
$$+ \frac{1}{2} \frac{\partial^2 S}{\partial w_1^2} \mathbf{M}_{ps} (\Delta w)^2 + \dots . \tag{14}$$

In order to calculate the averages $\mathbf{M}_{ps} \Delta w$, $\mathbf{M}_{ps} (\Delta w)^2, \dots$, we turn to (10). The process $y_t = s_t(x) + \xi_t$ entering into (10) has the *a posteriori* average $\mathbf{M}_{ps} y_t = s_1 w_1 + s_2 (1 - w_1)$ and the local variance $\mathbf{M}_{ps} (\Delta y)^2 = \varkappa \Delta + o(\Delta)$ ($\mathbf{M}_{ps} (\Delta y)^k = o(\Delta)$, $k > 2$). Thus from (10), applying the technique of averaging stochastic expressions developed by the author in [8], Sect. 4, we get

$$\mathbf{M}_{ps} w_1 = 0; \ \mathbf{M}_{ps} (\Delta w_1)^2 = \frac{(s_1 - s_2)^2}{\varkappa} w_1^2 (1 - w_1)^2 \Delta + o(\Delta); \ \mathbf{M}_{ps} (\Delta w)^k =$$
$$= o(\Delta) \quad (k > 2). \tag{15}$$

Consequently,

$$\mathbf{M}_{ps} S(w_1 + \Delta w, t + \Delta) = S(w_1, t + \Delta) + H(w_1) \frac{\partial^2 S(w_1, t + \Delta)}{\partial w_1^2} \Delta + o(\Delta),$$

where

$$H(w_1) = \frac{(s_1 - s_2)^2}{2\varkappa} w_1^2 (1 - w_1)^2.$$

After substituting this expression into (12) and passing to the limit as $\Delta \to 0$ we find

$$-\frac{\partial S}{\partial t} = C + H(w_1) \frac{\partial^2 S}{\partial w_1^2} \tag{16}$$

for

$$S(w_1, t) < \min [A w_1, B(1 - w_1)] \tag{17}$$

[compare with (10.44)].

In all other places, as follows from (12) with $\Delta \to 0$, the equation

$$S(w_1, t) = \min [A w_1, B(1 - w_1)]$$

is valid.

Assuming that the region where (17) is satisfied is a connected interval, we denote its boundary points by $f_1(t)$ and $f_2(t)$. This means that Eq. (16) is valid for $f_1(t) < w_1 < f_2(t)$ and to it correspond the boundary conditions

$$S(w_1, t) = \min[Aw_1, B(1 - w_1)]$$
$$\text{for } w_1 = f_{1,2}(t),$$

namely,

$$S(f_1(t), t) = Af_1(t),$$
$$S(f_2(t), t) = B(1 - f_2(t)), \tag{18}$$

if

$$Af_1 \leqslant B(1 - f_1); \quad Af_2 \geqslant B(1 - f_2)$$

(the latter assumption will be supported later).

It is possible to prove that at the boundary points the first derivative $\partial S/\partial w_1$ is continuous if $\partial S/\partial w_1$, $df_{1,2}/dt$ exist and are finite. Then, in addition to (18), the boundary conditions

$$\frac{\partial S}{\partial w_1}(f_1(t), t) = A; \quad \frac{\partial S}{\partial w_1}(f_2(t), t) = -B \tag{19}$$

will be satisfied.

Proof. From (12) is necessarily follows that the jump of the derivative at a boundary point, if it exists, can only be negative: $\partial^2 S/\partial w_1^2 = -\infty$ (i.e., the break is directed upward at an angle). If such a break exists, then, as we can see from the relation

$$\frac{S(w_1, t) - S(w_1, t + \Delta)}{\Delta} = \min\left\{\frac{1}{\Delta}\min[Aw_1, B(1 - w_1)] - \right.$$
$$\left. - \frac{1}{\Delta}S(w_1, t + \Delta), \ C + H(w_1)\frac{\partial^2 S}{\partial w_1^2}\right\} + o(1),$$

equivalent to (12), there we will have

$$-\frac{\partial S(f, t)}{\partial t} = -\infty \quad (f = f_{1,2}).$$

However, such an infinite value of the derivative is impossible because of the following considerations. Let us take the derivative

$$\frac{dS}{dt} = \frac{\partial S}{\partial t} + \frac{\partial S}{\partial w_1}\frac{df}{dt} \tag{20}$$

along the boundary, which obviously equals $A\frac{df_1}{dt}$ or $-B\frac{df_2}{dt}$ and thus is finite. If $\left|\frac{\partial S}{\partial w_1}\right|, \left|\frac{df}{dt}\right|$ are finite, then according to (20) the partial derivative $\partial S/\partial t$ should also be finite. Thus a break causing an infinite value of this derivative is not possible. The proof is completed.

If we denote

$$v(w_1, t) = \frac{\partial S(w_1, t)}{\partial w_1},$$

then from (16) will follow the equation

$$-\frac{\partial v}{\partial t} = \frac{\partial}{\partial w_1}\left[H(w_1)\frac{\partial v}{\partial w_1}\right], \quad (21)$$

which with the boundary conditions (19): $v(f_1, t) = A$; $v(f_2, t) = -B$ uniquely defines $v(w_1, t)$ as a functional of $f_1(t)$ and $f_2(t)$. In order to find the unknown functions f_1, f_2, additional conditions which we will introduce from (16) and (18) are required.

Conditions (18) obviously yield

$$S(f_2, t) - S(f_1, t) = \int_{f_1}^{f_2} v\,dw_1 = B - Af_1 - Bf_2. \quad (22)$$

Further, differentiating (18) with respect to t and taking into account (20), we find

$$\frac{\partial S}{\partial t}(f_1, t) + \frac{\partial S}{\partial w_1}(f_1, t)\frac{df_1}{dt} = A\frac{df_1}{dt},$$

from which, as a result of (19), we have $\frac{\partial S}{\partial t}(f_1, t) = 0$. Analogously, we can obtain $\frac{\partial S}{\partial t}(f_2, t) = 0$. Taking this into account, from (16) we will have

$$H(f_1)\frac{\partial v}{\partial w_1}(f_1, t) = H(f_2)\frac{\partial v}{\partial w_1}(f_2, t) = -C. \quad (23)$$

In this way the boundaries of the regions of termination $f_1(t)$, $f_2(t)$ can be found in the following manner. First, it is possible to solve Eq. (21) with boundary conditions (19) and (23), say, with conditions

$$v(f_1, t) = A; \quad H(f_1)\frac{\partial v}{\partial w_1}(f_1, t) = C,$$

assuming $f_1(t)$, $f_2(t)$ to be known. Then it is necessary to determine $f_1(t)$, $f_2(t)$ from the second condition of (19) and from (22).

Under the assumption that the "truncated" observation process definitely ends at the instant $t = T$, it is possible to prove that the boundaries of the regions of termination f_1, f_2 converge to one point:

$$f_1(T) = f_2(T) = f^* \equiv \frac{B}{A+B}. \tag{24}$$

At times $t < T$ the region of continuation of trials $f_1(t) < w_1 < f_2(t)$ spreads and as $T - t \to \infty$ tends to the limit region $a < w_1 < b$. It is easy to find the boundaries of the latter assuming $\partial S/\partial t = 0$ in (16) and taking into account (19). Substituting the solution of the resulting equation

$$v = A - C\int_a^{w_1}\frac{dw}{H(w)}$$

into the second condition of (19) and into (22), we find the transcendental equations

$$C\int_a^b \frac{dw}{H(w)} = A + B,$$

$$C\int_a^b \frac{w\,dw}{H(w)} = B, \tag{25}$$

which serve to define a and b. In case $A = B$ there remains but one equation

$$\int_a^{1-a}\frac{dw}{H(w)} = \frac{4\varkappa}{(s_1 - s_2)^2}\left[\frac{1-2a}{a(1-a)} + 2\ln\frac{1-a}{a}\right] = \frac{2A}{C}$$

$$(b = 1 - a).$$

Knowledge of the limit boundaries of the termination regions is sufficient if the duration of the observation process is not limited. In the case of the "truncated" trials it is sometimes suggested that an observation using the previous constant boundaries be carried out right up to the last moment T. The nonoptimal character of such a procedure is obvious. To obtain the optimal boundaries

$f_{1,2}(t)$ we need to solve the above problem. In view of the fact that an extended solution is difficult to obtain, one or another approximate method can be used. We will cite one such approximate solution producing an asymptotic expression for $f_{1,2}(t)$ for sufficiently small values $T-t$.

Since the functions $f_{1,2}$ near the end of the observation interval are close to their final values (24), within the region of observation $H(w_1)$ can be considered constant:

$$H(w_1) \approx H(f^*) \equiv H.$$

For $v(w_1, t)$ we will take a solution

$$v(w_1, t) = \frac{A-B}{2} - \frac{A+B}{2}\Phi\left(\frac{w_1 - f^*}{2\sqrt{(T-t)H}}\right);$$

$$\left(\Phi(x) = \frac{2}{\sqrt{\pi}}\int_0^x e^{-\varepsilon^2}\,d\varepsilon\right),$$

which exactly satisfies the equation $-\frac{\partial v}{\partial t} = H\frac{\partial^2 v}{\partial w^2}$ [see (21)], but only approximately satisfies the boundary conditions (19).

The functions $f_{1,2}(t)$ we determine using (23)

$$\frac{A+B}{2}\,\frac{2}{\sqrt{\pi}}\,\frac{1}{2\sqrt{(T-t)H}}\exp\left[-\frac{(f_{1,2}-f^*)^2}{4(T-t)H}\right] = \frac{C}{H}.$$

From this

$$f_{1,2}(t) = f^* \pm 2\left[(T-t)H\ln\left(\frac{A+B}{2\sqrt{\pi}C}\sqrt{\frac{H}{T-t}}\right)\right]^{1/2}. \tag{26}$$

If we do not take into account the difference between $H(w_1)$ and H, the solution (26) will be exact for the case of variable penalties

$$A(t) = \frac{A-B}{2} + \frac{A+B}{2}\Phi(x); \quad -B(t) = \frac{A-B}{2} - \frac{A+B}{2}\Phi(x),$$

$$x^2 = \ln\left(\frac{A+B}{2\sqrt{\pi}C}\sqrt{\frac{H}{T-t}}\right),$$

which can be seen by calculating $v(f_{1,2}, t)$. Using the asymptotic formula

$$\Phi(x) = 1 - \frac{e^{-x^2}}{\sqrt{\pi}x}\left[1 + O\left(\frac{1}{x}\right)\right],$$

we find

$$A - A(t) = B - B(t) = \frac{A+B}{2\sqrt{\pi}} \frac{1}{x} e^{-x^2} \left[1 + O\left(\frac{1}{x}\right) \right].$$

From this we see that for $x \gg 1$, $T - t \ll H \left(\frac{A+B}{2C}\right)^2$ the penalties $A(t)$, $B(t)$ are close to A, B and hence (26) is an asymptotic expression for the functions $f_{1,2}(t)$. Using various methods of successive approximations it is possible to determine them more precisely.

Finally, we will examine the conditional formulation of this problem, which is closer to the presentation given in the work of Wald [1].

Let us suppose we need to find the optimal sequential criteria $D(y)$, $d'_{DD}(y)$ which minimize the average observation time

$$\int D(y) \mathbf{P}(dy \mid x_1) \quad \text{or} \quad \int D(y) \mathbf{P}(dy \mid x_2) \tag{27}$$

with fixed errors of the first and second kind:

$$\int_{\Gamma_1} \mathbf{P}(dy \mid x_2) = \alpha; \quad \int_{\Gamma_2} \mathbf{P}(dy \mid x_1) = \beta. \tag{28}$$

Here Γ_i is the set of those trajectories $\{y_t\}$ which lead to the solution $d'_{DD}(y) = x_i$ $(i = 1, 2)$.

Choosing an arbitrary $0 < \Theta < 1$ and combining the average (27), we will seek the minimum of the expression

$$\Theta \int D(y) \mathbf{P}(dy \mid x_1) + (1 - \Theta) \int D(y) \mathbf{P}(dy \mid x_2).$$

Let us use the method of reducing the conditional extremum problem to a standard Bayesian problem. We minimize the average risk

$$R = \Theta \int D(y) \mathbf{P}(dy \mid x_1) + (1 - \Theta) \int D(y) \mathbf{P}(dy \mid x_2) +$$
$$+ \lambda_1 \int_{\Gamma_2} \mathbf{P}(dy \mid x_1) + \lambda_2 \int_{\Gamma_1} \mathbf{P}(dy \mid x_2),$$

where λ_1, λ_2 are undefined coefficients which will be found subsequently. If we interpret Θ and $1 - \Theta$ as *a priori* probabilities $\mathbf{P}(x_1)$, $\mathbf{P}(x_2)$, then

$$R = \int D(y) \mathbf{P}(dx, dy) + \frac{\lambda_1}{\Theta} \int_{\Gamma_2} \mathbf{P}(dy, x_1) + \frac{\lambda_2}{1 - \Theta} \int_{\Gamma_1} \mathbf{P}(dy, x_2).$$

This latter expression can easily be put into a sequential form:

$$R = \int \mathbf{P}(dx, dy) \left[\int_0^D dt C_{tt} + C'_{DD}(x, d'_{DD}) \right],$$

where

$$C'_{tt}(x_1, x_1) = C'_{tt}(x_2, x_2) = 0; \quad C'_{tt}(x_1, x_2) = \frac{\lambda_1}{\Theta} \equiv A;$$
$$C'_{tt}(x_2, x_1) = \frac{\lambda_2}{1-\Theta} \equiv B; \quad C_{tt} = 1. \tag{29}$$

Comparing (29) with (11), we see that the present problem coincides with the problem examined earlier. After its solution, relationships $A/C = \lambda_1/\Theta$, $B/C = \lambda_2/(1-\Theta)$ should be defined from conditions (28).

The optimal observation process consists of the fact that the observation is carried out while w_1 remains in the region $f_1(t) < w_1 < f_2(t)$. The observation terminates by the acceptance of the solution x_1 as soon as w_1 reaches the boundary $f_2(t)$, and the converse solution when the second boundary is reached. This applies also to the likelihood ratio l, since it is uniquely connected with w_1 by the relation

$$\frac{w_1}{1-w_1} = \frac{\mathbf{P}(x_1)}{\mathbf{P}(x_2)}\, l.$$

The region of continuation of observation here has the form

$$\frac{1-\Theta}{\Theta}\,\frac{f_1(t)}{1-f_1(t)} < l < \frac{1-\Theta}{\Theta}\,\frac{f_2(t)}{1-f_2(t)}. \tag{30}$$

Equations relating A and B, on the one hand, and α and β, on the other, are obtained from (28) by solving a more or less complex random walk problem with attainment of boundaries.

In stationary problems when $f_1(t) = a$, $f_2(t) = b$ are constant, it is not necessary to find a and b as solutions of Eqs. (25). In this case (30) in agreement with (9) has the form

$$\ln a' < \frac{s_1 - s_2}{\varkappa} \int_0^t \left(y_\tau - \frac{s_1 + s_2}{2} \right) d\tau < \ln b',$$

where

$$a' = \frac{1-\Theta}{\Theta}\,\frac{a}{1-a}; \quad b' = \frac{1-\Theta}{\Theta}\,\frac{b}{1-b}.$$

Calculation of the probabilities (28) of reaching boundaries using the function $\ln l$ with the hypotheses $x = x_1$, $x = x_2$ can be carried out by solving the corresponding Fokker-Planck equation. This yields the equations

$$a' = \frac{\beta}{1-\alpha}; \quad b' = \frac{1-\beta}{\alpha} \tag{31}$$

instead of the corresponding inequalities obtained by Wald for discrete time. The boundaries of the regions of termination a, b thus do not depend in this case on Θ. This indicates that both average times (27) are simultaneously minimized by (31).

3. **The complete Wald problem.** Let us now check the composite hypothesis $x \in \omega$ relative to the composite competing hypothesis $x \in \bar{\omega}$. The trials as before will be assumed independent. For simplicity, we will assume that the set $X = \omega \cup \bar{\omega}$ of possible values of the parameter x is a one-dimensional space and that ω is the half-line $x < 0$, although, of course, consideration of a more general case is possible.

In this case formulas (7)–(9) defining the *a posteriori* probability will also be valid if in them instead of $W(x)$, $\mathbf{P}(x)$ we write $W(dx) = w(x)\,dx$ and $\mathbf{P}(dx) = p(x)\,dx$.

In order for the conditional risk to depend on a finite set of parameters (sufficient coordinates), rather than on an infinite set, we need supplementary simplifying assumptions. Thus, let us assume that *a priori* distribution is Gaussian

$$p(x) = \frac{1}{\sqrt{2\pi}\,\sigma_0} e^{-\frac{(x-m_0)^2}{2\sigma_0^2}},$$

and that $s_t(x)$ is a linear function of $x: s_t(x) = q_t + r_t x$. Then the *a posteriori* distribution will also be Gaussian

$$w(x) = \frac{1}{\sqrt{2\pi}\,\sigma} e^{-\frac{(x-m)^2}{2\sigma^2}}, \tag{32}$$

where

$$\frac{1}{\sigma^2} = \frac{1}{\sigma_0^2} + \frac{1}{\varkappa}\int_0^t r_\tau^2\,d\tau;$$

$$m = \sigma^2\left[\frac{m_0}{\sigma_0^2} + \frac{1}{\varkappa}\int_0^t (\dot{y}_\tau - q_\tau)\,r_\tau\,d\tau\right]. \tag{33}$$

It is easy to see that these equations are equivalent to the equations

$$\begin{aligned} -\frac{2}{\sigma^3}\,d\sigma &= \frac{r_t^2}{\varkappa}\,dt; \\ d\left(\frac{m}{\sigma^2}\right) &= \frac{r_t}{\varkappa}(\dot{y} - q_t)\,dt \end{aligned} \tag{34}$$

with respective initial conditions $\sigma = \sigma_0$, $m = m_0$ for $t = 0$.

Let us suppose the solution $u = \operatorname{sign} x$ is required, with the same penalties for an incorrect solution and for observation time as in the preceding example:

$$C'_{tt}(x, u) = \begin{cases} A & \text{for } x > 0,\ u = -1; \\ B & \text{for } x < 0,\ u = 1 \\ 0 & \text{in other cases} \end{cases} \tag{35}$$

$$C_{tt}(x, u) = C.$$

The function $s'_{tt}(u'_{tt} \mid y_0^t) = \mathbf{M}_{ps} C'_{tt}(x_t, u'_{tt})$ [compare with (9.4)] now depends on y_0^t only through σ, m of (33). Taking into account (32) and (35) we find

$$s'_{tt}(u' \mid y_0^t) = \begin{cases} A\left[\dfrac{1}{2} + F(\mu)\right] & \text{for } u' = -1, \\ B\left[\dfrac{1}{2} - F(\mu)\right], & \text{for } u' = 1, \end{cases}$$

where $\mu = \dfrac{m}{\sigma}$, and $F(\mu)$ is function (3a).

The conditional risk, depending on σ and m, or equivalently, on σ and μ, is determined by Eq. (10.12), which takes the form

$$S(\sigma, \mu, t) = \min\left\{A\left[\frac{1}{2} + F(\mu)\right], B\left[\frac{1}{2} - F(\mu)\right],\right.$$

$$\left. C\Delta + \mathbf{M}_{ps} S(\sigma + \Delta\sigma, \mu + \Delta\mu, t + \Delta)\right\} + o(\Delta). \tag{36}$$

From (34) we obtain

$$d\mu = -\frac{r^2}{2\varkappa}\sigma^2 \mu\, dt + \frac{r\sigma}{\varkappa}(\dot{y} - q)\, dt.$$

In the averaging $\mathbf{M}_{ps}$ we replace $(\dot{y} - q)\, dt$ by $(rx + \xi)\, dt = rx\, dt + d\zeta$ here and take into account that $\mathbf{M}_{ps} x = m = \sigma\mu$, $\mathbf{M}_{ps}\xi = 0$, and hence

$$\mathbf{M}_{ps}\, d\mu = \frac{1}{2}\frac{r^2}{\varkappa}\sigma^2 \mu\, dt;$$

$$\mathbf{M}_{ps}(\Delta\mu - \mathbf{M}_{ps}\Delta\mu)^2 = \frac{r^2\sigma^2}{\varkappa^2}\mathbf{M}_{ps}(\Delta\zeta)^2 = \frac{r^2\sigma^2}{\varkappa}\Delta.$$

Thus

$$\mathbf{M}_{ps} S(\sigma + \Delta\sigma, \mu + \Delta\mu, t + \Delta) = S(\sigma, \mu, t + \Delta) +$$

$$+ \frac{\Delta}{2\varkappa} r^2\sigma^2\left[-\sigma\frac{\partial S}{\partial \sigma} + \mu\frac{\partial S}{\partial \mu} + \frac{\partial^2 S}{\partial \mu^2}\right] + o(\Delta). \tag{37}$$

(The first equation of (34) is used here also.)

Inserting (37) into (36) and passing to the limit as $\Delta \to 0$, we find that S satisfies the equation

$$-\frac{\partial S}{\partial t} = C + \frac{r^2\sigma^2}{2\varkappa}\left[\frac{\partial^2 S}{\partial \mu^2} + \mu\frac{\partial S}{\partial \mu} - \sigma\frac{\partial S}{\partial \sigma}\right],$$

when

$$S < \min\left\{A\left[\frac{1}{2} + F(\mu)\right],\ B\left[\frac{1}{2} - F(\mu)\right]\right\}. \tag{38}$$

In the remaining cases,

$$S = \min\left\{A\left[\frac{1}{2} + F(\mu)\right],\ B\left[\frac{1}{2} - F(\mu)\right]\right\}.$$

The region (38) is the region of continuation of the trials. On its boundaries $\mu = f_1(\sigma, t)$, $\mu = f_2(\sigma, t)$, $(f_1 < f_2)$, where

$$S(f_1) = A\left[\frac{1}{2} + F(f_1)\right],\ F(f_1) < \frac{1}{2}\,\frac{B-A}{A+B}; \tag{39}$$

$$S(f_2) = B\left[\frac{1}{2} - F(f_2)\right],\ F(f_2) > \frac{1}{2}\,\frac{B-A}{A+B}, \tag{40}$$

the trials terminate in the acceptance of the solution $u = -1$ (on f_1) and the solution $u = 1$ (on f_2). As in the preceding example, on the boundaries a continuity condition is satisfied for the derivative:

$$\begin{aligned} \frac{\partial S}{\partial \mu} &= \frac{A}{\sqrt{2\pi}} e^{-\frac{\mu^2}{2}} \quad \text{for} \quad \mu = f_1(\sigma, t); \\ \frac{\partial S}{\partial \mu} &= -\frac{B}{\sqrt{2\pi}} e^{-\frac{\mu^2}{2}} \quad \text{for} \quad \mu = f_2(\sigma, t). \end{aligned} \tag{41}$$

In those cases when the observation time is not limited and the parameters of the problem (r, $\varkappa$, A, B, etc.) are constant, the function S does not depend explicitly on time and hence satisfies the equation

$$\frac{\partial^2 S}{\partial \mu^2} + \mu\frac{\partial S}{\partial \mu} - \sigma\frac{\partial S}{\partial \sigma} + \frac{2\varkappa C}{r^2\sigma^2} = 0 \tag{42}$$

with boundary conditions (41).

The appearance of the factor σ with $\frac{\partial S}{\partial \sigma}$ simplifies the approximate solution of this problem and the finding of the boundaries $f_{1,2}(\sigma)$.

In the first approximation it is possible, disregarding the term $\sigma \frac{\partial S}{\partial \sigma}$, to solve the equation

$$\frac{\partial^2 S^{(1)}}{\partial \mu^2} + \mu \frac{\partial S^{(1)}}{\partial \mu} = -\frac{2\varkappa C}{r^2\sigma^2} \tag{43}$$

in order to find higher approximations using the formula

$$\frac{\partial^2 S^{(k+1)}}{\partial \mu^2} + \mu \frac{\partial S^{(k+1)}}{\partial \mu} = -\frac{2\varkappa C}{r^2\sigma^2} + \sigma \frac{\partial S^{(k)}}{\partial \sigma}.$$

The solution of Eq. (43) under the first condition of (41) has the form

$$\frac{\partial S^{(1)}}{\partial \mu} = e^{-\frac{\mu^2}{2}} \left\{ \frac{A}{\sqrt{2\pi}} - \frac{2\varkappa C}{r^2\sigma^2} \int_{f_1}^{\mu} e^{\frac{x^2}{2}} dx \right\}. \tag{44}$$

Taking the second condition of (41) into account, from this we obtain

$$\int_{f_1}^{f_2} e^{\frac{x^2}{2}} dx = \frac{r^2\sigma^2}{2\varkappa C} \frac{A+B}{\sqrt{2\pi}}.$$

The second equation for the determination of $f_1(\sigma)$, $f_2(\sigma)$ we find from the condition

$$S(\sigma, f_1) - S(\sigma, f_2) = \frac{A-B}{2} + AF(f_1) + BF(f_2)$$

[see (39) and (40)].

Integration of Eq. (44) thus yields

$$\frac{2\varkappa C}{r^2\sigma^2} \int_{f_1}^{f_2} d\mu e^{-\frac{\mu^2}{2}} \int_{f_1}^{\mu} dx e^{\frac{x^2}{2}} = \frac{A-B}{2} + (A+B) F(f_2).$$

In the symmetric case when $A = B$, we have $f_1 = -f_2$, where

$$\int_{0}^{f_2(\sigma)} e^{\frac{x^2}{2}} dx = \frac{r^2\sigma^2}{2\sqrt{2\pi}\varkappa} \frac{A}{C}.$$

For small $\sigma \ll \left(\frac{2\varkappa C}{Ar^2}\right)^{1/2}$, the asymptotic formula

$$f_2(\sigma) \approx \frac{1}{\sqrt{2\pi}} \frac{r^2\sigma^2}{2\varkappa} \frac{A}{C} \tag{45}$$

is thus valid.

On the basis of this solution it can be shown that the error $S^{(1)} - \min\left[A\left(\frac{1}{2}+F\right),\ B\left(\frac{1}{2}-F\right)\right]$ is of the order

$$\frac{2\varkappa C}{r^2\sigma^2} f_{1,2}^2 \sim \frac{A^2}{2\varkappa C} r^2\sigma^2.$$

Thus the term $\sigma\frac{\partial S^{(1)}}{\partial\sigma} \sim r^2\sigma^2 A^2/2\varkappa C$, which we disregarded, is $(r^2\sigma^2 A/2\varkappa C)^2$ times less than the term $2\varkappa C/r^2\sigma^2$ taken into account. Thus under the condition $\sigma \ll (2\varkappa C/r^2 A)^{1/2}$, the approximation carried out is valid.

In place of the termination region boundaries $m_\Gamma = \sigma f_{1,2}(\sigma)$ found in the (m, σ) plane, it is possible to consider boundaries in the (m, t) plane, since from the first equation of (34) the value of σ depends simply on t. Thus, with the initial condition $\sigma(0) = \infty$ and for constant r, we have

$$\frac{1}{\sigma^2} = \frac{r^2}{\varkappa} t.$$

Hence instead of (45) the equation for the termination boundaries takes the form

$$|m_\Gamma| = \frac{1}{\sqrt{2\pi}}\frac{A}{C}\frac{r^2\sigma^3}{2\varkappa} = \frac{1}{\sqrt{2\pi}}\frac{A}{C}\frac{\sqrt{\varkappa}}{2r} t^{-\frac{3}{2}}. \tag{46}$$

The method used here is also applicable in the case when the penalty function $C'(x, u)$ has a more general form than (35), for example,

$$C'(x, u) = \begin{cases} A|x|^k & \text{for } x > 0,\ u = -1; \\ B|x|^k & \text{for } x < 0,\ u = 1. \end{cases}$$

Then

$$\min_u s'_{tt}(u \mid y_0^t) = \min\left[A\sigma^k\varphi(-\mu),\ B\sigma^k\varphi(\mu)\right],$$

where

$$\varphi(\mu) = \frac{1}{\sqrt{2\pi}}\int_0^\infty \eta^k e^{-\frac{(\eta+\mu)^2}{2}}\, d\eta.$$

The further development is analogous to the preceding case and we will not carry it out. We will confine ourselves to quoting certain results applicable to the symmetric case $A = B$. Solution of Eq. (43) with the boundary condition

$$\frac{\partial S}{\partial \mu} = -A\sigma^k \left| \frac{\partial \varphi}{\partial \mu} \right| \quad \text{for} \quad \mu = f_2$$

yields the equation

$$\int_0^{f_2} e^{\frac{x^2}{2}} dx = \frac{r^2}{2\varkappa} \frac{A}{C} \sigma^{k+2} e^{\frac{1}{2} f_2^2} \left| \frac{\partial \varphi}{\partial \mu} \right|_{\mu = f_2},$$

which serves for the definition of f_2. In fulfilling the conditions $\sigma^{k+2} \ll 2\varkappa C / r^2 A$ we have $f_2 \ll 1$. Thus, taking into consideration that

$$\left| \frac{\partial \varphi}{\partial \mu} \right| \approx \frac{1}{\sqrt{2\pi}} 2^{\frac{k}{2}} \Gamma\left(\frac{k}{2} + 1\right) \text{ for } \mu \ll 1,$$

we find

$$f_2(\sigma) = \frac{1}{\sqrt{2\pi}} 2^{\frac{k}{2} - 1} \Gamma\left(\frac{k}{2} + 1\right) \frac{A}{C} \frac{r^2}{\varkappa} \sigma^{k+2}.$$

On the (m, t) plane, to this expression correspond the boundaries

$$|m_\Gamma| = \frac{1}{\sqrt{2\pi}} 2^{\frac{k}{2} - 1} \Gamma\left(\frac{k}{2} + 1\right) \frac{A}{C} \left(\frac{\varkappa}{r^2}\right)^{\frac{k+1}{2}} t^{-\frac{k+3}{2}}.$$

Comparison of the included term $2\varkappa C r^{-2} \sigma^{-2}$ with the term in Eq. (42) which we disregarded shows that the condition for application of the last result is $f_2 \ll 1$.

These latter formulas go over into formulas (45), (46), found previously, for $k = 0$, and for $k = 1$, to the case examined by Mikhalevich [1, 2].

This solution generalizes immediately to non-Wald problems in which the parameter x being estimated is variable. In this case, we first derive the differential equations for the derivatives $d\sigma/dt$, $d\mu/dt$ (from the theory of conditional Markov processes). Then, as before, we carry out their *a posteriori* averaging, which corresponds to the transition to the secondary *a posteriori* operator of the type (9.34). When the *a posteriori* distribution is not precisely Gaussian but is locally close to Gaussian, we can use an approximate theory which takes into account some finite number of parameters of the distribution.

4. **The problem of detecting the disorder.** We will examine a problem which in somewhat different form (conditional) was solved by Kolmogorov and Shiryayev.

Let us assume, as in problem 2, that $\dot{y}_t = s_t(x) + \xi_t$, where ξ_t is white noise, and $s_t(x)$ is a signal having two possible values:

$s_t(x_1) = s_1$ and $s_t(x_2) = s_2$. Now, however, we will assume that the parameter $x = x_1, x_2$ does not remain constant, but that Markov transitions from one value to the other are possible. Transition from x_2 to x_1 we will interpret as the occurrence of "disorder." If the reverse transition is not possible, the *a priori* prossibilities $p_1 = \mathbf{P}(x_1)$, $p_2 = \mathbf{P}(x_2)$ satisfy the equation

$$\frac{dp_1}{dt} = -\frac{dp_2}{dt} = \beta p_2, \tag{47}$$

where β is a parameter describing the frequency of occurrence of the "disorder." The *a posteriori* probabilities $w_1 = W(x_1)$, $w_2 = 1 - w_1$ of the presence or absence of the disorder are defined by the equation

$$\frac{dw_1}{dt} = -\frac{dw_2}{dt} = \beta(1 - w_1) + \frac{s_1 - s_2}{\varkappa}\left[\dot{y}_t - \frac{s_1 + s_2}{2}\right] w_1(1 - w_1) \tag{48}$$

[see (6.43) and (11.5)] which is somewhat more general than (10).

We need to determine whether there is a disorder and to stop the observation process if there is one. Here we take penalty A per unit time for the nondiscovery of a "disorder" and penalty B for a false alarm.

Choosing penalty matrices

$$\begin{aligned} C_{tt}(x_1) &= A; \quad C_{tt}(x_2) = 0; \\ C'_{tt}(x_1) &= 0; \quad C'_{tt}(x_2) = B, \end{aligned} \tag{49}$$

we can apply the general theory to this problem. The matrix (49) does not depend on u so that solutions d_{tt}, d'_{tt} [in addition to $\vartheta = D(y)$] do not need to be used.

Equation (10.12) takes the form

$$\begin{aligned} S(w_1, t) = \min\{&B(1 - w_1),\ Aw_1\Delta + \mathbf{M}_{ps}S(w_1 + \\ &+ \Delta w_1,\ t + \Delta)\} + o(\Delta), \end{aligned}$$

since $s_t = A\,w_1$; $s'_t = B(1 - w_1)$ in accordance with (10.11). Using (48), after computations analogous to (14)–(16), we obtain the equation

$$-\frac{\partial S}{\partial t} = Aw_1 + \beta(1 - w_1)\frac{\partial S}{\partial w_1} + H(w_1)\frac{\partial^2 S}{\partial w_1^2}, \tag{50}$$

$$\left(H(w) = \frac{(s_1 - s_2)^2}{2\varkappa} w^2(1 - w)^2\right),$$

which is valid where

$$S(w_1, t) < B(1 - w_1),$$

i.e., within the bounds of the observation region $w_1 < f(t)$. On the boundary $w_1 = f(t)$, of which there is now only one, as before the function and its derivative satisfy a continuity condition:

$$S(f, t) = B(1 - f);$$
$$\frac{\partial S}{\partial w_1}(f, t) = -B. \tag{51}$$

In the stationary case the boundary function becomes a constant: $f(t) = a$, and (50) becomes the equation

$$\frac{\partial^2 S}{\partial w_1^2} + \frac{\beta(1 - w_1)}{H(w_1)}\frac{\partial S}{\partial w_1} + \frac{Aw_1}{H(w_1)} = 0. \tag{52}$$

In the solution of this equation and the determination of a it is necessary that, in addition to (51), the boundary condition

$$\frac{\partial S}{\partial w_1} = 0 \text{ for } w_1 = 0 \tag{53}$$

be taken into consideration.

To prove this condition we note that if this is not the case, as can easily be seen by integrating (52), the derivative $\partial S/\partial w_1$ and the function $S(w_1)$ would take on unbounded values in the vicinity of zero, which does not make sense. In that case the asymptotic formula

$$\frac{\partial S}{\partial w_1} = \text{const} \exp\left\{\frac{2\varkappa\gamma}{(s_1 - s_2)^2}\frac{1}{w_1}\right\}$$

would be valid.

Solving (52) with the boundary condition (53), we find

$$\frac{\partial S}{\partial w_1}(w_1) = -A\int_0^{w_1} e^{\varphi(w_1) - \varphi(w)}\frac{w}{H(w)}\,dw, \tag{54}$$

$$\left(\varphi(w) = -\beta\int\frac{1 - w}{H(w)}\,dw\right)$$

and obtain a formula for determination of the boundary a:

$$\int_0^a e^{\varphi(a) - \varphi(w)}\frac{w}{H(w)}\,dw = \frac{B}{A}. \tag{55}$$

The expressions obtained by carrying out the integrations in (54) and (55) do not tend to finite limits as $\beta \to 0$ since the integral $\int_0^w w^{-1}\, dw$ diverges at the lower limit. However, for small $\beta \ll \frac{(s_1 - s_2)^2}{2\varkappa}$ the factor $\exp[\varphi(w_1) - \varphi(w)]$ serves essentially to exclude the small area near zero. Introducing a small value $\mu \ll 1$, it is possible to eliminate the exponential factor in (54) and (55), but as the lower limit of integration we need to take μ.

Then (55) takes the form

$$\frac{a}{1-a} + \ln \frac{a}{(1-a)\mu} \approx \frac{(s_1 - s_2)^2}{2\varkappa} \frac{B}{A}. \tag{56}$$

The function $S(w_1)$, obtained by integrating (54), will equal

$$S(w_1) = B(1-a) + \frac{2\varkappa A}{(s_1 - s_2)^2} \Big[\ln \frac{1 - w_1}{1 - a.} + \\ + H_0(w_1) - H_0(a) - (1 + \ln \mu)(a - w_1) \Big], \tag{57}$$

$$(H_0(w) = -w \ln w - (1 - w) \ln (1 - w)).$$

The value μ entering into (56) and (57), defined by the equation

$$\int_\mu^{w_1} \frac{dw}{w} = \int_0^{w_1} e^{\varphi(w_1) - \varphi(w)} \frac{dw}{w} \approx$$

$$\approx \int_0^{w_1} \exp\left[\frac{2\varkappa\beta}{(s_1 - s_2)^2} \left(\frac{1}{w_1} - \frac{1}{w} \right) \right] \frac{dw}{w} =$$

$$= -\exp\left[\frac{2\varkappa\beta}{(s_1 - s_2)^2} \frac{1}{w_1} \right] \mathrm{Ei}\left(- \frac{2\varkappa\beta}{(s_1 - s_2)^2} \frac{1}{w_1} \right),$$

turns out, where $2\varkappa\beta(s_1 - s_2)^{-2} \ll 1$, to equal

$$\mu \approx \gamma \frac{2\beta\varkappa}{(s_1 - s_2)^2} \quad (\gamma = 1.781\ldots).$$

Let us turn to the conditional formulation of this problem. Suppose that the penalties A and B are not assigned, but we are to find the optimal processing of the observed values which minimizes the average time of disorder

$$T = \frac{1}{1 - \alpha} \int_{D(y) > \tau(x)} [D(y) - \tau(x)]\, \mathbf{P}(dx, dy)$$

for a fixed false alarm probability

$$\int\limits_{D(y)<\tau(x)} \mathbf{P}(dx, dy) = \alpha. \tag{59}$$

Here by $\tau(x)$ we mean the time of appearance of the disorder.

Reducing the conditional problem to a standard one (Bayesian), we form the risk function

$$R = \int\limits_{D>\tau} [D(y) - \tau(x)]\, \mathbf{P}(dx, dy) + \lambda \int\limits_{D<\tau} \mathbf{P}(dx, dy) =$$

$$= \int \Big[\int\limits_0^D dt C_{tt}(x_t) + C'_{DD}(x_D) \Big] \mathbf{P}(dx, dy), \tag{60}$$

where

$$C_{tt}(x_1) = 1;\ C_{tt}(x_2) = 0;\ C'_{tt}(x_1) = 0;\ C'_{tt}(x_2) = \lambda.$$

The problem of minimizing the risk (60) is the same as the above problem if we assume $\lambda = B/A$. Observation would be carried on until w_1 reached the threshold value a. Equation (55) establishes a one-to-one connection between λ and a. Since λ is an undefined multiplier, λ or a should be determined from condition (59).

Having found the value a, we will calculate the false alarm probability

$$\alpha = \mathbf{P}[D(y) < \tau(x)] = \int\limits_0^\infty \mathbf{P}[D(y) < \tau | \tau]\, \mathbf{P}(d\tau), \quad \text{where} \quad \int\limits_{\tau>t} \mathbf{P}(d\tau) = p_2(t).$$

Taking into account (47), we have

$$\alpha = \beta \int\limits_0^\infty e^{-\beta\tau}\, \mathbf{P}[D < \tau | \tau]\, d\tau. \tag{61}$$

The probability $\mathbf{P}[D < \tau \mid \tau]$ obviously is taken for the observed signal $\dot{y}_t = s_2 + \xi_t$. This probability can be calculated knowing that w_1 satisfies Eq. (48), which takes the form

$$\frac{dw_1}{dt} = \beta(1 - w_1) + \frac{s_1 - s_2}{\varkappa}\left[\xi - \frac{s_1 - s_2}{2}\right] w_1(1 - w_1),$$

with the initial condition $w_1 = w_0 = 0$ at $t = 0$.

The transition probability density $f(w_0, w_1, t - t_0)$, $(t_0 = 0)$, related to $\mathbf{P}[D < \tau \mid \tau]$ by $\mathbf{P}[D < \tau \mid \tau] = 1 - \int\limits_0^a f(0, w_1, t)\, dw_1$, here satisfies the (first) Kolmogorov equation

$$-\frac{\partial f}{\partial t_0}=\frac{\partial f}{\partial t}=\left[\beta(1-w_0)-\frac{2H(w_0)}{1-w_0}\right]\frac{\partial f}{\partial w_0}+H(w_0)\frac{\partial^2 f}{\partial w_0^2}.$$

From this, integrating with respect to w_1 from 0 to a and with respect to t (after multiplying by e^{-pt}), we obtain the equation

$$H(w_0)\frac{\partial^2\Theta}{\partial w_0^2}+\left[\beta(1-w_0)-\frac{2H(w_0)}{1-w_0}\right]\frac{\partial\Theta}{\partial w_0}=p\Theta \tag{62}$$

for the characteristic function

$$\Theta(w_0, p)=p\int_0^\infty e^{-p\tau}\,\mathbf{P}[D<\tau|\tau]\,d\tau=$$

$$=1-p\int_0^\infty d\tau\, e^{-p\tau}\int_0^a dw_1 f(w_0, w_1, \tau).$$

To Eq. (62) corresponds the boundary condition

$$\Theta(a, p)=1. \tag{63}$$

Since $0\leqslant\Theta(w_0, p)\leqslant 1$ for all w_0 and $p\geqslant 0$, we will require the bound

$$|\Theta(0, p)|<\infty \tag{64}$$

at the other end of the interval.

It is not difficult to see that (61) corresponds to the specific value $\alpha=\Theta(0, \beta)$, hence in the future we will assume $p=\beta$.

Multiplying (62) by an integrating factor we have, after one integration,

$$\frac{\partial\Theta}{\partial w_0}(w_0, \beta)=\frac{\beta}{(1-w_0)^2}\int_0^{w_0} e^{\varphi(w_0)-\varphi(w)}\frac{(1-w)^2}{H(w)}\Theta(w, \beta)\,dw+$$

$$+\frac{C_1}{(1-w_0)^2}e^{\varphi(w_0)}. \tag{65}$$

Here $C_1=0$ on the strength of (64).

Equation (65) is convenient for obtaining an asymptotic solution for $\Theta(w_0, \beta)$ as $\beta\to 0$. The integrand in (65) is significant only for small w, where $\Theta(w, \beta)$ can be replaced by $\Theta(0, \beta)$, and $\varphi(w)$ by the asymptotic expression $\frac{2\varkappa\beta}{(s_1-s_2)^2}\frac{1}{w}$. Then we will have

$$\frac{\partial\Theta}{\partial w_0}(w_0, \beta)=\frac{\Theta(0, \beta)}{(1-w_0)^2}.$$

Integrating for the second time with condition (63) and assuming $w_0=0$, we find

$$\alpha = \Theta(0, \beta) = 1 - a.$$

In this manner the threshold value $a = 1 - \alpha$ and the other parameters of this problem are determined (expressed in terms of α).

Now we can also find the average time of disorder (58) using expression (57), found earlier. In fact, the risk (60) coincides (for $A=1$) with the value $S(0)$, thus

$$(1-\alpha)\, T = S(0) - \lambda\alpha = \frac{2\varkappa}{(s_1 - s_2)^2}\, a \left[\ln \frac{a}{(1-a)\,\mu} - 1\right].$$

If we take into account that $\dfrac{a}{1-a} = \dfrac{1-\alpha}{\alpha} \approx \beta T_0$ (T_0 being the average time between false alarms), this formula coincides with the asymptotic expression for the average delay time

$$T = \frac{2\varkappa}{(s_1 - s_2)^2}\left\{\ln\left[\frac{(s_1 - s_2)^2}{2\varkappa}\, T_0\right] - C - 1\right\}, \quad C = 0.577..,$$

obtained earlier by Shiryayev [1, 2].

References

Arrow, K. I., D. Blackwell, and M. A. Girshick

1. "Bayes and minimax solutions of sequential decision problems," *Econometrica*, v. 17, 1949, pp. 213-244.

Bellman, R.

1. *Dynamic Programming*, Princeton, Princeton Univ. Press, 1957.
2. *Adaptive Control Processes: A Guided Tour*, Princeton, Princeton Univ. Press, 1961.

Bellman, R., I. Glicksberg, and O. Gross

1. "Some Aspects of the Mathematical Theory of Control Processes," Rand Corp. Memo R-313, 1958.

Bellman, R. and R. Kalaba

1. "Dynamic programming and feedback control," First IFAC Congress, Moscow, 1960; *Proceedings*, London, Butterworths, 1961.

Blackwell, D. and M. A. Girshick

1. *Theory of Games and Statistical Decisions*, New York, Wiley, 1954.

Bol'shakov, I. A. and V. G. Repin

1. "Problems of nonlinear filtration. I. The case of one parameter," *Automation and Remote Control*, v. 22, no. 4, 1961, pp. 397-408.

Cameron, R. H. and W. T. Martin

1. "Nonlinear integral equations," *Ann. Math.*, v. 51, 1950, pp. 629-642.

Chandrasekhar, S.

1. Stochastic Problems in Physics and Astronomy, *Rev. Mod. Phys.*, v. 15, 1943, pp. 1-89.

Doob, J. L.

1. *Stochastic Processes*, New York, Wiley, 1953.

Dynkin, E. B.

1. "Markov processes and semi-groups of operators," *Theory of Probability and Its Applications*, v. 1, no. 1, 1956.
2. *Theory of Markov Processes*, Englewood Cliffs, Prentice-Hall, 1961.
3. *Markov Processes*, Berlin, Springer, 1965.

4. "The optimum choice of the instant for stopping a Markov process," *Soviet Mathematics*, v. 4, no. 3, 1963, pp. 627-629.

Feller, W.

1. "Semigroups of transformation in general weak topologies," *Ann. Math.*, v. 57, 1953.

Girsanov, I. V.

1. "On transforming a certain class of stochastic processes by absolutely continuous substitution of measures," *Theory of Probability and Its Applications*, v. 5, no. 3, 1960, pp. 285-301.
2. "Minimax problems in the theory of diffusion processes," *Soviet Mathematics*, v. 2, 1961.
3. "Some minimax problems in the theory of 'guided' Markov processes," *Theory of Probability and Its Applications*, v. 7, no. 2, 1962, pp. 223-224.

Gradshteyn, I. S. and I. M. Ryzhik

1. *Table of Integrals, Series and Products*, New York, Academic, 1965.

Hill, E. and R. S. Phillips

1. *Functional Analysis and Semigroups*, American Mathematical Soc.

Ito, K.

1. "Stochastic integral," *Proc. Imp. Acad.*, v. 20, 1944, pp. 519-524.
2. "On a stochastic integral equation," *Proc. Japan Acad.*, v. 22, 1946, pp. 32-35.
3. "On stochastic differential equations," *Memoirs Amer. Math. Soc.*, v. 4, 1951.

Kalman, R. E. and R. S. Bucy

1. "New results in linear filtering and prediction theory," *J. Basic Engin.* (*Trans. ASME*), v. 83, 1961, pp. 95-108.

Kolmogorov, A. N.

1. "Zur Umkehrbarkeit der statistischen Naturgesetze," *Math. Ann.*, v. 113, 1936, pp. 766-772.
2. "Interpolation and extrapolation of stationary random sequences," *Izv. Akad. Nauk USSR, Ser. Math.*, v. 5, no. 5, 1941, pp. 3-14.

Kolosov, G. E. and R. L. Stratonovich

1. "A problem in the synthesis of an optimal control, solved by the method of dynamic programming," *Automation and Remote Control*, v. 24, no. 9, 1963, pp. 1061-1067.

Kul'man, N. K. and R. L. Stratonovich

1. "Certain optimal devices for detection of a pulse signal of random duration in the presence of noise," *Radio Engineering and Electronic Physics*, v. 6, no. 9, 1961, pp. 1279-1288.

2. "Phase automatic frequency control and optimal measurement of narrow-band signal parameters with nonconstant frequency in the presence of noise," *Radio Engineering and Electronic Physics*, v. 9, no. 1, 1964, pp. 52-60.

Kushner, H. J.

1. M. I. T. Lincoln Laboratory Report JA 2123, March, 1963.
2. "On the dynamical equations of conditional probability density functions, with applications to optimal stochastic control theory," ***J. Math. Anal. and Appl.***, v. 8, 1964, pp. 332-344.

Kuznetsov, P. I., R. L. Stratonovich, and V. I. Tikhonov

1. "Passage of random functions through nonlinear systems," ***Automation and Remote Control***, v. 14, no. 4, 1953, pp. 375-391. (In Russian.)
2. "Passage of random functions through nonlinear systems," (Continuation), ***Automation and Remote Control***, v. 15, no. 3, 1954, pp. 200-205. (In Russian.) (Both available as Ch. 5, *Optimum Filtration*, Pergamon, 1965).

Langevin, P.

1. ***Comptes Rendus***, v. 14, 1908, p. 530.

Laning, J. H. and R. H. Battin

1. ***Random Processes in Automatic Control***, New York, McGraw-Hill, 1956.

Leonov, V. P. and A. N. Shiryaev

1. "On a method of calculation of semiinvariants," ***Theory of Probability and Its Applications***, v. 4, no. 3, 1959, pp. 319-329.

Loève, M.

1. ***Probability Theory***, Princeton, Van Nostrand, 1963.

Lyan Chzhi-Shuen

1. "On conditional Markov processes," *Th. of Prob. and Its* ***Appl.***, v. 5, no. 2, 1960, pp. 208-209.

Mikhalevich, V. S.

1. "Sequential Bayes solutions and optimal methods of receiving statistical control," *Th. of Prob. and Its Appl.*, v. 1, no. 4, 1956.
2. ***Sequential Bayes Solutions and Optimal Methods of Receiving Statistical Control***, Dissertation, Moscow University, 1956. (In Russian.)

Prokhorov, Yu. V.

1. "Convergence of random processes and limit theories of probability," ***Th. of Prob. and Its Appl.***, v. 1, no. 2, 1956.

Pugachev, V. S.

1. ***Theory of Random Functions and Its Application to Control Problems***, Oxford, Pergamon, 1965.

Shiryaev, A. N.

1. "Detection of spontaneously arising effects," *Soviet Mathematics*, v. 2, 1961.
2. "The problem of more rapid detection of breakdown of the stationary regime," *Soviet Mathematics*, v. 2, 1961.
3. *The Problems of More Rapid Detection of Breakdown of the Stationary Regime*, Dissertation, Mathematical Institute of the Acad. of Sci. of the USSR, 1961. (In Russian.)

Shmal'gauzen, V. I.

1. "Synthesis of an optimal servo system," *Automation and Remote Control*, v. 24, no. 8, 1963, pp. 971-977.

Skorokhod, A. V.

1. "On the differentiability of measures corresponding to random processes," *Th. Prob. and Its Appl.*, v. 2, no. 4, 1957.

Smirnov, V. I.

1. *Course of Higher Mathematics*, v. 2, Oxford, Pergamon, 1964.

Stratonovich, R. L.

1. "On the theory of optimal non-linear filtration of random functions," *Th. Prob. and Its Appl.*, v. 4, no. 2, 1959, pp. 223-225.
2. "Conditional Markov processes," *Th. Prob. and Its Appl.*, v. 5, no. 2, 1960, pp. 156-178.
3. "On conditional Markov processes," Report at the Sixth All-Union Conference on the Theory of Probability and Mathematical Statistics, *Conference Transactions*, Vilnius, Government Publishing House for Political and Scientific Literature, Lithuanian SSR, 1962. (In Russian.)
4. "On infinitesimal operators of Markov processes," *Transactions*, Sixth All-Union Conf. on the Th. of Prob. and Math. Stat., Vilnius, 1962. (In Russian.)
5. "On a functional of probability of diffusion processes," *Transactions*, Sixth All-Union Conf. on the Th. of Prob. and Math. Stat., Vilnius, 1962. (In Russian.)
6. "Optimal nonlinear systems realizing the discrimination of a signal with constant parameters from noise," *University Notes, Radiophysics*, v. 2, no. 6, 1959, pp. 892-901. (In Russian.)
7. "Application of the theory of Markoff processes in optimal signal discrimination," *Radio Engineering and Electronic Physics*, v. 5, no. 11, 1960, pp. 1-19.
8. *Selected Questions of the Theory of Fluctuations in Radio Engineering*, Moscow, Soviet Radio, 1961. (In Russian.)
9. *Topics in the Theory of Random Noise*, v. 1, New York, Gordon and Breach, 1963.
10. "Conditional distribution of correlated random points and the use of the correlation for optimal separation of an

impulse signal from noises," *Izv. Akad. Nauk USSR, Sec. for technical sciences*. Energetics and Automation, 1961, no. 2, pp. 148-158. (In Russian.)

11. "Optimal reception of a narrow-band signal with unknown frequency in background noise," *Radio Engineering and Electronic Physics*, v. 6, no. 7, 1961.
12. "Optimal filter discrimination of telegraph signals," *Automation and Remote Control*, v. 22, no. 9, 1961, pp. 1037-1047.
13. "Sampling of a variable frequency from the background noise," *Radio Engineering and Electronic Physics*, v. 7, no. 2, 1962, pp. 171-178.
14. "Conditional Markov processes in problems of mathematical statistics and dynamic programming," *Soviet Mathematics*, v. 2, 1961.
15. "Conditional Markov processes in problems of mathematical statistics, dynamic programming and game theory," Report at the Fourth All-Union Mathematical Meeting, Leningrad, 1961. *Transactions*, 1963, pp. 370-379. (In Russian.)
16. "Some extremal problems in mathematical statistics and conditional Markov processes," *Th. Prob. and Its Appl.*, v. 7, no. 2, 1962, pp. 216-219.
17. "On the optimal detection of disorder of industrial processes," *Bulletin of Moscow Univ., Math. and Mech. Ser.*, 1962, no. 2, pp. 63-71. (In Russian.)
18. "On the theory of optimal control. Sufficient coordinates," *Automation and Remote Control*, v. 23, no. 7, 1962, pp. 847-854.
19. "On the theory of optimal control. An asymptotic method for solving the diffusive alternative equation," *Automation and Remote Control*, v. 23, no. 11, 1962, pp. 1352-1360.
20. "Most recent development of dynamic programming techniques and their application to optimal systems design," Report at the Second IFAC Congress, Basel, 1963; *Proceedings*, London, Butterworths, 1964.
21. "Recursion relations for conditional risks in a measurable space," Report at the Seventh All-Union Conf. on Th. Prob. and Math. Stat., Tbilisi, 1963. (In Russian.)
22. "A new form of notation for stochastic integrals and equations," *Bull. Moscow Univ., Math. and Mech. Ser.*, 1964, no. 1, pp. 3-12. (In Russian.)

Stratonovich, R. L. and V. I. Shmal'gauzen

1. "Some stationary problems of dynamic programming," *Izv. Akad. Nauk USSR, Section for technical science. Energetics and Automation*, 1962, no. 5, pp. 131-139. (In Russian.)

Van der Waerden, B. L.

1. *Mathematische Statistik*, Berlin, Springer, 1965.

Wald, A.

1. *Sequential Analysis*, New York, Wiley, 1947.

Wald, A. and J. Wolfowitz

1. "Bayes solutions of sequential decision problems," *Ann. Math. Stat.*, v. 21, 1950, pp. 82-99.

Wentzel, A. D.

1. Report of the Seventh All-Union Conference on Probability Theory and Mathematical Statistics, Tbilisi, 1963.

Wiener, N.

1. *Extrapolation, Interpolation and Smoothing of Stationary Time Series*, New York, Wiley, 1949.

Yaglom, A. M.

1. "On the statistical reversibility of Brownian motion," *Mathematics Notes*, 1949, no. 24 (66), pp. 457-492. (In Russian.)

Yoshida, K.

1. "On differentiability and the representation of one-parameter semigroup of linear operators," *J. Math. Soc. Japan*, v. 1, 1948, pp. 15-21.
2. "An operator-theoretical treatment of temporally homogeneous Markov process," *J. Math. Soc. Japan*, v. 1, 1949, pp. 244-253.

Zadeh, L. A.

1. "Optimum nonlinear filters," *J. Appl. Phys.*, v. 24, no. 4, 1953, pp. 396-404.

Index